Hans Glapner

Plastics

Engineering

Handbook

Plastics

of

SPI

Engineering Handbook

THE SOCIETY OF THE PLASTICS INDUSTRY, INC.

BOOK DIVISION

REINHOLD PUBLISHING CORPORATION

NEW YORK

1954

Foreword

FROM TIME IMMEMORIAL man's accumulated store of knowledge in all fields of endeavor has been carefully recorded in written form for the benefit of contemporary and future generations. No activity has been more fortunate in that respect than the plastics industry.

Seven years ago The Society of the Plastics Industry's Handbook first made its appearance. It was rightly heralded at the time as a landmark in the literature of plastics—the outstanding result of the collective efforts and collaboration of hundreds of dedicated individuals and groups both from within and outside the plastics industry.

Now we have this impressive second edition, entitled "Plastics Engineering Handbook," which is largely new from cover to cover. We find ourselves indebted for its appearance to much the same sources as were responsible for the preparation of the original edition. We must again acknowledge with deep appreciation the generous cooperation of the American Society for Testing Materials, the Manufacturing Chemists' Association and the Laminated Products Section of The National Electrical Manufacturers Association, which has contributed much to the preparation of this volume.

Again we wish to single out for due honor those from within our ranks who labored so long and so well to produce this latest compilation of plastics lore. As an industry, we must rely greatly for our well-being on the intelligent application of the basic principles of the physical and chemical sciences to the many complex problems of a new field. The world of plastics, therefore, has been indeed richly endowed in its industrial pioneers who have not only created a modern industrial giant in a brief lifetime but have also demonstrated a stirring sense of public responsibility—one which has impelled them to share freely with others the same knowledge which they labored so mightily to obtain.

To all of them in gratitude and affection, we dedicate this result of their labors.

JOHN J. O'CONNELL, *President*
The Society of the Plastics Industry, Inc.

Introduction

THE SECOND EDITION of the Handbook of The Society of the Plastics Industry, Inc., represents a compilation of the best engineering knowledge available on the processing of plastics. The technicians who brought out the first edition have meanwhile kept up to date with the progress in their fields, and now give to the industry a new and more comprehensive treatise.

Our technical Handbook program dates back to December of 1943, when the SPI Engineering and Technical Committee organized and selected 10 chapter subcommittees. After the first edition came out in 1947, 10 new additional subcommittees were organized in order to include new plastics, data, standards, methods of processing, and uses. As a result, the second edition of the Handbook contains 20 chapters divided into 5 major sections:

Section I —Materials and Processes

Section II —Design

Section III—Finishing and Assembly

Section IV—Testing

Section V —SPI Standards

Some of the subcommittees were assigned the task of bringing the original chapters up to date on the basis of latest progress and developments. The other subcommittees were given the responsibility of compiling new chapters on subjects which have become of technical importance since the release of the first edition. We again point out that liaison between the various groups was made possible by appointing to the Engineering and Technical Committee the chairmen and alternate chairmen of the chapter groups. Periodic meetings of the steering committee made it feasible to avoid any duplication. Thus, the organization has been simple in its arrangement, but very effective.

A large number of technicians served actively and faithfully in bringing out this edition. To them goes full credit for continuing the Society's technical aims for the benefit not only of its membership, but of other industries and of educational institutions as well. It would be almost impossible to compute the man-hours and the money spent, and time taken in travel by the members of all the committees, as well as the time devoted by various companies who so graciously filled out numerous questionnaires and returned them to the respective subcommittees seeking values and data based on everyday experience. From its inception the project has had the full support of the entire industry, whether or not the personnel of a company was active on a committee.

While the subjects covered in this second edition of the Handbook are of primary importance to good engineering of plastics, they by no means cover the entire range. The present chapters will be revised from time to time to include new materials, methods, and applications. Also additional subject matter will be added as new chapters in succeeding editions.

The Society wishes that by its sponsorship of this technical program the quality of applications of plastics will be maintained throughout the industry.

On behalf of the SPI Engineering and Technical Committee, we want to thank C. L. Condit of SPI, who arranged our meetings and aided immensely in coordinating our technical progress. We also sincerely appreciate the cooperation of Alan Randolph of E. I. du Pont de Nemours & Co., Inc., in editing the Handbook.

N. J. RAKAS, *General Chairman*
Engineering and Technical Committee
The Society of the Plastics Industry, Inc.

PLASTICS ENGINEERING HANDBOOK COMMITTEES

ENGINEERING AND TECHNICAL COMMITTEE
(Steering Committee)

N. J. RAKAS, *General Chairman*
National Automotive Fibres, Inc.

E. F. BORRO
Durez Plastics & Chemicals, Inc.

R. B. BOWER
Indiana Plastics Co.

D. M. BUCHANAN
Bakelite Co.
Div. Union Carbide & Carbon Corp.

JOHN E. CURRIER
Diemolding Corp.

ANTHONY D'AGOSTINO
Birmingham Plastics, Inc.

JOHN DELMONTE
Furane Plastics, Inc.

FRANK J. DONOHUE
Monsanto Chemical Co.

T. C. DUMOND
Reinhold Publishing Corp.

D. R. FEGLEY
Consolidated Molded Products Corp.

A. F. FIELDS
General Electric Co.

W. BRANDT GOLDSWORTHY
Industrial Plastics Corp.

A. M. HANSEN
Chrysler Corp., Engineering Div.

B. F. HANTZ
American Insulator Corp.

TODD HARRIS
Creative Plastics Corp.

E. M. HAYDEN
Stanley Chemical Co., The

CHARLES B. HEMMING
U. S. Plywood Corp.

EMILE HEMMING
Plastics Products, Inc.

DONALD F. HOFFMAN
Evans-Winter-Hebb, Inc.

D. A. HURST
Rohm & Haas Co.

ALBERT A. KAUFMAN
Industrial Synthetics Corp.

G. M. KUETTEL
E. I. du Pont de Nemours & Co., Inc.

GARSON MEYER
Eastman Kodak Co., Camera Works

H. W. MOHRMAN
Monsanto Chemical Co.

CHARLES A. NORRIS, JR.
Bakelite Co.
Div. Union Carbide & Carbon Corp.

JOHN J. O'CONNELL
Consolidated Molded Products Corp.

KENNETH PERKINS
Diehl Manufacturing Co.

R. C. PLATOW
U. S. Plywood Corp.

ALAN F. RANDOLPH
E. I. du Pont de Nemours & Co., Inc.

ERIC SODERBERG
Newburgh Molded Products, Inc.

CLINTON RECTOR
National Engineering Products

C. R. STOCK
American Cyanamid Co.

G. REINSMITH
Narmco Metlbond Co.

E. J. STORFER
Chrysler Corp., Engineering Div.

HANS H. WANDERS
Northern Industrial Chemical Co.

ALAN F. RANDOLPH, *Editor*
E. I. du Pont de Nemours & Co., Inc.

CHARLES L. CONDIT, *Coordinator*
The Society of the Plastics Industry, Inc.

WM. T. CRUSE, *Executive Vice President*
The Society of the Plastics Industry, Inc.

CLASSIFICATION OF RIGID MOLDING MATERIALS

N. J. RAKAS, *Chairman*
National Automotive Fibres, Inc.

WILLIAM I. BEACH
North American Aviation, Inc.

E. F. BORRO
Durez Plastics & Chemicals, Inc.

H. E. BROOKS
Rogers Corp.

ROBERT BURNS
Bell Telephone Laboratories, Inc.

FRANK H. CARMAN
Manufacturing Chemists' Association, Inc.

W. C. GOGGIN
Dow Chemical Co., The

K. B. GOLDBLUM
General Electric Co.

J. C. KAZIMIER
Amos Molded Plastics Div.
Amos-Thompson Corp.

GORDON KLINE
National Bureau of Standards
U. S. Dept. of Commerce

G. M. KUETTEL
E. I. du Pont de Nemours & Co., Inc.

L. W. A. MEYER
Tennessee Eastman Corp.

G. REINSMITH
Narmco Metlbond Co.

L. E. SIEFFERT
Dept. of the Navy
Bureau of Ships

E. J. STORFER
Chrysler Corp., Engineering Div.

W. A. ZINZOW
Bakelite Co.
Div. Union Carbide & Carbon Corp.

COMPRESSION MOLDING

HANS H. WANDERS, *Chairman*
Northern Industrial Chemical Co.

ROBERT W. BAINBRIDGE
Durez Plastics & Chemicals, Inc.

B. F. HANTZ
American Insulator Corp.

JOHN H. BYGRAVE
Barrett Div.
Allied Chemical & Dye Corp.

JAMES J. MOYLAN
Barrett Div.
Allied Chemical & Dye Corp.

N. R. REYBURN
Applied Plastics Div.
Keystone Brass Works

EDWARD W. VAILL
Bakelite Co.
Div. Union Carbide & Carbon Corp.

GEORGE W. WHITEHEAD
Improved Machinery, Inc.

COLD MOLDING

EMILE HEMMING, *Chairman*
Plastics Products, Inc.

JOHN W. ANDERSON
Plastic Molding Corp.

GEORGE CARLSON
Arrow-Hart & Hegeman Electric Co., The

LEON R. EGG
Garfield Manufacturing Co.

TRANSFER MOLDING

FRANK J. DONOHUE, *Chairman*
Monsanto Chemical Co.

E. F. BORRO
Durez Plastics & Chemicals, Inc.

SVEN K. MOXNESS
Moxness Tool Works

HENRY R. MARSHALL
Cutler-Hammer, Inc.

S. E. TINKHAM
Shaw Insulator Co.

INJECTION OF THERMOSETTING MATERIALS

DONALD F. HOFFMAN, *Chairman*
Evans-Winter-Hebb, Inc.

INJECTION MOLDING OF THERMOPLASTIC MATERIALS

ERIC SODERBERG, *Chairman*
Newburgh Molded Products, Inc.

JAMES W. HENDRY
Jackson & Church Co.

W. A. OLSEN
Nixon Nitration Works

S. LEON KAYE
Kaye Plastics Corp.

ISLYN THOMAS
Newark Die Co.

A. R. MORSE
Injection Molders Supply Co.

GEORGE W. WHITEHEAD
Improved Machinery, Inc.

PREFORMING, DRYING AND PREHEATING

JOHN E. CURRIER, *Chairman*
Diemolding Corp.

B. B. BELDON
Baldwin-Lima-Hamilton Corp., The

DAVID M. BUCHANAN
Bakelite Co.
Div. Union Carbide & Carbon Corp.

A. R. BUTTERFIELD
General Electric Co.

S. E. GLICK
Knickerbocker Plastics Co., Inc.

B. F. HANTZ
American Insulator Corp.

A. A. HUTCHINGS
F. J. Stokes Machine Co.

J. J. KUX
Kux Machine Co.

W. T. LaROSE
W. T. LaRose & Associates, Inc.

A. S. MORECROFT
Diemolding Corp.

SVEN K. MOXNESS
Moxness Tool Works

EXTRUSION AND EXTRUSION MACHINES

ALBERT A. KAUFMAN, *Chairman*
Industrial Synthetics Corporation

C. P. FORTNER
Plax Corp.

D. R. WILLIAMS
Chippewa Plastics, Inc.

FORMING, DRAWING AND POSTFORMING

D. A. HURST, *Chairman*
Rohm & Haas Co.

ROBERT S. AMES
Goodyear Aircraft Corp.

WILLIAM I. BEACH
North American Aviation, Inc.

R. S. HALLAS
Bakelite Co.
Div. Union Carbide & Carbon Corp.

RALPH E. PORZER
Celanese Corporation of America

SIDNEY R. SMITH
E. I. du Pont de Nemours & Co., Inc.

R. L. THOMPSON
United States Rubber Co.

GEORGE E. VYBIRAL
St. Regis Paper Co.
Panelyte Div.

REINFORCED PLASTICS

JOHN DELMONTE, *Co-Chairman*
Furane Plastics, Inc.

W. BRANDT GOLDSWORTHY, *Co-Chairman*
Industrial Plastics Corp.

CECIL W. ARMSTRONG
Armstrong Products Co.

V. E. HASLER
American Cyanamid Co.

WILLIAM J. HOWELL, JR.
Owens-Corning Fiberglas Corp.

ROBERT MILBY
Flexfirm Products

ERVEN WHITE
Thalco

W. BURDETTE WILKINS
Ridgewood, N. J.

CASTING

CLINTON RECTOR, *Chairman*
National Engineering Products

L. R. MILLER
Rezolin, Inc.

WILLIAM E. WIRSCH
The Resinous Products Div.
Rohm & Haas Co.

TOOLING WITH PLASTICS

E. J. STORFER, *Co-Chairman*
Chrysler Corp., Engineering Div.

A. M. HANSEN, *Co-Chairman*
Chrysler Corp., Engineering Div.

FRANK BOGART
Marblette Corp.

E. F. BORRO
Durez Plastics & Chemicals, Inc.

MILTON BRUCKER
Zenith Plastics Co.

APPY JURAS
Rezolin, Inc.

HOWARD KASER
Murray Corporation of America

LOU LAMM
Fisher Body Div.
General Motors Corp.

JAMES LUNN
Lunn Laminates, Inc.

FRED LYIJYNEN
Chrysler Automotive Body Div.
Exeter Plant

L. R. MILLER
Rezolin, Inc.

R. C. PLATOW
U. S. Plywood Corp.

R. VOSS
Warren Plastics & Engineering, Inc.

WILLIAM WEAVER
Modern Pattern Works

W. C. WESTERGAN
Bakelite Co.
Div. Union Carbide & Carbon Corp.

S. J. WORTH
Northrop Aircraft, Inc.

EMBEDDING

TODD HARRIS, *Chairman*
Creative Plastics Corp.

G. R. FESSENDEN
Fessenden Process, The

D. L. GAMBLE
Ward's Natural Science Establishment, Inc.

A. C. LONERT   H. M. VERNON
General Biological Supply House, Inc.   Vernon-Benshoff Co.

WILLIAM WEERS
Castolite Co., The

VINYL DISPERSIONS

E. M. HAYDEN, *Chairman*
Stanley Chemical Co., The

H. E. ALLEN   R. W. QUARLES
Elastomer Chemical Corp.   Mellon Institute of Industrial Research
                                                    University of Pittsburgh

E. R. ERB
Paulsboro Manufacturing Co.   F. L. SCOTT
                                                    United Chromium, Inc.

EUGENE B. GREENSPUN   H. T. STARK
Geneve Manufacturing Corp.   Dept. of the Navy
                                                    Bureau of Ships

JUSTUS HOYT
Warwick Chemical Co.   GEORGE E. STEVENSON
                                                    Weymouth Art Leather Co.

IRA R. MESSER   W. D. TODD
Watson-Standard Co.   B. F. Goodrich Chemical Co.

DESIGN OF MOLDED ARTICLES

CHARLES A. NORRIS, JR., *Chairman*
Bakelite Co.
Div. Union Carbide & Carbon Corp.

D. M. BUCHANAN, *Alternate Chairman*
Bakelite Co.
Div. Union Carbide & Carbon Corp.

W. M. HOYT   WALTER E. RAHM
International Business Machines Corp.   Montclair, N. J.

T. S. HUXHAM   H. M. RICHARDSON
Bell Telephone Laboratories, Inc.   DeBell & Richardson, Inc.

FRED C. MEACHAM   W. B. ROSS
Northern Industrial Chemical Co.   Thermold Corp.

LOUIS PAGGI   H. T. STARK
E. I. du Pont de Nemours & Co., Inc.   Dept. of the Navy
                                                    Bureau of Ships
R. W. POST
Boonton Molding Co.   H. V. STEELE
                                                    Auburn Button Works, Inc.

STANDARDS FOR TOLERANCES ON MOLDED ARTICLES

ANTHONY D'AGOSTINO, *Chairman*
Birmingham Plastics, Inc.

R. B. BOWER
Indiana Plastics Co.

JOHN BRAUGHT
General American Transportation Corp.

JOHN DIETRICH
Great Lakes Plastics, Inc.

J. E. FALOON
General Electric Co.

HARRY MCGOWAN
Bakelite Co.
Div. Union Carbide & Carbon Corp.

L. J. MORRISON
Detroit Mold Engineering Co.

HAROLD SPAULDING
Brezo's Tool & Die

DESIGN STANDARDS FOR INSERTS

KENNETH PERKINS, *Chairman*
Diehl Manufacturing Co.

E. F. BORRO, *Alternate Chairman*
Durez Plastics & Chemicals, Inc.

MARION B. DAVIS, JR.
Davis & Hemphill

PHILIP J. GRAHAM
Worcester Moulded Plastics Co.

V. A. HEDBERG
Scovill Manufacturing Co.

ROLAND JOHNSON
Drexels Screw Products

ROY L. PEAT
Peat Manufacturing Corp.

WALTER E. RAHM
Montclair, N. J.

HAROLD SPAULDING
Brezo's Tool & Die

WILLIAM G. WALTERMIRE
Lamson & Sessions Co., The

A. L. WALTERS
General Electric Co.

MOLD DESIGN AND RECOMMENDED STEELS

A. F. FIELDS, *Chairman*
General Electric Co.

H. G. BECKER
Crucible Steel Company of America

JOHN W. BERTHOLD
American Insulator Corp.

FRED K. DAVIDSON
Boonton Molding Co.

THOMAS H. EYLES
Foster-Grant Co., Inc.

W. H. KEMPER
Carpenter Steel Co.

RICHARD F. LESCHER
E. I. du Pont de Nemours & Co., Inc.

L. J. MORRISON
Detroit Mold Engineering Co.

WALTER E. RAHM
Montclair, N. J.

C. KENNETH SWARTZ
Consolidated Molding Products Corp.

GORDON B. THAYER
Dow Chemical Co., The

HARRY TAYLOR
Newark Die Co.

HANS H. WANDERS
Northern Industrial Chemical Co.

C. H. WHITLOCK
C. H. Whitlock Associates

MACHINING, FINISHING, AND DECORATING

DONALD F. HOFFMAN, *Chairman*
Evans-Winter-Hebb, Inc.

JOHAN BJORKSTEN
Bjorksten Research Laboratories

ROBERT HOOPER
Vacuum Molding, Inc.

E. F. BORRO
Durez Plastics & Chemicals, Inc.

HENRY L. KELLNER
Lea Manufacturing Co., The

WILLIAM H. COX
Shaw Insulator Co.

MILTON SCHIMMEL
Conforming Matrix Corp.

JACK GRAHAM
Worcester Moulded Plastics Co.

C. J. SMITH
Hemco Plastics Div.
Bryant Electric Co., The

JAMES STEIN
Metaplast Process, Inc.

CEMENTING, WELDING, AND ASSEMBLY

R. C. PLATOW, *Chairman*
U. S. Plywood Corp.

W. R. GRANER
Dept. of the Navy
Bureau of Ships

H. F. WAKEFIELD
Bakelite Co.
Div. Union Carbide & Carbon Corp.

W. E. MANRING
B. F. Goodrich Chemical Co.

GEORGE A. WILKENS
E. I. du Pont de Nemours & Co., Inc.

J. C. SEARER
Durez Plastics & Chemicals, Inc.

R. R. WINANS
Material Laboratory
N. Y. Naval Shipyard

ASSEMBLY GLUING

CHARLES B. HEMMING, *Chairman*
U. S. Plywood Corp.

ARTHUR F. DRAPER
Remington Rand, Inc.

ROBERT HOPKINS
Rohm & Haas Co.

J. D. NELSON
General Electric Co.

CARL H. POTTENGER
Koppers Co., Inc.

WILLIAM J. POWERS
Picatinny Arsenal

H. RAWDON
Beech Aircraft Corp.

D. L. SWAYZE
X-Cel Finishing Corp.

H. V. THADEN
Thaden Engineering Co.

J. H. TIGELAAR
Haskelite Manufacturing Corp.

F. J. WEHMER
Rubber & Asbestos Corp.

TESTING PLASTICS ARTICLES

GARSON MEYER, *Chairman*
Eastman Kodak Co.
Camera Works

ROBERT BURNS
Bell Telephone Laboratories, Inc.

RAY B. CREPPS
Owens-Corning Fiberglas Corp.

L. M. DEBING
Monsanto Chemical Co.

FREDERIC L. FISH
U. S. Testing Co.

NORMAN L. GREENMAN
Rogers Corp.

A. J. KEARFOTT
General Motors Corp.

GORDON M. KLINE
National Bureau of Standards
U. S. Dept. of Commerce

ROGER MACDONALD
Koppers Co., Inc.

L. E. SIEFFERT
Dept. of the Navy
Bureau of Ships

LEONARD SMIDTH
Sylvan Plastics, Inc.

E. J. STORFER
Chrysler Corp., Engineering Div.

JOHN K. TOTTEN
Ford Motor Co.

A. C. WEBBER
E. I. du Pont de Nemours & Co., Inc.

F. E. WILEY
DeBell & Richardson, Inc.

Contents

SECTION II — DESIGN

SECTION III — FINISHING AND ASSEMBLY

SECTION IV — TESTING

Section I—Materials and Processes

1. Classification of Rigid Molding Materials

Introduction

The SPI Classification of Plastics is intended to promote and encourage the intelligent use of plastics. Until publication of the first edition of this book, there was no systematic classification of plastics comparable to the classifications of other engineering materials, such as rubber, metal or wood. This classification is intended to establish an engineering approach to the selection of the proper plastics for specific applications.

The classification, described in the text and presented in the accompanying table, characterizes the various rigid molding materials, primarily in terms of three physical properties believed to be usually of controlling significance, and also provides means of characterizing them in terms of other properties in cases where such further characterization may be required for a specific use.

The table is deliberately restricted to commercially available molding materials, thermoplastic and heat-setting, with and without filler. As new plastics reach commercial status, they will be included in subsequent editions of the book.

Likewise it is intended, in subsequent editions, to fill gaps in the present tabulation where reliable data are not now available, and to include data from other significant tests not now included, such as resistance to chemicals and solvents, and mechanical properties at extremes of temperature.

As with engineering data covering metals, wood or any other material, the technicians responsible for this classification table have assumed that it will be used principally by individuals with a working knowledge of plastics, including compounding, testing, molding and application, but the text contains brief statements of the significance of various properties on which the classification is based.

System of Classification

The SPI classification is based upon values for mechanical, electrical, optical, thermal, chemical and aging properties of molded plastics, derived from qualified sources such as the American Society for Testing Materials, the Plastics Materials Manufacturers Division of Manufacturing Chemists' Association, Inc., the National Bureau of Standards, and military plastics specifications.

Classification is based primarily on three properties of the molded materials, namely, heat-distortion temperature, impact strength, and tensile strength. While this is a somewhat arbitrary choice of basis, it is to be noted that these three properties are mentioned in one form or another in practically all ASTM, Federal, and military specifications for plastics.

The grade numbers in the first column of the table identify the various plastics by numbers in terms of their respective minimum values in these three properties. The grade numbers are arranged in the column in order of heat-distortion temperatures. Members of a group having the same heat-distortion temperature are arranged in order of impact strength. Prefixed to each numerical expression of these three properties are letter or letters identifying the type of plastic, in accordance with a system of abbreviations given on page 6.

Take as example of this basic classification the first plastic in the table, for which the grade number is CA 11143.

CA identifies this as a cellulose acetate molding compound. The first two digits, 11, represent its heat-distortion temperature at 264 psi fiber stress (110°F, with the last digit dropped). The third and fourth digits, 14, represent its impact strength (1.4, with the decimal point omitted). The fifth digit, 3, represents its tensile strength in thousands of psi (3,000 with three zeros dropped).

Thus the grade number, as given in the first column of the table, constitutes a general description of a material in terms of its type and of three of its properties.

But the requirements for a given use are likely to involve specifications for other properties also. Provision for coding such additional specification in conjunction with the grade number is made by a system of suffixes.

For this purpose, the categories of properties are coded as follows:

M — mechanical properties
E — electrical properties
O — optical properties
T — thermal properties
C — chemical properties
A — aging properties

These letters will be found at the head of groups of columns in the table.

Individual properties within any category are coded by the capital-letter designation followed by a small letter (thus, Ea for power factor at 60 cycles; Ei for volume resistivity; etc.). These code designations of single properties will be found at the head of single columns in the table.

If, now, for example, it is necessary, for a given use, to specify that this cellulose acetate molding material shall meet (in addition to the specifications inherent in its grade number CA 11143) a requirement of dielectric strength of at least 250 volts per mil, this fact is stated by suffixing the code letters Eg which head the column in which this value is given for material CA 11143.

If the four characteristics heat-distortion temperature, impact strength, tensile strength and short-time dielectric strength completely describe the requirements for the use in question, then the desired material is completely described by the code designation CA 11143 Eg.

If certain other specific characteristics are required, further suffixes are used. The code designation may become, for instance, CA 11143 EgTaAa, which would indicate the further requirements of coefficient of expansion not greater than 0.00016 and of loss of weight in the aging test not more than 7.5 per cent.

If all of the listed electrical properties of CA 11143 must be met, then capital E alone is used as suffix, rather than the whole list of Ea, Eb, etc.; the material is then specified as CA 11143 E; and similarly capital M, O, etc., if all of the values in any of these categories must be met.

And finally, if all of the unique properties across the table for any particular SPI grade number are desired, the letter Z is used, e.g., CA 11143 Z.

If, for a given purpose, one or more properties under the suffix-letter columns are of primary interest and values controlled by the grade number are of secondary importance, the table can be used in reverse manner. For example: if a minimum power factor at 10^6 cycles is required for an application, the user can trace down the Ec column and find a value 0.00005 for material HH 14201 and a value 0.0005 for materials PS 17026 and PS 18027. A choice between these, or other materials of low power factor, similarly found by search of column Ec, can then be made on the basis of such other properties as may be pertinent to the use in question, not forgetting such practical considerations as cost and adaptability to a practicable and economical technique of molding. Then the material chosen can be specified in terms of grade number and suffix, e.g., PS 18027 Ec.

In a few cases, there are two materials of the same grade number having different properties in the suffix columns. These are distinguished by suffixing -1 to one of them; e.g., UF 27026 and UF 27026-1.

As a proper safeguard, the values listed in the table, and on which the classification is based, are minima for those properties in which a maximum value is ordinarily desired; maxima for those properties in which a minimum value is ordinarily desired. The materials so classified will thus in general have properties on the safe side of the respective values. But of course further appropriate factors of safety must be applied in the design of the molded article, and account must be taken of the effect of the method of molding upon the properties of the article. (See Chapter 12 on Design of Molded Articles and Chapter 2 on Molding.)

Also, it is important to remember that the values used as a basis for the classification were obtained under standard test conditions. In applying the classification, account must be taken of the fact that conditions of service (particularly as to temperature and humidity) different from the standard conditions of test may change very considerably certain properties of certain plastics.

Official Specifications

Many of the materials identified by SPI grade numbers will meet certain specifications issued by other organizations. To show these relationships to other specifications, the table contains columns:

Sa, listing specification numbers of ASTM;
Sb, listing Federal L-P designations;
Sc, listing MIL-P- specification numbers.

The use of one of these suffixes with the SPI grade number indicates that material of the SPI grade number can be purchased under the respective specification. E.g., CA 11143 Sa means that material CA 11143 can be had under ASTM Specification D 706, type 3.

Plastics Included in the Classification

The following compounds included in the current table, and the codes used for their basic chemical identification, are listed below. In practically all of these, pigments or dyes may be present as coloring ingredients.

CA 11143, CA 11202, CA 11242, CA 11351, CA 12123, CA 12173, CA 13113, CA 14074, CA 14084, CA 14085, CA 15065, CA 16065, CA 17046 — cellulose acetate molding compositions, consisting of cellulose acetate esters and plasticizers

CAB 12253, CAB 12322, CAB 13153, CAB 13173, CAB 13222, CAB 14104, CAB 14114, CAB 14153, CAB 15104, CAB 16075, CAB 16085, CAB 18065 — cellulose acetate butyrate molding compositions, consisting of cellulose acetate butyrate esters and plasticizers

EA 35023 — general-purpose ester-alkyd compound

EA 35033 — glass-fiber-filled ester-alkyd compound

EA 40125 — flame-resistant ester-alkyd compound

EC 12283, EC 13244, EC 13354, EC 13403, EC 14186, EC 14204 — ethyl cellulose molding compositions, consisting of the ethyl ether of cellulose and suitable plasticizers, and mold lubricants

HH 14201 — polymer of halogenated hydrocarbon without plasticizer, filler, or stabilizer

MF 30027 — melamine-formaldehyde molding compound, cellulose-filled

MF 26035 — melamine-formaldehyde molding compound, mineral-filled

MF 27059 — melamine-formaldehyde molding compound, with filler of chopped cotton rag

MF 27098 — melamine-formaldehyde—phenol-formaldehyde (85:15 ratio) with filler of chopped rag

MF 29025 — melamine-formaldehyde molding compound unfilled and translucent

MF 26025 and MF 26035-1 — melamine-formaldehyde molding compounds, cellulose-filled, for electrical uses

MM 14048, MM 16048, and MM 19049 — methyl methacrylate molding compounds, consisting of methyl methacrylate resin

PA 13107 and PA 16069 — polyamides (nylon, i.e., synthetic linear condensation products of diamines and dicarboxylic acids)

PF 29026 — general-purpose wood-flour-filled phenol-formaldehyde molding compound

PF 29036 — general-purpose phenol-formaldehyde with cellulose filler (wood flour or cotton flock)

PF 29085 — phenol-formaldehyde of moderate impact strength, with cotton rag or other cellulose filler

PF 29176 — phenol-formaldehyde of medium impact strength, with cotton rag or other cellulose filler

PF 29406 — phenol-formaldehyde of high impact strengh, with cotton rag or other cellulose filler

PF 27034 — phenol-formaldehyde with mineral filler, having low loss at high frequencies

PF 23034 — phenol-formaldehyde with mineral filler, superior to PF 27034 in loss at high frequencies

PF 29064 — heat-resistant phenol-formaldehyde

PF 29024 — heat-resistant phenol-formaldehyde with mineral filler

PF 29026-1 — general-purpose wood-flour-filled phenol-formaldehyde

PF 29046 — general-purpose impact-resistant phenol-formaldehyde with paper, flock, or pulp filler

PF 29024-1 — heat-resistant mineral-filled phenol-formaldehyde of moderate specific gravity

PS 17026 — general-purpose compound consisting mainly of unmodified polystyrene and small amounts of mold lubricants

PS 16026 — lubricated general-purpose compound consisting of polystyrene

PS 18027 — polystyrene molding material of higher heat-distortion temperature

PS 15153 — molding compound of polystyrene and synthetic rubber of higher impact strength

PS 18039 — a polystyrene-acrylonitrile copolymer

S 50603 — silicone resin with filler of chopped glass fibers

UF 27026 — urea-formaldehyde molding compound consisting mainly of urea-formaldehyde resin and alpha-cellulose filler

UF 27026-1 — general-purpose molding compound with cellulose filler other than alpha cellulose

VC 13053 — vinylidene-chloride molding compound consisting mainly of polyvinylidene chloride resins

VCA 12027, VCA 12034, and VCA 13035—vinyl-chloride-acetate molding compounds consisting mainly of polyvinyl chloride-acetate resins

Practical Significance of Properties

The paragraphs which follow give brief statements of the practical significance of the various properties which form the basis of the SPI classification, and indicate the respective official methods of test. Descriptions of these tests, and of the controlled conditions of temperature, humidity, etc., under which each is made, will be found in ASTM Standards on Plastics and on Electrical Insulating Materials.*

The following three paragraphs deal with the three primary properties on which are based the SPI grade numbers listed in the first column of the table.

Heat-distortion temperature (°F) *at fiber stress of 264 psi* (ASTM D 648) is a statement of the temperature required to permit an arbitrary standard amount of deflection by a standard load, in a test in which the specimen is subjected to a gradually increasing temperature. It is thus an indication of the ability of a material to retain its stiffness, or resistance to deformation, against the weakening influence of high temperature. A similar test, under the lower load of 66 psi (ASTM D 648), in which, of course, a higher temperature is recorded, has similar significance for material subjected to lighter load. Values determined by this second test are shown, for some materials, in the 6th column of the table. A large difference between heat-distortion temperatures in these two tests gives warning of the need to pay particular attention to designing so as to minimize the stress in service of articles subjected to heat.

Impact strength, Izod (*ft-lb per in. of notch*) (ASTM D 256) is the energy required to break a notched test bar by means of a sharp blow, and thus is indication of the shock-resistance of a material. A brittle or notch-sensitive material has low impact strength.

Tensile strength (*psi*) (ASTM D 638), i.e., the force required to break by simple tension, is seldom of direct significance in the choice of a plastic for a specific application, because usually the design is governed by the need to avoid distortion, which occurs under much lower stresses, but it may serve as a preliminary indication of the general mechanical strength of a plastic, and as a guide in applications which are primarily structural.

---

* Published by American Society for Testing Materials, 1916 Race Street, Philadelphia 3.

The following two paragraphs describe tests which are frequently significant in applications involving service at higher than room temperature.

Recommended service temperature (°*F*) for molded articles subject to no stress cannot be stated in terms of any single definitive test. The values given in this column are based merely on general experience, and have no consistent relationship with respective heat-distortion temperatures under high and low loads. All three figures should be taken into account, and also, of course, the fact that continuous contact with water or chemicals may lower very much the temperature which a molded article can tolerate without distortion.

Heat-distortion temperature (°*F*) *at fiber stress of 66 psi* (ASTM D 648) has been mentioned above, in connection with the companion test at 264 psi.

The remaining paragraphs in this section refer to properties designated by suffixes at the head of respective columns in the table.

(Ma) *Flexural strength* (*psi*) (ASTM D 790) is a direct measure of the load required to cause failure by bending. Since usually a molded article must be designed to hold its shape under flexure, rather than merely not to break, a test for flexural stiffness, or for modulus of elasticity, is more generally significant than this one, but flexural strength is included here because it forms part of certain specifications for plastics.

(Mb) *Compressive strength* (*psi*) (ASTM D 695), the measure of compressive load required to cause failure, is seldom of direct significance for thermoplastic materials, since an article must usually be designed to resist deformation, which of course occurs under loads much less than that which will cause failure — and particularly so if the load is a permanent one, and large enough to cause cold flow, even though no immediate permanent distortion. Compressive strength, then, can serve usually only as a base to which to apply a large factor of safety.

(Mc) *Modulus of elasticity in tension* (*psi*) (ASTM D 638) is a measure of the force required to produce a given change in dimension. Thus a high modulus is associated with rigidity and ability to hold shape under momentary loading. Under prolonged loading, however, deformation may develop in a plastic through cold flow; and under repeated loading through fatigue. The moduli of the plastics are low in comparison with those of structural metals.

(Md) *Rockwell hardness* (ASTM D 785) expresses resistance to penetration by brief contact with a heavily loaded small spherical ball, and thus measures one type of hardness. It is not to be interpreted as a measure of scratch-resistance.

(Me) *Specific gravity* (ASTM D 792) is usually important only as affecting the number of articles obtainable per unit weight of material.

(Ea, Eb, Ec) *Dissipation factor at 60, 10^3 and 10^6 cycles per second* (ASTM D 150) is a measure of the percentage of AC electrical energy lost as heat within a material used as a dielectric. A low dissipation factor is desirable in electrical insulation because it minimizes not only the waste of energy but also the immediate and cumulative effects of heat upon the material. On the other hand, a material of very low dissipation factor cannot be pre-heated or heat-sealed by high-frequency methods of heating.

(Ed, Ee, Ef) *Dielectric constant (specific inductive capacity) at 60, 10^3 and 10^6 cycles per second* (ASTM D 150) of a material is the ratio of the capacitance of a capacitor in which the material is the dielectric to the capacitance of the same capacitor with vacuum as the dielectric; thus, dielectric constant is directly a measure of the value of the material as dielectric in a capacitor.

(Eg, Eh) *Dielectric strength short-time and step-by-step (volts per mil)* (ASTM D 149) are measures of the voltage required to cause puncture, and thus are indicative of the thickness of insulation required to withstand a given voltage. (Actually, the thickness is usually more likely to be governed by mechanical considerations than by electrical.)

(Ei) *Volume resistivity (megohm-cm)* (ASTM D 257) is a measure of internal electrical resistance, i.e., resistance to steady passage of current through the material (not resistance to puncture), and thus a measure of suitability to serve as an insulator.

(Ej) *Insulation resistance (megohms)* (ASTM D 257) is a more realistic measure of insulating value, since it is calculated from the current passing both through the material and along its surface, and is determined on specimens conditioned at 50 per cent relative humidity.

(Ek) *Arc-resistance (seconds)* (ASTM D 495) is a measure of suitability for use under arcing conditions.

(Oa) *Index of refraction* (ASTM D 542) influences the "brilliance" of a transparent plastic, determines the limit of curvature in a light-piping system, and is a necessary factor in the calculation of the shape of a lens or reflector.

(Ob) *Light-transmission (per cent)* (ASTM D 791) is important in applications in optics and illumination.

(Oc) *Haze (per cent)* (ASTM D 1003) is a factor in the appearance of transparent plastics, and important in applications in optics and illumination.

(Ta) *Coefficient of linear thermal expansion per °C* (ASTM D 696) represents the magnitude of change in dimensions with change of temperature, which may be important in a device graduated for accurate measurement, or in an assembly of plastic with metal or other material, where differential expansion must be considered. Also it is a factor in the shrinkage of molded articles from the dimensions of the mold, and hence in the design of molds to yield articles of desired dimensions.

(Tb) *Rate of burning (in. per minute)* (ASTM D 635), i.e., the rate of propagation of flame in a test piece, is less important than the separation, by this test, of materials which when ignited will continue to burn and those which will not support combustion — i.e., are self-extinguishing.

(Ca) *Water-absorption* (*per cent*) (ASTM D 570) is usually important only because of the effects of absorbed water on other properties, e.g., impairment of electrical properties; swelling and warpage; impairment of rigidity; enhancement of toughness and impact strength.

(Aa) *Weight loss* (*per cent*) is a measure of the tendency of a plastic to lose weight upon aging, through evaporation of plasticizers or softeners. It is determined by weighing a specimen, heating it at $180 \pm 2°F$ for 72 hr, reweighing, and calculating the percentage loss in weight.

2. Molding

COMPRESSION MOLDING

History

History has failed to establish definitely the date of origin of the art of molding. It might be said that the art of molding originated with prehistoric man when he learned how to form pottery from clay, using the pressure of his hands to form the shape and the heat of the sun to harden the clay.

The earliest application of compression molding as a manufacturing process was early in the 19th century, when Thomas Hancock perfected a process for molding rubber. The first patent on a molding process in the United States was issued in 1870 to John Wesley Hyatt, Jr., and Isaiah S. Hyatt.

Dr. Leo H. Baekeland's development of phenol-formaldehyde resins in 1908 gave the industry its first synthetic molding material, which is even today one of the principal materials used in the compression-molding process.

As a result of recent developments in the art of molding thermosetting materials, the transfer or plunger method has to a certain degree replaced the original compression method and has made it possible to produce articles of more intricate design, and also to work to closer tolerances. However, compression molding still is, and will be for a long time to come, the standard conventional method of producing molded articles from thermosetting plastics.

Materials Used in Compression Molding

Both thermosetting and thermoplastic materials can be molded by compression, but thermoplastics can generally be molded more economically by injection, and hence compression molding is mostly confined to the thermosetting materials.

Thermosetting materials are softened by the initial application of heat, but further application of heat causes a chemical reaction within the materials, which hardens them permanently so that they cannot be remolded. The maintenance of pressure on the material during the molding prevents the development of porosity by any gases evolved by the reaction.

Most commonly known thermosetting materials are made from phenol-formaldehyde, urea-formaldehyde and melamine-formaldehyde resins. Of late, a new important material has been produced from alkyd resins. Silicone resin with glass-fiber filler is another molding compound for highly specialized applications. Also, polyester resins are thermosetting, but these are used mostly in low-pressure molding, which is covered in Chapter 6 on Reinforced Plastics.

Thermoplastic materials soften when heated and remain soft until cooled. They do not undergo a chemical change during molding, and can, therefore, be remolded.

Examples of thermoplastic materials are cellulose acetate, cellulose acetate butyrate, ethyl cellulose, acrylics, vinyls, polystyrene, styrene copolymers, nylon, polyethylene and fluorocarbons.

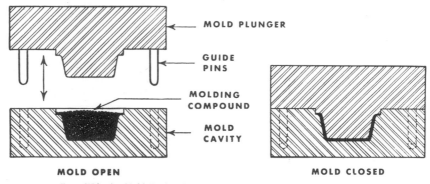

MOLD OPEN   MOLD CLOSED

From "Plastics Mold Engineering", Courtesy The American Technical Society, Publishers

Fig. 2-1

General Description of Compression Molding

Compression molding is the art of producing an article of definite shape from a molding material by loading the material into an open heated mold, shaping it by closing the mold under pressure, and hardening it in the mold under pressure (Fig. 2-1).

In modern plastics practice, the molding material is supplied in comminuted form, and the softening of the material by heat in the mold serves to permit the pressure to weld it into a continuous mass and to force this mass to take the shape of the cavity of the mold. The hardening of the molded mass under pressure is accomplished, for thermoplastics, by cooling it, and for thermosetting materials by continuing the heating until the hardening has been effected by chemical change or "cure".

Advantages of Compression Molding

Thermosetting and thermoplastic materials can be molded by this method. Large production is possible through the use of multiple-cavity molds. Large articles, such as trays, radio cabinets and industrial switch bases, are molded

Courtesy of Chicago Molded Products Corporation

Fig. 2-2

by this method (Fig. 2-2). The size of the article which can be molded is limited only by the tonnage and size of the available press equipment. This method is best suited for quantity production from thermosetting materials.

Limitations of Compression Molding

In the case of very intricately designed articles, containing undercuts, side draws and small holes, the compression method may not be practicable, because of the necessity of complicated molds and the possibility of distorting or breaking pins during the flow of the material under high pressure. Also, compression molding may be unsatisfactory for production of articles having extremely close dimensional tolerances, especially in multiple-cavity molds, particularly in relation to the parting line of the molded article. In both cases, it is recommended that the plunger or transfer method of molding be used in preference. For details regarding this method of molding, see the section in this chapter on Transfer Molding.

For thermoplastics, compression molding is usually economical only when articles are too large, in either weight or projected area, to be produced on available injection-molding machines. However, a combination of injecting the correct amount of the thermoplastic material into the mold and then applying pressure on the softened material through a compression force plug is being used with considerable success. This is especially desirable for thermoplastic moldings with very heavy cross-sections. The action of the compression force plug keeps the material under pressure while setting, and thus prevents development of air bubbles and shrink marks.

Molding of Phenol-Formaldehyde Compounds

The details of the procedure of molding thermosetting materials can conveniently be covered by a description of the molding of phenol-formaldehyde compounds. The minor differences in procedure required for handling other thermosetting materials will be pointed out in later sections.

A typical mold is made in two parts which when brought together enclose a cavity representing the article to be molded. The parts are mounted, in register, in a hydraulic press which serves to open and close the mold and to apply pressure to its contents. Usually the mold is cored for circulation of steam under pressure, since steam provides the most satisfactory heating, especially in large complicated molds, because it automatically replaces itself as it condenses, and holds the mold at an even temperature.

Electrical heating is sometimes used, and gives good results with molds in which uniform distribution of heating elements of sufficient capacity is possible. Heating of molds by other media, such as oil and hot water, has been successfully used in a limited manner.

In molding, an amount of molding material required for the molded article is placed in the lower part of the open heated mold, and the mold is closed by operation of the hydraulic press. The molding material becomes heated by the hot mold, and thereby plastified. The pressure consolidates it into a continuous mass and forces it to flow into the shape of the mold and completely fill the cavity formed between the two parts of the mold. A slight clearance is allowed between these, in order to allow a slight excess of molding compound to escape; usually a clearance of 0.002 to 0.005 in. is sufficient. The material filling the cavity is held under heat and pressure to harden it, and then the mold is opened and the molded article removed. Thermosetting materials, having been hardened by a chemical change through application of heat, can be ejected after the proper curing cycle without need of cooling the mold. Only occasionally is a slight cooling of the mold advisable with thermosetting materials in order to improve the dimensional stability of the articles.

The proper molding procedure produces properly cured articles of sound, uniform structure. Before these can be used, they must be finished, by operations described in Chapter 16 on Machining and Finishing.

General-purpose phenolic molding compounds are supplied in granular form, and can be loaded into the mold in this form, in weighed or measured charges. But in commercial operation there is economy in preforming such material into tablets of the correct size and weight by means of automatic preforming equipment. This is less expensive than weighing out individual charges; the tablets are easily handled, and conveniently loaded into the mold cavities by loading boards; and frequently the cavity of the lower half of the mold can be made less deep than it would have to be in order to hold the charge in the form of loose granules having a bulk several times that of the molded article.

High-impact phenolic molding materials, which contain fabric as reinforcement for the molded article, cannot be handled by preforming equipment, and must be loaded as weighed charges.

The time required to cure the article in the mold, and the pressure required for molding, may sometimes be reduced by preheating the molding material before it is loaded into the mold. And when this is done by so-called high-frequency heating, which develops heat within the body of a preform, there is the further advantage that the molded article may be more uniformly cured than by heat introduced only by conduction from the hot mold.

Metal parts, or inserts, placed in the mold and held firmly in position, can be molded into the article. See Chapter 14 on Design Standards for Inserts.

Molding of Urea-Formaldehyde and Melamine-Formaldehyde Compounds

The techniques employed in handling and molding urea-formaldehyde and melamine-formaldehyde are in general similar to those used for phenol-formaldehyde, but some differences in practice are frequently required.

Since these are usually light-colored materials, attention must be directed to avoiding contamination which will show up in the molded article. Dust from adjacent presses, the soiling of preforms, and the incomplete removal of flash from the mold are frequent sources of contamination. By making the necessary provisions to prevent contamination, urea and melamine can be run with a low percentage of rejection for dirt.

The design of the article and of the mold is particularly important in molding urea and melamine, because their translucency and light color fail to conceal flow-marks and gas pockets which may be present but undetected in the dark, opaque phenolic materials. Hence it is desirable, whenever possible, to design both the article and the mold to minimize such defects in appearance. Ribs, variations in thickness, louvers and molded holes can be molded satisfactorily in urea when the article and mold are properly designed.

In molding these materials, it is frequently necessary to open the mold slightly and briefly, after it has been initially closed, to promote the escape of gas formed in the reaction of curing.

In the majority of cases, the actual molding cycle involves simply loading the mold, closing the press, degassing and completing the cure. However, there are applications which require more elaborate techniques, such as a slow close or a dwell period, to give the best results. In such cases, no over-all rule may be prescribed; the cycle must be worked out for each job.

Both urea and melamine may sometimes advantageously be preheated before being put into the mold. Melamine-formaldehyde may be electronically preheated very successfully, but urea does not react so well to electronic methods. For urea, heating by conduction, such as in a rotary-canister preheater or, for automatic presses, in an oil-bath heater, have gained more favor. Infrared lamps also have been used with some success.

Molding of Alkyd Materials

The techniques of molding alkyd thermosetting materials are sufficiently different to warrant a brief description of them as a separate category of thermosetting materials.

It is of primary importance to use a fast-closing press, since the extremely fast-setting characteristic of the alkyd resins requires that the pressure be applied on the materials within 3 to 4 seconds at the most. Because they give off no volatiles, there is no necessity for degassing or "breathing," nor for a dwell at partial pressure before closing the mold. For the granular material, molding pressures of about 800-1200 psi will be found satisfactory, although on occasion higher pressures may be desirable. The putty-type alkyd material has the same molding characteristics as the granular, with the exception that extremely low pressures (50-250 psi) may be used to mold satisfactorily around delicate inserts.

Molding of Thermoplastic Materials

The general procedure is the same as for thermosetting materials, but the molded article is hardened by cooling in the mold under pressure, i.e., by shutting off the steam and circulating cold water through the coring of the mold. Some experimentation will be necessary to establish at what point in the cycle the cooling should be begun, and how long it must be continued to harden the article sufficiently.

Thermoplastic molding compounds can usually not be preformed.

Details of Molding Procedure

The sequence of operations constituting the molding cycle is as follows:

1. open the mold;
2. eject the molded article(s);
3. place articles in shrink or cooling fixtures, if very accurate dimensions are required;
4. remove all foreign matter from the mold, usually by air blast, and lubricate mold if necessary;
5. place inserts or other loose mold parts, if any;

6. load molding compound (powder or preforms, cold or preheated) ;

7. close the heated mold;

8a. for thermosetting materials, hold under heat and pressure until cure is complete, and cool under pressure if desirable, principally for better dimensional control.

8b. for thermoplastic materials, hold under pressure and cool to harden the article.

The temperature of the mold and the pressure applied are extremely important, and it is advisable to follow the recommendations of the manufacturer for each grade of material used.

Phenolic materials used in compression molding can be classified as conventional and low-pressure materials (the latter should not be confused with materials used in low-pressure molding of impregnated laminates).

There are five very important variables in the compression molding of phenolic materials which determine the pressure required to produce the best molding in the shortest length of time. These are as follows:

1. Design of the article to be produced

    (a) projected area and depth

    (b) wall thickness

    (c) ribs

    (d) obstruction to vertical flow (such as pins, louvers and sharp corners)

2. Speed of press in closing

    (a) use of slow- or fast-acting self-contained press

    (b) use of fast-acting press served by hydraulic line accumulator system

    (c) capacity of accumulator to maintain constant follow-up of pressure on material

3. Plasticity of material

    (a) degree and type of preheating

    (b) density of charge (preform or powder)

    (c) position of charge in cavity

    (d) mobility of resin under pressure

    (e) type of filler (woodflour, cotton flock, macerated fabric, asbestos or mica)

4. Over-all temperature of mold

    (a) temperature variations within cavity and force of mold

5. Surface condition of mold cavity and force

(a) highly polished chrome-plated surface

(b) polished steel

(c) poor polish (chromium plating worn; pits, gouges and nicks)

Conventional phenolic materials loaded at room temperature, i.e., without preheating, require a minimum pressure of 3000 psi on the projected land area for the first inch of depth of the molded article, plus 700 psi for each additional inch of depth. Efficient high-frequency preheating, however, may reduce the required pressure to as low as 1000 psi on the projected land area, plus 250 psi for each additional inch of depth. The pressure required on high-impact materials may reach 10,000 to 12,000 psi. These recommendations of pressure are predicated on fast travel of the press, approximately 1 in. per second. The flow characteristics of thermosetting molding materials are changing continually during the molding, and the effect of this is particularly noticeable in slow-closing presses.

Low-pressure-molding phenolic materials, efficiently preheated by high-frequency, require a minimum of 350 psi on the projected mold area, plus about 100 psi for each additional inch of depth.

The following table may be used as a guide for pressures required in accordance with the depth of the molded article.

PRESSURE TABLE

Pressure, Psi of Projected Land Area

Depth of Molding (in.)	conventional phenolic		low-pressure phenolic	
	preheated by high-frequency	not preheated	preheated by high-frequency	not preheated
0 - $\frac{3}{4}$	1000 - 2000	3000	350	1000
$\frac{3}{4}$ - $1\frac{1}{2}$	1250 - 2500	3700	450	1250
2	1500 - 3000	4400	550	1500
3	1750 - 3500	5100	650	1750
4	2000 - 4000	5800	750	2000
5	2250 - 4500	*	850	**
6	2500 - 5000	*	950	**
7	2750 - 5500	*	1050	**
8	3000 - 6000	*	1150	**
9	3250 - 6500	*	1250	**
10	3500 - 7000	*	1350	**
12	4000 - 8000	*	1450	**
14	4500 - 9000	*	1550	**
16	5000 - 10000	*	1650	**

* Add 700 psi for each additional inch of depth; but beyond 4 in. in depth it is desirable (and beyond 12 in. essential) to preheat.
** Add 250 psi for each additional inch of depth; but beyond 4 in. in depth it is desirable (and beyond 12 in. essential) to preheat.

The wide range of pressures given in the second column is necessary to cover the variety of molded pieces and of types of press equipment used. For example, an article of comparatively small area and great depth requires pressures at the lower end of the range given; an article of large area and great depth may require the upper end of the range. Also, the thickness of wall of the article influences the pressures required; thin sections require more pressure than heavier sections. On deep draws, fast-closing presses with ample supply of high pressure (self-contained or from an accumulator system) for the full stroke will make it possible to use lower pressures.

The time required to harden thermosetting materials is commonly referred to as the cure time. Depending upon the type of material, preheat temperature and thickness of the molded article, the time may range from seconds to several minutes.

Types of Compression Molds

For most economical production, molds are made from high-grade steels so that they can be hardened and polished.

A *hand mold* is so constructed that it must be removed from the press manually, taken apart to remove the molded article, and assembled again for the next molding cycle. These molds are used primarily for experimental or small production runs, or for molding articles which by reason of complexity require dismantling of mold sections in order to release them. These molds are usually small and light, and contain not more than a few mold cavities.

Semiautomatic molds are self-contained units and are firmly mounted on the top and bottom platens of the press (Fig. 2-3). The operation of the press opens and closes the mold and also operates the ejector mechanism provided for the removal of the molded piece from the mold. This type is employed particularly for multiple-cavity work and for articles too large or too deep in draw for hand molding. It is designed for thermoplastic and thermosetting materials of all types.

Fully automatic molds are of special design and adapted to a completely automatic press. The complete cycle of operation, including the loading and unloading of the mold, is carried out automatically. A multiple-cavity mold may be used, and usually the molded article contains no insert or metal part. It is designed only for general-purpose thermosetting materials or medium-impact materials having bulk factor of 3.5:1, and is not suitable for impact-resistant materials.

For details regarding the design of molds, see Chapter 15 on Mold Design, which describes fully each type of mold.

Machinery and Equipment

Presses. Presses for hand molds range from small laboratory presses to production equipment of capacities from 15 to 100 tons. The heating plates are fastened directly to the top and bottom press platens. The mold is placed between these plates for the transfer of heat and pressure to it during the molding operation.

Fig. 2-3

Presses for semiautomatic molds range in size from 15 to 4000 tons and up. These presses have top and bottom platens with grids and parallels so that the molds can be readily mounted. The presses are provided with either mechanical or hydraulic ejecting apparatus to remove molded articles from the molds (Fig. 2-4).

Hydraulic System. Hydraulic presses may be provided with individual sources of hydraulic power, or a group of presses may be operated from a single line. A pump driven by steam or electricity provides the necessary volume of water at the required pressure, and an accumulator maintains a reserve sufficient to serve all the presses on the line without fluctuation of pressure.

In some cases, a high-and-low-pressure accumulator system is used, for economy. The low-pressure system is especially advantageous for operating presses with a long stroke; the low pressure can advance the moving part of the mold up to the point where the material takes pressure, and then the high pressure is thrown on to complete the molding cycle.

Heating and Cooling of Molds. A hand mold is heated and cooled by contact with cored platens mounted in the press. Heat for automatic and semi-

Courtesy Chicago Molded Products Corporation

Fig. 2-4

A compression molding press equipped with automatic cycle control. Here the removal of the molded part and the charging of the mold are done manually. The remainder of the cycle—closing the press, degassing, curing cycle, and reopening—are controlled by an electro-pneumatic timing mechanism, shown at the right of the press. The mold installed in the press is for producing a washing machine agitator.

automatic molds may be supplied by steam flowing through channeled mold sections or by electric heaters installed in the platens of the mold or press. Other means of heating, such as oil and water, have also been used.

For chilling thermoplastics, or for the chilling occasionally required for thermosetting materials, a supply of cold water is required, which flows through the same channels used for heating by steam.

Air-Compressor. Compressed air is very essential, being employed for removing flash and scrap from the mold, for lifting some molded articles from the molds, and for operating auxiliary equipment. Air pressure should be between 90 and 125 psi.

Preforming Press. A preforming press is usually required, in order to save time and labor in preparing charges of molding material for multiple-cavity molds.

Preheating. Preheating equipment, such as steam or electric ovens, infra-red lamps, and high-frequency units, may be required for rapid economical production.

Miscellaneous. Miscellaneous equipment includes items such as loading boards for preforms and inserts, scales for weighing powder, brass, leather or plastic hammers, and brass chisels for removing flash.

COLD-MOLDING

History and General Considerations

Cold-molded plastics were introduced in this country in 1908, just about the same time phenolic molding compounds came into being, and both were recognized as better electrical insulation than any other products available at that time. The materials and the methods of molding them, however, were quite different and each soon found its separate field of importance and activity. The term "cold-molding" has persisted through the intervening years because it describes a *method* rather than a *type* of plastics, and it must not be confused with current *cold-setting* resins and cements which have come into use recently for casting and laminating. The ingredients are utterly different and so are the results.

In fact, cold-molded plastics are entirely different from those produced by conventional hot-molding methods, both in the mix and in the technique employed to form and cure them. Therefore, this discussion will be confined strictly to the refractory and nonrefractory types of cold-molded plastics, which find their greatest service in the electrical insulating field, and in handles for pots and pans, where greater heat-resistance is required than other plastics can provide.

The definite need for an efficient commercial heat-resisting molded insulating material for the electrical and automotive industries inspired the research work which resulted in the development of the cold-molding process. For many years porcelain was popular for such purposes because it was the only fireproof, heatproof and waterproof material available to electrical engineers, and its low cost was a strong recommendation for its use. Unfortunately it was brittle, as are all ceramics, and could not be used in many places where its insulating properties would otherwise prove valuable.

Needless to say, many attempts were made to extend the field of insulating materials. Vulcanized fiber, hard-rubber compounds, shellac and various other combinations were devised, but each of them had limitations. Ultimately these materials were superseded by cold-molding.

Once developed to the point of manufacture, cold-molded materials became an important member of the plastics family. They are inexpensive as compared with hot-molded insulation, and certain types are capable of a much higher rate of production because they are not cured in the press.

Contrary to conventional molding, where molding compounds are manufactured by materials suppliers and shipped in drums to molders, cold-molding compounds are mixed on the spot by the companies which use them and are not available from other suppliers at all. The reason for this is that cold-molding compounds contain much higher moisture content when they go into the press and each batch is mixed and used within a period of hours, before it dries out. The very nature of the mix prohibits its preparation very far in advance, and thus it cannot be shipped and stored as other compounds are.

Methods of preparation are relatively simple when compared to hot-molding compounds. There is no need for polymerization kettles or stills. The ingredients, consisting variously of bitumens, synthetic resins, drying oils, fillers and solvents, are combined in conventional mixers and sometimes rolled to get thorough homogenization. Binders are often heated before mixing to make them workable. After these simple mechanical operations, the compounds are ready to use. Other compounds consist largely of asbestos, cement and water, and these will be explained later on.

Molding is done in conventional presses (Fig. 2-5), except that no provision has to be made to heat or cool the molds. The prepared compound is accurately weighed or measured in the exact amount required for the finished piece, placed in a cold mold and subjected to pressures from 2,000 to 12,000 psi. The pressing operation is continued just long enough to compress the cold-molding material thoroughly into the desired shape. Then it is removed from the mold and transferred to a heating oven and baked until it becomes hard and infusible. Finishing operations consist of removing fins or excess compound by sanding, filing, etc., after the piece is baked.

Cold-molded parts do not have the luster usually associated with hot-molded or cast plastics, nor is this necessary, because the prime requirement of insulating material is to resist arcing, moisture and heat.

Those cold-molded products in which phenolic resin is used as a binder have a somewhat smoother surface, but, generally speaking, cold-molded

Courtesy American Insulator Corp.

Fig. 2-5

products are more or less dull and unattractive in appearance. Colors are usually dark brown, black or gray, although for coffee-pot handles and other kitchen utensils reds and greens sometimes appear. Color in cold-molding is secondary to function, and the finish or surface of cold-molded parts is satisfactory for all practical purposes unless the mold is old or worn.

Cold-Molding Materials and Their Preparation

Cold-molding compounds ordinarily are divided into two distinct groups according to the binder and filler used. These are *nonrefractory* (*organic*) and *refractory* (*inorganic*).

(1) Nonrefractory (Organic). In general, the binders suitable for non-refractory cold-molding compound are asphalts, oil derivatives, coal-tar pitches, stearine pitches, residue from distillation of oils and fats, various solutions of gums or resins, oxidized oils, wax compounds, etc. Fillers consist for the most part of asbestos fibers, silica and magnesia compounds. To transform these materials into molding compound, the solid binders must first be dissolved into a liquid or viscous state. This is done by adding solvents such as coal-tar oils, petroleum oils, drying oils, naphtha, benzine, turpentine, etc., and cooking the mixture in a large kettle until the proper viscosity is reached. The solution is poured into a mixer, where it blends with the filler. If coloring pigments are to be included, they are added to the mix. The resulting compound is then ground and screened to get uniform particles for molding, after which it is allowed to "age" for a brief period, during which time the solvents evaporate and the material is conditioned for molding.

The aging process is critical and often presents problems because the molding mixture must be conditioned to the consistency best suited for molding, so that the articles will come from the press neither too soft nor too hard to prevent their safe removal from the mold. It should be remembered that cold-molded articles are uncured when they come from the mold; therefore they may be easily damaged unless the molding compound is of proper formulation and age to prevent sticking. They must be handled with considerable care until they have been baked.

This problem is not as acute in conventional hot-molding because dry powder is fully cured by heat and pressure in the mold before being removed. But cold-molding compounds are already plastic when placed in the mold. Their moisture content must be carefully controlled in order that the pressure applied in the press will bring them into intimate contact with all portions of the mold to give them shape. Since no chemical change takes place in the mold, and since no heat is applied to cause the compound to dry out, the exact amount of compound must enter the mold each time if duplicate products are to be obtained. The compound must not be allowed to dry out beyond the point where it will flow readily under pressure. Since it is also affected by atmospheric conditions it must not be exposed too long before molding, as it is likely to harden to some extent and fail to mold properly.

Experience alone is the guide used by cold-molders, and they vary their compounds from time to time to achieve the best results in molding articles of various designs. A composition of binder in which phenolic resin is used comes under the heading of nonrefractory compounds and the procedure for mixing and preparing the material is much the same as with natural binders.

(2) Refractory (Inorganic). Refractory cold-molding compounds basically are mixtures of cement, lime or silica, as the binder, with a filler of asbestos, blended together with water. This mixture, like other cold-molding compounds, depends upon pressing to shape, then baking to cure or dry. The presence of cement in the mixture, however, requires somewhat different treatment in the drying process. The mixture itself is blended by any suitable mechanical process, but the resulting compound is difficult to weigh or measure accurately because the long fibrous fillers have a tendency to hang together when wet. It is also very abrasive on the mold when the tremendous pressures required to mold it are applied.

It is even more critical during the curing period because, if dried too quickly, cement has a tendency to crack. Therefore, molded articles as they come from the press are stacked and covered with canvas or burlap and kept moist for a considerable time before they are placed in the oven to cure. Even in the oven they are dried during the first period in a moist humid atmosphere provided by permitting steam to circulate throughout the oven. This steam bath is gradually diminished as time goes on, and the final cure, requiring several days, is accomplished in dry hot air. Once cured, refractory cold-molded articles are exceedingly dense and hard, and will stand considerable abuse.

Cold-Molded Insulation

Among the properties which recommend cold-molding materials to the electrical field, for which they were primarily developed, are good arc-resistance and superior resistance to heat. Another advantage lies in the fact that the raw materials for cold-molding compounds are plentiful and cheap and, once the formula is established, may be mixed without the necessity of excessively costly equipment or highly skilled labor. Fewer molds are required also, and this reduces mold cost to a minimum right at the start. Production runs can be made economically and rapidly in a single-cavity mold, because the molding cycle is short. It consists simply of filling the mold, closing the press, and removing the article. No time is required to cure the article in the press, and since no gases develop, which would have to be allowed to escape during the molding operation, the press may be closed rapidly and full pressure applied at once. The operation may be likened to preforming more than to conventional molding, and may be done as rapidly as the operator can remove pressed articles and refill the mold.

Larger articles frequently require more time in loading the mold because the material has to be distributed largely by hand, since it does not flow. It cannot be bunched in the center of the mold with the hope that it will distribute itself evenly throughout the cavity when pressure is applied. This is especially true of refractory compounds in which asbestos and cement are used. On the other hand, some cold-molding compounds are capable of more rapid production than in any other form of molding. Ink-bottle tops, buttons, and similar small items have been molded in a conventional preforming press, where a continuous flow of nonrefractory organic compound is fed into the cavity from a hopper and some six hundred molded articles discharged from the press every minute during the operating period. These are discharged upon metal trays as they come from the press, then placed in an oven to cure. Much more oven capacity is required than press capacity, and a prodigious number of pieces are produced in a single press.

Limitations of Cold-Molded Articles

Detracting somewhat from the desirable qualities of cold-molded plastics are certain limitations which must be taken into account whenever use of the material is planned. Unless molds are watched carefully, and repaired or renewed when they become worn as a result of the heavy pressures required and the abrasive action of the materials, molded articles may have uneven surfaces and burrs which must be removed after the articles have been baked. This entails more expensive finishing operations than otherwise would be necessary, and runs up the cost per article. Unavoidable shrinkage is another factor which may cause trouble. The evaporation of solvents during the baking and curing is responsible for shrinkage anywhere from 0.002 to 0.020 in. per in., and sometimes the finished product is slightly warped. Taking shrinkage into consideration in the design of the cold-molded article, however, reduces this hazard to a minimum. Wall thickness must be more carefully planned and specified than for hot-molding, because the shrinkage takes place after the piece has been removed from the mold and at a time when no follow-up pressure may be applied. If wall thickness is not planned to avoid more rapid drying in one part of the piece than in other parts, trouble may result. Positioning of inserts and holes for attachment is likewise critical in design and should be carefully planned before the molds are made.

Other possible drawbacks which distinguish cold-molded articles include dull finish, lack of brilliant color, low tensile strength, and the restriction that cold-molding compounds are not available unless mixed on the spot and used almost as soon as they are made.

Molds and Fixtures

It has been pointed out that cold-molded articles are still soft when they come from the mold. They are merely compressed to shape and have very little strength; therefore, the mold must be designed and made to permit easy removal of the delicate parts without damage. In general, exactly the right amount of compound is placed in a positive mold. The upper plunger descending upon the material forces it into all parts of the mold and high pressure is exerted to squeeze and compress the compound into the exact shape of the mold. After the piece has been formed, the lower plunger, which forms the base of the mold cavity, rises to bring the piece up out of the mold, and it may be safely removed. Conventional knockout pins used in hot-molding would likely destroy the article if they were used in cold-molding operations; thus the mold is constructed so that the lower plunger acts in their place. The walls of the mold are tapered slightly to facilitate removal of the articles.

Special steels having high carbon and high chromium content are usually used in making molds, because of their greater resistance to the abrasive action of the raw materials that go into the mix. The greatest single factor, perhaps, in assuring the successful operation of a mold is to have it built by the molder who is to produce the articles. In this way it can be tailored to accommodate his particular brand of mix, and his experience with his own compounds will prompt its proper design to handle the mix expediently and turn out evenly dense parts. It will also be built to accommodate the pressures he has available without distorting, and, as a result, the mold will have a longer life. Molds can be built by any engineer, of course, but he must have all the facts before him when the design is laid out and he must understand the special requirements of the cold-molding compounds to be pressed and have full knowledge of the presses on which they will be used.

Fillets or corners should never be sharp, because they may be too easily damaged when the comparatively soft material is removed from the press or during curing processes. Walls should be sufficiently thick to stand expected strains, and a generous bevel, or draw, should be provided for easy removal of the pieces. In general, if these principles are followed, quite intricate cold-molded parts can be successfully made. Obviously, there is not space in this brief chapter to detail the many variations of mold-construction, but it is safe to leave them in the hands of an experienced cold-molder who is familiar with the requirements and will be able to provide the proper mold to do any cold-molding job.

Finishing Operations

As in all molded plastics, parting lines on cold-molded pieces are often removed to improve the appearance of the article and facilitate assembling. Parting lines are caused by excess material which squeezes out where the plunger enters the mold, and as the mold wears this becomes more acute. Such flash is removed by sanding, or buffing with a wire brush wheel, and sometimes it is removed with a file. Surfaces may be ground flat to improve assembly, but drilling and threading cold-molded articles is not easy. They are sometimes tumbled if better appearance is desired. This removes small burrs and other defects from the surface, and a final tumbling with waxed shoe-pegs gives a smooth polished appearance. Glass, diamonds, metallic carbides, etc., are required for cutting tools in finishing operations because ordinary steel, or chromium steel, soon dulls and becomes useless as a result of the hard abrasive character of the surface of cold-molded pieces. For a more detailed description of the finishing of cold-molded products, see Chapter 16.

Advantages of Cold-Molded Articles

While cold-molded plastics exhibit excellent insulating properties for electrical equipment of various sorts, and possess good resistance to moisture and heat, it must not be assumed that they will serve in all fields of electrical insulation. Nor should they be chosen for definite applications until their limitations as well as their advantages have been carefully checked with the known facts regarding their physical characteristics. Their low cost and rapid manufacture recommend them where demands beyond their capacities are not required, but they are in no sense to be considered as the ideal insulation for all electrical needs. Perhaps the best way to indicate suitable applications where cold-molded plastics will serve with complete satisfaction is to illustrate typical examples which have demonstrated their worth to the electrical industry (Fig. 2-6). They are sometimes used in mechanical applications, such as pot- and pan-handles, where their resistance to high temperature gives them an advantage over other plastics which might easily char, burn, or decompose.

Fig. 2-6

Closed-Mold Technique

1. TRANSFER MOLDING

Definition

The term "transfer molding" is now generally applied to the process of forming articles in a closed mold from a thermosetting material that is conveyed under pressure, in a hot, plastic state, from an auxiliary chamber.

History

Prior to the development of transfer molding, thermosetting materials were handled only in compression molds by methods adapted from the prior art used in forming articles from rubber, shellac and cold-molded compositions. The compression method is still widely used and is entirely suitable for the production of a great variety of small and large articles of relatively simple outline and plain cross-section.

However, compression molding does not readily permit of the forming of articles having intricate sections, thin walls and fragile inserts, and those on which close tolerances must be held. When compression molding is applied to such articles, the usual results are high costs of molds and maintenance, due to excessive wear and breakage.

To overcome these difficulties, transfer molding was introduced by Shaw Insulator Co., Irvington, New Jersey, in 1926.* At that time, the process was carried out in conventional single-ram compression presses, with three-piece molds, as described later. To promote flow, it was frequently necessary to employ special, long-flow, premium molding compounds, and to preheat in an oven. This type of transfer molding is now usually referred to as "pot type."

·Later, presses equipped with two or more rams were developed for transfer molding. In these the main ram is attached to the lower or upper press platen in the usual manner, and holds the mold closed. One or more auxiliary rams are used to force the material into the closed mold. This form of transfer molding is frequently called "plunger molding."

In the most commonly used American molding presses, the main ram is attached to the lower press platen and operates upward. When these presses are equipped for transfer molding, the auxiliary rams may be mounted on the side columns, operating at right angles to the main ram, or on the press head, operating downward in a direction opposite to that of the main ram, or on the press bed or within the main ram, operating upward and in the same direction as the main ram.

---

* Numerous U. S. patents covering transfer molding have been granted to Shaw Insulator Co. Included among these are 1,916,495, 1,919,534, 1,933,942, 1,997,074, 2,274,279, 2,279,208, 2,293,633, 2,351,582, 2,436,065.

Inverted-ram or downstroke presses are used in some American plants and more widely in England. In these the main ram operates downward. When presses of this type are employed for plunger molding, the transfer cylinder is attached to the bottom of the press frame and the transfer ram operates upward through an opening in the lower press platen.

The introduction of high-frequency dielectric preheating and steam pre-heating, during and after World War II, greatly accelerated the growth of transfer molding, particularly with auxiliary-ram presses. Speeds of transfer and of cure were markedly increased, and lower pressures could be used for transfer and for clamping the mold. As a result, the process of transfer molding has spread widely in the last six years, and prospects of further growth are very favorable.

This progress in molding technology and in equipment has been matched by the development of improved materials, particularly phenolics, which are better suited to the large multiple-cavity transfer molds now in use than were the special transfer materials previously used. These new materials have more rapid rates of flow and shorter cure times than those previously available for transfer molding. With the aid of dielectric or steam preheating, they exhibit the same total flow as the special transfer materials once required, but accomplish this flow in a much shorter time. Rigidity on discharge from the mold has also been greatly improved. This all makes for faster production and lower molding costs, and further enhances the usefulness of transfer molding.

Description of Process

In transfer molding, of either the pot or plunger type, the material, usually preformed, and preheated dielectrically or by steam, is introduced, in a softened, semiplastic state, into a chamber called a "pot" or "well," separate from the mold cavity. From this it is forced by pressure through one or more orifices into the heated mold cavity or cavities.

In certain pot-type transfer molds, intended for operation in compression presses, the orifice from the pot connects with channels called runners leading to the individual mold cavities; in others, operated also in compression presses, the orifice leads directly into the mold cavity, without any intervening runners. In some large multiple-cavity molds of this type, an individual pot may be used for each cavity. The M-52 fuse molds used during World War II were of this multiple-pot type, in most cases (Fig. 2-7).

That portion of the material which fills the orifice from the pot is called the sprue; the term runners is applied both to the channels leading from the sprue bushing, or the well, to the cavities, and also to the material occupying these channels. The gates are those points at which the runners join the cavities. At these points, the cross-section of the channel is usually reduced to a minimum, to facilitate removal of excess material from the pieces in finishing operations.

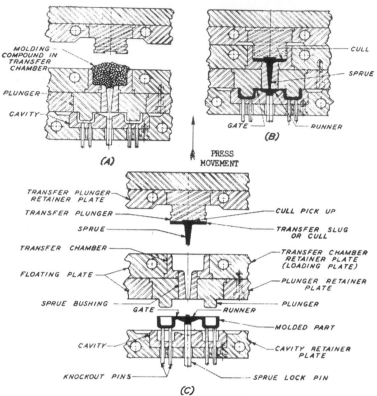

From "Plastics Mold Engineering," Courtesy of The American Technical Society

Fig. 2-7

In plunger-type transfer molds, designed for operation in auxiliary-ram presses, the runners lead directly from a central well, which forms part of the mold, to the mold cavities, often arranged in a radial cluster around the well (Fig. 2-8).

Transfer molding of thermosetting materials is roughly analogous to injection molding of thermoplastics, but there are certain important differences. In pot-type transfer, the taper of the sprue is the reverse of that used in injection molding, since it is desired to keep the sprue attached to the cull, rather than to the piece.

Because of the heat-hardening characteristics of thermosetting materials, it is not ordinarily feasible to hold any considerable mass of the material at a high temperature in a heating cylinder before molding. The material would polymerize to a solid, infusible mass in the cylinder under such treatment. Hence in both pot and plunger transfer only sufficient material for a single

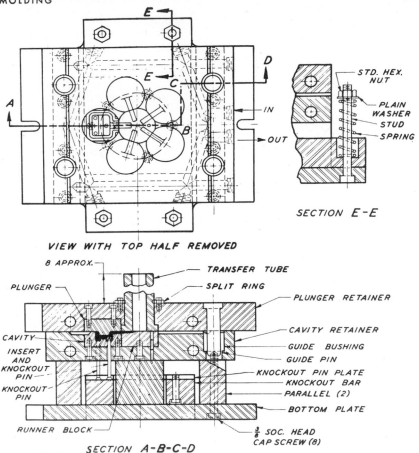

VIEW WITH TOP HALF REMOVED

SECTION E-E

STD. HEX. NUT
PLAIN WASHER
STUD
SPRING

IN
OUT

8 APPROX.

PLUNGER

CAVITY

INSERT AND KNOCKOUT PIN

KNOCKOUT PIN

RUNNER BLOCK

TRANSFER TUBE
SPLIT RING
PLUNGER RETAINER
CAVITY RETAINER
GUIDE BUSHING
GUIDE PIN
KNOCKOUT PIN PLATE
KNOCKOUT BAR
PARALLEL (2)
BOTTOM PLATE
$\frac{3}{8}$ SOC. HEAD CAP SCREW (8)

SECTION A-B-C-D

Fig. 2-8. Plunger-type transfer mold.

shot is heated at one time, and the pot or well is cleaned out completely between shots.

Jet molding, still carried out in a few places, is the only variant of transfer molding in which a mass of granular thermosetting material is heated in an adjacent cylinder, prior to molding. Here, however, the temperature in the cylinder is well below the point of active polymerization. Also, the inside diameter of the heating cylinder is considerably less than in conventional injection molding, and the amount of material heated much less. Additional heat is supplied to the material by means of a special electrode as it passes through the nozzle.

Transfer Molds. *Loose-Plate Molds.* This classification may be subdivided into hand and semiautomatic types, depending on the method of mounting and operation.

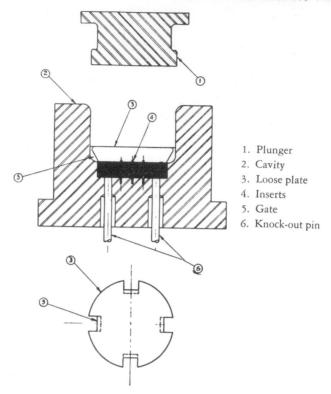

1. Plunger
2. Cavity
3. Loose plate
4. Inserts
5. Gate
6. Knock-out pin

Fig. 2-9. Loose-plate or hand-transfer mold.

One of the first and simplest hand-transfer molds is illustrated in Fig. 2-9. This mold is especially useful where the molded piece contains a group of fragile inserts extending completely through it. The mold consists of a plunger, a loose plate with orifices around its perimeter, and the cavity. The space in the cavity above the loose plate serves as the pot or transfer chamber.

In operation, the inserts are loaded into the loose plate and this is then inserted into the cavity so that the lower ends of the inserts enter the proper holes. The compound is loaded into the mold above the loose plate and is transferred by the plunger through the orifices into the closed mold. After curing, the molded piece, loose plate, and cull are ejected by knockout pins for further disassembly at the bench. Two plates may be used to speed up production.

These molds are most useful when the cost of the mold must be as low as possible, and when volume of production is small.

Figure 2-10 shows a semiautomatic mold assembly of the loose- or floating-plate type. In this case, the floating plate is carried more or less perma-

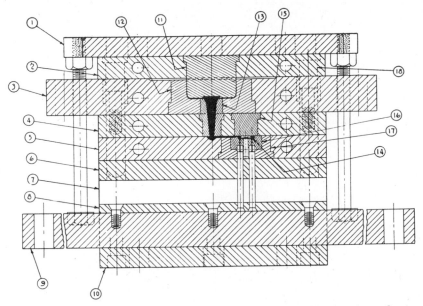

Fig. 2-10. Design of transfer mold for use in a transfer press. The press has a floating platen that will receive transfer chambers of several standard sizes.

1. Top plate	7. Parallel	13. Sprue plug
2. Upper force plate	8. Pin plate	14. Molded article
3. Floating platen	9. Knock-out bar	15. Force
4. Force plate	10. Bottom plate	16. Cavity
5. Cavity plate	11. Upper force	17. Chase
6. Backing-up plate	12. Loading chamber	18. Guide pin

nently in the press and has a central opening that will accommodate stock-transfer pots and plungers of various sizes, as required by different molds. In this way the design of the mold itself is simplified. Presses equipped with these floating plates have been called transfer presses, but are not to be confused with auxiliary-ram transfer presses. Movement of these loose plates may be accomplished either by latches or bolts built into the mold, or by auxiliary pneumatic or hydraulic cylinders attached to the press.

Integral Molds. As the name implies, these molds are self-contained; each one has it own pot and plunger. This frequently increases the efficiency of the mold, since the transfer pot can be designed for best results with a specific cavity. A simple type is illustrated in Fig. 2-11.

Molds of this type can be designed for either manual or semi-automatic operation. The transfer chamber may be located above or below the mold cavity, and the material may flow through a sprue, runner and gate to the cavity, or the sprue may enter the cavity directly, as in the illustration.

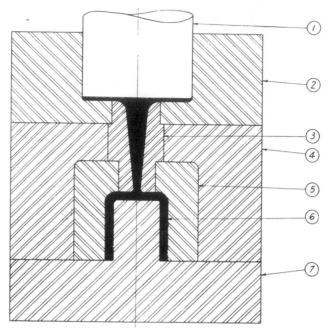

Fig. 2-11. The "integral" or "accordion" type of transfer mold.

1. Plunger   5. Cavity
2. Loading chamber   6. Molded article
3. Sprue   7. Force
4. Cavity plate

Auxiliary-Ram Molds. A mold of this type is illustrated in Fig. 2-12. This is an integral mold, in which the transfer plunger is operated by a separate double-acting cylinder mounted on the press head. As mentioned previously, this transfer cylinder and plunger, may, in alternative designs, be mounted on the bottom press platen, within the main ram, or even on the tie rods or side columns of the press.

These various methods of mounting are usually described as top-ram, bottom-ram, and side-ram mounting, and the molds are designated accordingly.

In comparing the virtues and shortcomings of the various designs of auxiliary-ram molds, it is difficult to generalize because of limiting factors in each design and method of operation. The statements that follow are therefore made with reservations, and with the realization that special conditions in individual plants may alter considerably the conclusions given here.

Top-ram molds are frequently awkward to load, because of the restriction of space between the bolsters and press head, at the upper opening of the transfer tube. Aside from this, and particularly where manual controls are

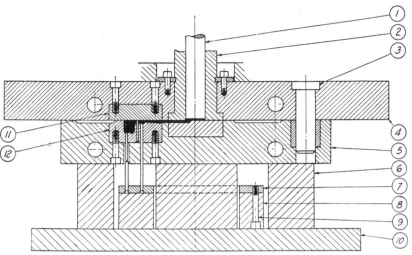

Fig. 2-12. Design of a pressure type of transfer mold which makes use of the conventional press for clamping pressure only. Transfer is effected by means of an auxiliary ram.

1. Plunger	5. Cavity plate	9. Pin-plate screw
2. Loading chamber	6. Parallel	10. Bottom plate
3. Guide pin	7. Pin plate	11. Force
4. Force plate	8. Knock-out bar	12. Cavity

used, top-ram molds will normally permit a faster cycle, after loading, since the mold is already closed at the start of the cycle. There are certain exceptions to this statement, however, as noted later.

Another factor to be considered in any appraisal of top-ram molds is the difficulty of using top ejection mechanisms with this design, because of the space required for the transfer cylinder and ram.

Bottom-ram molds are easier to load, since they are open and the transfer well readily accessible at the beginning of the cycle. However, where manual controls are used, the molding cycle may be longer, because the mold must be closed, after loading, before the transfer ram is actuated. On the other hand, on presses equipped with automatic cycle-controls and timers, bottom-ram molds have shown cycles about 15 per cent faster than top-ram molds in comparative tests.

When a bottom-ram mold is mounted in a conventional upstroke compression press, some of the stroke and opening must be sacrificed to provide mounting space on the lower press platen for the transfer cylinder. In some cases this can be offset by the use of longer side columns or strain rods.

In certain newer bottom-ram transfer presses, the transfer cylinder and ram are contained within the main ram. This saves opening or daylight in the press but usually increases problems of maintenance and repair.

Side-ram molds are less common, and are used primarily where the design of the molded article requires injection of material at the parting line. Theoretically, this design permits use of the full clamping area of the mold, but in actual practice, unless the molding material is extremely soft and fluid and the transfer pressure low, there is a distinct tendency for the mold to spring and flash as a result of localized, unbalanced transfer pressure near the gate.

Whatever method of mounting is used, it is now generally conceded that the auxiliary-ram transfer method permits the highest production with lowest mold cost and minimum loss of material in sprues, runners and culls. Other advantages, common to this and other types of transfer mold, are mentioned below.

Advantages of Transfer Molding. *Molding Cycles.* Loading time is usually shorter in transfer molding, since fewer and larger preforms are used. These can be preheated most rapidly and effectively in dielectric and steam preheating equipment. Also, dielectric preheaters have been designed for use with multiple-cavity compression molds (loading-board preheaters), but they are more expensive.

In entering the mold, the material flows in thin streams through small runners and gates. This promotes heat-transfer, and may also momentarily add some heat to the material through friction and mechanical work. Most phenolic materials are also homogenized thereby, and volatile matter, which might otherwise remain in the piece and necessitate a longer cure to avoid blistering, is reduced in passing through these small channels and by escape through vents and clearance spaces around movable pins. All of these factors contribute to substantially shorter molding cycles than are possible in compression molds, without preheating.

Tool and Maintenance Costs. Deep loading wells are not necessary with transfer molds, and mold sections can be thinner than in compression molds, since they are not required to withstand the higher stresses present during closing of the latter. This obviously permits initial savings in tool costs.

There is less wear on the mold and much less tendency toward breakage of pins. Core pins having a length-to-diameter ratio of 10:1 can be used in transfer molds; the largest ratio that can safely be used in compression molds is about 3:1. Transfer molds retain their original accuracy and finish considerably longer than do compression molds.

Molding Tolerances. Since the articles are produced in closed molds which are subjected to less mechanical wear and erosion by the molding material than are compression molds, closer tolerances on all molded dimensions should be possible in transfer molding. This is particularly true of dimensions perpendicular to parting lines, because of the very small amount of flash in properly designed and operated molds of this type.

Also, it should be possible to hold closer tolerances on diameters of holes and dimensions between holes, since forces in the mold tending to distort or displace pins or inserts are much less.

This is the theoretical ideal which could be attained, if no other factors than those mentioned above were at work in the process. Actually, warpage and dimensional variations have occurred in numerous instances in plunger-molded articles, and it was not possible in these cases to maintain the close dimensional tolerances hoped for.

Careful study of these problems has indicated that these difficulties were caused, in most cases, by abnormal shrinkage and internal strains set up in the molded articles by improper gating and excessive transfer pressure. In some instances, the article, although complicated in outline and section, did not lend itself to transfer molding because of peculiarities of its design.

Those who have studied the auxiliary-ram transfer process most thoroughly are convinced that in most instances close tolerances can be held, and optimum dimensional stability realized if, and only if, the preheating, the plasticity of the material and the transfer pressure are accurately controlled, and if the runners and gates are so located, and of such size and shape, as to permit rapid, free flow of the material into the closed mold.

Finishing Costs. Transfer molding reduces costs of finishing of all thermosetting materials, and especially of those having cotton flock and chopped fabric as filler. In an article molded from these latter in a compression mold, the flash is frequently heavy, tough, and expensive to remove; this condition becomes even worse as the mold wears. In a transfer-molded article, assuming a properly designed mold with adequate clamping pressure, the flash is quite thin or altogether absent.

Gates, except in certain cases with fabric-filled phenolics, can usually be made sufficiently thin, and can be so located, that their removal is easy and inexpensive. It may be possible to gate into a hole in the molded piece and to remove the gate by drilling.

Limitations of the Process. As might be expected, there are certain intrinsic limitations in transfer molding. These are detailed below.

Mold Costs. The statements concerning lower mold costs apply particularly to auxiliary-ram transfer molds. Pot-type transfer molds may, in some cases, be more expensive than equivalent compression molds, without offsetting advantages.

Loss of Material. The material left in the pot or well, and also the sprue and runners, is completely polymerized and must be discarded. This loss of material is unavoidable, and for small articles can present a sizable percentage of the weight of the pieces molded. In the auxiliary-ram molds, this cull is reduced to a minimum and the sprue is eliminated.

Transfer molding is not well suited to production of small molded items such as buttons and closures, because of this loss of material. These items can be molded in much larger volume and more cheaply in multiple-cavity compression molds or high-speed automatic compression-molding machines.

Effect on Mechanical Strength. With woodflour-filled materials, no significant loss of mechanical strength attributable to the transfer-molding process has been observed in laboratory tests on standard ASTM specimens. This conclusion has correlated reasonably well with general production molding experience.

Some instances of cracking around inserts and at weld lines have been noted in production-molded articles, especially with mineral-filled phenolics and melamine materials, which have inherently lower mechanical strength.

Changing the design and location of gates, altering the cycle of preheating, or reducing volatile content of the plastic material, when tried separately or in combination, have overcome these difficulties in many cases; in some severe cases, however, no practicable remedy could be found within the framework of the transfer-molding process, and it was necessary to mold the articles by compression in order to overcome the trouble.

With improved-impact materials containing fibrous fillers, a definite and sometimes marked decrease from values obtained in compression molding has been noted by a number of investigators.

At first this was believed to be due to orientation of the fibers of the filler, or to shredding or degradation in passing through small runners and gates. Later experimental work tends to disprove this, and the theory currently held is that this effect is due to additional impregnation or saturation of the filler occurring during flow through small runners and gates, because of the high transfer pressures used. It is indicated that this effect on strength can be minimized by the use of lower transfer pressures and larger gates, and can be substantially eliminated by employing less absorptive fillers which do not permit this secondary impregnation to occur.

Royalty Charges. Licenses are issued to cover applications of transfer molding, under Shaw patents. Where applicable, the royalty charges must be included as an additional item in the cost of the job.

Materials Used

Phenol-formaldehyde and melamine-formaldehyde molding compounds are the most widely used materials in transfer molding. General results with these are excellent.

Urea-formaldehyde materials have been transfer-molded quite successfully in some cases, principally small articles, but because of their reactivity and critical behavior in dielectric preheating, the process has not been found as generally satisfactory with them as with the phenolics and melamines.

Some improvement in behavior of the ureas in transfer molding has already been achieved, and research is continuing in this direction.

The newly introduced alkyd or polyester molding materials have been tested extensively in transfer molds. In certain cases they have proved suitable for smaller articles, but their extremely fast rate of reaction has prevented their use in larger molds and in articles where considerable plastic flow is required.

Phenol-Formaldehyde Materials. Phenolic materials of all of the standard types, containing any of the usual fillers, can be successfully molded by transfer. The principal types used are listed below:

Type	Filler
general-purpose	woodflour
heat-resistant	asbestos
medium-impact	cotton flock or fabric
high-impact	cotton fabric
highest-impact	chopped cotton cord
low-electrical-loss	mica

For satisfactory use in transfer molding, a phenolic material must be extremely fluid at molding temperature, in order to flow readily through runners and gates and form dense homogeneous molded parts. For most economical production, this flow should be accomplished in the shortest possible time, i.e., the material should have a rapid rate of flow.

Phenolic materials now available possess these properties and, with the aid of dielectric or steam preheating, give excellent results in transfer molds of all types.

Melamine-Formaldehyde Materials. Mineral-filled, cellulose-filled and fabric-filled melamine materials have been employed in transfer molding with good results. Certain melamine-urea formulations have also shown good characteristics in transfer molding.

Melamine materials may require some modification of basic properties in order to produce best flow in transfer. These compounds as a class show greater after-shrinkage than do phenolics. This tendency exists more or less independently of the method of molding; it can be considerably reduced by proper control of the resin and its compounding, and by suitable preheating before molding.

Theoretical and Design Considerations

There are many and diverse opinions within the industry, concerning design of transfer molds, and molding pressures and molding techniques, and a decided lack of authoritative and specific data. Because of the many factors involved, no hard and fast rules can be given to serve as infallible guides in the design and operation of these molds. The principal factors are listed below, and recommendations based on experience and successful current practice are given.

Mold Design. It is considered good practice in multiple-cavity plunger-type transfer molds to mount the mold cavities, forces and runners as separate hardened steel inserts in the mold chases or retainer plates. This permits removal of individual mold cavities and runner blocks for repair or replacement when wear or breakage occurs. Where not precluded by other features of design, such as location of steam channels and ejector pins, a circular layout of mold cavities with short radial runners from the central well is preferred. However, there are numerous examples of successful transfer molds having various ladder and multiple-"T" arrangements.

The center pad beneath the pressure well should be hardened and well supported, to prevent deflection and consequent flashing of the mold. For the same reason, all mating mold surfaces should be ground smooth and perfectly flat to provide uniform contact. It is not imperative that cavities and runners be chrome-plated, but this is usually advisable, to improve release from the mold, and to reduce wear, particularly in the runners.

Runners, Gates and Vents. The design of runners and the size and location of gates are some of the most controversial subjects in this field. The recommendations given below are in accord with current practice, but are not intended to be infallible pronouncements.

Main runners are usually $1/4$ to $5/16$ in. wide and $1/8$ in. deep, and semicircular in section; branch runners, where used, should be about $1/8$ in. wide and $3/32$ in. deep. These runners are located in the half of the mold containing the ejector pins; this is usually the plate opposite the pressure well. The runners should be kept to minimum length and should extend into the pad at the bottom of the pressure well at least $1/2$ in.

Location, size and shape of gates are quite important to proper operation of the mold. While there are many conflicting opinions concerning location, and while striking individual exceptions may be found on particular jobs, it is considered good practice to place the gate at the thickest section of the molded article and, whenever possible, at a readily accessible point on the article, so that it can be removed by simple sanding or filing.

The size of the gate will vary with the type of material molded, the size of the piece and the molding pressure available. For small pieces, and where general-purpose woodflour-filled phenolics are used, it is recommended that the gate be 0.80 to 0.100 in. wide and 0.015 to 0.020 in. deep. With mineral-filled materials, a gate 0.125 in. wide and 0.030 in. deep is usually necessary.

The shape of gates for transfer molds has recently received considerable study. Experimental work by Borro with gates and runners of varied shape and cross-section has indicated that a circular section is the most desirable. This permits rapid transfer at moderate pressures. Such gates must usually be located at parting lines and must be cut into both halves of the mold. This will increase machining costs somewhat, but this consideration would be of minor importance if the beneficial effects indicated are attained.

Because of the coarseness of the fillers used in high-impact materials, larger gates are usually necessary, both to lessen the transfer pressure required and to prevent reduction in mechanical strength of the molded articles. In these cases, a width of 0.500 in. and depth of 0.125 in. may be needed.

These are general recommendations; it may well be necessary, in individual cases, to enlarge gates beyond these dimensions, depending on circumstances. It is always easier, in any case, to remove metal from a mold than add it.

Vents are almost equally important, to permit escape of air, moisture and other volatiles, as the materials fill the mold cavity. It is frequently found that without proper vents the mold cavities will not fill properly even under high transfer pressures.

Vents should be located on the same half of the mold as the runners, and opposite the gate. They are usually 0.003 to 0.005 in. deep, and about ⅛ in. wide, and are extended to the outer surface of the mold block.

Selection of Material. The problem here is threefold—to choose the type of material that will yield the desired physical properties in the molded article, e.g., impact strength, heat-resistance, or low electrical loss; next, to choose from among a number of formulations of this type the one having the proper preheating and molding characteristics for the mold in question; finally, to choose the proper plasticity, which will provide the fastest transfer and cure. This last cannot be decided in advance; it must be determined by experiment.

Choice of the proper plasticity is very important. A material which is unduly stiff will be extremely critical in behavior during preheating, and may not fill the mold; a material that is too soft may flash the mold or require excessive preheating to attain a satisfactorily rapid cure.

A maximum transfer time of 10 to 15 seconds at a mold temperature of 320 to 350°F, with a preform temperature of 220 to 260°F, is usually found satisfactory. It will be realized that individual conditions may depart somewhat from these values, but these represent the average of general experience.

Molding Pressures. It would be extremely difficult, if not impossible, to measure accurately, or to calculate theoretically, the magnitude and distribution of pressure within thermosetting material flowing in a transfer mold. If all of the factors involved were in perfect dynamic balance, there would be no unbalanced fluid pressure in the mold cavity, at the moment of complete filling.

Initially, with either pot or plunger molds, fluid pressure in the hydraulic line to the press is converted to mechanical motion and then to mechanical pressure on the molding material, as the latter is compressed and forced into the closed mold. As the mold fills, and polymerization of the material continues, this pressure builds up to a maximum. Ideally, at the moment when the mold is filled completely, all of the material will have hardened to infusibility, and the transfer pressure, transmitted through the hardened material, would be balanced exactly by the clamping pressure applied to the closed mold by the main ram.

Actually, no such ideal equilibrium is attained. Usually, even after the mold is filled, the material is still in a semiplastic state, and for a few seconds, at least, exerts an indeterminate fluid pressure on the interior surfaces of the mold. If this were not counterbalanced by external clamping pressure, the mold would open and the material would flash excessively at the moment of filling. To take care of this condition, it is necessary to provide excess clamping area, or pressure more than that theoretically necessary.

Pot-type transfer molds are usually provided with only one source of molding pressure, the main ram; plunger molds, on the other hand, usually have two, more or less independent, sources of pressure, for the main and transfer rams. It is usual, therefore, in designing transfer molds, to equate transfer area to total mold-clamping area for the pot type, and transfer pressure to clamping pressure for the plunger type, and then to allow 10 to 15 per cent excess clamping area, or pressure, to prevent opening of the mold, and flashing. Usually, if the mold is properly supported in the press, this margin will be sufficient.

Because of the many variables in design of article and of mold, and in molding conditions, involved in each application, it is practically impossible to calculate the minimum transfer pressure required to mold a given article. Only empirical assumptions can be made, based on limited experimental data and on previous production molding experience.

For soft-plasticity general-purpose phenolic material, which is electronically preheated, minimum transfer pressures of 8000 psi for plunger-type and of 12,000 psi for pot-type transfer molding are generally recommended. This assumes a total runner area of about 0.05 sq in., and is valid primarily for quantities of material of the order of 100 grams. When preheating is done in an oven, it will usually be necessary to increase transfer pressure by 100 per cent and, for quantities of material greater than 100 grams, to enlarge runner and gate areas by 50 to 100 per cent.

For fabric-filled phenolic materials also, a 50 per cent increase in transfer pressure will usually be required to keep transfer time to an economical minimum. Here, too, larger gates, as recommended previously, should be used to avoid the secondary impregnation and consequent embrittlement of the material.

Design Calculations. The various factors included in design of plunger transfer molds in so far as pressure is concerned, can be defined and illustrated as follows:

1. *Line pressure.* The pressure in psi in the hydraulic line to the press, supplied either by a self-contained pump or from a central pump and accumulator system.

2. *Clamping-ram pressure.* The total pressure delivered by the main ram. It is found by multiplying the ram area by the line pressure.

3. *Injection-ram pressure.* The total force applied by the injection ram, expressed in pounds, determined by multiplying the ram area by the line pressure.

4. *Plunger pressure.* The pressure exerted on the material in the transfer chamber by the plunger. It is equal to the injection-ram pressure divided by the area of the plunger.

5. *Mold-clamping pressure.* The effective pressure which holds the mold closed against the pressure exerted by the material within the mold cavities and runners. It is expressed in psi and is determined by dividing the clamping-ram pressure by the total projected area of cavities and runners in square inches.

These factors can be shown symbolically as follows:

L $\quad$ = line pressure, psi

A_M $\quad$ = area of mold cavities, lands and runners, sq in.

A_R $\quad$ = area of clamping ram, sq in.

A_I $\quad$ = area of injection ram, sq in.

A_P $\quad$ = area of plunger, sq in.

CRP = clamping-ram pressure = $A_R \times L$, lb

IRP = injection-ram pressure = $A_I \times L$, lb

PP $\quad$ = plunger pressure = $\dfrac{A_I \times L}{A_P}$, psi

MCP = mold-clamping pressure = $\dfrac{A_R \times L}{A_M}$, psi

By definition, to ensure safe operation and avoid flashing: mold-clamping pressure = plunger pressure + 15 per cent, or:

$$MCP = 1.15\ PP$$

Practical application of this simple equation is demonstrated in the following example.

Example

How many cavities can be placed in a mold which is to operate under the following conditions?

projected area of molded article = 3 sq in.

estimated runner area per cavity = 1 sq in.

total area per cavity = 4 sq in.

diameter of main ram = 14 in.

diameter of injection ram = 6 in.

plunger diameter = 3 in.

line pressure = 2,000 psi

Let x = the number of cavities

L $\quad$ = 2,000 psi

A_M = $4x$

$$A_R = \frac{3.1416 \times 14^2}{4} = 154 \text{ sq in.}$$

$$A_I = \frac{3.1416 \times 6^2}{4} = 28.3 \text{ sq in.}$$

$$A_P = \frac{3.1416 \times 3^2}{4} = 7.0 \text{ sq in.}$$

$$CRP = A_R \times L = 154 \times 2{,}000 = 308{,}000 \text{ lb}$$
$$IRP = A_I \times L = 28.3 \times 2{,}000 = 56{,}600 \text{ lb}$$

$$PP = \frac{A_I \times L}{A_P} = \frac{56{,}600}{7} = 8{,}085 \text{ psi}$$

$$MCP = \frac{A_R \times L}{A_M} = \frac{308{,}000}{4x} = \frac{77{,}000 \text{ psi}}{x}$$

$$MCP = 1.15 \, PP$$

$$\frac{77{,}000}{x} = 1.15 \times 8{,}085$$

$$x = \frac{77{,}000}{1.15 \times 8{,}085} = 8.3 \text{ or 8 cavities}$$

In designing pot-type transfer molds, where the only source of external pressure is the main ram, the pot area is equated to the total mold area and, as mentioned previously, the latter is increased by 15 per cent to prevent flashing.

Let L = line pressure, psi

A_R = area of main ram, sq in.

A_P = area of pot or material chamber, sq in.

A_M = area of mold cavities, lands and runners, sq in.

CF = clamping force = $A_R \times L$, lb

$$MCP = \text{mold-clamping pressure} = \frac{A_R \times L}{A_M}, \text{ psi}$$

Then, for equilibrium, with the factor of safety:

(1) $A_M = 1.15 \, A_P$

(2) $A_M = \dfrac{A_R \times L}{MCP}$

(3) $\dfrac{A_R \times L}{MCP} = 1.15 \, A_P$

Other Considerations. It has been assumed in the foregoing discussion of transfer-molding pressure that flashing will be prevented if sufficient clamping pressure or area is provided. This is generally true if the mold is properly supported, particularly under the transfer chamber. However, if insufficient bolstering is used at this point, or if the mold is not properly aligned or hardened, deflection can occur and permit flashing, in spite of the excess clamping pressure provided in the design.

Transfer pressure should be sufficient to fill the mold, under ordinary circumstances, in 10 to 15 sec. Excessive transfer pressure should be avoided— it may cause flashing, it will probably cause undue wear of gates and runners, and it may decrease normal molding shrinkage to the point where articles are outside normal tolerances.

The rate at which a phenolic material will preheat in a dielectric pre-heater depends, among other factors, on the high-frequency output of the machine and on the electrical-loss characteristics of the material involved. Woodfloor-filled compounds, having a higher electrical-loss factor, will preheat more rapidly than mica-filled materials. Modern dielectric preheaters of 2 KW output are designed to heat approximately one pound of woodflour-filled material from room temperature to 250°F in one minute.

Where a number of preforms are being preheated at one time, the uniformity of preheating of the material is quite important. This is related directly to the hardness and density of the preforms. If these are not uniform in density, their temperatures will vary considerably and their behavior in transfer will be erratic. Once established, optimum preheating conditions should be maintained as nearly constant as possible for a given batch of material.

Numerous other factors affect transfer molding, but these are already familiar to molders employing this method, and need not be described in detail. It has been the purpose of this article, rather, to point out some of the important features of this method and the advantages in increased production and lowered production costs that may be achieved with it, if certain fundamental considerations are known and observed.

2. INJECTION OF THERMOSETTING MATERIALS

About 1940, modifications of injection molding were developed for molding of the thermosetting materials. These processes are called jet, flow, and offset injection molding. Each, with its minor variations, was developed for the production of small articles, especially those requiring inserts. They provide means of molding articles comprising thin and heavy sections, and articles having long holes of small diameter. The resulting molded articles have a uniform density throughout all sections and, in general, the maximum physical characteristics of the material from which they are molded.

In the jet process, the problem of preventing premature hardening of the thermosetting materials is solved by (1) holding the temperature of the heating cylinder at a point at which the molding material is made plastic without being polymerized appreciably; (2) using sufficient pressure on the injection plunger to force the viscous mass through the nozzle orifice; (3) utilizing

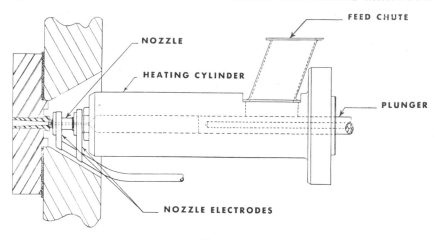

Fig. 2-13

the heat of compression, as well as the frictional heat caused by the flow of the material as it is forced through the nozzle; and (4) applying additional heat to the plastic mass as it passes through the nozzle.

The accompanying sketch (Fig. 2-13) illustrates some of the principal features of a jet-molding machine. The design of the mold-clamp and the general construction of a jet machine are similar to those of a conventional injection-molding machine. It is possible to install jet attachments on most injection machines.

The nozzle is an important part of the jet machine. It must be instantly heated and thereafter cooled, during each molding cycle. The nozzle must heat the material, as it passes through the orifice, to the temperature required for polymerization. The heating of the nozzle is accomplished by energizing a low-voltage transformer, which develops current between the electrodes to heat the nozzle, almost instantaneously, to about 285°F. The nozzle is cooled by running water through the electrodes. The temperature of the nozzle must be raised rapidly to heat the material, and then at the end of the stroke quickly reduced to prevent polymerization of the material that remains in it and also to prevent bleeding of soft material from the open nozzle after the injection cycle has been completed.

The front and rear sections of the nozzle are cooled independently. Cooling at the front offsets heat conducted from the mold block, and controls the break-off point of the sprue; cooling at the rear prevents heat from the hot nozzle from reaching the material in the cone end of the nozzle, and polymerizing it.

General-purpose and nodulated high-impact materials can be fed from the hoppers in general use on standard injection machines. But fabric-filled materials from CFI-5 to CFI-40 must usually be loaded by hand into the feed cylinder. This is done in the interval during the cure of the article in the mold. The charges of such materials should be weighed, to keep molding conditions constant, and to prevent overloading of the cylinder.

Glass-reinforced alkyd compounds are readily molded by jet. They must be loaded by hand. Also, these compounds require a highly polished chromed-plated cylinder. The nozzle electrodes are not required as the frictional heat developed during the injection stroke is adequate to plastify the material to the proper degree.

High-impact compounds containing asbestos are more difficult to handle, some impossible to mold, by this process, because of their low thermal conductivity. Furthermore, the jet process tends to break the fibers of the asbestos and thereby impair the strength of the molded article.

Urea-formaldehydes are readily molded by jet. But the period of heating the heating cylinder is likely to discolor the pastel colors.

In general, the melamine-formaldehydes can be jet-molded, but not economically, because of their gassing.

Over-all cycles, on converted standard machines, range ordinarily from 30 sec to 2 min, depending on the type of the material and the limitations of the machine. In general, the rate of molding is faster than that of compression or transfer, through saving of time in handling material. And because all of the material is subjected to the same temperature, thick sections can be cured as rapidly as thin sections; this is an advantage in articles which combine thick and thin sections.

The size of pieces produced by this method has been limited by the capacities of the available converted machines, the largest being 16 oz. Articles weighing over 2 lb have been produced on an experimental machine. A mold-shot may be injected into one large cavity, or divided into many small cavities, within the limit of the capacity of the mold clamp.

Typical articles made by jet molding are shown in Fig. 2-14.

Jet molding can be used also for thermoplastic materials and for compounds of natural rubber. The same general procedure is followed as with thermosetting materials, but the plunger pressure is usually lower. However, molding cycles are considerably longer than in standard injection molding, and hence the method usually proves to be too costly. The process appears to be advantageous, however, for some of the newer critical thermoplastic materials.

For molding thermoplastic, the temperature of the heating cylinder is held substantially below that required for conventional injection molding, and the necessary additional heat is applied at the nozzle, but only to the amount of material injected into the mold in each cycle. The cooling of the nozzle between shots acts as a valve to prevent further flow of the material.

With compounds of natural rubber, the curing is faster than in the conventional compression method. Rubber compounds have been molded at approximately the same speed as the phenolics, whereas 15 to 30 minutes was required for the same materials when molded by compression.

Courtesy Evans-Winter-Hebb, Inc.

Fig. 2-14

Flow molding is very similar to jet molding with the exception that the use of electrodes on the nozzle, and of special nozzles, is eliminated. In some instances band heaters on the cylinder have been replaced by circulation of hot oil, steam, or high-pressure hot water, on the assumption that band heaters cause local overheating and premature setting up of a thermosetting compound.

Offset injection molding is so named because the injection plunger instead of pressing material directly into a mold forces it sideways into passages offset along its path. A heated preform is dropped into a yoke fastened to the front of the stationary platen of an injection machine, directly ahead of the plunger. The plunger passes clear through the stationary half of the mold and forces the soft preform into runners and cavities at the sides, where it quickly sets. As in jet and injection molding, the return stroke opens the mold and automatically ejects the molded parts. Excess flash is removed from the mold by compressed air. Some machines have built-in high-frequency terminals for preheating preforms, which are then automatically fed ahead of the plunger.

Advantages of the offset process are a fast cycle, large capacity, and low plunger pressure. With comparatively light machinery it molds pieces of a size previously thought to be possible only with huge presses, prohibitive cycles, and expensive molds with numerous cavities.

INJECTION MOLDING OF THERMOPLASTIC MATERIALS

History

The process of injecting plastics can be traced back to 1872 with the invention of the stuffing machine by John Wesley Hyatt and his brother Isaiah. The important feature of the machine was the heating cylinder, which consisted of a steam-heated chamber provided with a discharge nozzle and a hydraulically operated plunger. The machines were used for extruding rods, sheets or tubes of cellulose nitrate plastic. In 1872 I. S. and J. W. Hyatt were awarded a patent* covering the molding of individual pieces by injecting the material from the stuffing machine into a closed mold held in a vertical hydraulic press mounted alongside the stuffing machine.

The instability of cellulose nitrate limited its utility in this early form of injection molding. The restriction on operating temperatures imposed by this instability made it necessary to use volatile solvent in the mix in order to achieve the degree of plastification required for molding; and the removal of this solvent by the subsequent step of seasoning caused irregular shrinkage and warpage of the molded article. This distortion was acceptable only in some articles of inherently irregular contour, such as imitations of stag horn for cutlery handles.

The advent of cellulose acetate, with its superior stability under heat, made possible the development of injection molding in the absence of volatile solvent—a mixture of cellulose acetate with a percentage of plasticizer, appropriate to provide the mechanical properties desired in the molded article, will tolerate the temperature required to soften it enough to be injected into the closed mold.

The first successful work on the injection molding of cellulose acetate appears to have been done by Dr. Arthur Eichengrün in 1919, with simple hand-operated presses. In the early twenties Eichengrün enlisted the cooperation of Eckert und Ziegler, who had considerable experience in the building of die-casting machines. By adapting from the die-casting process certain features, such as mechanisms for closing, clamping and adjusting molds, they constructed successful machine-type injection presses.

The present state of injection molding is the result of parallel development in injection-molding equipment and molding materials, largely since 1935.

Process

Injection molding takes advantage of the characteristic of thermoplastic materials, that they are softened by heat and harden when cooled. No chemical change takes place when the material is heated or cooled, the change being entirely physical. Hence the cycle of softening and hardening can be repeated

* U. S. Patent No. 133,229.

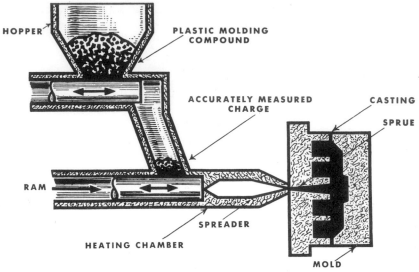

HOPPER

PLASTIC MOLDING
COMPOUND

ACCURATELY MEASURED
CHARGE

CASTING

SPRUE

RAM

SPREADER

HEATING CHAMBER

MOLD

Fig. 2-15

any number of times, within the limits imposed by any cumulative degradation caused by exposure to heat.

Most of the principles of injection molding have been borrowed from the older art of die casting.

Granular molding material is fed into one end of a heated cylinder, is heated and thereby softened (plastified) in the cylinder, and is pushed out of the other end of the cylinder into a relatively cool closed mold, in which it hardens, and from which the molded article is then removed (see Fig. 2-15).

In order to provide time for the heating of each successive charge of the molding material (which is a poor conductor of heat), the cylinder is designed with capacity and length to hold a number of charges, from four to eight as a rule, and is kept filled by metering the feed, either by volume or weight, to balance exactly the delivery of softened material into the mold. Thus, at all times the cylinder contains a number of successive charges in progress from the cold feed end through the heating zones to the delivery end.

Within the cylinder, at the approach to the delivery end, is mounted a spreader or "torpedo" which diverts the material into constricted channels where it may be more uniformly heated and softened.

The delivery end of the cylinder is fitted with a nozzle containing a small orifice, which during injection fits tightly against a bushing which gives entry into the closed mold. This opening into the mold is known as the sprue. In a single-cavity mold, the sprue delivers the plastic, through a constriction termed the gate, into the mold cavity. In multicavity molds, intermediate channels, known as runners, carry the material from the sprue to the gates of the cavities.

The terms "sprue," "runner," and "gate" are used not only to designate these channels themselves, but also to designate the corresponding parts of the single continuous piece of hardened plastic as removed from the mold.

The gate is constricted to facilitate separation ("degating") of the molded article from the runner or sprue.

Usually there is provided, in direct line at the end of the sprue, a small cavity known as the "cold-slug well," which serves to trap a tiny slug of material which has hardened in the injection nozzle between shots, and thus to prevent it from blocking a runner or gate. In most molds this well is provided with an undercut and serves also as a sprue-puller.

The mold, in two parts accurately fitted to each other to prevent escape of material under injection pressure, is closed and opened by a clamping device, which must exert enough pressure to hold the mold tightly closed against the hydrostatic pressure transmitted by the injection plunger over the total projected area of cavities and runners.

The pressure required to push the material through the heating cylinder and into the mold can vary from 10,000 to 25,000 psi. Suitable controls are used to adjust this pressure to fit the molding operation. It is variously estimated that from 25 to 75 per cent of this injection pressure is transmitted to and must be resisted by the mold clamp.

In detail, the following sequence of steps takes place:

The clamping device closes, causing the moving half of the mold (retained on the moving platen) to close against the stationary half of the mold (retained on the stationary platen).

The nozzle of the injection cylinder comes into contact with the sprue bushing of the mold. The injection ram or plunger then enters the material cylinder and pushes the new charge of material, fed by the metering device, into the heating cylinder, and in so doing displaces a like weight of material from the cylinder into the mold. The injection ram maintains pressure on the material as it cools in the mold. At the end of the required time, the injection ram returns to its neutral position.

At a desired time after the injection and the return of the ram, determined by the time required to fully harden the moldings, the clamping device opens the mold (see Fig. 2-16). The molded article is retained usually in the moving half, and is ejected from the mold by pins, sleeves or plates when the knockout plate of the mold makes contact with the knockout bars of the machine.

The molded article is removed from the mold and the machine is then ready for the next cycle. The clamping device closes the mold and the cycle is repeated.

These operations may be carried out by manually actuating the various control levers. But the general practice is to operate the machine automatically, by means of adjustable timing clocks, which operate solenoids, which in turn actuate the control levers in accordance with the desired timing of the sequence.

Courtesy The Hydraulic Press Mfg.Co.

Fig. 2-16

The temperature to which the material has to be heated in the heating cylinder depends on several factors, but is usually between 350 and 575°F. Thermoplastics, except nylon, and possibly the new polystyrene "alloys," do not have a clearly defined softening point, but rather become progressively more fluid over a wide range of temperature; the higher the temperature, the lower the viscosity of the material, and the more readily it can be pushed into the die. Intricate pieces, large pieces, numerous cavities, and long runners all tend to increase the temperature required, but overheating tends to degrade the plastic and embrittle the molded article.

The temperature to which cellulosics must be heated is largely determined by the type and amount of plasticizer used in the material. Soft-flow formulations with high plasticizer content require lower cylinder temperature than do the hard formulations, and are easier to mold. They also have higher impact strength and greater elongation than the hard-flows. But in all other physical properties the hard-flow materials are superior.

Cylinder temperature affects the strength of molded articles of cellulosics of any formula. As the temperature is raised, within the allowable range for the formula, the impact strength and elongation increase, while the tensile and flexural strength decrease. This applies also, to a less marked degree, to polystyrenes and acrylics. The use of lubricants and high cylinder temperatures to make the material flow more easily impairs the ultimate physical properties of the molded article.

The maximum and minimum temperatures between which a material can be molded may be only 10 degrees apart or they may be as much as 100 degrees apart, depending on the design of the mold, the machine, the material, and the article to be molded. Below the minimum temperature, the pieces will not be completely filled out, will show obvious weld and flow marks, and will have a dull, lusterless surface. Above the maximum temperature, the surface will show birds'-eyes, striation, scales, burns, and sink marks; there will be more flash than the mold should allow, and even discoloration and decomposition. Exact control of cylinder temperature is a vital part of injection molding.

The temperature of the mold will always be held low enough to cause the molded article to harden so that it can be removed from the mold. But the mold is not always literally cold; frequently, because of the nature of the molding, or of the material being used, it is necessary to use a warm mold. Mold temperatures as high as 240°F are used in some cases, especially with nylon.

In most cases it is important to hold the temperature of the mold at an optimum level by circulation of water or other medium. All too often, the need for exact control of mold temperature is disregarded.

Mold temperatures on the high side permit the use of lower injection pressures and lower cylinder temperatures, and minimize internal strains in the molded article, and warpage after molding. Since higher mold temperature often means longer cycles, the general practice is to run the molds as cool as possible.

Finishing Operations

Injection-molded articles require very few finishing operations. The major operation is degating, and this is often accomplished at the press by the press operator, particularly in the case of novelty merchandise, on which perfection of finish is not required. If the gate has to be trimmed more carefully, this can be done with a shearing die, knife, routing cutter, wet sander or burnishing wheel. Seldom does the mold-parting line on the piece have to be touched, because the mold is closed before the material is introduced, and hence only a very slight mark is left on the molding.

Molds

The sizes and locations of runners and gates play an important part in the success of a mold. The runner is the channel through which the material flows from the sprue to the cavity. There is no satisfactory formula for predetermining how large a runner should be. A good starting point for an average mold is a diameter of $\frac{1}{4}$ in.; for very large molds, $\frac{3}{8}$ to $\frac{1}{2}$ in.; for very small molds $\frac{1}{8}$ in. If the runner is larger than necessary, too much material is wasted, sometimes taxing the capacity of the machine, and often lengthening the cycle by the necessity of chilling the unnecessarily thick section. If the runner is too small, resistance to flow is greater, the material is cooled too much before it reaches the cavity, and cylinder temperature has to be raised to allow for this drop.

Runners should be well polished, and rounded at all turns. Wherever possible, they should be cylindrical, with one half cut in each side of the mold. Where this is not practicable, they should be trapezoidal, with the depth almost equal to the width. In no case should they be wide and shallow. The ratio of perimeter to area should be as small as possible.

It is advisable to plan the layout of a multicavity mold so that it is symmetrical, with all cavities equidistant from the sprue. This helps to get all cavities filled at the same time, and with equal pressure.

The gate, or opening through which the material enters the cavity of the mold, must also be variously designed to meet specific requirements. The smallest gate is the easiest to trim off; hence it is wise to keep it as small as possible, consistent with good molding. In polystyrene, pieces weighing more than a pound have been satisfactorily molded through a gate of diameter 0.030 in., but some molders insist that a gate $\frac{1}{8}$ in. wide by 0.050 in. deep should be minimum. Very small gates are commonly called restricted or pin-point gates. They work well also with cellulose acetate butyrate, polyethylene and vinyls, and in some cases with cellulose acetate and acrylics. It is well to remember that it is easier to enlarge a gate that is too small, than to reduce one that is too large.

The location of the gate is very important. It has always been recommended that a large gate enter the piece at the heavier sections. The recently recognized restricted gates, however, work much better when they feed into the thinnest section, and best of all when the entering material impinges on a wall of the cavity before it spreads to the rest of the cavity.

In planning the location of the gate, consideration must be given to the path which the material will follow as it proceeds to fill the cavity. This pattern of flow determines the occurrence and location of flow marks, weld lines, and air pockets.

Since the mold is tightly closed before the material is injected, provision must be made for getting rid of the air in the cavity. If the last part of the cavity to fill is at the parting line, a groove, 0.002 to 0.004 in. deep, can be ground from that point to the outer surface of the mold. If the last part to fill is not at the parting line, an ejector pin may be located at that point and provided with several flats, ground to a depth of 0.002 in. Such vents can usually be effectively and accurately located only after the mold has been tried out. If the cavity is not correctly vented, proper filling is difficult, a poor weld may result, or the trapped air may even be compressed enough to overheat and burn the material.

To facilitate removal of articles from the mold, it is necessary to provide adequate draft on the surfaces of the mold, usually ½ to 1 degree on a side. But consideration must be given also to molding technique, since injection pressure, cycle, temperature of material and mold all influence the ease of ejection from the mold. If the pressure is too high, or is left on too long, the article tends to adhere to the mold.

Often it is necessary to use a mold lubricant to achieve proper release from the mold. Vegetable oils and silicone oils are effective. They can be swabbed or brushed on, or sprayed on diluted with a flash solvent. Or stearate powder can be dusted on. Caution must be observed in the use of such mold-release agents, however, since they may affect the finish of the molded piece by leaving spots, cause crazing, or interfere with such secondary operations as painting or cementing.

Characteristics of Molding Compounds

Special consideration must be given to the characteristics of the various molding compounds.

Polystyrene, for example, is the most difficult to release from the mold, and requires a draft angle of 1 to 2 degrees.

Vinyls tend to be decomposed chemically by prolonged exposure to high temperature; the corrosive character of the products of this decomposition necessitates the use of chrome-plated injection cylinders, or cylinders made of corrosion-resistant alloys, and even then it is wise to purge hot material from the cylinder during a shut-down. Some molders manage to use standard cylinders by planning their vinyl jobs well within the rated capacity of their machines, and then using extra caution not to overheat the material.

Nylon has a very sharp softening point and is very fluid at its molding temperature; with it, the clearance between mating mold parts must be made extremely small, to preclude flashing. Special precautions must be taken to prevent drooling of the fluid nylon from the nozzle between shots. This is accomplished by using a reverse-taper nozzle with very closely controlled temperature. A filter plug is often used in the nozzle to prevent unmelted particles of nylon from coming through.

Cellulosic and vinyl materials absorb moisture readily, and this moisture causes unsightly surface blemishes on the moldings. It is therefore necessary to dry these materials immediately before molding. This can be done by conveying the material slowly under infrared lamps, or by storing for 2 to 3 hours, in shallow trays, in circulating warm-air ovens at a temperature of about 180°F, or by using a warm-air dryer mounted directly on the material hopper.

Polystyrene and acrylics absorb very little moisture. But occasionally, under very humid conditions, moisture condenses on the surface of the granules of these materials; this must be removed by the same procedure as with the cellulosics, except that the time required for drying is much shorter.

Injection Presses   (Figs. 2-17 and 2-18)

There are several makes and varieties of injection machines, and to each one molders have added innovations. The injection machine consists essentially of two units. One unit, the clamping unit, supports, opens, and closes a mold, and maintains it in the closed position under suitable clamping pressure. The other unit, the injection unit, converts the plastic from solid particles into a continuous semifluid or fluid mass and injects it into the closed mold.

The clamping unit comprises supporting frame, clamping head, clamping devices, moving platen, stationary platen and knockout devices.

The injection unit comprises a supporting frame or base, the injection head and piston, the injection plunger or ram, the heating cylinder and the feeding device.

To make the clamping unit and the injection unit operate in proper sequence, auxiliary equipment is needed, such as the power unit, timing-controls and temperature-controls. Injection machines in general are self-contained, but some may be operated from a central hydraulic system, or a source of compressed air. Conventionally, an injection machine has its own hydraulic system, employing oil. The hydraulic power is developed by one or more pumps, driven by an electric motor. Suitable valves control the sequence of operation.

Courtesy Reed-Prentice Corp.

Fig. 2-17

Injection-molding machines are usually classified by their "capacity," i.e., the quantity of molding material that the heating cylinder will deliver in one stroke of the injection ram. This capacity is expressed in ounces. Other important specifications are:

1. the amount of material which the heating cylinder will heat and deliver per hour;

2. the injection pressure, in psi, developed on the material by an injection ram of a specified diameter;

3. the clamping pressure (expressed in tons), i.e., the maximum total pressure available on the clamping unit;

4. the mold space available, which determines the maximum length and width of the mold, and its maximum and minimum thickness;

5. the mold opening, i.e., the distance which the moving platen travels between open and closed positions;

6. the capacity of the feed hopper;

7. the specifications of the motor;

8. the physical dimensions of the machine.

Machine ratings range from a fraction of an ounce to 300 oz.

Courtesy Watson-Stillman Co.

Fig. 2-18

Variations of the standard machine described and shown are numerous.

Horizontal platens aid in loading inserts, while vertical platens make it easier to discharge finished work.

Some machines have used up to four injection cylinders to handle a large mass of material, but were found to be impractical.

In one machine, a measured amount of material is injected through a sprue on the parting line of a partially closed mold, which is afterwards closed by an auxiliary plunger. This closing cuts off the gate. This machine is capable of molding very thick and complicated articles.

In recent years, considerable attention has been given to the idea of heating the molding material to molding consistency in a separate unit before feeding it into the injection cylinder. Thus the cylinder does not have to serve as a heating unit, and performs only its mechanical function of filling the mold. This technique has been variously designated "presoftening," "premelting," "preplasticizing."

The technique of preplastifying in a separate unit offers several advantages.

It makes the molding cycle independent of the plastifying capacity of an injection cylinder. In conventional equipment, the molding cycle must sometimes be lengthened beyond the potential minimum cycle of the mold, because the heating cylinder is unable to plastify the material fast enough. Preplastifying removes this restriction, and thereby may increase the hourly output of the mold.

Preplastifying ensures thorough softening of the plastic to an optimum condition for molding, and thereby makes practicable the use of lower injection pressures. This reduces the development of strains in the molded articles. Also it enables the clamping device to handle molds of larger projected area, and thus may increase the productive capacity of the machine.

Preplastifying does away with the need of expending pressure to overcome the frictional resistance involved in moving unheated granular material, as in the conventional cylinder.

Various methods and devices for preplastifying are in use or under development. At present, preplastifying in one form or another is being used with practically all molds 120 ounces or larger, in order to avoid the need for excessively large heating cylinders of conventional type.

Choice of Materials

Although all thermoplastic materials are adaptable to injection molding, the potential user, before deciding on the material for a specific application, should consult with both the material-manufacturer and the molder, to make sure of selecting the best material for the job.

Whenever a project is mapped out for a molded plastic, one of the first questions is the choice between thermosetting and thermoplastic materials. If a thermosetting material is specified, then injection molding is not practicable.

If a thermoplastic material is specified, then in almost all cases injection molding will be used, even though compression or transfer molding is used for thermoplastics in special cases.

Advantages and Limitations

Since the molding cycle in injection molding is short, the labor cost per article tends to be low, and it may not be necessary to provide a large number of mold cavities. On the other hand, the size of the machine is very large in proportion to the size of the article produced, and machine overhead, based on cost of the machine and operating costs, tends to be high.

Since theromplastics undergo merely physical change in the molding operation, the rejects, sprues and runners may be ground and reused, provided they are kept clean, and not mixed with material of different color or composition. There is, therefore, practically no waste of material in the injection process.

Since speed is one of the main advantages of injection molding, complicated molds with inserts should be avoided when possible.

3. Preforming, Drying and Preheating

PREFORMING

Introduction

Definition. Preforms are cold-compressed tablets of thermosetting molding materials, used, instead of loose powder, for loading compression and transfer molds, for reasons given below. They are often referred to as pills, tablets, biscuits, premolds, etc. A preform can be of almost any shape or size, and is generally designed to fit the cavity of the mold or transfer pot. Preforms are produced in machines designed for the purpose, in which loose powder is dispensed usually automatically, by volume, to provide units of the desired weight, and these units compacted under high pressure in cavities of the desired shape.

Reasons for Preforming. The principal purposes and advantages of preforming may be summarized as follows:

(1) to shorten the cycle of molding;

(2) to control the weight of the charge;

(3) to facilitate handling of the molding material;

(4) to facilitate preheating by decreasing the bulk of the charge;

(5) to save material;

(6) to obtain thinner cutoff through control of weight;

(7) to simplify construction of molds.

Reasons for not Preforming:

(1) The cost of preforming is not always justified.

(2) Some materials cannot be preformed because of high bulk factor.

(3) Some molds of intricate shape are more effectively filled by powder.

(4) For mottled articles, powder often gives a better pattern of flow.

Types and Shapes of Preforms

The four types of preforms, and reasons for choosing among them, are discussed in the following paragraphs.

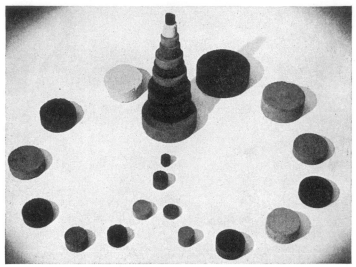

Courtesy of Diemolding Corp.

Fig. 3-1

Standard Round Flat-Faced Preforms. This shape is probably the most commonly used. The dies are the least expensive to make and the least troublesome to run. This preform can be satisfactorily heated by any method. Breakage and loss of weight through abrasion and chipping during handling are small. Fig. 3-1 indicates the variety of die diameters that may be available.

Courtesy of Diemolding Corp.

Fig. 3-2

Rectangular Preforms. Fig. 3-2 shows rectangular preforms, some with rounded corners. The heaviest preforms can be made in this shape. Since these preforms when placed on edge present a uniform dimension, they are particularly adapted to being preheated dielectrically.

When the length, width, and thickness of a rectangular preform are properly proportioned, it often gives the best possible distribution of load in the mold cavity.

Rectangular preforms with rounded corners (sometimes called oval) have some of the advantages of both the round and rectangular. In many cases, they will give good distribution of load in the mold. The die is comparatively inexpensive, and makes a durable preform.

Ball-Shaped Preforms. The best preform from the standpoints of loss of weight and breakage in handling is the ball-shaped (Fig. 3-3 is a sketch of the preforming punches). Also, it is the easiest to load into a loading board (Fig. 3-4), and often the easiest to load into the mold. But it is difficult to heat, dielectrically, because of its lack of a uniform dimension and density.

Preforms of Special Shapes. Preforms should be designed in the shape which will best meet the problem of molding the article.

Typical Sample Tablet

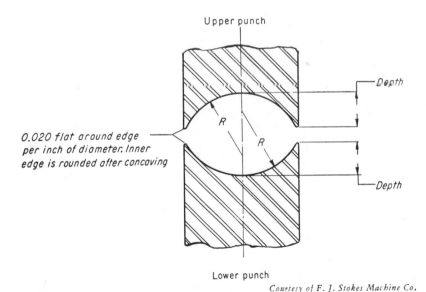

Fig. 3-3. Modified Ball Punches.

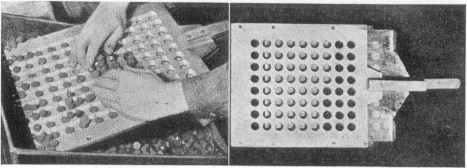

Grooved Preform Loader.　　　　　　　　　　　Preform Loader.

Fig. 3-4

In some cases it is advantageous to make the preform as nearly as possible the shape of the molded article. Thus, the material is put as near as possible to its final destination before the mold begins to close. This minimizes flow in the mold cavity, and makes it feasible to use the stiffer materials, which cure more rapidly and yield better finish. When preforms are designed in this way, the flash lines from compression molds tend to be least noticeable. However, any dirt which has settled on the surface of the preform will probably appear on the surface of the molded article; any pockets which are completely covered by the preform are likely to trap gas, which may prevent filling out of the cavity; and staining of the mold is greatest when flow is at a minimum.

In other cases, flow is desirable, and preforms of simple compact shapes are used. There is some indication that the appearance of the article is improved by flow in the mold. Contamination due to dirt on the surface of the die or preform is minimized. Some molds can be filled more easily; but softer molding compound is needed. The thickness of the flash, with compression molds, is apt to be excessive, and a somewhat larger charge of material may be needed. Some shapes cannot be molded satisfactorily from preforms of this type.

Whenever flow of plastic does occur, it should be out of unvented pockets and toward the flash line or vent. Probably it is best to design the preform to fit closely in unvented pockets to ensure flow toward the flash line. Even successful attempts to force material to flow into dead-end areas aggravate staining of the mold, and often require a breathe or slow close.

1. The "dog bone" shape is almost universally used for molding rectangular boxes or small trays with deep draws.

2. If inserts are to be molded into the finished article, or if the mold contains delicate pins, cored preforms may be advantageous in that they serve to ensure even distribution of pressure on mold pins and inserts so that these will not be distorted or displaced by unbalanced flow; to permit

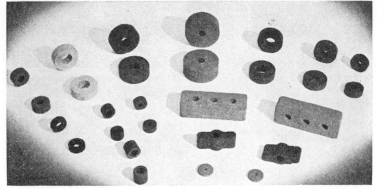

Courtesy of Diemolding Corp.

Fig. 3-5

Courtesy of F. J. Stokes Machine Co.

Fig. 3-6

the preform to be seated in the cavity, rather than to rest upon pins or inserts, and thereby to reduce entrapment of gas; to avoid weld lines, which are likely to result when the flow of plastic is divided by a pin and must be reunited beyond the pin; to permit the molding of through holes, with the use of spring-loaded mold pins. Cored preforms are shown in Figs. 3-5 and 3-6.

3. Preforms of various irregular shapes are designed to locate material where it will be finally molded. They reduce the amount of material required (Fig. 3-7) or fill pieces which could not otherwise be filled (Fig. 3-8).

Preforms of irregular shapes are subject to breakage and may require special handling. For a given weight of material they require larger plates

Courtesy of Diemolding Corp.

Fig. 3-7

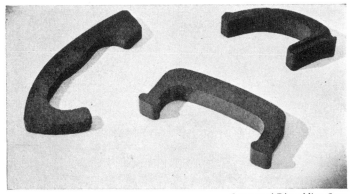

Courtesy of Diemolding Corp.

Fig. 3-8

for dielectric heating and they may have variations in height and density which constitute problems in preheating by that method.

Preforming dies for producing irregular shapes are discussed on p. 85.

4. Button preforms may be concave or convex, or have a preformed rim, to aid in positioning them in the mold. Fig. 3-9 illustrates a typical button punch.

Typical Problems

A variety of special preforms is shown in Fig. 3-10.

1. With flash-type compression molds the shape of the preform is always important. Even though a mold can be operated satisfactorily with a standard preform of simple shape, it may be possible to save material by adopting a specially shaped preform. Fig. 3-7 shows a preform of simple but special shape, and the rectangular preform which it replaced, with appre-

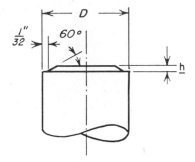

D	$\frac{3''}{8}$	$\frac{7''}{16}$	$\frac{5''}{8}$
h	0.030	0.032	0.035

Courtesy of F. J. Stokes Machine Co.

Fig. 3-9. Special button face for punches.

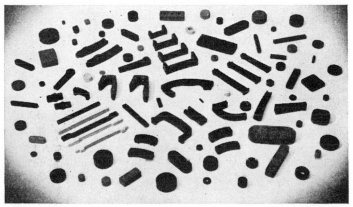

Courtesy of Diemolding Corp.

Fig. 3-10

ciable saving because material was concentrated at the point of use. If the preform is properly designed, it has been found that about 0.2 g of excess material is required per inch of open flash line.

2. Long through holes are most easily molded by using two preforms having locating indentations which will match up and completely enclose the arbor before the mold begins to close (Figs. 3-11 and 3-12). Right and left preform dies are required (Fig. 3-11), unless the preforms are made symmetrical about the arbor (Fig. 3-12).

Courtesy of Diemolding Corp.

Fig. 3-11

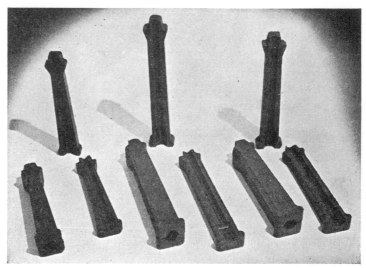

Courtesy of Diemolding Corp.

Fig. 3-12

3. Usually a single preform per article is the most economical.

The preforms shown in Fig. 3-13 are used to mold a handle with a through hole. Originally two preforms were used in the manner illustrated in Fig. 3-11. However, it was found that by using an excess of material the article could be made satisfactorily with a single preform, containing a half-round groove to accommodate the pin in the mold; under pressure, the material flows around the pin and encloses it. Cost analysis showed that savings in direct labor more than covered the increase in material used.

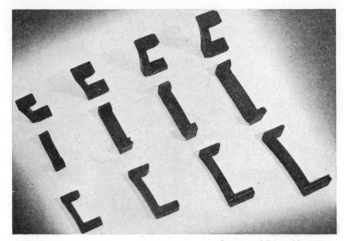

Courtesy of Diemolding Corp.

Fig. 3-13

4. Preforms should be designed with regard to the type of preheating which may be used, and vice versa. Dielectric heating requires that the preform be of fairly uniform density, and that at least one dimension be constant. Providing one constant dimension allows the operator to set the plates of the dielectric heater at a fixed distance, and thus reduces one of the variables in preheating. The best results may be obtained when this dimension is a die dimension, since variations in thickness of the preform will not affect the heating.

Courtesy of Diemolding Corp.

Fig. 3-14

On the left in Fig. 3-14 is a preform with a locating bump made by a recess in the punch. When this preform was heated flat, it became much hotter at the center than at the outside. The sides of the preform were cut off (by making a new die) and the preform was heated on edge. The tempera-

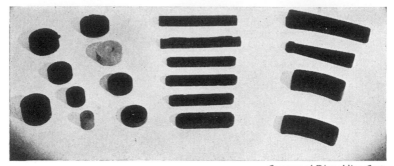

Courtesy of Diemolding Corp.

Fig. 3-15

ture throughout the preform was then fairly uniform. Preforms having small, shallow indentations, such as most of those in Fig. 3-15, can be heated dielectrically without trouble, but those having very deep indentations, such as the preform on the extreme left of Fig. 3-15, cannot. Cored preforms present no problem if they are heated with the holes perpendicular to the plate.

5. The more complicated a preform becomes, the more fragile it will be. Ball-shaped preforms can be rolled out of the preform machine into drums and dumped into hoppers for delivery to the operator. Preforms of the type shown in Fig. 3-8 must be stacked in tote boxes as they are made, and carefully handled until they are placed in the mold. When a molding shop is set up to handle preforms in bulk, attempts to handle large, fragile preforms may result in a disappointing amount of breakage.

Influence of Properties of Powder on Preforming

The ability of molding material to be preformed satisfactorily is influenced by its bulk factor, uniformity of granulation, pourability, content of lubricants and moisture, and its temperature.

Bulk factor is the ratio of the volume of a given weight of molding compound in loose powder form to its volume in molded form. Some materials of high-impact type, containing fabrics or coarse fibers as fillers, cannot be fed automatically in standard preforming equipment, and require either manual feeding or special preforming presses.

Pourability of molding powders, which can be expressed in terms of rate of flow through a standard funnel, is a prerequisite to the proper loading of preforming dies by gravity flow.

Ideally, the mixture of various sizes should be such that each size, starting with the smallest, occupies the voids between particles of the next larger size. Too large a percentage of coarse particles is unfavorable to preforming, because the voids will be inadequately filled and the resulting preform will be weak and brittle. Too large a percentage of extremely fine particles is objectionable because it causes bridging in the feeder and entrapment of air in the preform. The fines also tend to jam the clearance between the punch and the die.

Lubricants, added to molding compounds to reduce chattering in ejection of the preform from the die, may impair the strength of the molded article.

Since some segregation of coarse and fine particles may occur during shipment of powders, it is desirable to homogenize each batch, before preforming, by rolling the drum on a drum-roller or by putting the material through a blender.

Since high moisture content of a molding material may affect the quality of the molded article, and also impair its flow in preforming equipment, the moisture content should be at an acceptable level before preforming is done. The temperature of the material at the time of preforming is directly related to the pressure required to compact a preform to any given density.

The density of a preform will be governed by the specific problem of molding. The desired density is obtained by adjusting the pressure applied by the preforming machine. Usually the material is compressed to about 80 per cent of its maximum density. Preforms of such density can be preheated effectively, and are strong enough to withstand handling.

Charts of Weights, Sizes, and Thicknesses

Charts 3-1 through 3-8 show relationships of dimensions and weight for preforms of general-purpose phenolic having a molded specific gravity of 1.35 to 1.40, and of medium heat-resistant phenolic of specific gravity 1.55 to 1.60, in small and large preforms of round, rectangular and irregular shapes.

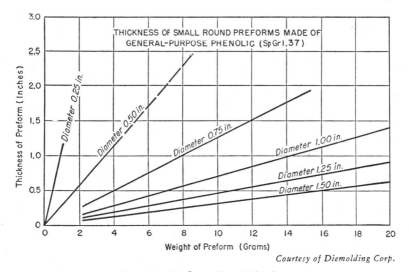

Courtesy of Diemolding Corp.

Chart 3-1. Preform size-weight chart.

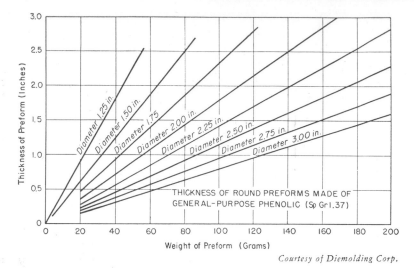

Courtesy of Diemolding Corp.

Chart 3-2. Preform size-weight chart.

Chart 3-9 can be used for figuring required thickness of a preform of given size when the molded density of the material is known.

Chart 3-10 is an alignment chart for estimating the depth of fill required, when the apparent density of the loose material is known.

Charts 3-1 through 3-8 are conservative; that is, they are for fairly soft preforms. Approximately 10 per cent more material than is shown can

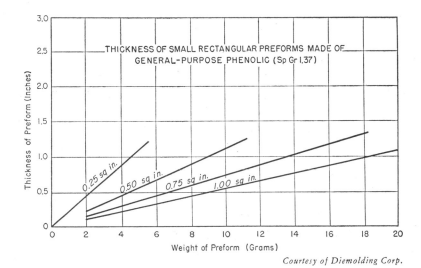

Courtesy of Diemolding Corp.

Chart 3-3. Preform size-weight chart.

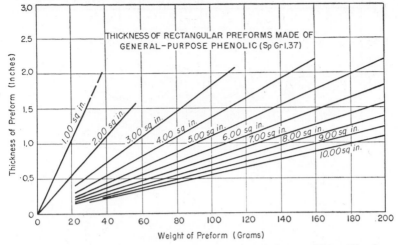

Chart 3-4. Preform size-weight chart.

be put into a preform of specific size. Obviously variations in material will cause slight difference, but it is believed that satisfactory preforms with the size-weight relationships shown can be made from any good batch of material.

Example (1): What will be the approximate thickness of a round preform which weighs 45 g made from standard phenolic? The diameter cannot

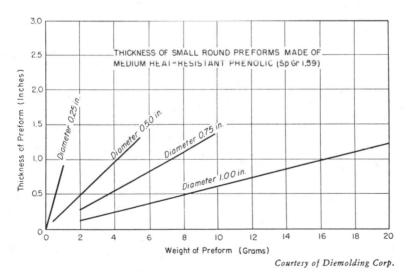

Chart 3-5. Preform size-weight chart.

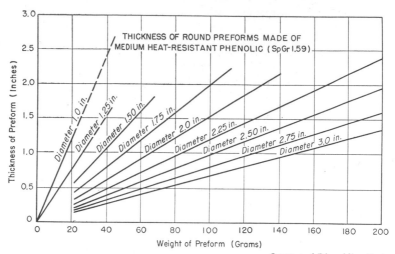

Chart 3-6. Preform size-weight chart.

exceed 2 in. On Chart 3-2, find 45 at bottom of chart. Draw a vertical line.
Read the thickness for the desired diameter:

diameter	thickness
2.0	0.8
1.75	1.1
1.5	1.4

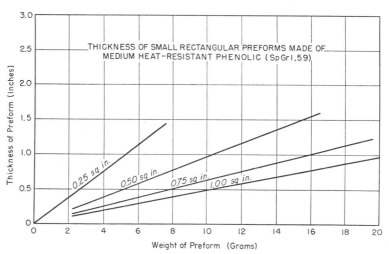

Chart 3-7. Preform size-weight chart.

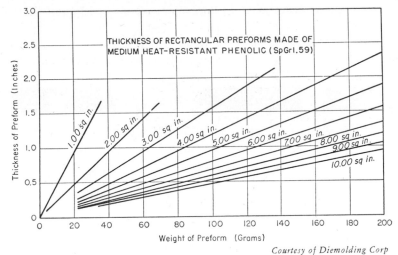

Courtesy of Diemolding Corp

Chart 3-8. Preform size-weight chart.

Example (2) : How large an area must a preform die have if the preform cannot be more than 7/8 in. thick and weighs 120 g? The material is a medium heat-resistant phenolic with a specific gravity of 1.60. On Chart 3-8, a vertical line from 120 g at the bottom and a horizontal line from 7/8 in. at the left

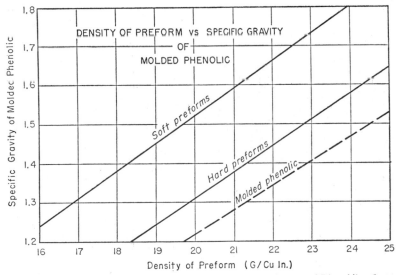

Courtesy of Diemolding Corp.

Chart 3-9

intersect about midway between the lines representing 6 and 7 sq in. The die must, therefore, have an area of at least 6.5 sq in.

Example (3): What depth of fill is required to make a preform of diameter 2 in. and weight 31 g from material with a powder density of 11 g/cu in.?

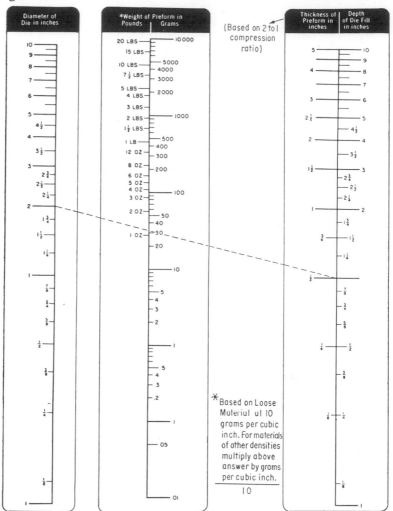

Courtesy of F. J. Stokes Machine Co.

Chart 3-10. Preform diameter, weight and depth of fill chart. To assist plastics molders who use preforming presses, this chart is a ready calculator. Briefly, if the diameter of a die is 2 in. (left scale), and the weight of the preform is to be 31 g (middle scale), based on loose material at 10 g/cu in., then the depth of fill will be 1 in. (right scale). For materials with densities other than 10 g/cu in., divide the answer from the chart by the density of the material expressed in g/cu in. and multiply by 10.

On Chart 3-10, draw a line through 2 in. diameter and 31 g, and read 1 in. of fill in the right-hand column. Multiply 1 in. $\times$ $1\%_{11}$ to get .90 in. for the required depth of fill.

Example (4): If the preform machine has a maximum depth of fill of 2 in., how heavy a preform can be made in a 2.5-in. die? The powder has a density of 10 g/cu in. Draw a line through 2 in. in the right-hand column and 2.5 in. in the left-hand column. Read the answer, 95 g, in the center column.

Preforming Presses

Single-Stroke Presses. Single-stroke preforming machines have a production rate of 8 to 60 strokes per min, depending on size of preform and type of material. They are generally classified into three types:

(a) Eccentric presses (Fig. 3-16) in which the head of the machine

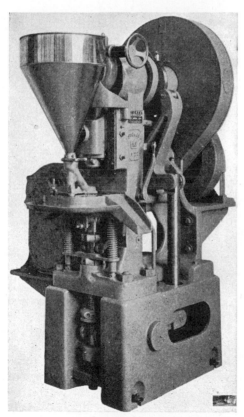

Courtesy of F. J. Stokes Machine Co.

Fig. 3-16

is operated directly off a crank. Presses of this type are available in capacities from 10 to 60 tons.

(b) Reciprocating presses (Fig. 3-17) in which the head is mounted on four columns operated by a mechanism located below the die table. Presses of this type are available in capacities from 30 to 200 tons.

(c) Hydraulically operated presses are available in standard models (Fig. 3-18) with capacities of 25 to 200 tons. They may be either single- or double-acting.

Rotary Preforming Machines. Rotary presses (Fig. 3-19) generally use from 15 to 33 sets of dies mounted in a rotating member, and have

Courtesy of Baldwin Lima Hamilton Corp.

Fig. 3-17

production rates of 250 to 1200 preforms per min. The material is compressed from top and bottom simultaneously, as both the upper and lower punches will pass between two sets of pressure rolls at the same time. Rotary preform presses are rated at from 2½ to 35 tons.

Presses for Material of High Bulk Factor. Special machines have been developed to handle bulky high-impact-strength materials (see Fig. 3-20). Materials of medium impact strength, for which information can be obtained from their suppliers, can often be handled on eccentric and reciprocating machines by the use of special feeding mechanisms.

Courtesy of F. J. Stokes Machine Co.

Fig. 3-18

Courtesy of F. J. Stokes Machine Co.

Fig. 3-19

Operation of Preforming Presses

As preforming is generally a very dusty operation, and since molding compounds are highly abrasive, lubrication is of first importance in the maintenance of a preform press. Before starting a day's run, a thorough check should be made to see that oil is reaching all moving parts in an adequate supply.

When operating a preforming press, care should be taken to see that no more than the required pressure for the job is being used. High operating pressures not only reduce the life of punches and dies, but subject the machine to undue stress and wear. When switching to the production of preforms having less weight or a small diameter, pressures should always be checked to see that they have been reduced correspondingly.

When setting up for a run, it is also good operating practice to approach the final desired pressures slowly. In fact, it is usually best to turn the machine over by hand before applying power and bringing it up to speed. This will prevent damage to punches and dies in case they are not in perfect

Courtesy of Kux Machine Co.

Fig. 3-20

alignment, and prevent the machine from overloaded and jamming. Care should also be taken to check the clearance of the feed shoe and the upper punch. This is particularly important when inserting punches and dies for the production of larger preforms.

Preforming Dies

Proper design of preforming dies is one of the most important factors in obtaining good preforms. The use of properly hardened steels having very smooth or polished die surfaces, and the provision of proper clearances of top and bottom punches, will not only promote production of good dense preforms, and facilitate their ejection, but also prolong the life of the die.

Since most plastics are abrasive, a tool steel of high chrome content should be selected for dies, and it should be hardened to 58-62 Rockwell on the C scale.

The punches are subject to impact load, and hence should be made from a good tool steel that will withstand impact. The punches should be hardened to 50-60 Rockwell on the C scale.

Clearances between the top and bottom punches and the die will sometimes have to be varied according to the size of the preform and the type of material to be preformed. Chart 3-11 shows typical clearances for dies of various diameters. The clearance should be maintained for a distance of 0.5 in. along the shank from the face of each punch. Beyond this distance, the punch should be machined smaller, to prevent binding.

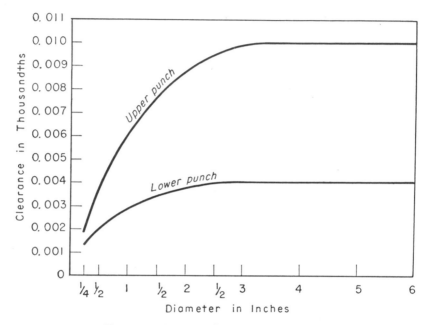

Chart 3-11. Clearances for preforming punches.

The die should be tapered 0.001 in. per in. on a side, or 0.002 in. per in. on the diameter, to aid in ejection and to lengthen the life of the die. An untapered die often becomes barrel-shaped from excessive wear. Then the preform may be larger than the space through which it is to be ejected. This condition may cause overloading of the machine, and the preforms will be broken during ejection.

Figures 3-21, 3-22 and 3-23 show typical details of a preform die.

It is desirable to chamfer or radius the top edge of the die at least $\frac{1}{32}$ in., to prevent the breaking off of corners of the preform during ejection; also it helps in introducing the upper punch into the die during the setup.

Polishing the die axially to remove circular grinding marks will aid in ejection of the preform. In most cases, chrome-plating the die cavity will prolong the life of the die. When a die that has been chrome-plated starts to show wear, it can be stripped and replated for further service.

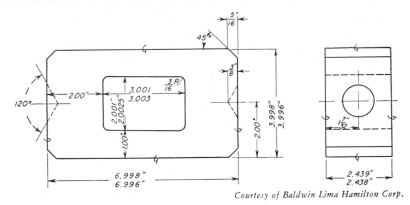

Courtesy of Baldwin Lima Hamilton Corp.

Fig. 3-21

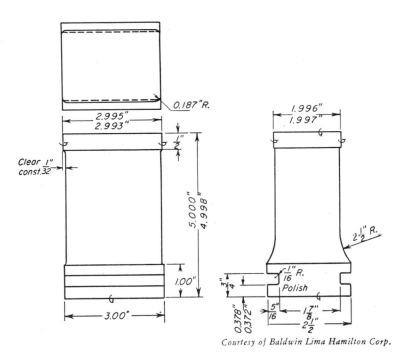

Courtesy of Baldwin Lima Hamilton Corp.

Fig. 3-22

The life of any set of punches and dies will depend upon the pressure applied and the abrasiveness of the material.

If very abrasive materials are to be preformed, or if exceptionally long wear is required, carbide-tipped punches and carbide-lined dies should be used. In general, carbide linings will wear about ten times as long as the best type

Preforming Operating Difficulties and Remedies

Symptoms	Possible Causes	Remedies
Poor ejection. The preforms show vertical score marks and horizontal cracks on sidewalls. In severe cases, the top of the preform flakes off during ejection, and the machine labors and pounds excessively.	1. *Worn preform dies.* From long use at a given depth setting, the cavity has developed a larger inside diameter at the bottom than at the top. The preform is forced during ejection through the smaller area at the top of the die, and binds or breaks.	1. Die must be ground to uniform inside cross-section, polished and plated back to size; or new die must be built.
	2. *Insufficient lubricant in the molding material.* A small amount of lubricant is added to standard material to aid preforming. In certain cases involving large preforms, because of greater ratio of area to volume, this standard amount may not be sufficient. This cannot be determined readily in advance.	2. Increase the amount of lubricant in small increments until the optimum amount is found. Avoid an excess, since this will reduce cohesion and tend to produce soft preforms. A marked excess will also impair the appearance of the molded article.
Poor cohesion. Preforms are soft, when preformed with normal pressure, and crumble on handling. Increasing the pressure, in an effort to make them harder, causes sticking during ejection.	1. *Nonuniformity of granulation.* This causes low apparent density (high bulk factor). Pill cannot be compressed to proper hardness even at maximum stroke and die opening.	1. Roll the drum, to blend the material thoroughly; or obtain material of more uniform granulation.
	2. *Tight clearance between punches and cavity walls in the preform die.* This tends to trap air in the material.	2. Increase clearance. A die clearance of 0.003 in. on one side or radius of the top and bottom punch is recommended. This clearance should be maintained for a distance of 1/2 in. along the shank from the face of each punch. Beyond this point, additional shank clearance should be provided by relieving the punch to allow flash to escape.

3. *Preforming speed is too rapid.* Field tests on single-stroke preformers with the same pressure setting have shown that at higher preforming speeds softer preforms are produced because entrapped air is less effectively removed.

3. Reduce the speed. The usual practice is to operate single-stroke preformers at 30 to 50 strokes per min.

Variation in weight of preform. Uniform weight cannot be maintained within accepted tolerance without frequent adjustment of the preformer.

1. *Preforming speed is too rapid.* In this case, variation occurs because there is not sufficient time during the interval the feed shoe is over the cavity for powder to flow into and fill it adequately and uniformly.

1. Reduce the speed. With multiple-cavity dies, use baffle plates in feed shoe to direct flow of powder uniformly to all cavities, particularly those at the front of the die.

2. *Poor pourability of the material.* Instead of feeding smoothly from the hopper, the material cascades. In other cases, it bridges at the hopper throat, breaking loose and flowing irregularly. In granular material, this behavior is due to excess fines or an improper combination of coarse and fine material. In flock-filled material, the poor pourability is caused by the fluffy texture and tendency of the fibrous particles to felt or interlace.

2. Improve granulation by providing a properly graded distribution of particle sizes. Use magnetic vibrators on hopper and feed shoe of preformer. The inside of the hopper should have smooth polished surface. With flock-filled material, use strong, positive agitation instead of magnetic vibrator.

Vibrators tend to pack the material. Hence they should not be operated continuously, but only during each feeding.

3. *Material has stratified in drums during shipment.* Distribution of particle size is not uniform. Feed is irregular.

3. Transfer to a larger drum and roll for 20 min to 1 hr at approximately 25 rpm before using. Drum rollers can be made inexpensively.

4. *Material is removed from cavities by feed shoe on return stroke.* This phenomenon is most noticeable with flock-filled material when preformed in multiple-unit dies.

4. Relieve leading edge of feed shoe to provide extra clearance between it and the die table.

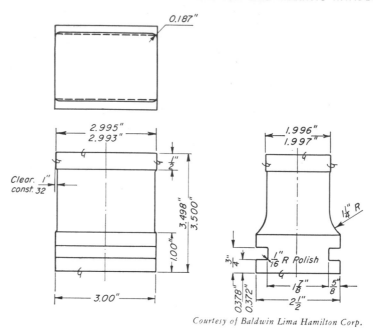

Courtesy of Baldwin Lima Hamilton Corp.

Fig. 3-23

of steel but, because they are brittle, they must be treated carefully when the dies are installed and removed.

Dies for cored preforms are usually relatively expensive to make and to run. Many of the advantages of cored preforms can be secured by putting projections on the upper punch of the preforming die, to form indentations on the preform; obviously they cannot form holes. Fig. 3-15 shows a number of special preforms of this type.

In the construction of dies for preforms of irregular shape, the irregularities should, if possible, be incorporated into the preforming die proper, and both the top and bottom punches left flat. Two of the preforms in Fig. 3-8 follow this pattern.

Operating difficulties which may be encountered in preforming together with their remedies are shown on pages 88 and 89.

DRYING AND PREHEATING

For various reasons, molding materials, both thermoplastic and thermosetting, are sometimes heated prior to the molding operation.

When the material is heated simply for the purpose of driving off moisture or other volatile, the operation is properly called drying. When the purpose is to deliver the material to the mold, the transfer pot, or the feed hopper in a warm or hot condition, the operation is properly called preheating. In some cases both purposes are achieved in a single operation.

It must be recognized that any operation of drying or preheating represents an exposure to contamination. Precautions against contamination, in methods of handling and in general housekeeping, are obviously most important with light-colored materials and in molding of large articles.

Conditioning of loose powders, as to temperature and moisture content, can be achieved to some degree by merely storing them in bags or in drums with the covers loose, for a week or so in a dust-free room at 100 to 120°F.

Thermoplastics

In the case of thermoplastics, the purpose of heating may be solely to remove moisture which would cause troubles in molding and impair the quality of the molded articles; i.e., the operation is simply one of drying. The cellulosics and nylon, in particular, but also, to a lesser extent, some of the other thermoplastics, tend to absorb moisture during storage in bags or other unsealed containers, and any of the molding materials, whether absorptive or not, may pick up moisture by simple condensation if they are brought from winter temperature into a warmer moist atmosphere. If excess of moisture is not removed before the material is molded or extruded, the product is likely to be marred by dullness of surface, "orange peel," "splash marks," "mica specks" or "silver streaking."

In the case of some of the cellulosics, the removal of moisture also restricts the odor developed during molding.

With nylon, the presence of more than about 0.25 per cent of moisture results not only in bad appearance of the molded article, as stated above, but also in deficiency in toughness. Nylon powder exposed to ordinary indoor atmosphere for as little as two hours is likely to absorb enough moisture to cause serious trouble in molding.

With thermoplastics in some cases the purpose of heating may be to deliver the material to the molding machine already hot or warm, so as to shorten the time required for heating it to molding temperature in the machine, or to provide the benefit of a uniform temperature of feed. This is properly called preheating.

Obviously, if a material freshly dried is delivered to the molding press while still hot, the operation of preheating as such is not additionally required, unless there is need of a higher temperature than that at which drying was done.

In drying thermoplastics, the temperature must be limited to avoid lumping or caking. Also the combination of temperature and time of exposure must not result in discoloration or other breakdown of the material. Hot spots in driers must be avoided.

Nylon molding powder is subject to discoloration and deterioration if heated in contact with air; it should preferably be dried in vacuum equipment. Nylon molding powder is, however, dried by the manufacturer, and shipped in airtight containers, so that drying in the molding shop is seldom necessary, except for sprues and runners accumulated for reuse. Containers of new material should not be opened until they are to be used, and the amount of material in the hopper should be restricted to 30-min supply unless the hopper is covered and moderately heated (150°F) to prevent absorption of moisture from the air.

Sprues and runners of nylon, if put into moistureproof containers as made, can be ground and reused without drying. When drying is required, a one-inch layer of material ground to about quarter-inch size can be dried under vacuum in about 4 hr at 212°F, or 8 hr at 185°F.

Acrylics, polyethylene, vinyl resins and polystyrene may occasionally require drying for removal of condensed moisture. For this purpose, or for preheating for the sake of uniformity or of reducing the time needed to plastify them in the heating cylinder, heating at 160 to 200°F for $\frac{1}{2}$ to 2 hr in an oven, or for 15 to 20 min under infrared, will usually suffice.

Thermosetting Plastics

In the case of thermosetting materials, the chief purpose of preheating is usually to shorten the cycle of molding and thereby to increase hourly production and decrease operating costs per article. But other economies also may be important.

Preheating promotes uniformity of molding and thereby reduces the percentage of rejections.

Preheating promotes free flow of the material in the mold, and this results in economies: thickness of flash is reduced, with economies in material and in cost of finishing; a reduction in the unit pressure required may make it feasible to use a press of lower tonnage for a given job, or to install more mold cavities in a press of given capacity; the molding of articles of large size and deep draw is facilitated; compounds of poor flow characteristics are molded with less difficulty; wear and tear on the mold is reduced.

Preheating is beneficial also to the properties of the molded article. By promoting uniformly high density in the molded article it improves mechanical, chemical and electrical properties. The better flow promotes accuracy of dimensions and, by minimizing stresses in the article, promotes its dimensional stability. Preheating makes also for uniformity of color in the molded article.

Drying of molding compound, incidental to preheating or as a separate operation, frequently improves the electrical properties of the molded article.

Equipment and Operation

For drying and for preheating, equipment and techniques of several types are available:

hot plates
ovens (conductive type)
    dry heat
    steam or moist atmosphere
    vacuum
infrared radiation
    belt or conveyer type
    stationary
dielectric heaters
hopper preheaters

Hot Plates. A metal plate or platen, heated to a controlled temperature electrically or by gas flame or circulating steam, is placed adjacent to the press. The preformed charge is placed on the heated surface, covered with flannel cloth, and regularly turned by the operator to promote uniform heating from both sides. Several successive charges are stacked on the plate and used in rotation, a new charge being added when a preheated charge is removed to the press.

Courtesy of Despatch Oven Co.

Fig. 3-24

Ovens with Circulation of Air. An oven having forced circulation of hot air, properly designed and with proper control of temperature, can be used for drying or for preheating (see Fig. 3-24).

The source of heat may be electrical resistances or steam coils. There should be a suitable fan to keep the hot air in motion. Temperatures from 100 to 450°F can be maintained.

For drying thermoplastics, the oven may be equipped with shallow trays, up to about 3.5 in. deep, of size convenient to be carried to the injection machine and having spout ends for convenience in emptying. If the molding powder is loaded not more than about 1 in. deep in the tray, it does not need to be stirred during drying. Temperatures up to about 200 to 230°F will dry the material adequately in from 1 to 3 hr.

The trays are unloaded in a regular sequence, and immediately reloaded. Thus the time of exposure of material in the oven is always the same.

If the dried material is emptied directly into the hopper of the injection machine or extruder, the additional benefit of preheating is gained.

Ovens of this type can be used for preheating of thermosetting materials, in the form of loose powder or of preforms, to appropriate temperatures, usually in the range 160 to 250°F, predetermined by the type of material and by the molding cycle to be followed.

Heating with Live Steam. This is a variant of oven heating, in which the atmosphere of the oven is maintained at operating temperature (270 to 300°F) by production of live steam within the oven. Figure 3-25 is a photograph of a steam preheater.

The interior of the steam oven is kept supplied with live steam by the flash vaporization, within it, of water admitted at a controlled steady rate by a metering device. The oven should not be pressure-tight, but nearly enough so to maintain the desired temperature.

Preforms are handled in a series of racks, each of which holds enough for one shot. Loaded racks are put in sequence into a heated tube surrounding the oven proper, and the preforms are there warmed to about 150°F for about 45 min before being put into the steam oven. This warming effects some drying, causes essentially no polymerization, and saves time in the subsequent preheating to molding temperature. When properly preheated in the oven, the preforms are transferred promptly to the press. Preforms to be preheated by this method should be made not more than 1 in. thick, and preferably thinner. Their density should be as low as possible, consistent with handling, to enable the steam-laden air to penetrate easily. Graphite-filled phenolics, which cannot be preheated dielectrically, respond very well to steam preheating. Most general-purpose, heat-resistant, and impact grades are satisfactorily handled by this process.

Optimum operating conditions—operating temperature, proper dosage of water, duration of preheating, etc.—must of course be established by trial and experience, and then be maintained.

Heating in Vacuum. Drying of materials in a vacuum is a practice of long standing in many fields, because it effects rapid vaporization of the volatiles at temperatures below their normal boiling points. With thermosetting materials, the greatest advantage of drying in vacuo is that it rapidly removes most of the moisture and volatiles at a temperature below that which

Courtesy of Minneapolis Honeywell Regulator Co.

Fig. 3-25. Typical Steam Preheater.

will cause polymerization of the materials. The small percentage of moisture remaining is generally expelled during the molding at higher temperature.

Drying in vacuo may be done in a container of bell-jar type, e.g., a steel vessel with a wide flange. An electrical band heater with thermostatic control on the outside of the vessel supplies heat. The material to be dried is held in a wire-mesh basket suspended within the vacuum vessel. A gauge indicates the vacuum. The cover consists of a heavy steel plate with its lower surface ground, and equipped with a handle. It is placed on the top of the jar, with a soft silicone-rubber gasket between. The weight of the cover is sufficient to create a nearly perfect seal, and as the vacuum is applied a perfect seal is made.

Vacuum of 28 to 29 in. may be supplied by a Venturi steam aspirator with water-cooled condenser. Vane-type vacuum pumps are apt to become contaminated by the volatiles removed and are not recommended for continued use.

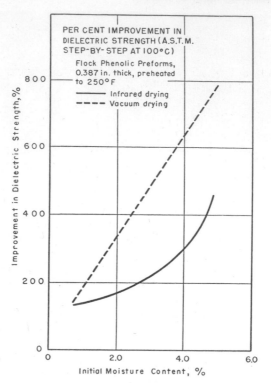

Fig. 3-26. Improvement in dielectric strength.

The vacuum in the vessel may be broken across a moisture trap to prevent re-absorption from the atmosphere.

Figure 3-26 shows the improvement effected in dielectric strength of flock phenolic compound with various percentages of moisture by heating for 30 min under 28 in. of vacuum at 175°F, as compared with heating with infrared radiation at 250°F.

Heating by Infrared Radiation. Radiant heat can be provided by a source of infrared. Control of temperature of the material is based on the wattage and distance of the source, and length of time of exposure.

Infrared heat is radiant heat and heats the immediate area and the exposed surface of the material; with some materials it penetrates to some degree beneath the surface. It is available in stationary, rotary and conveyor-type equipment. (Fig. 3-27.)

Molding material in bulk can be dried or preheated batchwise or continuously.

For batch operation, the material can be spread in a shallow layer (not more than 2 in.) in a pan, which is placed under a battery of infrared lamps.

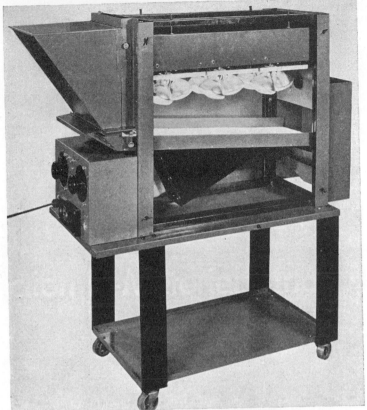

Fig. 3-27. Conveyor-type infrared equipment.

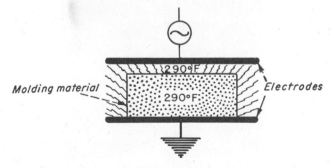

Fig. 3-28. Molding material being heated uniformly and evenly throughout its mass between two electrode heating plates of dielectric preheater.

Courtesy of W. T. LaRose & Associates, Inc.

Fig. 3-29

Courtesy of W. T. LaRose & Associates, Inc.

Fig. 3-30

The powder should be stirred frequently, either by hand or by means of a vibrator attached to the tray, which keeps the powder in motion, to expose fresh surfaces, to ensure uniformity of heating, and to prevent agglomeration.

Still another piece of equipment is a drum rotated on a horizontal axis, into which a row of lamps can be introduced. Baffle plates in the drum ensure continuous thorough mixing of the contents.

For drying in continuous manner, loose powder may be fed in a thin layer (0.25 in.) on a moving belt which passes under a bank of infrared lamps.

In all of these installations, drying is promoted by blowing air over the material while it is being heated.

Dielectric Heating. When a molding material is placed in a high-frequency electrical field, the resulting molecular friction or hysteresis results in generation of heat within the material, and under favorable conditions the heating is uniform throughout the material (Fig. 3-28).

This method of preheating has been applied mostly to preforms, and it

Courtesy of The Girdler Corp., Thermex Div.

Fig. 3-31

has been established that for best results it requires that the preforms have one dimension uniform throughout, and uniform density. The method can, however, be applied to loose powder also.

There are available several basic types of equipment:

general-purpose heaters
loading-board preheaters
specialized equipment adapted to operations of rotary and
    fully automatic presses.

General-purpose units are available (Figs. 3-29, 3-30 and 3-31) to handle large or small loads of preforms.

Loading-board preheaters are designed to accommodate preforms for standard multiple-cavity compression molding, or single loads of powder or preforms for transfer and plunger molding.

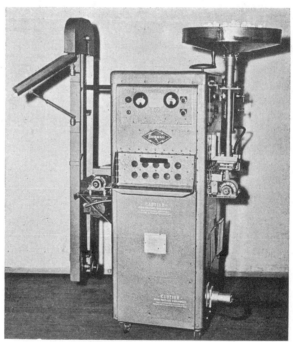

Courtesy of W. T. LaRose & Associates, Inc.

Fig. 3-32

The rotary press unit (Fig. 3-32) has equipment for controlling the cycle of operations and the temperature, and for metering a preheated charge into the mold cavity.

In preheaters for fully automatic flat-bed presses (Fig. 3-33), the material, as preforms, is fed into the preheater and thence, automatically, to the mold.

Material in the hopper of an injection or extrusion machine can be heated to some small extent, or at least prevented from cooling (if already hot) and from absorbing moisture, by means of infrared lamps mounted directly above.

Courtesy of W. T. LaRose & Associates, Inc.

Fig. 3-33

Hopper Preheaters. Loose powder can be heated in a container mounted directly upon the hopper of an injection or extrusion machine, and supplied from below with a constant current of hot air (Fig. 3-34). Thus, it can be dried and preheated, or at least prevented from cooling and absorbing moisture, and maintained at constant temperature. This is, of course, a variant of a circulating-air oven. Air is supplied by a small centrifugal blower or from a line, and passed over a fin heater.

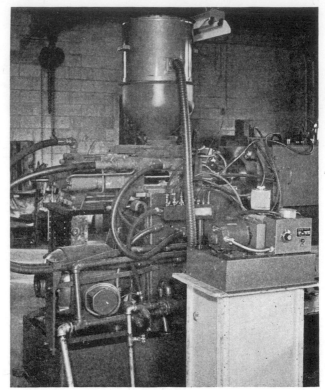

Courtesy of Thoreson-McCosh, Inc.

Fig. 3-34

This device, if it provides sufficient drying and/or preheating, can be loaded directly from the drums or bags in which the material is received, and its large capacity makes loadings infrequent. Thus it has an advantage of minimizing exposure to contamination. With polystyrene, its capacity to preheat may run as high as 150 lb/hr.

4. Extrusion and Extrusion Machines

Extrusion

Extrusion is a process of molding used to produce tubes, rods, filaments, film, and shapes with a wide variety of profiles. In dry, hot extrusion (i.e., extrusion in which heat alone, and not solvent, is used to soften the material), which is a continuous process, the material is fed from a hopper into the machine cylinder, which has closely controllable temperature zones; a screw rotating inside the cylinder forces the heated plastic through a die orifice which has the approximate shape of the desired profile; and this extruded form is carried through cooling media by the take-off mechanism, which is generally a conveyor, a capstan, or squeeze rolls, with variable speed.

Thermosetting materials have been extruded commercially here as well as abroad, but most commercial extrusion at this time is done with thermoplastics, as listed below:

acrylic	rods and shapes for decorative applications; sheeting; tubing; beads (ground from small-bore tubing)
cellulose acetate and acetate butyrate	architectural shapes, trim; tubing ($\frac{3}{32}$-in. inside diameter) to large pipe; transparent sheeting (0.003 to 0.030 in. thick); transparent vials and containers; beads (as above)
ethyl cellulose	tool handles
polyvinyl chloride and copolymers of vinyl chloride	electrical insulation on wire and cable; garden hose; shoe and upholstery welting; novelty belting; window channels, and gaskets; preforms for records (rigid); rigid pipe
polyvinyl alcohol	oil- and solvent-resistant tubing
polyvinyl butyral	continuous sheeting (safety-glass interlayer)
polyvinylidene chloride (saran)	oriented monofilament for weaving window screening, automobile seat covers, webbing and upholstery; chemical pipe and tubing; bristles
polystyrene	rods; tubes; fluorescent-light shields; oriented flexible sheeting; sheeting for forming

polyethylene	insulation of coaxial and carrier-frequency cable; film up to 108 in. wide; oriented monofilament for weaving; television and auto radio lead-in wire; chemical and air pipes; thin-wall lay-flat tubing; bottles (by extrusion blow-molding)
silicone rubber	gaskets, valve seats
nylon	oriented monofilament for "bristle" in brushes, for weaving and other pseudo-textile uses, for fishing lines and leaders, for racquet string, for sutures; thin-wall electrical insulation; rods; tubes
tetrafluoroethylene resin ("Teflon")	electrical insulation; rods; tubes
trifluorochloroethylene resin ("Kel-F")	electrical insulation; film; rods; tubes

These various materials require various ranges of temperature, from as low as about 93°C (200°F) to as high as 410°C (770°F). Tetrafluoroethylene resin requires temperatures around 354 to 410°C (670 to 770°F), and special equipment.

Uniformity of size of granule, and of temperature, as well as low moisture content of the material, are important for producing extruded goods of accurate dimensions and good surface. Drying before extrusion is essential for some materials, such as the cellulosics. Nylon is dry and ready for extrusion as shipped; very few extruders have the required vacuum equipment for drying nylon without discoloration.

Continuous preheating (infrared, dielectric, hot air, etc.) increases the rate of production with most materials.

An extrusion-machine cylinder which is electrically heated and has a sufficient number of independently controlled heating and cooling zones may be successfully used for a wide range of thermoplastic materials. However, for optimum results in dimensional uniformity and in rate of production, the screw should be designed, in length, and in depth and pitch, for a specific material. Different types of screws are used for saran, nylon, polyvinyl chloride, cellulose acetate, cellulose acetate butyrate, and acrylics.

Some materials, nylon, for example, require a screen-pack and breaker plate to build up back pressure in order to obtain uniform flow and good mixing. Acrylics require a breaker plate, but no screen. For others, such as saran, screens and breaker plate are harmful, in that they accelerate decomposition.

The design of the die is different for different plastics, and cannot be treated within the scope of this article. One fact has, however, to be stated, and that is that stretch-down of any shape from an oversize die, or blow-up or stretch-down in the manufacturing of tubing and pipe, are to be applied with caution, since they may cause stresses and strains and other inferior mechanical properties. In polyethylene tubing, however, a proper amount of stretching, both longitudinally and laterally, produces an orientation which is beneficial. And in some materials, such as nylon, a stretch-down is necessary to produce any shape because of the very low viscosity of the material in its molten stage. Recommendations have been made, by suppliers of material, for design of extrusion dies for the various plastics.

In the extrusion of tubing, a die forms the outside, and a core or mandrel, supported by a spider, forms the inside. It is possible to introduce air pressure through a rib of the spider to the core to maintain the round shape of the tubing until it has cooled. Accurate controls of air pressure are important, especially in production of film by the "expanded tube" method explained below.

Courtesy of Hartig Engine & Machine Co.

Fig. 4-1. 8-in. extruder with die for polyethylene film.

Wide film is produced in different ways. It may be extruded through a slit die accurately machined and sometimes equipped with a sizing bar to adjust thickness, and of slightly greater width than the width of the desired film. A gooseneck (90-degree elbow) holds the wide die, which thus extrudes vertically downward into a cooling trough. Control of temperature of the setup is critical (Fig. 4-1). Polyethylene film 0.0005 in. thick and 108 in. wide has been extruded by this method.

Such film may be produced also by the expanded-tube method. In this process, a tubing of relatively small diameter and heavy wall is extruded, generally vertically upward. A controlled amount of air is supplied into this tubing so that it is blown up to many times its original diameter, with correspondingly greatly reduced wall thickness. The air is held inside this tube by a set of nip rolls, the speed of which may be varied (Fig. 4-2). The resulting tubular film can be rolled up on a mandrel as "lay-flat" tubing or can be slit and rolled up as a sheet.

Polyvinyl chloride film of a wall thickness of less than 0.001 in. has been successfully produced by this method.

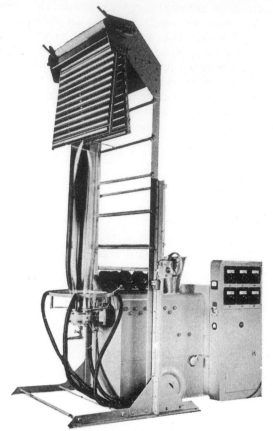

Courtesy of Modern Plastics Machinery Corporation

Fig. 4-2. Installation for production of lay-flat film tubing: expanded-tube method.

Another method of producing thin film utilizes an annular die of large diameter, which produces directly a tube of large diameter.

The softness of the material after leaving the die necessitates supports and fixtures to retain or obtain the desired shape during the cooling. The emerging shape may be cooled in hot or cold air or in a liquid, depending upon the chemical character and/or the viscosity of the material. Rigid materials, such as cellulose acetate and acetate butyrate, polystyrene, methyl methacrylate and rigid vinyls, should not be quenched in cold water, since too rapid cooling of the outer surface may cause vacuum bubbles to form inside. Also it may impair surface appearance and set up undesirable stresses and strains. Other materials, such as elastomeric vinyls, polyethylene, nylon, and saran, may be and sometimes have to be cooled in cold or cool water, particularly in the case of monofilament which is to be oriented by stretching.

The rate of take-off in comparison with the rate of extrusion influences the dimensions of the extruded shape, and a proper balance between the two is used to control the dimensions. But excessive stretch is to be avoided, because it sets up stresses and strains and may result in undesired orientation.

It is possible to produce extruded goods with stripes or layers of more than one color, by several methods. By one method several small screw extruders are set up to deliver materials of different colors to a common die. This effect may be obtained also by hydraulic cylinders which force a different-colored compound into the extrusion die. This compound may be an ink or a plastisol.

Another type of multicolor extrusion can be achieved by twin-cylinder extrusion or by using the crosshead (see below) as a continuous heat-sealing device. In the latter case one color is extruded separately, and fed through the guider tube, to meet and become joined with material of the second color as it passes through the die. This process has proved successful in extrusion of flexible polyvinyl chloride compounds, but can be applied to other materials also.

Extrusion Equipment

Screw-type extrusion machines for plastics, and their auxiliary equipment, operate to give continuous straight-line production. Although used primarily for the extrusion of shapes, they are being used also for preforming, extraction, pelleting, continuous compounding, and blow molding, and even to some extent in injection molding. Machines are made with screws of diameters from 1 in. (laboratory size) up to 8 in. for extrusion of shapes and for wire-covering, and up to 20 in. (Fig. 4-3) for compounding. The most commonly used for extrusion of shapes have screws of diameters 2 to 4½ in.

Courtesy of Farrell-Birmingham Co., Inc.

Fig. 4-3. 20-in. compounding extruder.

Basically, a machine for dry hot extrusion consists of a cylinder suitably equipped for heating and cooling the material to desired temperatures; a screw rotating inside the cylinder, which kneads the plastic to uniform consistency and impels it toward the die orifice; and a slow-starting, preferably variable-speed motor, which drives the screw. Mechanical drives of the variable-sheave type or AC-DC motor-generator units may be used as means of varying the speed.

Cylinders are heated by steam, oil, "Dowtherm" or the like, or by electrical heaters; each system has its advantages and limitations. Steam, for example, does not give a high enough temperature for certain plastics. Heat-transfer oil, heated electrically or by gas, requires a thermostatically controlled circulating system. Other newer heat-transfer liquids, such as the silicones and "Dowtherm," are being used.

**CALROD RANGE-TYPE
HEATING ELEMENTS**

**FINNED, CAST ALUMINUM
JACKET**

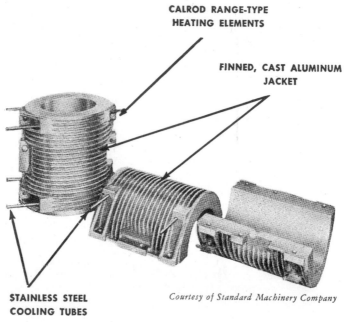

**STAINLESS STEEL
COOLING TUBES**

Courtesy of Standard Machinery Company

Fig. 4-4. Auxiliary cylinder equipped with cooling coils and fins for dissipation of heat.

The trend is now toward direct electrical heating of cylinders by band, strip or cartridge heaters. This method imposes no top limit on operating temperatures, and is efficient, clean and self-contained. Cooling is accomplished through fins (Fig. 4-4), sectional coring (Fig. 4-5) or helical grooves in the cylinder, which house tightly fitting cooling coils, etc.

The bore of the cylinder should be fitted with a ground hard liner, preferably made of a hard, corrosion-resistant alloy such as "Xaloy," "Xaloy" 306,

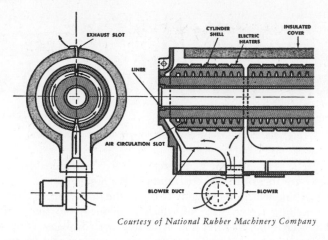

Courtesy of National Rubber Machinery Company

Fig. 4-5. Cylinder section electrically heated, blower cooled.

or "Hastelloy" A or B. For extrusion of saran, "Z" nickel is frequently used.

The design of the front section of the cylinder should permit easy and rapid mounting and dismounting of dieholders, crossheads, etc.

Screws in single-screw machines are made preferably of stainless steel. The lands of the flights are hard-surfaced with "Stellite," "Toolweld," or other extra-hard alloys. The axis of the screw should be bored hollow to allow heating or cooling.

The clearance between screw and cylinder is kept at a minimum to prevent adhesion of the plastic to the cylinder, and also because too great clearance decreases the rate of production. The screw is shallow, to permit the maximum contact between the plastic, which is a poor conductor of heat, and the heated wall of the cylinder. The efficiency of the screw is determined by the helix angle of the flights. The longer the pitch, the less positive the advance and the lower the pressure developed, since the material can backslip more easily. Hence the single-flight screw generally provides a greater yield than the double-flight type. The bulk factor of the plastic as fed to the screw determines the depth and pitch of the screw at the feed end, and the rate of the necessary decrease in pitch and/or depth toward the delivery end, i.e., a gradual decrease in the cross-section of the thread.

A torpedo or muller, sometimes specially shaped, and located at the outlet end of the screw, may help to complete the homogenizing of the material just before it enters the die. Breaker plates may be used at this point to equalize variations of flow of the material from the screw, and to support screens when necessary. Separately driven metering devices are successfully used to eliminate pulsations of flow.

Extruders were all of cylindrical design until the recent development of a machine with a conical heating jacket and screw having a taper of more

Fig. 4-6. Screw construction of intermeshing twin-screws.

than 10 degrees. This machine minimizes undesirable frictional heat, provides more positive advance of the material, and yields a higher output.

One machine which has recently come on the market incorporates two or three intermeshing screws, each of which is divided into three sections of successively decreasing diameter and increasing root diameter (Fig. 4-6). A variable volumetric feeding unit, directly geared to the screw system, ensures that the feed will match the delivery. It is claimed for this machine that the metered feed and the continuous positive forward movement ensured by the intermeshing screws provide uniform and nonpulsating delivery to the die, and that the machine provides superior homogenizing at lower power-consumption.

Multiscrew (twin-screw or triple-screw) extrusion machines have embodied a number of new concepts. The designers have attempted to obtain the advantages of a twin-screw extruder in plastifying and pumping action, and in greater latitude in dimensions.

One design, which has completely departed from the continuous screw, incorporates several sets of helicoidal gears arranged one above the other, and completely enclosed. The successive sets have different pitch and different intermeshing clearance. The plastic is forced from one set into the next, and thereby gradually plastified and positively pumped to and through the orifice of an extrusion die (Fig. 4-7). It is reported that this machine (of Italian design) will be produced in the United States by an established American manufacturer.

For extruding otherwise than straight out along the axis of the machine, attachments are made to the head. The crosshead is an adaptor which directs the flow of the material at an angle (usually 90 degrees) to the axis of the machine. It is used in covering wire and cable with insulation, and in coating other materials, such as rope, cotton, pipe, etc., with thermoplastics. For such purposes, the crosshead is equipped with a guider tube, in the axis of the delivery of the die. The material to be covered is fed continuously into this tube and through it to and through the die. Thus it becomes encased in the plastic extruded from the die.

Crossheads are now being made at angles of 45 degrees and even 30, instead of 90, to provide better and more uniform flow of the material to the die.

Fig. 4-7. The "Pasquetti" Machine.

Such coating can be accomplished without a crosshead, for the sake of the benefit of straight-line flow, but this is seldom done because ordinarily it would require a hollow screw in lieu of the guider tube.

Goosenecks are used to deliver material vertically upward or downward. Typical examples are in the extrusion of monofilament, and in the production of film by the "wide sheet" method.

Auxiliary equipment consists of take-off mechanisms such as adjustable-speed conveyors, capstans, or squeeze rolls equipped with accurate variable-speed controls. Conveyor belts are sometimes made of polished stainless steel. Means of cooling include heated or cooled air, tanks of liquid with temperature-controls, sprays of liquid, and cooled forming dies through which the extruded material is drawn to cool and shape it. In production of monofilament, take-ups consist of multispindle spooling units which are generally combined with the orienting mechanism. Constant-tension take-up reels are used in the production of cords, sheets, and coated wire. Semiautomatic and automatic devices for cutting to length are sometimes combined with the take-off mechanism.

Continuous inspection devices are frequently used, such as sparking equipment for electrical testing of insulation, and roll-equipped or electronic gauges for continuous dimensional inspection.

The general trends are toward larger machines, and toward increasing the efficiency of smaller machines to produce more pounds per hour per horsepower.

The applications of extrusion machines in the plastics industry have broadened considerably from their original purpose — the continuous production of shapes. In the applications listed below, the use of extrusion machines results in a great improvement, in production capacity and/or versatility of performance, over conventional methods. This list indicates the successful performance of extrusion machines in some of the more important of the newer uses to which they have been put.

1. Production of thin-walled films down to 0.0005 in., which cannot practicably be produced on calenders; especially lay-flat, thin-wall tubing of large diameter, which has opened new possibilities in the field of packaging.

2. Use as a preheater and preforming machine in connection with continuous vacuum forming; heavy extruded strips while still hot are shaped into such articles as shoe heels.

Courtesy of Welding Engineers, Inc.

Fig. 4-8. Twin-screw extruder for extraction.

3. Coating of paper with plastic (e.g., polyethylene), without the use of solvent or spreading devices. An extruded web of the resin falls upon a web of paper passing beneath the die, and is anchored to the paper while still in soft, tacky condition.

4. Extraction or evaporation of moisture or solvents (Fig. 4-8).

5. Continuous heating (preheating) of thermoplastics; as a preheater, an extrusion machine is used in certain compounding techniques; also prior to extrusion of shapes and as the preheating and fluxing unit for injection-molding machines.

6. Compounding, generally in conjunction with pelleting equipment (Fig. 4-9).

7. Extrusion of a finished product from a powder mix or dry blend, without previous hot milling and granulating, is performed by extrusion machines of special design or by supplementary fluxing attachments on existing extrusion machines. Single-screw and multiscrew machines successfully perform this function.

8. Extrusion of pipe, both semiflexible and rigid, which in this country is being commercially produced up to 8 in. in diameter, and abroad, it is

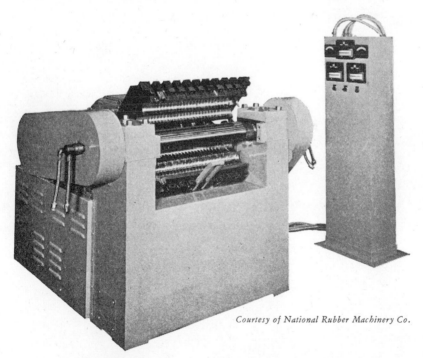

Courtesy of National Rubber Machinery Co.

Fig. 4-9. The "Millstruder," open, showing screw flights on cylinder.

reported, up to 24 in. The twin- and triple-screw machines have opened the field of rigid polyvinyl chloride for pipe. It is reported, however, that there are single-screw machines with special screws and fluxing attachments which perform satisfactorily at high rates of production.

Further extensions may be expected in the use of extrusion machines to perform their functions of continuously heating plastics and of pumping plastic or viscous masses. Modifications and adaptations will keep pace with the demand of current and new applications. And improvements in basic design can be expected to result from current effort to approach problems of design from the viewpoint of the theory of plastic and viscous flow.

5. Forming, Drawing and Postforming

Foreword

The methods described herein are intended to be suggestive of the types of operations which can be used with available plastics to produce articles of commerce. They do not include all the methods which have been developed, but rather those most generally used.

Information is included on the types of tools, equipment and operations which are required. Although some of the art of forming plastics is very old and has been borrowed from practices in other industries, new and novel methods are constantly being developed. This was especially true during World War II, when the need for such methods was acute. There are some methods which are applicable only to specific types of plastics, while others can be adapted to a wide variety of plastics.

Methods of heating and forming cannot be described with the same definiteness with which one can describe a piece of equipment. For instance, in speaking of a press, a long account can be given as to the purpose for which it was designed, its capabilities and its improvements. It is a press for a definite purpose — finished. With methods, it is a different story. They are never finished, but are always being changed and improved and adapted, so that any written instruction is not final but fundamental, and success in practice depends upon the resourcefulness and ingenuity of the personnel of the plant seeking and applying this instruction. Every plant has, among its personnel, men who are versatile; they develop their own techniques, their tricks; they are ingenious. It is suggested that when and wherever such genius is found it be developed and encouraged, and used to supplement any written directions. The scientist uses pyrometers and other instruments to determine correct operating conditions. The man in the plant learns, by sense of feel, the proper temperature for the job at hand.

Some plants have their own tool rooms, with toolmakers, layout men and machinists to design and build their own tools. The smaller plant may not have these facilities, but in every community there are specialists who make one kind of tool, such as male and female dies, clicker dies, hollow dies and other jigs. These are not only sources of supply; they also act in an advisory capacity in helping to apply any written methods. Manufacturers of plastics also have experts who are usually very willing to supply technical information, cooperating with the fabricator in the use of their materials.

Some fabricators have refrained from discussing techniques which they believe are peculiarly their own. With the increasing dissemination of information on methods of forming plastics, it is becoming increasingly apparent that many of these techniques are being applied by others, and that much might be gained by frank discussion of practices within the industry.

Preparatory Operations

Sheets of plastics are generally cut, routed or otherwise shaped to a predetermined contour suitable for forming, drawing and postforming operations. Some machines are built to perform a sequence of operations, e.g., to prepare the blank and form it without removal from the press. It is sometimes necessary to warm the sheet prior to blanking or cutting. A brief description of some of these preparatory operations is given below.

Blanking and Die-Cutting. Blanking and die-cutting of plastics are efficient methods of preparing the sheet for forming. In large-scale production, the use of a blanking technique, rather than sawing or turning, can result in a saving of as much as 40 to 50 per cent in cost of cutting. The amount of this saving will vary, according to the quantity of items produced, the type of plastic used, the efficiency of the over-all operation, and possibly other factors. Since first-class blanking dies cost only about one dollar per inch of edge to be cut, a simple measurement of a proposed article and a knowledge of the number of pieces which are to be produced will determine whether one is justified in using this procedure. Obviously, even the low cost of a blanking die will not be justified if only a few articles are to be manufactured.

The various plastics differ widely in the ease with which they can be blanked or cut, in the temperatures to which they should be preheated, and in the thickness of sheets which can be cut.

The temperature will depend upon the type of plastic that is to be cut, and must be increased as the thickness of the stock is increased.

Cellulose acetate sheet up to about 0.060 in. thick can usually be blanked very satisfactorily without being heated above 70°F. Other thin sheet materials which may be blanked at room temperatures of 70°F or above are cellulose nitrate, polyvinyl butyral, polyethylene, and flexible vinyl sheet. Most plastics in thicknesses of 0.080 in. or greater require heating to produce a clean cut without cracking or chipping. Thus, cellulose nitrate 0.250 in. or thicker must usually be heated in a water bath at 210°F prior to blanking. On the other hand, in cutting thick sheets of polyethylene it may frequently be necessary to use lower than room temperature, in order to make the material more rigid and to prevent the cut edges from being concave.

Low room temperature, or storage in very dry atmosphere, will cause cellulose acetate sheet to crack or shatter under impact of the blanking die. Consequently, suitable temperatures and humidities must be maintained in storing this sheeting prior to blanking it.

Cellulose acetate, rigid vinyl sheeting, and butadiene-acrylonitrile-styrene copolymers* all require similar conditions for blanking and die-cutting. Recommended temperatures for blanking these materials vary from 100°F, for thicknesses 0.060 to 0.125 in., to 180 to 225°F, for 0.750 in. Acrylic sheet can be cut after being heated in an oven at 320°F for the general-purpose grade and at 350°F for the heat-resistant grade. The edges of acrylic sheet 0.060 to 0.080 in. thick can be squared after cutting by heating the sheet to the forming temperature. Recommended conditions for cutting methacrylate sheeting are as follows:

thickness (in.)	minutes in oven at recommended temperature	pressure (lb per linear in.)
0.250	8	165
0.375	10	165
0.500	12	235

Masking paper should be removed from both surfaces prior to heating and blanking unless the blanked article is to be tumble-ashed and polished. In the latter case, the paper will be removed by the tumbling operation. In the former case, masking paper is removed by simply pulling it away from the surface of the sheet. Then the sheet is wiped with a soft cotton batting or cotton wool flannel moistened with hexane or kerosene.

The choice of a press for a given job will depend upon the size of the pieces which are to be cut and the rate of production. Large pieces or heavy sections are usually blanked at slow speeds with a heavy press. A cutting board made of a soft material such as brass, aluminum, vulcanized fiber, or end-grain wood is mounted on either the base or the head of the press, to prevent dulling of the edges of the cutting die.

It is generally possible to blank plastics with an accuracy of approximately $\pm$ $\frac{1}{64}$ in. In some cases considerably better accuracy has been attained, but due allowance must be made for thermal shrinkage, since it is generally necessary to preheat all but the thinnest of sheet material. At room temperature, thin sheets can be punched to an accuracy of $\pm$ 0.002 in. or better.

The economical use of sheet materials in the production of blanked parts depends almost entirely upon a proper layout of the work. Best results can be obtained by a careful geometric analysis and an actual to-scale layout of the outline of the desired piece on a sheet of the available size. Frequently, several paper or cardboard patterns cut to the outline of the blanked piece can be used to advantage in quickly ascertaining the most economical way of cutting the sheet, through actually placing these patterns on the sheet itself. Such a study pays dividends, in that it is often possible to obtain a considerably greater number of pieces from a given area than is apparent from a casual calculation. Sometimes it is found advisable to blank pieces from sheets in successive steps, taking the largest piece first, and then the smaller pieces

---

* More precisely, these are mixtures of two copolymers, i.e., butadiene-acrylonitrile and styrene-acrylonitrile.

afterwards from the so-called "skeleton" or scrap. Irregularly shaped objects may be interlocked and spaced to leave a frame or skeleton from which smaller objects can then be cut.

Either ovens or tables can be used for heating most sheet materials. The preferred method of heating acrylic sheet is in a forced-air circulating oven equipped with automatic controls. Tray-type ovens are required for heating sheeting of butadiene-acrylonitrile-styrene copolymer. For cellulose nitrate, steam or hot water is to be preferred because of the flammability of the material. In using tables heated by steam, electricity, or gas, the temperatures of the heated sheets can in some measure be regulated through the use of insulating and covering pads of canvas or cotton cloth. Heavy sheets heated on tables must be turned over so that they become thoroughly heated through.

In laying out equipment for blanking and punching thermoplastics, it is essential that the ovens, tables, or other heating equipment be located adjacent to the presses in which the work is to be done. Extremely large units to serve a battery of presses are not desirable, and better over-all yields will be obtained if equipment of a suitable size to serve an individual press or pair of presses is placed directly adjacent thereto. This prevents cooling of the work between the heating unit and the press, and thus permits a greater number of pieces to be blanked or punched before it is necessary to reheat the sheeting. In a properly worked-out installation, it is quite frequently feasible to blank an entire sheet, or at least a precut portion of a sheet, without returning it to the oven or heating tables. Similarly, blanking presses should not be placed near windows or doors where drafts are likely to cause the surface of the sheets to cool between heating units and presses. It is, of course, essential to blank material as rapidly as possible, since the length of time between the removal from the heating unit and the actual cutting determines the number of pieces that can be blanked cleanly with a smooth edge.

The types of dies and blanking operations most commonly used are classified as follows:

Outline or Open-Faced Die. Such dies are made from tool steel, about $\frac{1}{4}$ to $\frac{3}{8}$ in. thick at the base or blunt end. It is of utmost importance to construct all dies with the same over-all height, which should be standardized at $2\frac{3}{4}$ in. This practice (a) permits safe operation, since it allows sufficient clearance for the operator's hands and wrists, (b) eliminates the otherwise frequent necessity of changing the height of the ram, (c) prevents the breaking and bending of dies which result when dies of various heights are used in the same press, (d) makes it possible to interchange dies of different size on the same sheet, e.g., for brush backs, mirror-handles, and handles for small articles, without removing the sheet from the press, and (e) permits the more economical production of dies, since smaller stocks of steel bars in a single width are required and since set-ups of machinery do not have to be changed.

These dies can be used for either large or small production runs, and are accurate in dimensions and economical to maintain. In spite of their initial cost, they are more economical to use than those of the lighter, less expensive types. Dies of this type are ordinarily not fastened to the press, but are handled by the operator and can be moved around at will. This form of working is called freehand blanking (Fig. 5-1). The dies are ground and polished on the inside. They pick up the cut piece as the result of a slight chisel-beveling on the inside of the die at the cutting edge (Fig. 5-2).

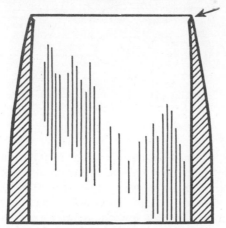

Courtesy of E. I. du Pont de Nemours & Co., Inc.

Fig. 5-1

Courtesy of E. I. du Pont de Nemours & Co., Inc.

Fig. 5-2. Cross section of open-faced die showing "chisel-bevel."

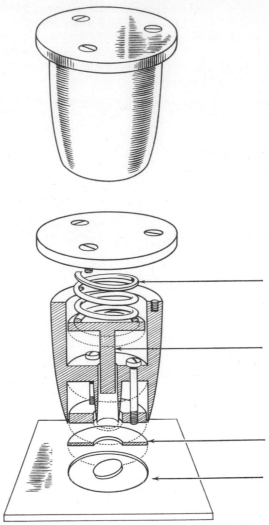

Courtesy of E. I. du Pont de Nemours & Co., Inc.

Fig. 5-3. Ejecting, outline-blanking die.

The ejecting, outline-blanking die (Fig. 5-3) is similar in construction to the open-faced die, but its inner wall is ground differently and provision is made for the die to eject the cut work rather than to pick it up. It is usually made from tool steel of the same types and generally has about the same cross-sectional configuration. It is most useful for sections having a center cut-out, such as a washer. It may be used for free-hand blanking or may be mounted on the base or on the ram of the press.

Steel-Rule Die. Steel-rule is the name applied to a type of steel ribbon quite generally employed in the leather and paper industries. Cutting dies can be easily and cheaply constructed to any desired contour by using this ribbon of steel mounted in a block of wood with its cutting edge protruding. A sponge-rubber pad inserted in the die serves to eject the cut blank from the die. The die is mounted in a press and cuts against a block of end-grained hardwood, or of metal such as saw steel. The die can be used for blanking large pieces for which an outline die would be too costly, or where production

Courtesy of E. I. du Pont de Nemours & Co., Inc.

Fig. 5-4. Steel Rule Die.

will be small. The principal use of equipment of this type (Fig. 5-4) is for trimming to shape previously cut rectangular pieces. It should not be used on sheets of thickness greater than 0.080 in. Such dies can be used in the blanking of pieces of large area, for which the cost of a steel die is prohibitive.

Clicking Die. The die is similar to the steel-rule die but is made from

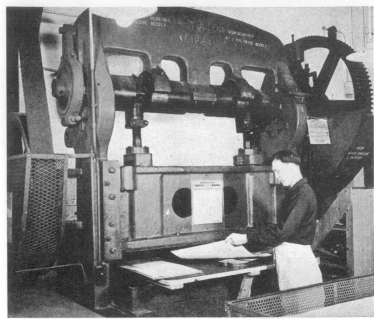

Courtesy of E. I. du Pont de Nemours & Co., Inc.

Fig. 5-5. Clicking Die.

heavier ribbon and is a more permanent die. A clicking die (Fig. 5-5) may
be used for material up to 0.125 in. thickness. Like the steel-rule die, it is
made up of a thin steel ribbon bent to the desired pattern and mounted in or
around a plywood backing plate. The exposed edge is razor-sharp, and at
intervals along the periphery, or inside the pattern itself, there are rubber
stops to hold the plastic in place prior to cutting and to eject it from the die
afterward. The thickness of the steel ribbon is determined by the thickness
of the plastic which is to be cut, as well as by its nature.

Knockout Die. The knockout, or ejector, die is a modification of a blanking die, consisting of a lower section called the die block and an upper section
called the punch, mounted in a suitable press, and provided with a mechanism
for ejecting the blank. The cutting edge of a knockout die is usually $\frac{5}{16}$-in.
steel tapered to a sharp blade. In some cases, knockout dies, which are used
on stock up to 0.080 in. thick, are fastened to the press, and the sheet of
material is fed underneath on the up-stroke of the press. In other cases, the
die is placed on the material, which rests on a cutting board, and the two are
inserted together into the open press. After the press has completed its stroke,
they are removed, and either the die is shifted to another location on the sheet
or the cut sheet is removed and the next one put in position. In still other
cases, the operator shifts the position of the die on the sheet while it is still

in the press, timing his motions to the automatic strokes of the press. Dies used in this way should be equipped with a flange at the top to eliminate any danger that the operator's hand can be caught between the press and the die.

Dinking Die. This is generally constructed as a hand tool having a ground tapered cutting edge and a shank on which a mallet is used to force the die through the sheet. Suitable means of knockout is provided, to remove the blank from the die. Sometimes these dies are used in multiple in a press.

Punch and Die. These usually are small dies used to punch holes in the blank. Punching dies are mounted with the die fastened to the base of the press and the punch to the movable member. The die usually has an open bottom, and the punched work is forced through by the successive strokes of the press. Frequently a jet of air is played against the work, to blow the piece clear of the next stroke of the press.

Punch and die should be constructed of tool steel having a high carbon content, and made to accurate dimensions so that pieces, or holes in pieces, can be expected to have a precision of dimensions not usually obtainable by blanking. This technique is often used where the finished piece must fit accurately over or into another part, or when there are several holes that must be definitely aligned or spaced.

Sawing. Sawing is the method most generally used for cutting sheets of plastics. The types used for cutting wood and soft metal can be used for cutting plastics. Sharpening of the saw blades is very important, and if the saws are being used for cutting more than one material, it is advisable to reserve certain saw blades for the cutting of plastics. Selection of the best type of saw for cutting depends upon the plastic to be cut, and the shape of the piece.

With the exception of cellulose nitrate, plastics can be sawed dry, but smoother cuts can be made with the aid of a lubricant, such as a light coat of oil applied to the saw blade by means of a brush. A jet of air can be directed against the saw blade to prevent overheating. Liquid cooling agents are helpful in cutting thick sheets of thermoplastics. Masking paper must be removed from the sheet immediately after cutting with the aid of liquid lubricants, because absorption of the lubricant by the paper, and possible softening of the adhesive, makes later removal a difficult problem.

The rate of feed for all types of sawing can best be learned by experience. In general the rate is slower for plastics than for wood, and it is advisable to slow down at the finish of the cut, to assure a smooth edge and to avoid chipping. Smearing and excessive smoking during sawing may indicate too rapid feed, or the wrong saw, but with some materials may be unavoidable.

Circular Saws. Hollow-ground circular saws are preferred for straight cutting of plastics. Stiffening collars should be used to support the blade. The collars and stem of the arbor should be well fitted to make the saw run perfectly true. As the thickness of the material or stock increases, the saw should have fewer teeth, larger diameter, and more set. There should be 45 to 60 degrees of clearance and no rake on the teeth.

The selection of the saw blade is important, as it determines both the efficiency of the cutting operation and the quality of the sawed edge. When finishing operations are to be performed, a smooth saw cut reduces the time required for polishing.

In cutting acrylic sheet, large circular saws (15 to 16 in. diameter) stay sharp longer and do not gum up as quickly as smaller ones. For cutting acrylic sheet, circular saws should run at surface speeds from 8000 to 12,000 fpm (that is, a 12-in. saw should run about 3400 rpm). For cutting cellulose acetate sheet $\frac{1}{4}$ in. thick and over, a saw of diameter 10 to 14 in., having 4 to 6 teeth per in., and run at a spindle speed of 2400 to 3000 rpm is recommended. For the same stock under $\frac{1}{4}$ in., a suitable saw has a diameter 6 to 9 in., and 8 to 10 teeth per in., and is run at a spindle speed of 2100 rpm. For cellulose nitrate, saws require more set than for cellulose acetate sheet. The set should be rather heavy for thick sheet. When cutting cellulose nitrate sheet, a heavy stream of water must be used on the saw blade. For the sawing of postforming laminates, surface speeds up to 13,000 fpm can be used. Saws having 4 to 8 teeth per in., ground square and with liberal clearance are used for sawing material up to 2 in. thick. For the sawing of rigid vinyl plastics, an underwater saw having a surface speed of 3500 to 4000 fpm is recommended. Saws of 12 in. diameter with 10 to 14 teeth per in. are used. The teeth should have no set.

When cutting thin stock (less than $\frac{1}{4}$ in.), blades sufficiently hollow ground do not require set teeth, and consequently produce a smoother cut and make a narrower kerf. For thicker materials, a spring set is required. The teeth should be side dressed on the machine, after sharpening, to obtain a smooth-edged cut. Teeth should be of uniform height, to prevent excessive chipping of the sheet and possible cracking of the blade. Saws should be kept sharp by machine filing or grinding, and all teeth should be of the same shape.

For cutting thick stock, a swaged-tooth saw is recommended. Swaged teeth should also be side-dressed to obtain a cleanly cut edge. Flat-ground spring-set saws $\frac{1}{8}$ in. thick and having 4 to 6 teeth per in. may also be used for cutting thicker sheets.

The height of the saw blades above the table should be slightly greater than the thickness of the material, to prevent chipping. Good sawing practice requires firm holding of the material, in alignment parallel with the saw blade, and uniform rates of feed. A hold-down should be provided to prevent chattering, which will cause uneven cutting and chipping. In some cases, a slitter directly behind the saw blade will prevent the kerf from closing on the retreating edge and causing a burned cut. A burned cut not only destroys the good surface of the cut but also tends to heat and dull the saw. The rate of feed should be reduced as the blade is leaving the cut, to avoid chipping of the corners.

In cutting sheets having masking paper on them, a sliding jig made of plywood or hard composition board is arranged to slide on the saw table. The sliding jig is useful in preventing damage to the masking paper which might result from sliding the sheet over the saw table on which chips are located, or otherwise damaging the paper as a result of handling the sheet on the saw table. The sliding jig is made by fastening a steel bar to the under surface of the plywood in such a manner as to permit the bar to ride in the grooves on the saw table. This has been a very useful jig. Lubricants such as soap or tallow can be used to reduce the friction. In multiple-sawing of sheets having masking paper, the adhesive tends to dull the saw. The gumming of the blade can be minimized by applying to it a small amount of oil or grease. This may be done with wick oilers or, more simply, by touching a stick of tallow or white soap against the revolving blade. If a deposit starts to collect on the saw, it should be cleaned off before it builds up to such an extent that it fills the clearance space.

Multiple sawing, especially with suitably designed jigs, can prove economical and will more than pay for the increased power used. Thin stock can be stacked to about 1 in. in thickness for sawing.

Circular saws require more power for cutting plastics than for cutting wood. A three-horsepower motor is recommended to drive a 10- or 12-in. saw. Hand feeding is the best method for controlling the rate of sawing, since the operator can "feel" the stock and adjust to give the best results. Some hydraulic devices are available, by which the feed can be controlled by a valve regulated to suit the work.

A small stream of cooling agent directed against the blade as it enters the cut will prevent heating and give a smooth cut. The use of a cooling agent reduces the amount of side clearance required, and thus extends the use of hollow-ground saws to thicker material. In continuous cutting operations, the use of cooling agents improves the quality of the cut and retards the dulling of the saw. The use of 10 per cent of a water-soluble cutting oil in the cooling agent prevents rust, but too high a percentage of soluble oil causes trouble in cleaning mastic off acrylic sheets sawed with the masking paper left on. Masking paper should be removed immediately after sawing with coolants.

Saws should always be guarded, and particularly so when cooling agents are used.

Air jets can also be used for cooling.

Because cellulose nitrate sheet is flammable, friction caused by a saw not properly cooled can cause the material to burn. Heavy work requires a heavy stream of water constantly directed on the saw blade at the cutting point. For thin stock, a light jet of water directed against the lower part of the blade is generally sufficient.

Water must not be used in sawing cellulose acetate unless the surface has not been finished or unless each piece is immediately dried, since drops of water allowed to remain on cellulose acetate will spot the surface. On the other hand, overheating will cause cellulose acetate to soften and to become gummy.

Band Saws. A straight cut can be made also with a band saw. Where flat sheets are to be cut in curves, or where formed parts are to be rough-trimmed, band saws should be used. Large saws with a 30- to 36-in. throat are best for production work, although the smaller home-workshop saws will do for small work. Some of the newer band saws are arranged so that the speed can be changed to suit the work. This is an advantage, since in general the speed must be less with the thicker material, to ensure against overheating. Speed, feed and thickness of stock should be such that each tooth cuts a clean chip. If the speed is too high in proportion to the feed, the teeth will rub and heat up, rather than cut freely. For cutting acrylic sheet, the blade should run at speeds of from 2300 to 5000 fpm. For cellulose acetate, a speed of 1500 fpm is recommended. For sawing postforming laminates in thicknesses greater than 2 in. and up to 10 in., band saws having a surface speed of 8000 fpm are recommended. Saws should have from 5 to 8 teeth per in., with a medium set for straight sawing and a heavy set for curved sawing.

Metal-cutting blades stay sharp longer than the softer woodworking blades. They cannot be sharpened and should be thrown away when dull. Thickness, width, and number of teeth will depend on the size of the saw, the thickness of the material to be cut, and the minimum radius to be cut. For curved work the best band widths are $\frac{3}{16}$ to $\frac{3}{8}$ in. For ripping and cutting work of large radius, widths of $\frac{1}{2}$ to $\frac{3}{4}$ in. are generally satisfactory.

Skip-tooth metal-cutting band saws are one of the newest developments in saws for cutting plastics at high speeds. These saws have coarse teeth and will keep sharp for a long time. There are 2, 3, 4, or 6 teeth per in.; the thinner the material, the greater the number of teeth required. The manufacturers of saws of this type can supply tables showing recommended sawing speeds for all types of plastics.

Band saws with spiral blades can be used for cutting stock over $\frac{1}{4}$ in. thick.

Jig Saws. A jig saw may be useful for making cuts that cannot be made on a band saw. Jig saws are used for cutting closed holes in thin stock. They do not cut well through thick sheets or multiple sheets. If it is necessary to use a jig saw, the feed must be light and the teeth cleared often.

Veneer Saws. Small circular saws 3 to 4 in. in diameter are called veneer saws. They are used in portable tools to trim large formed acrylic pieces. They should be driven at from 10,000 to 15,000 rpm to give a surface speed of from 8000 to 15,000 fpm. Great care must be taken in using veneer saws, since they cannot be guarded. They must be well balanced and run true. Do not use a veneer saw if there is vibration when the motor is running at full speed.

Veneer saws can be used also in a woodworking shaper or router, for trimming the flanges from formed pieces. The height of the saw is adjusted to the proper distance above the table, and the work moved by the revolving blade. No jig is required and a high rate of production is possible.

Hole Saws. A hole saw is a tubular tool with saw teeth filed on its lower end. The teeth have a set, so as to cut a groove wider than the thickness of the wall. A shaft is fastened to the top of the tube so that it can be mounted in a drill press which is used to drive the saw. Usually a pilot drill and guide are provided in the center to locate and center the hole saw. Knockout holes are located in the top of the tubular saw to allow removal of the discs. Hole saws are made in sizes from ⅝ to 4 in. in diameter.

Routing. Routing of blanks is often required, to bevel or square-rout them to size or to produce variously shaped edges, such as channels and steps. The stationary type of router is the most common, although portable routers designed for pattern work in wood, and for trimming, can also be used to advantage on formed pieces.

Courtesy of United States Rubber Co.

Fig. 5-6

A vertical cut can be accomplished on a router as shown in Fig. 5-6. The depth of the cut is governed by the roller which rides on a track off to one side of the cutting tool. A guide pin, riding in a track on the bottom of the fixture, guides the cut in relation to the contour (see Fig. 5-7). This par-

Courtesy of United States Rubber Co.

Fig. 5-7

ticular setup on 0.093-in. butadiene-acrylonitrile-styrene copolymer is run at 20,000 rpm with a high-speed steel cutter of ¼-in. diameter, and at about 40 fpm on a 60-in. cut.

Speeds. The best rates of production can be obtained with heavy routers running from 5000 to 10,000 rpm, and with light routers running 10,000 to 22,000 rpm, with no load on the spindle. High-speed routing with small cutters (less than 1.5-in. diameter) will give a smooth cut, provided all of the teeth are identical; if one tooth projects farther than the others, it will cause a rough cut. Chips can be removed from the cutters by an exhaust blower or air jet. Exhaust blowers should never be used with cellulose nitrate plastics, because of the danger of dust explosions. The speed of a portable router is about 19,000 rpm.

Cutters. Standard routing cutters should be used. They must be kept sharp. For acrylics, they should have a back clearance angle of about 10 degrees, and no rake. Trimming of cellulose acetate stock is done with a straight-edged cutter of diameter 1.5 in., having 6 blades, with a clearance angle of about 35 degrees. This operation brings blanked-out work down to size, although further rounding of corners is usually necessary.

Channeling requires a cutter with clearance on three faces. The clearance on the rim face is about 30 degrees, while that on the side faces should not be more than 10 degrees. High-speed steel is used because of its resistance to wear. The largest cutter generally used in production work is 2½ in.

Carbide-tipped cutters are recommended for routing postforming laminates. Milling cutters should be ground with a negative rake up to 10 degrees, and should be operated at surface speeds up to 1000 fpm.

In a portable router, the cutter is chucked directly to the motor shaft. Stationary routers are generally belt-driven. Standard high-speed end mills also have been used. The depth of the cut is controlled by a spacing collar inserted on the spindle, either above or under the cutter. The difference in radius between the cutter and the collar governs the depth of cut. As the cutters are worn down by sharpening, it is necessary to change the size of the collar.

Square-routing is sometimes necessary, to square the edges after blanking or rough trimming, and is performed with a straight-edge cutter. Tolerances of plus or minus 0.015 in. can be maintained in depth or toe of rout in a single operation. Tolerances of plus or minus 0.030 in. or better can be held in the length of the shoulder of the rout. Close tolerances cannot be maintained both in toe and in depth of rout on sheets having wide differences in thickness. It is advisable to grind a slight radius on the corner of the cutter so that it will be duplicated in the shoulder of the rout. This reduces the possibility that cracks will develop at this point. Work should be fed slowly and continuously to avoid any tendency to chip or overheat the plastic.

Cutting, Shearing, and Breaking. Some plastics in certain thicknesses can be cut with a scissors-type cutter. Shearing generally refers to the cutting action of a knife blade which has some lateral motion. Such blades may contact the sheet progressively across its width or may contact the sheet evenly and move transversely across it as pressure is applied.

Standard cutters of the guillotine type or a metal-cutting power shear can be used for cutting some plastics, but these are not satisfactory for acrylics. The guillotine knife is used for cutting continuous sheets of cellulose acetate as they are unwound or stripped from the drum. Postforming laminates in thicknesses up to ⅛ in. can be cut on a guillotine, depending upon the type of fabric base that is used.

In some cases the sheet can be scored and broken to produce the desired shape.

Some plastics have to be conditioned before these operations are performed, especially in cold weather. Recommendations for this depend upon the type of plastic. Temperatures above room temperature and controlled humidities are generally required.

Accessory Equipment and Supplies

Heating Equipment. Most forming, drawing and postforming operations require that the plastics first be heated to forming temperature. At this temperature the plastics are pliable and can be easily shaped. Various plastics have different forming temperatures, and in some cases one method of heating works better than others. In general, the simple bends and slight three-dimensional bends are made at a lower temperature than are the more deeply drawn or difficult compound curved sections. The thinner material must be heated to a higher temperature than the thicker material, since the amount of heat stored in the sheet, and hence the time available for forming, are much less than for thick sections. Automatic temperature-controls must be provided, and temperature-recording devices are desirable, although not absolutely essential. Brief descriptions of the most common methods of heating plastics for forming are given below.

Ovens. Ovens are the preferred means for heating acrylics and certain other plastics for forming operations.

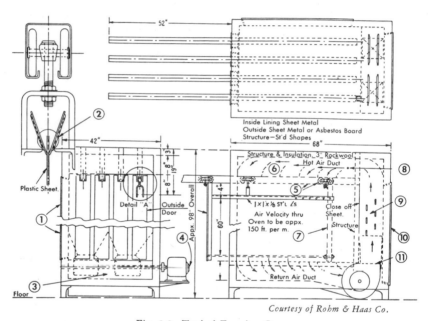

Courtesy of Rohm & Haas Co.

Fig. 5-8. Typical Forming Oven.

1. Access door for flattening.
2. Hunt clip No. 4 to hang plastic sheet.
3. Blowers (1 or 2) approximately 3000 cfm total.
4. ¾-Hp motor approximately.
5. Track and trolleys.
6. Deflectors, adjusted to give uniform flow.
7. Inside door; adjustable to close when rack is all the way out.
8. Thermostat. On-off or modulated. To control temperature 250-500 watt units.
9. Heaters (electric).
10. Access door to blowers and heater.
11. Blowers.

Courtesy of E. I. du Pont de Nemours & Co., Inc.

Fig. 5-9. Sheet Heating Oven.

The most commonly used type of oven consists of a chamber of sufficient size, insulated against heat losses and provided with a forced circulation of air and a means of heating. A typical forced-circulation air oven is shown in Fig. 5-8. A tray-type sheet heating oven is shown in Fig. 5-9. Steam, gas or electricity may be used to heat the oven. Temperatures above 400°F are not generally recommended. The optimum temperature can be learned from the manufacturer of the plastic. It is impracticable to use steam for the highest operating temperatures. The oven should be provided with suitable controls, so that the temperature can be varied to meet the different operating requirements.

The time required to bring the sheet to the proper temperature depends on the temperature of the oven, the velocity of the air in the oven and the thickness of the sheet. The oven temperature should not be much higher than the desired forming temperature of the plastic, since excessive temperatures may damage the surface of the sheet.

The doors of the ovens should be small, to minimize cooling of the ovens while loading and removing the sheets. It is also desirable to have one door in one section of the oven sufficiently large to permit the introduction of large formed pieces for reheating if re-forming is necessary.

Forced circulation of air and suitable baffles are necessary to distribute the heat throughout the oven so that each sheet will be heated uniformly over its entire surface and so that all sheets will be heated to the same temperature. Gas ovens designed to use flue gases as a heating medium are not recommended. Air velocities across the surface of the sheet should be in the range of 150 ft per minute. The oven should be constructed with the air inlet from the back or side, in order to prevent cold air from being drawn in when the door is opened. Air outlets are provided on both sides near the doors of the oven, or over the supporting racks if a down-draft circulating system is used.

The sheets are hung vertically from racks or supported in trays lined with soft cloth or woven glass-fiber cloth to protect the surface of the plastic from scratching. Overhead racks may be equipped with tracks and trolleys to facilitate handling of the sheet.

The manufacturers of ovens will supply engineering information on equipment which they manufacture.

Infrared Radiation. Infrared radiation can be used for the heating of sheet plastics to the desired forming temperature. Sources of such infrared radiation are electric lamps, electrical resistance units, glass plates, gas heat and a heating panel comprising electrical resistance wire, woven glass-fiber tapes and tubing, and covered with glass-fiber cloth.

Electric lamps are usually operated at relatively low temperatures for maximum efficiency. Such lamps tend to focus the radiation, and thus may cause spotty heating if the lamps are too close to the sheet or improperly spaced or directed. This can be avoided by shielding the plastic from direct radiation by placing an absorbing plate between the lamps and the plastic. The plate can be sheet steel, which will absorb and re-radiate at a lower temperature. Too-rapid heating of thick sheets must be avoided, since it may overheat the surface. Localized heating is sometimes desirable. For this purpose portable lamps are used, usually with reflectors built in. In some cases, additional reflectors are used.

Ovens can be constructed with banks of infrared lamps mounted in the ceiling, on each side, or on one side with a suitable reflector on the other side. Installations can be built to permit the sheet to pass through the oven continuously, or sheets can be hung in the oven or placed on a stationary tray. In some installations the lamps are so mounted that the radiation does not strike the surface of the sheet at 90 degrees. It is claimed that this permits greater absorption and higher efficiency of operation. Furthermore, the lamps can be arranged on a mechanism which will cause them to oscillate, and thus distribute the heat more uniformly over the surface of the sheet. Arrangements which either permit such movement of lamps or provide for passage of the sheet between the banks of lamps have the advantage of giving uniform heating, which is important if the optics of the formed shape are critical.

Ovens built with walls of a woven mat of glass fiber and resistance wire have the advantage of providing a large radiating area of uniform surface temperature. It is claimed that the temperature can be controlled at any point in the range from 120 to 700°F. Sheets heated by this method are reported to be free of hot or cold spots. Such infrared-radiation heating panels can also be used horizontally for thinner plastic sheets and films. It is reported that 10-mil vinyl film heated underneath such a panel requires only 10 to 12 seconds to reach forming temperature.

Plastics differ in their ability to absorb infrared radiation. Thicker sheets may behave quite differently than thin sheets, in that the center does not heat up as rapidly as the surfaces. This difference can sometimes be corrected by moving the banks of lamps or panels farther from the sheet.

To ensure efficient installation of infrared lamps or of panels of glass fiber and glass resistance wire, it is desirable to consult companies experienced in manufacturing and installation of such equipment for the heating of plastics.

Narrow Band Heaters. Certain forming operations require only a narrow zone of the sheet to be heated. Electric strip heaters, cartridge heaters, open-coil electric heaters or a small steam pipe are used for such work. The sheet may or may not be placed in direct contact with such heaters. Localized heating of some types of plastics should be done with caution, and the manufacturer should be consulted about the best method of handling his material.

Electric strip heaters are available in widths up to about 6 in. and are designed to operate at temperatures from 750 to 1500°F, or higher. For the heating of plastics a maximum of 350°F is generally required, and rheostats are used to control the temperature within the desired limits. Cartridge heaters are round tubes packed in various ways for heating electrically. Such units may be mounted within a pipe having a larger diameter than the unit, and the sheet can be placed on this pipe for heating.

Open-coil electric heaters also are used. These are sometimes constructed with multiple coils to give the desired width of band and also with adjustable flanges on each side of the heaters. The sheet is placed on these flanges to avoid direct contact with the hot wires. The width of the heated band can be varied to suit the requirements.

A blast of hot air can sometimes be used to produce a localized heating effect.

It is desirable to heat both sides of the sheet. Preferably, the face of the sheet which will be on the outside of the bend should be heated over a greater area and to a slightly higher temperature than the face which will be on the inside.

Hot Bath. A hot bath can be used to heat plastics to the forming temperature. Water kept hot by bubbling in steam can be used to heat some plastics. Such materials as glycerine or glycol can be used in the water to raise its boiling point. Hot oil baths are satisfactory except for the difficulty in handling the sheet and the need of cleaning to remove the oil afterward. The use of a hot bath has the advantage of giving uniform heating, provided it is equipped with efficient stirrers.

Hot-Plate Radiation. Hot platens are used quite extensively for the heating of sheet plastics. The platens can be cored for heating with either steam or hot water under pressure. Electric hot plates are also used, equipped with rheostats to control the temperature. Sometimes two hot plates are mounted so that the plastic can be hung between them. If only a single platen is used, it is necessary to cover the sheet on both sides with cloth or other insulator during the heating, in order to produce more nearly uniform heating.

Electronic Heating. Electronic heating works only on plastics which absorb high-frequency radiation. Several companies are now building apparatus suitable for this work. The initial expense in setting up such equipment is large, but for some types of plastics the method is rapid and the cost may be justified for large production.

Materials for Molds and Mold Covers.   Materials used in the construction of molds for the forming of plastics are described below:

Wood. Either plywood or solid wood may be used in the construction of molds for short production runs. It is essential that the wood be dry, and preferable that it should be hard. Kiln-dried wood, such as mahogany or maple, can be used when available. If comparatively few pieces are to be made, a mold can be economically constructed from cheaper wood, such as dry white pine. Even good wood will change shape and dimensions with atmospheric changes, and therefore it should be sealed. Since shellac and regular varnish will melt at forming temperatures, synthetic resins, high-temperature varnish or casein should be used.

Since contact with end-grain wood may produce distortion in the finished pieces, wooden molds should be constructed so that the side grain of the wood is on the surface throughout. In constructing molds from wood, it is generally necessary to glue the pieces together and carefully finish the surface. The heat-curing glues are preferred, since they will not soften under the heat of subsequent forming operations. The surface of the mold is usually covered with a soft material such as felt or suede rubber.

Some impregnated and compressed woods make excellent molds for the forming of plastics. Such woods have low shrinkage and can be used for construction of large molds.

Metal. Metal is used most in making forming molds for simple items. Its advantages are ease of fabrication to exact contours, ability to be polished to a smooth surface, and relatively high dimensional stability under conditions of use.

Several types of metals, such as brass, steel, aluminum or low-melting alloys, are used in making cast forming molds. Either sheet metal or solid die stock also can be used. In some cases bar stock is used as a reinforcing medium in making molds from other materials, such as plastic.

Low-melting alloys have the advantage of ease of fabrication for duplication of design or pattern. Two types of low-melting alloys are most generally used. These are alloys of lead, antimony, bismuth and tin, melting in the range of 300 to 400°F, and alloys of aluminum and zinc, melting in the range of 600 to 800°F.

The disadvantages of metal molds are relatively high initial cost and high thermal conductivity. The heat capacity and thermal conductivity of the metal are important factors in mold design. Most metals have higher heat conductivity than plastics, and for that reason it is sometimes necessary to heat metal molds to 140 to 180°F so that heat will not be dissipated from the plastic too rapidly. The thermal shock of forming against a cold mold may cause optical distortion resulting from strain, and also such strains result in poorer dimensional stability at elevated temperatures. This is especially true for the more complex shapes made from more rigid plastic sheets. But good results with rigid vinyl sheets may generally be had with unheated metal molds.

Plastics. Thermosetting plastics, usually phenolics, have been used quite successfully in making molds for forming of thermoplastics and for the post-forming of thermosetting laminates. Fillers such as asbestos are used to reduce shrinkage and give added strength to the mold.

Low-viscosity furane resins also have been used to impregnate foundry-type molds of sand. It is necessary to use an accurately controlled amount of a phenolic-resin binder in the raw sand shape, in order to obtain a strong core which does not soften too much during impregnation, and which is sufficiently porous to soak up a large amount of furane resin. After curing, the final smooth finish is obtained by applying a filling coat of a medium-viscosity furane resin containing finely-divided china clay.

Special plastics with low shrinkage have been developed for the making of molds. The dimensional stability of such molds is generally satisfactory, but some have a tendency to crack after long use in forming operations. These special mold materials have low coefficients of heat-transfer and are uniform throughout. This is important in the forming of transparent thermoplastic sheet materials, in which strains caused by unequal cooling may cause optical defects.

Ceramics. The types of artificial stone used by dentists for making investments can also be used to make forming molds. These are available from dental-supply houses. These materials are relatively expensive, but have the advantage of fine texture, which gives excellent detail for reproduction of pattern such as grain in wood. Less expensive materials that have found more extensive use are gypsum cements, some of which are harder than others.

In making a mold with one of the hard materials, the cement is mixed with only sufficient water to make a paste of a consistency to be worked. Excess of water causes high shrinkage and makes the material difficult to handle. The molds are reinforced by means of chicken-wire, long-fiber sisal hemp, or burlap. In some cases the mold is constructed with a reinforcing framework of scrap metal bar stock. Such molds are often constructed as a shell only a few inches in thickness. All surfaces to be used in forming are carefully smoothed and dressed to the desired contour. After baking to harden, the mold may be finished by sanding or coating. Such materials may be used when a few hundred parts are to be made from the mold.

Mixtures of gypsum plaster with Portland cement are sometimes used to make molds. Molds may be made from mixtures of 30 to 40 parts of Portland cement with 70 to 60 parts of gypsum plaster. Such molds are good for long production runs. After long use, cracks may develop in the molds, possibly as a result of dehydration of the plaster.

"Keene" cement, a British product, is one of the best and most economical materials for making molds. It is readily obtainable at any building-supply house. The shrinkage factor is quite low, and it needs very little water for mixing, much less than ordinarily used for mixing common plaster.

Ordinary plaster of Paris is not a satisfactory material for making molds to form sheet plastics, being not strong enough to withstand the forces involved.

A special metal-casting plaster, known as "P.M.C.," has been found useful for forming some thermoplastics. It is many times more porous than ordinary casting plasters, and this eliminates the necessity of incorporating a system of vacuum holes in the mold for vacuum forming. "P.M.C." can be cast in 1 to 2 hr, but is relatively fragile, and is not recommended for long production runs.

Magnesite, an oxychloride cement, has been used to make hard, stone-like, nonporous molds which show good heat-resistance and good reproduction of detail.

In the production of molds for vacuum drawing, and to allow evacuation of entrapped air in blow molding, it is necessary to have a number of fine holes in the mold through which the air can escape quickly. These air holes must be no larger than 0.04 in. in diameter, since the rigid sheet will form down into larger orifices. The number of holes is determined by computing the volume of air between the mold surface and the rigid sheet, and then approximating the number of holes necessary to evacuate this volume of air in less than one second. The holes should preferably be located in the deep draws, to ensure optimum drawing into them.

Since magnesite and many other casting materials are very hard and difficult to drill after they have set, it is generally desirable to incorporate "Monel" metal rods with tapered points, or twenty-penny nails, into the casting. The most efficient method is to drive the nails at predetermined distances through a board or jig which can be placed over the fresh casting, and so allow the nails to penetrate the casting and provide a hole through to the master mold. These nails or rods are removed after the cast mold has set. Also, a small pipe is usually embedded partially in a horizontal position into what will later be the bottom of the cast mold, so that the vacuum line can be connected to it.

After the mold has set and the various inset nails removed, the bottom of the mold is covered with two layers of 1/8-in. hardware cloth. A sheet of 0.029-in. aluminum is mounted over the hardware cloth and taped to the side of the mold to form a vacuum seal. The wire mesh forms a connecting link between the holes and the pipe previously laid. The end of the pipe outside the mold is connected to a vent and to the vacuum system. A blanket of 1/4-in. sponge rubber is mounted over the aluminum sheet to cushion the mold from undue impact and to compensate for any nonlevel surfaces on the back of the mold.

"Masonite." "Masonite" die stock is available in a variety of thicknesses and sizes. This is a material prepared from wood chips. It can be worked with conventional tools to produce the desired contours and smoothness. One quite general application is for the construction of flanges for vacuum-forming equipment. The material is uniform and has low heat-conductivity.

Rubber. Rubber can be used in a number of ways for the construction of molds. Sponge rubber is used as a medium to force the sheet plastic into intimate contact with molds of intricate shape. Soft rubber is used as diaphragms in applying pressure where desired. Soft rubber bands are frequently used to hold the edges of a sheet formed by simple bending or draping. Hard rubber has not been used to any great extent as a mold material.

Flock rubber is used extensively as a covering for plaster or wooden molds. When the flock rubber has to be stretched over a mold surface having compound curvatures, it is important to use a grade of flock rubber that has sufficient elasticity, and on which the flock is evenly distributed when the material is stretched.

Felt. Felt is used as a covering for molds made from other materials, such as wood, plaster or plastics. It may also be used to retain grease used in grease-forming operations. Such felt is generally $\frac{1}{16}$ or $\frac{1}{8}$ in. thick and has a fairly high density.

To cover a male mold, the felt is saturated with water, stretched over the mold, tacked beyond the trim line, and allowed to dry. To cover a female mold, the felt is cemented to the mold with a waterproof linoleum cement.

Cotton Cloth. Cotton cloth is used in the form of cotton flannel to cover molds or to line drawers in ovens to prevent mark-off on the sheet. Special types of cloth are used for miscellaneous jobs, such as wiping dust and lint from the sheet just prior to forming.

Presses. Practically all of the conventional types of presses have been used in the forming of sheet plastics.

Air-Operated Arbor Press. These presses are very useful in forming deep-draw sections and large sections which require more pressure than is available on small hand-operated presses.

The air-operated press is generally constructed with a large air cylinder mounted vertically over and attached to the ram. A supply of air, ample in volume and pressure, is required with this equipment.

The capacity of such presses is determined by the size of the cylinder and the air pressure available.

A press of this type can readily be equipped with a cylinder on the bottom of the bed, which acts as a force for use in drawing operations. Presses are built from channel iron as shown in Figs. 5-10 and 5-11.

Hydraulic Presses. Hydraulic presses are standardized for the plastics industry and need not be described in detail. Both small and large presses

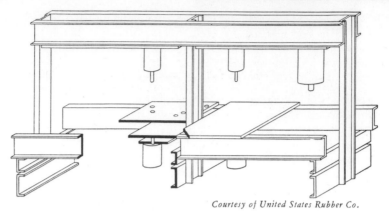

Courtesy of United States Rubber Co.

Fig. 5-10. Air-operated Press (light).

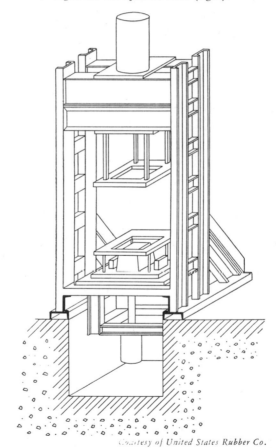

Courtesy of United States Rubber Co.

Fig. 5-11. Air-operated press (heavy) with lower cylinder.

are used and, when necessary, presses built to specifications are quite easily constructed.

Oil is the usual force used, but water, on a high-pressure system, can be used if all of the equipment is adapted to it.

The hydraulic press has an advantage over the air press in that more pressure is usually maintained in a hydraulic system. This allows use of male and female molds for embossing and similar operations requiring great force.

Courtesy of E. I. du Pont de Nemours & Co., Inc.

Fig. 5-12

Toggle Press. The toggle press is of standard design and comes in various sizes. This press involves the use of cranks with lever mechanisms to actuate slides on which cutting dies or molds for drawing of plastics are used. Both single-crank and double-crank presses are used. The latter may be used for combined blanking and forming operations (see Fig. 5-12).

Cam Press. A modification of the toggle press involves the use of cams instead of levers for actuating the sliding mechanisms.

Cam presses can be built to provide correct rate of draw and dwell for forming, depending upon the design of the cam. Multiple-cam presses are available for performing a series of operations. It is frequently necessary to design the cams to suit the requirements of a particular forming operation.

Foot Press. Foot presses are used extensively in the forming of plastics, especially those of the cellulose derivatives. These are usually small presses operated by pedals, and are oftened designed to meet requirements of an individual application.

Arbor Press. This is a small machine generally mounted on a bench and having a hand-operated mechanism consisting of a rack meshed with a pinion to which a hand lever is attached. It is useful for a great many operations in connection with the forming of plastics.

Courtesy of United States Rubber Co.

Fig. 5-13. Punch Press with die mounted for piercing and trimming.

Hat Press. Small presses used in the hat industry have been adapted to the postforming of laminated thermosetting sheet. These are generally small light presses operated by hand levers and pedals.

Punch Presses. Punch presses of the double-action variety can be used in forming some plastic sheet materials when the forming and drawing are not too severe. With such a press, the primary motion forms the part between

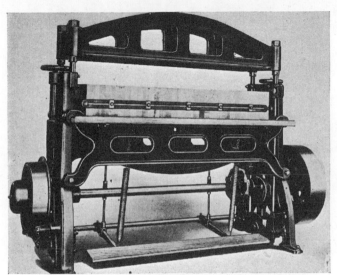

Courtesy of E. I. du Pont de Nemours & Co., Inc.

Fig. 5-14. Clicking Press.

the male and female molds, and then dwells at the end of the stroke to allow for cooling. The secondary motion then trims, pierces, etc. (see Fig. 5-13).

Clicking Press. The type of press shown in Fig. 5-14 is commonly used for guillotine cutting, and for mounting of dies of the steel-rule or clicking type.

Trimming Press. The press shown in Fig. 5-15 is used for mounting of trimming dies or steel-rule dies.

Miscellaneous Tools and Equipment. *Clamps.* Clamps of several types are used in the fabrication of articles from sheet plastics. These include the conventional "C" clamps, wood clamps, pattern-makers' clamps, toggle and vise-grip pliers, and quick-acting clamps. Clamps are used to hold the sheet during some forming operations and also for the clamping of molds.

Vacuum Apparatus. Vacuum apparatus is required for certain forming operations. Such apparatus may consist of the conventional radial or vane-

Courtesy of E. I. du Pont de Nemours & Co., Inc.

Fig. 5-15. Trimming Press.

type vacuum pump connected with an accumulator tank of sufficient capacity to prevent large fluctuations in the vacuum available. This tank should have a capacity at least one-and-one-half times that of the largest forming chamber to be used. Rotary-type vacuum pumps are suitable for use and are available with large capacities.

Other pumps may be used, such as a steam vacuum jet of the Venturi type operating from a high-pressure steam line and having a capacity of at least 25 cu ft of air per minute at 25 in. of vacuum.

Milking machines can be used to produce vacuum, and for a small forming chamber a two-stage compressor can be used in reverse, with connection made at the intake.

A vacuum gauge is required to determine the vacuum. Connections between the tank and the forming chamber can be made with rigid or flexible metal-reinforced tubing. Flexible connections are more convenient to handle when more than one chamber is to be used in the system. Suitable valves must be inserted in the vacuum lines to control the amount of vacuum and to release the vacuum by admitting air to the system. One method of accomplishing

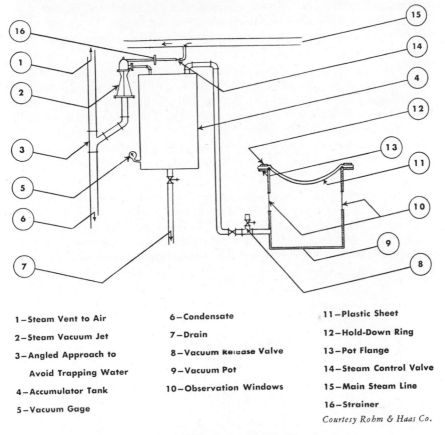

1 – Steam Vent to Air

2 – Steam Vacuum Jet

3 – Angled Approach to
     Avoid Trapping Water

4 – Accumulator Tank

5 – Vacuum Gage

6 – Condensate

7 – Drain

8 – Vacuum Release Valve

9 – Vacuum Pot

10 – Observation Windows

11 – Plastic Sheet

12 – Hold-Down Ring

13 – Pot Flange

14 – Steam Control Valve

15 – Main Steam Line

16 – Strainer

Courtesy Rohm & Haas Co.

Fig. 5-16. Equipment for Vacuum Forming.

this is to insert a plug or gate valve in the vacuum line and put a T with a second valve between the chamber and the first valve (Fig. 5-16). These valves are mounted within easy reach of the operator.

The vacuum chamber is preferably constructed from sheet steel. If only a few articles are to be formed, a vacuum chamber can be constructed from lighter, less expensive materials, such as plywood reinforced with two-by-fours. The joints can be filled with caulking compound and covered with an adhesive tape to prevent leakage of air.

The flanges of the vacuum chamber are preferably constructed from a material such as "Masonite" die stock. These have low thermal conductivity, and hence do not cause rapid chilling of the sheet during the forming. Plywood may be used when only a few pieces are to be made. The flanges may also be constructed from metal, with a small rod welded to the top and around the opening. When the sheet of plastic is clamped to the vacuum chamber, a tight air seal is obtained between it and the metal flange. Either pneumatic or mechanical clamping rings can be used to hold the sheet in contact with the metal frame.

Pressure Apparatus. Pressures above atmospheric are sometimes used in the forming of sheet plastics. Single- or two-stage compressors with auxiliary tanks having sufficient capacity to provide uniform line pressure can be used. Pressure gauges, lines, and valves for regulation of the pressure are required.

The forming chamber must be designed to withstand the pressures developed during forming of the sheets. Heavier construction is required than for vacuum chambers, as a factor of safety, even though pressures of only a few pounds per square inch are generally required.

Automatic Control Equipment. Either pneumatic or electric equipment can be used to control automatically the pressure used.

In the pneumatic system use may be made of an indexing pin which is touched by the sheet when it reaches the correct depth. This contact operates a solenoid valve, which in turn controls the modulating valve on the vacuum line. An alternate method, using a perforated piston in a cylinder for the

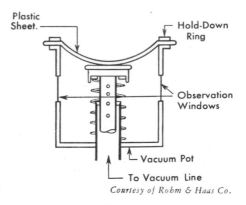

Courtesy of Rohm & Haas Co.

Fig. 5-17

vacuum-line connection inside the forming chamber, is shown in Fig. 5-17. When pushed down by the plastic sheet being formed, the perforated piston acts as a shut-off valve between the forming chamber and the vacuum accumulator tank, and thus controls the depth of forming.

In the electric system the solenoid valves are actuated by photo-electric cells or micro switches (see Fig. 5-18). When the sheet interrupts the beam of light, the change in current operates the solenoid valve. In this system, it is possible to use an auxiliary valve on the vacuum line to balance the rates of intake and exhaust of air in the forming chamber, and thus to control the rate of forming.

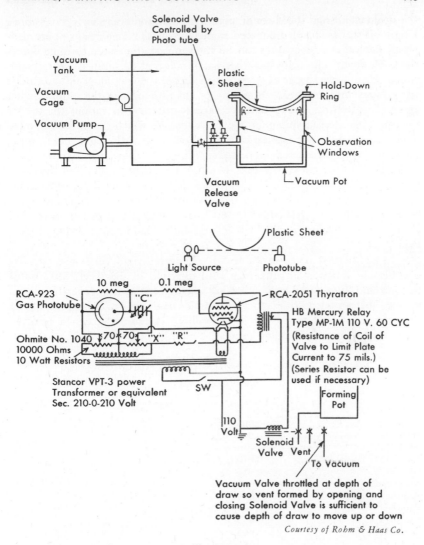

Fig. 5-18

Methods for Forming Thermoplastic Sheet Materials

The nomenclature used here to describe the various methods of forming thermoplastic sheet materials is believed to be the one in most common use, but some of the methods are known also by other names. Many combinations employing the principles of these various methods can be used for the forming of thermoplastic sheet materials, and no effort is made to cover all of them.

Cold Bending. Cold bending of rigid thermoplastic sheets into various cylindrical shapes, which are then fastened into position by means of metal or plastic fasteners or adhesives, is one of the simplest and fastest forming operations. However, with many materials, small radius of curvature or sharp bends create high concentrations of stress which exceed the maximum recommended service stress and may result in crazing or embrittlement of the material upon aging. Research has shown that for various materials in various thicknesses there are characteristic minimum radii of curvature which should be respected in designing articles for fabrication by this technique. Minimum cold-bending radii for vinyl rigid sheets are reported in Table 5-1. In general, recommended bending radii for rigid vinyl sheets are a function of the thickness of the sheet, its formulation, and its form, i.e., calendered or planished. It is not desirable to cold-form acrylic sheet unless the material is thin. The minimum cold-bending radius for acrylic sheet is 180 times the thickness of the sheet. For example, a 16-in. piece of acrylic 0.250-in. thick should not be deflected more than ¼ in.

In addition, as noted in Table 5-1, calendered rigid vinyl sheets exhibit considerable variation in properties with direction in the sheet. Because of this fact and the possibility of other influencing factors, it is generally recommended that an adequate number of samples or models of an application be prepared, aged, and tested for serviceability. If failure occurs, a bend of larger radius, or a hot-bending process, should be utilized.

TABLE 5-1. MINIMUM RECOMMENDED RADII FOR COLD-BENDING

RIGID VINYL SHEETS

Surface	Thickness (in.)	Direction of Sample*	Radius of Bend (in.)
calendered	0.005	L	½
calendered	0.005	T	2
calendered	0.010	L	1
calendered	0.010	T	6½
calendered	0.015	L	3
calendered	0.015	T	9
planished	0.010	L & T	12
planished	0.020	"	12
planished	0.030	"	14
planished	0.040	"	14
planished	0.050	"	18

* L = longitudinal or machine direction; T = transverse direction, with reference to the manufacturing process for rigid sheets.

Creasing, Beading and Forming of Thermoplastic Sheets for Packaging Applications. Transparent containers made from thermoplastic sheets are finding increasing demand for many types of consumer goods. The containers not only provide individual showcases to stimulate the sale of the goods, but they also offer protection from soiling by handling, and increase shelf life. Many types of containers can be made; rectangular boxes, cylindrical containers, and a variety of other shapes. Combinations with cardboard and other materials are also possible. Because of the limitations on the drawing of plastic sheets, most of these containers are made by creasing and bending prepared blanks and cementing the seams, much in the same way as in making cardboard boxes.

The most common materials used are cellulose acetate and ethyl cellulose plastics, which are available in sheets and continuous rolls in a range of gauges from 0.005 to 0.20 in. The thicknesses most used are 0.0075 and 0.010 in.

While automatic machines have been developed that blank out, crease and cement the material fed from a roll, and discharge a completed container body or top, by far the majority of containers are made by performing the successive operations as separate steps.

Description of Processes. The first step is to prepare blanks of proper shape to form the container. Rectangular blanks may be cut from stacks of sheets of the material with a guillotine-type cutter knife. Shaped blanks, i.e., nonrectangular blanks for folded rectangular boxes with cementing flanges, circular discs for bottoms of cylindrical containers, etc., are usually cut out with blanking dies. These operations are described more fully under "Preparatory Operations," on page 116.

Beading. For many types of containers it is desirable to bead the top and possibly the bottom edge of the body. The bead lends a more attractive appearance than a raw edge, and also contributes strength and rigidity to the container. As an inside bead, it may be used to seat the bottom of a cylindrical container.

The beading is usually formed on the blanks before creasing and may be turned to the inside or to the outside of the container. Beading machines are available that turn either one edge or both edges of the blank. These machines can be equipped with dies for turning out a great many sizes and shapes of bead (Fig. 5-19). The blanks are fed by hand to the machine or, if desired, a continuous bead can be formed on roll stock slit to the proper width.

Cylindrical containers may be beaded before or after cementing. In many cases it is simpler to bead after cementing the longitudinal seam rather than to telescope the ends of a beaded blank in making the seam. In simplest form for hand operation, a heated die and a mandrel are required to turn the bead. The die is a brass plate with a machined circular groove of desired diameter with the leading side inclined at an angle of about 60 degrees and the other side inclined at about 20 to 30 degrees, while the bottom of the groove is rounded. The depth and width across the top of the groove are the same and should equal the desired diameter of the bead plus twice the thickness of the material. An inside or outside bead is formed, depending upon whether the leading side of the groove is on the outer or inner circumference of the groove. A fiber collar is placed around the outside of the groove to guide the cylinder more readily into the groove.

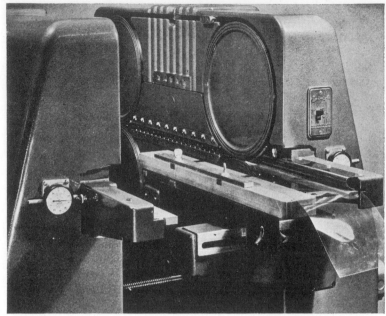

Fig. 5-19. Double edge beader. Operates on blank strips or roll material.

The mandrel is made of wood and serves to support the plastic cylinder during the beading. Its diameter is such that it allows a snug fit in the cylinder and its length is less than that of the cylinder by the amount needed to form the bead. A collar at the top of the mandrel acts as a stop.

The die is usually placed on a steam table or hot plate and heated to a temperature of about 250 to 300°F. To form the bead, the edge of the cylinder with the inserted mandrel is slowly turned under slight pressure in the groove of the die until the bead is completely formed.

For large production, cylinder-beading machines are available on the market. These machines are designed to bead one end, or both ends simultaneously, of preformed cylindrical bodies (Fig. 5-20). The cylinder beader can be set up together with a cylinder fabricator so that both operations can be performed by one attendant.

Creasing. The usual machine setup for creasing is a hand press, foot press, or cam press with a die consisting of a thin blade of tool steel tapered to a blunt edge mounted on the top plate of the press which cooperates with a V-type groove cut in the bed plate. The die plate is heated, usually by resistance heating elements, to about 230 to 260°F, depending upon the type and thickness of the material used. In operation the blank is placed in position under the blade and the heated blade is lowered to press the material into the V-groove to form the crease. The angle of crease may be varied somewhat

Fig. 5-20. Cylinder beader. Designed to bead one or both ends simultaneously of preformed cylinders. Equipped with automatic ejector.

by varying the speed of the machine or the temperature of the blade. In some cases it may be desirable to use a sponge-rubber pad on the base plate of the machine instead of the V-groove. In this case the crease is formed when the blade presses the material into the sponge rubber. The angle of crease will depend upon the depth to which the material is pressed into the rubber. Creasing machines designed for this type of work are available (Fig. 5-21).

Creases are usually made one at a time. Beaded blanks or strips can be creased through the beading. This would apply to a container with a cemented seam on the side wall, with top and bottom edges beaded, the bottom beading turned in to supply a cementing surface for the bottom.

After creasing, the container is placed on a holding block or jig, with corner flanges or seams together, and cemented. Cementing is usually a hand operation, and the cement is applied with an applicator or brush. Quick-acting solvent-type cements for the material are used. They give a strong bond under slight pressure.

For longitudinally-seamed cylindrical containers, a rectangular blank is wrapped around a mandrel of proper diameter with a slight overlap. A pressure bar under light pressure holds the seam in place while cement is applied along the edge of the seam. The cement is drawn between the surfaces of the overlap by capillary action, to cement the surfaces. Or the cement may be applied with an applicator before the blank is wrapped over the mandrel. Cylinder-fabricators are available with expanding mandrels which may be adjusted to cover a great many sizes of cylinders and which permit the production of cylindrical bodies with repetitive uniformity (Fig. 5-22).

Courtesy of Taber Instrument Corp.

Fig. 5-21. Thermocreaser designed to produce a 90-degree crease from precut blanks.

Courtesy of Taber Instrument Corp.

Fig. 5-22. Cylinder Fabricator.

Draping and Hot Bending. One of the oldest methods for forming sheet plastics consists of draping a hot, pliable sheet over a form of the desired shape and allowing it to cool, while restraining the edges from curling. Two-dimensional shapes can be made with cheaply constructed molds (Figs. 5-23 and 5-24).

Courtesy of Bakelite Co.

Fig. 5-23. In the manufacture of a large drinking-glass shaped advertising display, pre-heated vinyl rigid sheets are rolled on a metal cylinder and cooled so that the cylindrical shape is imparted to the rigid sheet.

Description of Process. The sheet is heated to the forming temperature by means of a forced-circulation air oven or other suitable means. Different temperatures are generally required for various types of plastics, and the recommendations of the manufacturers of the sheet should be followed. Depending upon the type and thickness of sheet material, the temperature will generally be between 150 and 300°F. For general-purpose acrylic sheet, temperatures of 230 to 240°F can be used, and for heat-resistant acrylic sheet, the temperature should be 285 to 295°F. Recommended temperatures of the heating apparatus for hot bending or draping vinyl rigid sheets range from 160 to 212°F. Time required for preheating ranges from 10 seconds to 120 seconds; recommendations for various thicknesses are given in Table 5-2. These recommended cycles were determined with a hot-air oven; other means of heating may require some modification of these specific cycles.

Courtesy of Rohm & Haas Co.

Fig. 5-24. Draping form and acrylic part.

TABLE 5-2. PREHEATING CYCLES FOR USE WITH VINYL RIGID SHEETS PRIOR TO BENDING

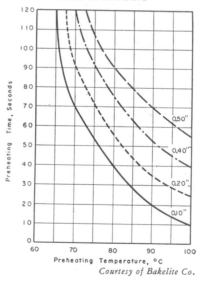

Courtesy of Bakelite Co.

NOTE: Recommended cycles for a given material thickness are those combinations of time and temperature which fall above and to the right of the line representing that thickness.

After the sheet has been uniformly heated to the desired temperature, it is draped over the mold, and its edges are held in place by rubber bands. An electric fan or blower can be used to accelerate the cooling of the sheet. When the sheet has cooled to approximately room temperature, it can be safely removed from the mold.

Equipment. The equipment required for draping is relatively simple and may consist of molds of wood covered with felt, flock rubber, or cloth. More expensive mold materials can be used if desired for long production runs where close tolerances are required. A machine for cutting the sheet plastic to the shape desired and a suitable means for heating it are all of the auxiliary equipment necessary for this method.

Materials which can be Formed by Draping. Draping is used on all types of sheet plastics, including cellulose derivatives, acrylics, vinyls, and butadiene-acrylonitrile-styrene sheet.

Advantages and Limitations. Advantages of draping include the relatively low costs of tools, and the fact that in most cases no finishing is required. The use of several cheap molds may help reduce the labor cost per article.

A limitation of draping is that generally only pieces having relatively simple curvatures can be made by this method. Also, the optical quality of articles made by draping may not be sufficiently good for critical specifications. The defect known as mark-off, i.e., imperfections caused by small imperfections in the surface of the mold, can sometimes be avoided by slightly cooling the sheet just prior to draping it over the mold.

In some cases, sheets have been draped with a masking material left on. Temperatures are much more critical when this is done. Also the masking can cause imperfections in the surface of the sheet when the masking is uneven in thickness or the temperature conditions are incorrect.

Applications. This method can be used for forming display cases, aircraft parts, safety guards, lighting-fixture parts, and other simply curved sections.

Die-Pressing. Die-pressing is substantially a molding process performed on thermoplastic sheets in the form of precut blanks having as nearly as practicable the size and shape of the finished article. Die-pressing effects a change in the configuration of the blank through plastic flow of the material. It is one of the earliest methods of forming thermoplastics and dates back to the early history of cellulose nitrate plastics.

Description of Process. The first step in the process is the preparation of the blank having approximately the size and shape of the finished article. Blanks are usually cut out of sheet stock by any suitable blanking method, with presoftening, if necessary. For some shapes blanks may be sawed from rod or tube stock.

Blanks must be clean before pressing, as surface dirt and contamination will show in the finished article. Their sharp corners must be rounded off, in order to prevent folding in the die. The cleaning and rounding are accomplished by tumbling with abrasive, usually wet pumice. Then the pumice must be removed by washing, conveniently by tumbling in water.

The blanks are then preheated or softened on trays in an oven or on a hot plate, at a temperature depending upon the type of plastic, until sufficiently soft for pressing. They are then put in the die or mold, which may be either hot or cold, and the die is closed under pressure up to about 2000 psi and cooled.

The article is then finished by any of the usual methods, such as tumble-polishing, hand buffing or dip-polishing.

Equipment Required. Die-pressing requires blanking equipment, preheating facilities, pressing dies or molds, presses, finishing equipment and such other auxiliary equipment as is necessary for efficient control of temperature and pressure and the handling of materials.

Methods and equipment for blanking, heating and finishing are described elsewhere in this book.

Pressing dies or molds are usually flash, semipositive or positive compression molds. They may be hand molds (that is, molds that are heated, loaded and unloaded outside of the press), or they may be mounted in the press itself. Molds that are fixed in the press are usually cored for heating and cooling.

Hydraulic or toggle presses are used. They may be manually operated or automatically operated on a predetermined cycle.

Materials. Die-pressing is applicable to any of the thermoplastics that are available in the form of sheets in a wide range of thicknesses, or in rods or tubes that can be readily blanked or precut, such as cellulose nitrate, cellulose acetate, acrylic, and vinyl chloride-acetate. The temperature of pressing will vary with the type and formulation of the material.

Advantages and Limitations. Die-pressing is widely used with cellulose nitrate plastics, as these cannot be molded, in the form of powder, by compression or injection molding. With other thermoplastics that are available also in the form of molding powders, it may offer advantages for limited production runs of rather massive articles of simple shape.

The process is limited to those shapes and sizes that can be approximated in the precut blank, so that no great amount of plastic flow is required to fill out the die.

Applications. A few typical applications are toothbrush handles, brush backs, typewriter keys, pipe-bits, buttons, harness rings, ferrules and dentures.

Drawing Thermoplastic Sheets. The earliest record of a practicable process for drawing thermoplastic sheet material is probably the patent* issued in 1901 to Charles H. Thurber, for a "process of manufacturing

* U. S. Patent No. 669,331.

articles of hollow ware from sheets of pyroxylin compounds." Improvements in the process since that time have been largely in better die design and introduction of semi-automatic and fully automatic presses. Also new types of materials have been made available for drawing, which have broadened the usefulness of that process.

Description of Process. In its simplest form the drawing process consists of placing a blank of thermoplastic sheet on a heated die plate having an opening corresponding to the projected outside dimensions of the article to be made, and lowering a plunger or "former," having the exact shape of the article, so as to draw the material into the die and shape it around the "former." A hold-down or pressure plate is required to hold the blank on the die and keep it from wrinkling as it is drawn into the die. As the "former" is usually kept cool, the material sets after drawing and holds its shape when removed from the "former." The flange remaining between the die and hold-down plates may be sheared off in the drawing die or it may be cut off afterwards.

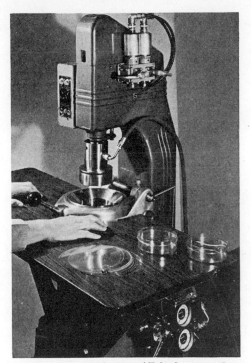

Courtesy of Taber Instrument Corp.

Fig. 5-25. Drawing press with adjustable electronic controls.

The drawing operation may be performed (1) in a hand press, operated by hand lever or pedal, on precut blanks, (2) in a semiautomatic hand press (Figs. 5-25 and 5-26) which automatically feeds a strip of material across

Courtesy of Taber Instrument Corp.

Fig. 5-26. Drawing Press.

the die opening, (3) in an automatic press with automatic feeding and ejecting devices, or (4) in hydraulic or pneumatic presses for heavy sheets.

To draw thermoplastic sheets they must be heated to the drawing temperature just prior to and during the drawing cycle. After being drawn they must be cooled to harden on the die. The material may be heated on the die plate itself, or it may be preheated on a hot plate, or in an oven or heating tunnel, or a combination of preheating and heating in the die may be used. The die and hold-down plates are usually heated, while the "former" is kept cool or only slightly warm. Frequently a chilling box or cold plate is attached to the under side of the die plate, and well insulated from it, to set the material more quickly at the end of the draw.

The drawing temperature will vary with the type and thickness of the material, the size of the article and the depth of draw. The best temperature for a job must be determined by experiment. Too high a temperature may cause heat-marks, unmolding of the surface, or tearing, while too low a temperature may result in wrinkles and fractures. The drawing temperature of the various thermoplastics will usually be found in the following ranges:

Material	Temperature (°F)
cellulose acetate	225 - 275
cellulose acetate butyrate	200 - 250
cellulose nitrate	195 - 240
ethyl cellulose	225 - 275
acrylics	250 - 330
vinyl chloride acetate	185 - 250
butadiene-acrylonitrile-styrene copolymer	225 - 325

The "former" is usually operated at a temperature of about 90 to 100°F.

The function of the hold-down plate is to heat the stock and to keep it smooth and free from wrinkles as it is drawn into the die. If the pressure on the hold-down plate is too great, the stock will bind and be prevented from slipping into the die, and will tear. If the pressure is too light the stock will wrinkle. The proper pressure must be determined by trial. Pressure may be exerted on the hold-down plate by springs or through a treadle, or in some cases by the weight of the plate itself.

After the piece is drawn it may be removed from the "former" either under or over the die. If the flange is sheared off in the die the piece may be stripped from the "former" under the die by means of stripping fingers, or it may be blown off by compressed air blown through the "former." If the flange is left on, the piece is removed above the die by air pressure or by raising the "former" above the hold-down plate, which acts as a stripping plate.

In a properly operated hand or foot press the operator brings the plunger down slowly until he feels the stock yield, and presses just hard enough to follow the stock down into the die without rupturing it. Then with a short stroke he makes the cutoff. This may be followed by a short dwell, if necessary, to cool the drawn piece. He then returns the plunger to the starting position. An operator quickly becomes sufficiently skillful so that he can judge by the feel of the stock the best operating temperature and timing of the drawing operation.

Equipment Required. The most important part of the equipment is the drawing die. It consists essentially of an open die plate, a hold-down plate and a shaped "former." It may also have a cooling plate or box.

The "former" is usually made of brass or machine steel and must be smooth and free from surface imperfections. The dimensions and shape of the "former" are those of the finished article. For a straight draw, it is tapered about 0.003 in. per in. to facilitate stripping. It may be vented to prevent entrapment of air between the stock and the "former," and may have air ports for blowing off the drawn piece. The "former" is fastened to a top plate which acts also as a support for the hold-down plate. The top plate and "former" may be cored for cooling.

If the flange of stock formed between the die and hold-down plates is to be cut off in the die, a cutoff member is mounted between the top of the "former" and the top plate. It is made of hardened tool steel and has the shape and dimensions of the opening in the die plate, with very slight clearance at the operating temperature, so that it will telescope into the die opening and shear off the flange. In another type, the cutoff member is made slightly larger than the die opening so that the stock is pinched off between the edge of the cutoff member and the rounded edge of the die opening.

The die plate is generally made of machine steel, and is cored for heating by steam or electrical heating elements. The opening in the die plate corresponds to the projected dimensions of the "former" plus an allowance for clearance. The clearance is equal to the thickness of the stock plus about 0.002 to 0.010 in., depending upon the thickness of the stock. This clearance should be measured at the operating temperature of the die. The top edge of the die opening should be slightly rounded.

The hold-down plate is made of machine steel and is cored for heating. The opening in the hold-down plate is slightly larger than that in the die plate. If the opening is too large, wrinkling may occur. The hold-down plate is attached to the top plate on the "former" by guide rods passing through the plate and supported by stop nuts at the end of the guide rods. Springs may be inserted over the guide rods between the plates to exert pressure on the hold-down plate during the draw.

It is important that adjacent surfaces of the die and hold-down plate be smooth and parallel. It is advisable to lap in the two surfaces while the plates are hot.

A cooling plate may be mounted under the die plate and well insulated from it. The cooling plate has an opening slightly larger than the opening in the die plate and is cored for cooling water. Stripping fingers may be mounted in the plate to strip the finished piece off the "former" as it is withdrawn.

The drawing press may be hand- or foot-operated, pneumatically or power-driven, and may be automatically controlled. It consists essentially of a bed plate and a ram actuated by suitable means to reciprocate between guides.

The die plate is mounted on the press bed, and the "former" with top and hold-down plates is attached to the ram. The alignment between the openings in the die and hold-down plates and the "former" must be perfect, as the clearances are small. Improper alignment will cause tears and wrinkles as the stock is drawn into the die.

A hand or foot press is generally used with thin material. Individual blanks may be fed by hand to the die in the hand press, or an automatic feed, which passes strip material through a heating tunnel and across the die opening, may be attached to the hand or foot press.

A pneumatic press may be used on heavy sheets. A long-stroke air cylinder is preferred to hydraulic for greater speed. The cylinder is mounted vertically with the ram operating downward. The "former" is attached to the end of the ram.

Recently fully automatic drawing presses have been designed, and used to produce small ammunition components at a high rate of speed. In such a press, the action of the hold-down plate, the drawing, cutoff, ejection and advance of stock are all actuated by cams so that they may be controlled at will in any desired cycle. The cams are specially designed and cut for each job, but the press is so designed that they can be cheaply made and installed. The stock used is in the form of a strip wide enough to leave a small web that will hold the material together after the piece is drawn. The stock is preheated on its way to the die by being passed between heated platens. Finished pieces are ejected automatically into a work basket. The rate of production will depend upon the size and shape of the piece and the depth of draw. Small pieces have been produced at a rate of 100 per minute in these presses. One operator can tend 4 to 6 presses.

Auxiliary equipment will include connections and controls for heating the die and hold-down plates and for cooling the "former" and cold plate.

Other equipment may consist of steam tables or heating ovens for pre-heating materials, and blanking dies and presses for cutting blanks. These are described elsewhere.

Modifications. The drawing die and process described above are of the simplest type, employing an open die and a simple draw. If the "former" has cutout sections or indentations, the stock tends to bridge across these areas when it is drawn into the die. In such cases it is frequently possible to modify the die to shape these areas. In an extreme case a closed die may be used. This is to be avoided if possible, because contact of the stock with two opposing die surfaces increases the possibility of surface imperfections. In addition the drawing cycle will be longer if it is necessary to alternately heat and cool the die. It may be possible when drawing some shapes to place a sponge rubber pad or other elastic material under the die to press the stock against the "former" during its travel through the die. In other cases a shaped receding plate operating against spring pressure may be placed under the die opening.

Materials. Practically all of the thermoplastic sheetings can be drawn. The following are available in a wide range of thickness in the forms of sheets and continuous rolls:

Material	Thicknesses (in.)	
	Sheets	Rolls
cellulose acetate	0.003 - 0.250	0.003 - 0.020
cellulose acetate butyrate	0.003 - 0.006	0.003 - 0.006
cellulose nitrate	0.003 - 0.250	0.003 - 0.010
ethyl cellulose	0.003 - 0.020	0.003 - 0.200
acrylics	0.060 - 0.500	
vinyl chloride acetate	0.010 - 0.125	0.005 - 0.015
butadiene-acrylonitrile-styrene copolymer	0.032 - 0.500	0.010 - 0.062

Limitations. The drawing process has its limitations, and for articles of certain types and shapes other processes are more practicable. In general the depth of draw does not exceed $1\frac{1}{2}$ times the diameter of the article. Sharp corners cannot be formed easily because of the tendency to tear. Complicated shapes that cannot be made by simple drawing can sometimes be made by a combination of processes, such as drawing and blowing in the same die.

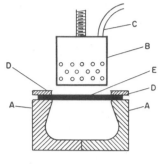

1 - Blank clamped in place

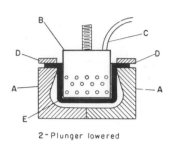

2 - Plunger lowered

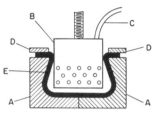

3 - Steam introduced

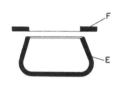

4 - Finished article

A, A -   Split mold
B -   Perforated plunger operated
         by screw
C -   Steam connection
D, D -   Clamp
E,   Blank and blown article
F -   Scrap removed

Fig. 5-27

Applications. Containers, clock crystals, radio crystals, trays and other concave shapes.

Blow-Die Operations (Fig. 5-27). The operation known as blow-dieing is employed mainly for making from sheet stock bowl-shaped articles in which the perimeter of the sides is larger than the opening or neck. Articles usually associated with this method of die-forming are hollow toys, small manikins, etc.

Equipment. A split two-piece die is necessary, whose inside surface is shaped and finished to determine the shape of the finished articles. It is halved, usually vertically, so that the blown article may be removed. The die is dovetailed to be airtight when closed.

In addition there is a ring clamp to hold the blank against the die, and a plunger with a screw to lower and raise it, and with an opening for admitting steam.

Description of Process. The sheet plastic is cut or blanked to a predetermined shape which is suitable for inserting in the split two-piece die used in blow-die operations.

With the plunger out of the die and the two halves of the die locked together, the prepared blank is fastened between the clamp and the die, and the entire assembly placed in boiling water for long enough to soften the blank. An experienced operator can tell by the resistance of the stock against the plunger as it is lowered into the die whether it is soft enough.

After the stock is properly softened, the plunger, whose sides have a slight taper, is lowered as far as it will go, and high-pressure steam is admitted through the opening of the plunger to force the softened blank out against the die, causing it to take the shape of the interior of the die. After about 2 min, with steam pressure still on, the entire assembly is taken from the boiling water and placed in a tank of cold water until the metal has chilled sufficiently to set the plastic. The steam is then turned off while the die is in the chill bath. The die is taken out of the bath, the plunger raised, the die opened, and the article removed.

On removal from the die, the article should be thrown immediately into cold water to complete the chilling. If the excess material on the article has not already been trimmed off by a trimmer attached to the die, this may be done by a small saw mounted on a vertical spindle.

Materials. The types of sheet plastics most commonly shaped by blow-die operations are the cellulosics, such as cellulose nitrate or acetate, vinyl, the thinner acrylics, and others.

Advantages and Limitations. This method can be used to produce shapes which are difficult or impossible to obtain by other methods, such as a hollow sphere, or a container having a shoulder.

The method is not generally applicable to large articles or thick sheets.

Applications. Christmas-tree ornaments, balls, bottles, hollow toys and small manikins can be made by the blow-die.

Veneering and Hand-Forming. Veneering involves application of sheet plastic material over forms ordinarily constructed of wood, usually birch or maple. Since this is generally done by hand it may also be called hand-forming.

Description of Process. First the sheet plastic is conditioned by either the "wet," or solvent, method, or the "dry," or vapor-box, method.

For softening by the wet method, the blanks are immersed in a solution consisting of one part of acetone and two parts of water, until they are of about the consistency of wet chamois and can be stretched like thin rubber. This requires usually about 20 min. The softened blanks are removed from the solution, and wiped off before being cemented.

The equipment required for the dry method consists of a galvanized iron box, kept at a temperature of 90 to 100°F by steam coils at the sides or on the bottom. Inside the box are drawers set one above the other. A pan containing acetone is placed below each drawer. Each drawer has a bottom of wire netting, over which a piece of cheesecloth is laid to support the stock.

The blank is placed in the drawer, and the latter closed. In 10 or 15 minutes the material has absorbed enough acetone vapor to become soft and pliable.

The softened blank is painted lightly with amyl acetate as a cement. A piece of cheesecloth is preferred to a brush, as the latter is likely to cause streaks unless great care is taken. The amyl acetate is a high-boiling solvent which keeps the stock soft and sticky while it is being stretched over the wooden form, e.g., a toilet seat.

The top of the form is covered first. No cement is applied to the wood except on the flat surface where the ends are cemented down. All the cement necessary is applied on the stock itself. The wood must be covered quickly, as the stock tends to harden in a few minutes. Too much cement causes roughness and waviness of the covered article, which require considerable sandpapering to smooth off.

At the end of this first operation, there should be over the top, in the case of a toilet seat, a smooth cover, which is folded over the bottom and cemented to keep it tight until it sets. This requires drying overnight at room temperature. The rough underpart, which has been turned in, is trimmed off the next morning with a sharp knife, to make the edge of the plastic flush with the flat bottom of the seat.

The bottom piece is then applied by painting it with amyl acetate, placing it on a soft pad of 1-in. felt, and then forcing the seat down tightly on it. Then it is well to paint with amyl acetate around the edge so as to give a very good weld between the top cover and the bottom cover.

The article may then be removed from the clamp which is holding it tightly, and laid aside until the next day. Then the projecting edge of the bottom cover is trimmed off flush with the curved surface. This is done with a sharp knife, and usually on a small rotating stand. The article is then dried at room temperature for about 2 days (forced drying at higher temperatures is likely to induce porosity).

After this drying, the rough edges may be smoothed with fine sandpaper. Then the article is ashed and polished.

Success in covering wooden cores, such as those of toilet seats, depends largely upon promptness in putting the sheet on the core after it is removed from the solution or the conditioning cabinet. The stock must be cemented underneath at the same time that it is stretched, and then worked around the seat, beginning at any point in the circumference. One hand is used in stretching it down and the other hand in holding it until the amyl acetate painted underneath cements it fast to the wood.

The plastic used need not be thoroughly seasoned. However, the wood to be covered must be well seasoned to avoid subsequent shrinkage.

Use of Sprayed Sheeting. Sheeting for covering toilet seats is sometimes colored, on the surface next to the wood, by a spray of colored opaque lacquer containing pearl essence. Such sprayed pearl sheeting is used quite extensively for colored pearl effects because of its economy over the composited type of sheeting and because it enables the fabricator to change from one color to another without maintaining large inventories. The spraying operation follows the practice used for any lacquer or enamel, with care to apply a uniform coating. Lacquers and lacquer thinners have a solvent action on the plastic. Consequently, it is necessary that the opaque backings be put on in two or more successive layers rather than attempting to obtain the opacity in one coat. With a little experience the operator will be able quickly to determine the proper procedure.

The use of this sprayed sheeting necessitates a change in the technique of cementing, since brushing or wiping amyl acetate on the sprayed surface will disturb the backing. Instead, the bond to the wood is obtained by painting the wood with a heavy-bodied cement immediately before the cover is stretched over it.

Equipment. Special equipment for conditioning and clamps for holding the sheet are required. The apparatus is simple and probably the least expensive of any used for forming.

Materials. Cellulose nitrate and cellulose acetate sheet materials are extensively used in veneering and hand-forming operations. The thickness of sheet is usually either 0.010 or 0.020 in. In the case of pearl sheeting composited with a colored backing sheet, the total thickness is usually 0.020 in. (pearl 0.010 in. and backing 0.010 in.).

Applications. Veneering and hand-forming are used in the manufacture of toilet seats and hamper tops, and in the covering of wooden heels for women's shoes.

Stretch-Forming. Thermoplastic sheets can be formed by being stretched, while hot, over a mold, and then cooled. Both simple and compound curvatures can be obtained by this method (Fig. 5-28).

Description of Process. The sheet is heated in an oven at a controlled temperature from 250 to 325°F, until it becomes stretchable. The time and temperature will depend upon the type and thickness of material being formed. When stretch-forming over a dry mold, lower temperatures are generally used, in order to reduce mark-off, than is the case when the stretch-forming is done over a greased mold. Higher temperatures are required for thin sheet material, since it cools more rapidly upon being removed from the oven.

The sheet is removed from the oven and placed over the mold quickly, before it becomes chilled. For some shapes, it is a general practice to clamp

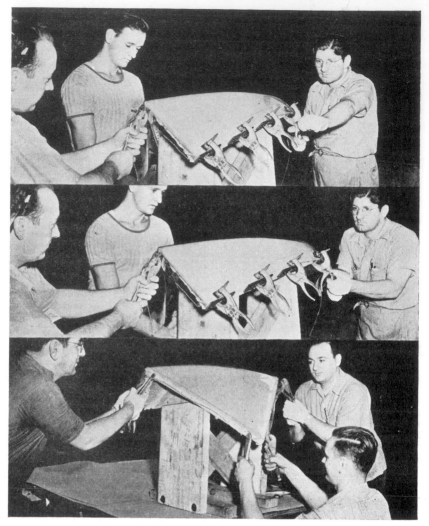

Courtesy Celanese Plastics Corp.

Fig. 5-28

one side of the sheet rigidly and stretch it by pulling from the opposite side. In some cases the stretching is done by a number of operators, who pull the sheet by means of quick-acting clamps or carpenter's clamps attached to its edge at intervals of 6 to 10 in. Slow, steady pull should be exerted as uniformly as possible in order to avoid producing thin spots in the formed article. The forming of large articles may require as many as 10 men. After the sheet has been stretched to the desired shape, a metal ring is clamped around the edge, to hold it in place while it cools.

Where compound curvature is not excessive, but where a considerable number of pieces are to be made, it is practicable to provide some mechanical means for stretching the sheet. For example, the heated sheet can be clamped in a yoke which grips the sheet outside the final trim line and then be pulled down around the form by means of screw clamps, screw jacks, air or hydraulic pressure devices, or other mechanical means. To minimize mark-off, the lowest pressure which will form the sheet should be used. The yoke tends to equalize the stretching around the edge of the piece and produces, in general, more nearly uniform thinning out than can be achieved by manual operation.

In some cases, the male form is mounted on the ram of a press and forced down through a stationary yoke. In other cases, the yoke is mounted on the press, and the male form is kept stationary. The choice of method will depend on the equipment at hand and the particular shape being formed. Often the sheet is clamped between two rings held together by toggle clamps operated manually or by air. Sometimes one of the two rings is fixed and the sheet is clamped or released by moving the second ring. This movement may be controlled by the main ram of the press, or by a secondary system. It is also possible to clamp the hot sheet between two fixed rings by means of a flexible pneumatic or hydraulic hose which can be inflated to exert the required pressure.

Modifications. If there is any flat surface on the mold which would allow an air pocket to be formed between the sheet and the mold, it is necessary to drill a very small vent in the mold at this point to allow the air to escape. In some cases, the male mold and clamping-ring assembly are mounted in a jig which can be placed in an oven, and as the sheet softens, the male mold is gently lowered to shape the sheet. The entire jig and formed piece are then removed from the oven and allowed to cool to room temperature.

During World War II, a modification of the stretch-forming process was developed by Bell Aircraft Corporation. This provides for motion of the mold relative to the sheet as it is brought into contact with the sheet to be formed. For a circular article, this is generally a continuous rotation. Other shapes are produced by a lateral to-and-fro movement of the mold during the forming. It is claimed that superior optical properties are obtained by this method, since mark-off is negligible. Variations in thickness also are greatly reduced by this method.

Equipment. The mold should be constructed so that its depth exceeds that of the article to be made. For small production, the mold can be constructed of wood covered with a soft cloth such as billiard felt, imitation chamois, or outing flannel. More substantial molds can be constructed from "Masonite," reinforced plaster, or metal. Suede rubber provides suitable coverings for such molds.

The molds should be braced to maintain the correct contour. If no ring is used, the edges of the mold should be flanged sufficiently to permit application of clamps to hold the sheet.

Presses should have sufficient rigidity and capacity to exert a steady force in stretching the sheet. A fast-acting ram is desirable, but must be carefully used, since some sheet materials may tear if stretched too rapidly.

Some sheet materials, such as cellulose acetate, can be advantageously handled by locating the mold under a duct through which either warm or cool air can be blown. Dampers are installed in the duct to change from warm to cool air. During the forming, air at 170 to 180°F at the duct outlet is blown at 350 to 500 fpm over the sheet to prevent too rapid cooling. Cool air is then blown on the sheet to bring it to about room temperature.

Materials. Sheet plastics which can be stretch-formed include the acrylics, cellulosics such as cellulose acetate or cellulose acetate butyrate, and vinyl chloride acetate.

Advantages and Limitations. Close tolerances can be held on stretch-formed articles. When a relatively small number of parts are to be made, the low tool cost is an advantage in stretch-forming. If power equipment is used, the tool cost is higher, but the labor cost is reduced.

Since the sheet is formed in contact with the mold, there is the possibility of mark-off on the finished part. The method is limited to forming relatively simple curves, or compound shapes having no reverse curves.

Applications. This method of forming has been used to make articles such as aircraft parts, box lids or others where contours and fitting are important considerations.

Plug-And-Ring Forming. This method of forming is similar in principle to the use of embroidery hoops. It is the basic method for many important industrial applications of thermoplastic sheet today.

Description of Process. The method is a modification of the stretch-forming procedure. The heated sheet is placed over the plug, which is a male mold having a contour corresponding to the inside of the finished article, and a ring is brought down over it. The ring is made to fit over the outside of the plug, with allowance for the thickness of the sheet. The sheet can be drawn in this way even deeper than the smallest dimension of the ring opening, before it starts to wrinkle. The fact that it will eventually wrinkle is also of interest, for, by using a larger or smaller plug, it is possible to make dish shapes with wavy edges (Fig. 5-29).

In some cases, the male plug is mounted on the ram of a press and is forced into the sheet held by means of rings which are engaged as the plug is lowered. The section of the street light globe shown in Fig. 5-30 was formed with a plug made of "Hydrocal" plaster reinforced with steel. A ring of "Masonite" was constructed to the outside dimensions of the globe. The plug was mounted on a double-action air-cylinder press having a 5-in. bore and an 18-in. stroke.

In forming of translucent sheet, unsightly thin spots can be avoided by

Courtesy of Rohm & Haas Co.

Fig. 5-29. Plug and Ring.

drawing the sheet as far as practicable by means of vacuum before pushing the ring into position.

Equipment. To control the amount of air going into the cylinder of the air press, a pressure-regulator can be inserted in the line by means of a T, and the air hose attached to the other side. Air pressures within the range of 80 to 150 psi are generally used for plug-and-ring forming. Total pressures required for shallow formed articles range from 20 to 30 lb per linear in. of circumference (Fig. 5-31). For example, in forming single letters with nearly vertical returns 4 in. in depth, the total circumference of the letter is multiplied by 30 lb per linear in. to obtain the total force required to form the letter. A shallow pan-shaped article such as a large sign face having embossed letters would require a force equal to the combined circumference of the sign face plus the circumference of all of the letters multiplied by 20 lb per linear in. of circumference. An acrylic sheet 54 in. × 108 in. formed to a depth of 3 in. with letters having a total circumference of 126 in. would require 9000 lb total pressure.

The schematic diagram shows the design of a simple tool for plug-and-ring forming of rigid vinyl sheet (Fig. 5-32).

Molds have been constructed with the plug having the shape of letters or other contours, and having a shearing action when it completes the forming

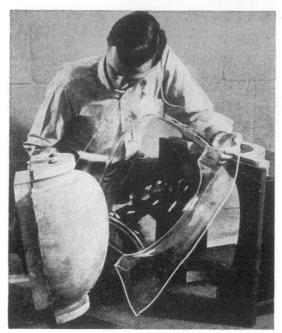

Courtesy of Rohm & Haas Co.

Fig. 5-30. Plug and Ring Forming.

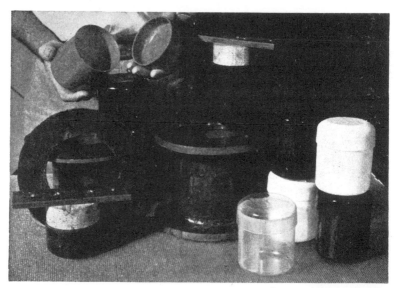

Courtesy of Rohm & Haas Co.

Fig. 5-31. Plug and Ring.

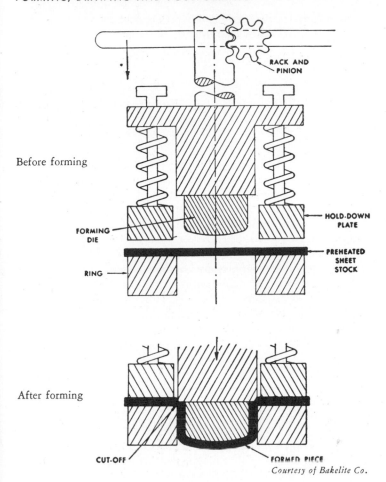

RACK AND PINION

Before forming

FORMING DIE

RING

HOLD-DOWN PLATE

PREHEATED SHEET STOCK

After forming

CUT-OFF

FORMED PIECE

Courtesy of Bakelite Co.

Fig. 5-32. Plug and ring forming of vinyl rigid sheets.

cycle, to trim the excess. Pins can be inserted for piercing the sheet to provide holes for mounting purposes. Thus forming, piercing and cutting to size can be done in one operation.

The plug may be constructed from metal, wood, reinforced "Hydrocal," or other material. Female molds made of "Masonite" may have plywood reinforcement on the back.

Materials. All thermoplastic sheetings can be formed by this method.

Advantages and Limitations. Tool costs are low, and the method is adaptable to forming shapes that are difficult to make. Plug-and-ring forming has the disadvantage of producing excessive mark-off, usually at the inside corners of the formed article. For sections in which optical properties are not important, this disadvantage does not apply.

Applications. This method is used for making signs, lighting equipment, containers, and industrial articles of many types.

Methods Employing Differentials of Air Pressure. Differentials of air pressure have been extensively used in forming thermoplastic sheeting. Some work on these methods was done in Europe prior to 1935, but the art has been advanced to its present state since that time in the United States. The literature contains numerous references to these methods, and includes several patents.

Either vacuum or air at above atmospheric pressure may be used to produce the desired differentials of pressure. The sheet material may either be formed in free space or be made to conform to the shape of a mold. The choice between vacuum and air under pressure will depend upon many factors, which include shape of the article, the optical quality desired, the maximum forming pressure required, and accuracy of conformance to contours of the mold. The maximum pressure differential available with vacuum is 14.5 psi, and in practice a maximum of 10 psi is generally used with vacuum methods, but sometimes as much as 13 psi. When this is not enough, then positive air pressures must be used.

Vacuum-Forming Methods. Vacuum forming methods use the atmospheric pressure of air to force a heated sheet into an evacuated space. These methods are discussed below:

1. Vacuum Forming in Free Space. Sheet made ductile by heating can be formed in free space by fastening it over a vacuum chamber and applying vacuum. This technique has been called "free blowing," since the surfaces of the sheet do not touch any solid surface. The shape produced is a function of the surface tension of the ductile plastic. The method is similar in principle to the formation of a soap bubble (Fig. 5-33).

Description of Process. The sheet plastic, cut to suit the finished article, is heated in an oven at a temperature from 160 to 350°F, depending upon the type and thickness of the sheet. For acrylics of thickness 0.250 in., recommended oven temperatures are 275°F for general-purpose, and 295°F for heat-resistant sheet. Slightly higher temperatures will be required to form sheets thinner than 0.250 in., because the sheet cools rapidly after it is removed from the oven. Oven temperatures must not exceed 320°F for general-purpose and 350°F for heat-resistant acrylics. When the sheet has been heated uniformly throughout, it is removed from the oven and clamped over the vacuum chamber so as to provide an airtight seal. In many cases, the sheet is permitted to drape into the chamber rather than being clamped in a taut condition. Then vacuum is applied, and the sheet is formed in free space by atmospheric pressure which forces it down into the vacuum chamber.

A large variety of shapes can be made by varying the shape of the opening of the vacuum chamber. Thus, a round opening will produce a circular article, while a square, triangular, elliptical, or rectangular opening will produce the corresponding shape. Still further modification can be obtained by providing an opening and corresponding flange with a contour in three dimensions. Thus three-dimensional shapes of numerous designs can be produced.

Courtesy of Rohm & Haas Co.

Fig. 5-33

It is necessary to make allowance for thinning of the sheet by stretching. For example, in a hemisphere, the thickness at the point of deepest draw will be about one-third of that of the original sheet.

The contour of the finished article is controlled not only by the shape of the opening in the vacuum chamber and the amount of draping of the sheet into the chamber when it is clamped, but also by the depth to which the sheet is drawn. This depth may be controlled manually by manipulating a valve in the vacuum line and observing the depth of draw through calibrated sight glasses located in the sides of the vacuum chamber. It may also be automatically controlled, either electrically or mechanically — with the aid of a solenoid valve actuated by a photoelectric cell, or of a pneumatic valve actuated by a pin which is touched by the sheet when it has reached the desired depth of draw. Other automatic mechanisms can be used — for example, micro switches could be adapted to control the depth and rate of forming by this method.

The rate of forming must be determined by experience. It should be rapid enough to produce the desired contour before the sheet cools too much, yet not so rapid that the sheet is torn.

In some cases, banks of infrared lamps have been used to supply additional heat during the forming of large sections, with care to prevent localized heating which would result in optical distortion.

After the desired depth of draw has been reached, electric fans can be used to assist in cooling the article.

Equipment Required. The vacuum equipment will be the same for all of the vacuum-forming methods, but details of the tools will be different.

Any suitable method may be used for producing vacuum, such as a piston pump driven by a motor, rotary or vane-type pumps, steam ejector, air or water Venturi, to maintain at least 22 in. of vacuum at the rated volume of the system. A piston pump would not generally be suitable for handling the largest articles. For most production work a pump having a capacity of 25 cu ft of air per minute at 27-in. vacuum is sufficient. The vacuum line should be connected directly to a tank or reservoir to provide additional capacity, especially for the forming of large articles or when a number of smaller vacuum chambers are connected on the line. A reservoir serves also to prevent excessive fluctuations in the air pressure, which would result in optical distortion in the formed piece. Galvanized-steel domestic hot-water tanks may be used or any tank that will withstand external pressure of 15 psi. A tank with capacity of 100 gal will be large enough for most production work. A drain should be provided to remove condensate from the storage tank.

Large-sized pipe (1½- or 2-in. iron pipe) should be used to make the connections between the vacuum chambers and the storage tank. A flexible metal hose can be used to connect the vacuum chamber to the large vacuum line. For permanent setups, these connections can be made with standard iron pipe and standard fittings, omitting the flexible connections.

Within arm's reach of the vacuum chamber, a T should be inserted in the pipeline for insertion of a valve which can be used to open the line to the atmosphere. A second valve should be inserted in the line adjacent thereto in order to control the supply of vacuum. By manipulation of these two valves, the rate of drawing can be controlled. And, after the piece has been formed and has started to harden, the release of air into the vacuum chamber through the first valve promotes the cooling of the plastic. Vacuum chambers can be made from various materials, such as sheet steel, plywood, "Masonite" die stock, plaster of Paris, and cast liquid resins. For large articles, the vacuum chambers should be constructed of sheet metal and reinforced to resist the pressure differential. The most satisfactory method is to cut the flanges from $\frac{1}{2}$-in. plate and construct the remainder of the chamber from thinner metal. The sides and ends should be constructed from 10-gauge steel, while the bottom can be made from $\frac{3}{16}$- or $\frac{1}{4}$-in. steel to make it more rigid.

When the vacuum chambers are constructed of steel or other metal, all seams should be welded to form an airtight joint. If other materials are used, such as plywood or "Masonite" die stock, the joints are sealed by applying a caulking compound to all edges before assembly. This method of sealing the joints allows a certain amount of movement as the pressure is reduced within the chamber, and still maintains the seal. If a glued joint is used, the deflection often cracks the glue and causes leakage. As an additional sealing, "Scotch" tape is applied on the outside of all seams.

Where detachable flanges are used, a tubular gasket is applied between the metal flanges and the flange of "Masonite." The greater the pressure differential on such a seal, the tighter the joint.

In certain cases, particularly where a variety of articles are to be made in the same vacuum chamber, it is desirable to make a detachable flange. The preferred materials for constructing this removable flange are "Masonite" and phenolic laminates. Flanges made of metal chill the plastic too rapidly, and wood is unsatisfactory because it is affected by atmospheric changes. Because of its lower heat capacity and conductivity, the "Masonite" does not chill the sheet as quickly as does a steel flange, and thus a more uniform draw is secured.

A clamping ring is usually supplied to hold the sheet to the flange of the vacuum chamber. For satisfactory permanent equipment, this should be a rigid ring accurately fitted to the flange of the vacuum chamber and clamped by single or multiple air-operated cylinders. A less expensive setup uses a bent iron pipe, approximately $\frac{3}{4}$ in., which can be held on top of the sheet by quick-acting clamps. These have the advantage of being readily adjustable and quick and easy to operate. It is simplest to use "C" clamps or wood clamps. The pressures required for clamping are not great. Experience will indicate the pressures required to keep the sheet from slipping.

Since variations in the rate of drawing produce wide variations in the finished article, in both shape and thickness, a definite procedure covering every step in the operation for each individual piece is required for best results, and a sweep-second-hand electric clock should be required with each large piece of equipment so that the operator can follow the prescribed cycle.

Materials. Acrylic, cellulose acetate, and rigid vinyl sheet materials can be formed by this method.

Advantages and Limitations. A principal advantage of this method is that mark-off is reduced to a minimum, since the sheet does not come into contact with any solid surfaces except around the flange and pressure ring which hold it on the vacuum chamber. Another advantage is that it provides a means of forming an integral flange on the article. This method is limited to the forming of spherical contours. If other shapes are desired, a modification of the present procedure is employed.

Applications. Aircraft parts such as astrodomes for navigation purposes, large canopies, and sighting domes are made by this method. Very large hemispheres have been made for display cases, for architectural uses such as skylights, and for aquaria. Picture windows for homes also have been formed by this method.

2. Vacuum Snapback Forming. Thermoplastic sheet materials, such as those of an acrylic base which possess elastic memory, can be formed by allowing an extended hot sheet to contract over a male form to the desired contour. The contraction of the sheet has been referred to as "snapback" and the method as "snapback forming." Reverse curvatures and difficult contours can be obtained by combining vacuum snapback with subsequent application of air pressure to the external surface of the piece (Fig. 5-34).

Description of Process. The forming temperatures required in the vacuum snapback method range from 225 to 325°F, depending upon the type and grade of thermoplastic sheet material. After the sheet has been heated to the temperature recommended by its manufacturer, it is clamped to a vacuum chamber in the manner previously described and drawn into the chamber by vacuum. The drawing should be just fast enough to allow the sheet to remain soft, but slow enough to prevent excessive reduction in its thickness in the section adjacent to the clamping ring. A male form of the desired contour is then lowered into the cavity formed by the distended sheet and in close proximity to its surface. The pressure differential is then reduced sufficiently to permit the normal contractive forces, due to elastic memory, to act during cooling of the thermoplastic sheet to make the sheet conform to the shape of the male mold. The sheet is then cooled until sufficiently hard to hold its shape when the male mold is removed. It can then be removed from the vacuum chamber.

Precautions must be taken to minimize surface defects. When the sheet has been drawn to the desired extent, it should be carefully wiped with Canton flannel, or other suitable soft material, to remove any dust or lint from its upper surface. Similar care should be taken to remove any dirt or lint from the surface of the male mold. And in order to prevent imperfections, such as

Courtesy of Rohm & Haas Co.

Fig. 5-34. Vacuum snapback formed with the addition of applying 8-lb air pressure in the chamber after vacuum was released.

mark-off, on the article, the vacuum should be reduced very gradually to prevent uneven contact of the sheet against the male form.

The thickness at the point of deepest draw can be controlled to a limited extent by allowing the male form to touch the sheet as it is being stretched. This causes localized cooling of the sheet and reduces the amount of stretching. The thickness can be controlled also by designing the clamping ring to permit some slippage of the sheet through the ring during the initial stages of the operation. Thickness can be controlled also by localized heating or cooling of the sheet prior to or during the forming, but this procedure is not generally recommended, because it may cause local imperfections, such as optical distortions. Thus, infrared lamps may be so placed as to produce localized heating of the sheet just prior to and during the stretching; this will result in thinning out of these locally heated sections. On the other hand, cooling a section by the local application of asbestos pads, to prevent it from reaching the temperature of the rest of the sheet, will result in a thicker section.

Equipment Required. Equipment similar to that required for the vacuum-chamber method can be used for snapback forming. In addition to the vacuum chamber, vacuum equipment, and ovens for heating the sheet, a satisfactory male form is required. The form should be constructed with sufficient draft (approximately 3 degrees) to permit easy removal of the formed article. In order to permit escape of air which may be entrapped between the form and the sheet, small vents should be provided in the form. The form can be constructed of any one of several types of materials, such as polished metal, wood, cement, and plaster. It is preferable that the cross-section of the base of the mold approximate the cross-section of the vacuum chamber at the rim. If metal molds are used, they should be polished, and preferably chromium-plated. Wooden or plaster molds should have smooth surfaces and be covered with a suitable material, such as flock rubber having a suede surface. Good optical quality can sometimes be obtained by using two layers of flock rubber over a wooden mold.

Materials. The method is applicable to thermoplastics which tend to contract to their original shape when they have been heated and distended. Sheet materials most generally formed by this method are the acrylics and butadiene-acrylonitrile-styrene copolymers.

Advantages and Limitations. It is possible to maintain closer tolerances on the formed article by snapback forming than by free blowing or vacuum forming. Tolerances of $\pm \frac{1}{8}$ in. are possible, as compared to $\pm \frac{1}{4}$ in. to $\pm \frac{1}{2}$ in. for some vacuum-formed articles. Three-dimensional shapes, which cannot be produced by the previously described vacuum-chamber method, can be made more readily by the snapback method. A flange can be formed integral with the formed article to provide a means of mounting it.

A limitation of this method is that it will not form reverse curves or sharp changes in contour. Articles formed by this method have some imperfections, such as mark-off, and the optical quality is generally not so good as that obtained by the vacuum-chamber method.

Applications. The vacuum-snapback method was extensively used during the war, to produce transparent enclosures for airplanes. It has not been widely used since, except for making articles with contours difficult to form by other vacuum-forming methods.

3. Ridge-Forming. This is an adaptation of features of the foregoing vacuum methods, designed for the production of articles of compound curvature. It has been developed since World War II.

Description of Process. A heated thermoplastic sheet is clamped over the opening in a vacuum chamber and the chamber evacuated to produce the desired depth of draw. A skeleton framework or recessed mold is then lowered into the cavity and is pushed into the sheet to stretch certain portions to desired contours (in some cases, the skeleton mold alone is used to stretch the sheet, in which case, the technique is quite similar to stretch-forming). After the mold has been locked in the desired position, the vacuum may be

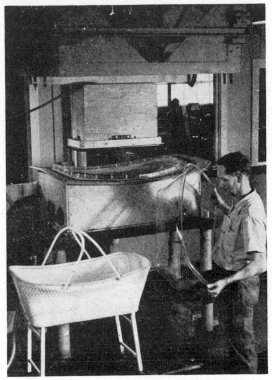

Courtesy of Rohm & Haas Co.

Fig. 5-35

released to allow the sheet to snap back around the frame or recessed mold (Fig. 5-35).

There are many possible variations of tooling in ridge-forming to produce unusual design in finished articles. A single board may be pushed into the sheet, or a combination of the board with a suitably constructed vacuum chamber can be used to cut off vacuum on one section and thus produce asymmetrically free-blown parts. The vacuum chamber can be divided into several sections with independent vacuum controls to produce more complicated shapes (Fig. 5-36).

By manipulation of the vacuum, it is possible to produce flat or rounded sections. The use of a recessed die with a vent hole in the recess permits either vacuum or air pressure to be applied to that section, and thus to shape the sheet to desired contours.

After the skeleton or recessed mold has been locked in position, it is sometimes desired to release the vacuum and to apply a slight air pressure to force the sheet into close conformity with the mold. In some cases, this is accomplished by mechanical means.

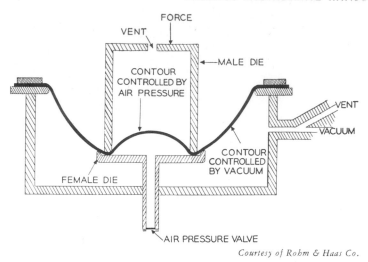

Courtesy of Rohm & Haas Co.

Fig. 5-36

Equipment Required. The vacuum-producing equipment is the same as that previously described. The vacuum chamber is equipped with the usual clamping ring and may be used, if desired, for long production runs.

A mold for ridge-forming should be constructed with generous radii on corners and edges. The radius should be at least twice the thickness of the sheet, to reduce the possibility of tearing. The mold must be suitably braced, and the area of the framework which will touch the sheet should be small. Materials of low thermal conductivity, such as phenolic laminates, "Masonite" die stock, and wood, are good materials for such a mold. To minimize the thinning of deeply drawn articles, the skeleton form may be constructed of smooth stainless-steel pipe through which water at 180°F may be circulated. These pipes keep the sheet soft so that it can more easily slip past the ridges. Rollers or other devices also can be used to facilitate slipping of the sheet.

The pressure differentials which may be used with this method are limited by the tensile strength of the hot sheet as it is stretched across the dividing partition or ridge. A more positive seal can be made between the several zones of curvature if ridges in a male mold hold the sheet between grooves in a female mold.

A suitable press, such as an air-cylinder type, is required in which to mount the mold. Air cylinders 12 in. in diameter, operated with air pressure of at least 40 psi, will handle most work.

Materials. The ridge-forming method was developed primarily for acrylic plastics. It can be used with other sheet materials such as cellulose acetate or vinyls, within the limitations of their characteristics.

Advantages and Limitations. Large articles can be formed, having large ratio of depth to diameter. The formed articles generally have very little mark-off, since the sheet touches a minimum of mold surface. Sharp corners and flat surfaces can be produced by this method. The method often results in more nearly uniform thickness within the article than is possible with other methods of forming compound curvatures. The principles of ridge-forming can be applied to both male and female molds, so that reverse curves, flanges, and flutes can be formed with a minimum of distortion.

Applications. Ridge-forming or skeleton-forming has been adapted to produce articles such as bassinets, baby-carriage bodies, large developing tanks, bell-jars, and housings.

4. Vacuum Drawing, or Blowing, into a Mold. In this method, the pre-heated sheet is clamped to the periphery of a female mold, and the article

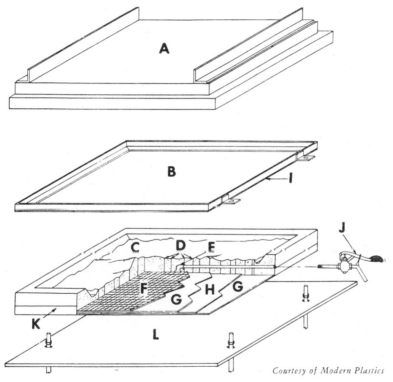

Courtesy of Modern Plastics

Fig. 5-37. Vacuum Forming Equipment.

A. Superheater	G. Aluminum sheet—0.032 in.
B. Angle-iron frame	H. Sponge rubber ¼ in.-⅜ in.
C. Mold	I. Sponge rubber gasket
D. Vacuum holes	J. Poppet valve
E. Vacuum pipe	K. Heat-resistant tape
F. Wire mesh—2 layers	L. Aluminum plate—½ in.

is formed by application of vacuum or compressed air. The mold is constructed with small holes through which air can pass.

Description of Process. There are several modifications of procedure for vacuum drawing, or blowing, into a mold. One of the simplest is to clamp the preheated sheet over a mold such as shown in Fig. 5-37, and apply

Courtesy of Bakelite Co.

Fig. 5-38. Relief map. Vacuum molded from vinyl rigid sheet.

vacuum to draw the sheet into the desired shape, such as a relief map (Fig. 5-38).

While most blow- and vacuum-forming molds are negative molds, the advantages of positive molds for vacuum-forming operations should not be ignored. In forming such complex articles as relief maps, the use of a positive mold often ensures better register, and a stronger product because of a better uniformity of thickness.

When a positive mold is used, the first part of the mold with which the sheet comes into contact during the forming is that part which would in a negative mold be the deepest and hardest portion of the mold to fill out. For example, in a negative mold a pointed mountain would be a very deep valley,

POSITIVE TYPE VACUUM MOLD

FRAMING WALL

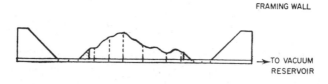

→TO VACUUM RESERVOIR

NEGATIVE TYPE VACUUM MOLD

→TO VACUUM RESERVOIR

- - - - -VACUUM HOLES

Courtesy of Bakelite Co.

Fig. 5-39

but in a positive mold it is still a mountain (Fig. 5-39). Since the rigid sheet is drawn down over the most difficult portion first, register is greatly enhanced by use of the positive mold. Also, the thickness of the sheet in the final product is more nearly uniform—the regions of the deepest draw are relatively large areas, and thus excessive localized thinning-down at deep draws is avoided.

Molds should have air-vents at the points of deepest draw.

For molding rigid vinyl sheets by this method, cycles are suggested in Table 5-3, as a guide in establishing optimum conditions for production.

Depending upon the size, detail, and depth of the mold, and to some extent upon the material to be formed, it may be necessary, for a given thickness of sheet, to use the higher temperature and pressure conditions indicated by the curve next beyond that suggested in the table.

TABLE 5-3

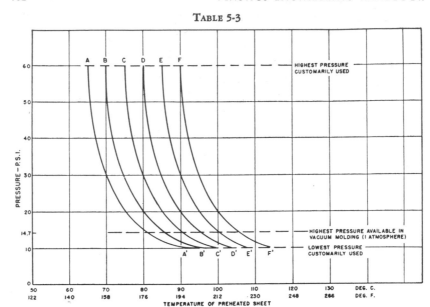

GENERAL PRESSURE AND TEMPERATURE CONDITIONS FOR BLOW
MOLDING AND VACUUM MOLDING VINYL RIGID SHEETS.

Courtesy of Bakelite Co.

Curves indicate approximate minimum pressure needed for forming rigid vinyl sheets, as a function of thickness, temperature of preheating, and depth of draw or detail of mold.

Curve	Thickness of Rigid Sheet (in.)	Depth of Draw
A-A′	0.005 - 0.020	shallow
B-B′	0.005 - 0.020	deep
	0.020 - 0.035	shallow
C-C′	0.020 - 0.035	deep
	0.035 - 0.050	shallow
D-D′	0.035 - 0.050	deep
	0.050 and up	shallow
E-E′	0.050 and up	deep
F-F′	suggested upper limit to avoid defects caused by high temperatures	

Acrylic sheet materials are extensively formed by this method (one modification known as grease-forming is described as a separate method).

Pan-shaped signs or signs with raised letters are formed by this method. Such signs may be made from acrylic sheet having pigments incorporated in it, or they may be painted.

Painting may be done, either before or after the forming, by means of an air brush. Painting before forming requires the use of a paint which has sufficient elasticity to withstand the stretching of the sheet without cracking. Best results are obtained when the mold does not come into contact with the colored coating during the forming.

In making painted signs of this type, a template is first prepared, which serves (1) to determine the outlines of a silk screen used in the painting, and (2) for indexing the sheets prior to forming. First, the indexing pins on the mold are replaced by short studs, and with these a preheated sheet is marked to show the location of the indexing pins. This sheet is then formed against the mold in the manner and under the conditions of the subsequent production of the signs. It is then scribed to define the outlines of each raised letter and all details of copy on the front surface of the formed face. Holes are drilled in it, for indexing, at the locations of the marks made by the studs. The sheet is then heated to allow it to resume a flat shape. Next, with the scribed marks on the flattened sheet as a pattern, a silk screen is made, which is used in applying silk-screen paint to sheets used in production of the sign.

Manufacturing procedure then involves the following steps: (1) the blank is heated and slowly cooled; (2) index holes are drilled in it with the aid of the template; (3) the blank is silk-screened on the surface which will be inside the sign; (4) after the paint has dried, the blank is formed, using the index holes to locate it on the mold.

The molds should have as few as possible sharp corners and deep indentations, so as to avoid excessive localized thinning or stretching.

Split female molds made of "Hydrocal" and inserted in a 16-gauge metal cone can be used for pressure blowing when the article is difficult to remove from the mold (Fig. 5-40). The heated sheet is clamped to the top of the

Courtesy of Rohm & Haas Co.

Fig. 5-40. Split mold for blowing.

mold before the pressure head is attached. In order to produce the ¼-in. beading around the top of the dentist's wastes-receiver, the bottom of the pressure head is constructed with a rubber plug screwed into a small section of pipe welded to the head. Air pressure at 45 psi is used to force the sheet into the return section by expansion of the rubber.

Equipment Required. Either vacuum equipment or air-compressors with storage tanks of sufficient capacity are required. For forming of large signs, molds may be mounted in either hydraulic or pneumatic presses. Air pressures of 20 to 45 psi are generally sufficient for blowing into a female mold. In some cases the mold is mounted on the bed of the press with springs to facilitate removal of the formed article.

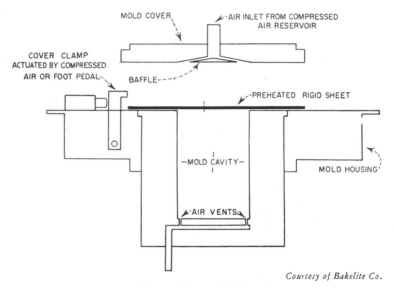

Courtesy of Bakelite Co.

Fig. 5-41. Blow molding of rigid vinyl sheets.

Schematic diagrams of equipment for blowing into a mold are shown in Figs. 5-41 and 5-42. The apparatus in Fig. 5-41 utilizes a preheated sheet, while that in Fig. 5-42 preheats the rigid vinyl sheet by steam after the sheet is inserted in the mold and prior to the forming. The use of heated metal molds is advantageous in preventing a cold metal mold from chilling the sheet before it can be formed.

Although generally air is used directly as the pressure medium, in some methods air is used to expand a rubber bag which presses against the plastic (Fig. 5-43).

The heating apparatus, whether oven, hot plate or other means, should be as close to the mold as possible, so that a minimum of cooling occurs before the air pressure is applied.

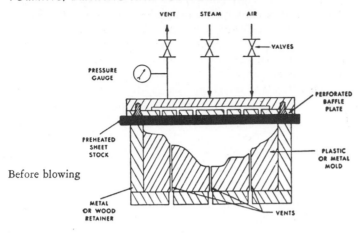

Before blowing

After blowing

Courtesy of Bakelite Co.

Fig. 5-42. Blow molding of rigid vinyl sheets.

Courtesy of Bakelite Co.

Fig. 5-43. Blow welding a hot-formed cylinder of vinyl rigid sheet into the form of a large drinking glass. The air pressure is applied by means of a rubber pressure bag.

In some operations, it is entirely feasible to heat the sheet after it has been clamped in the mold, as discussed previously. This can be accomplished by means of circulating steam, infrared lamps, electric resistance heaters, etc.

Cooling can be accomplished by allowing the formed rigid sheet to stand in the open mold at room temperature under a blast of air from fans. Ordinary portable room fans, and directional fans such as used in hair-dryers, have been used with good success. It is desirable to have the fan mounted on an adjustable or rotating arm, so that it may be conveniently swung over the mold.

Materials. Most thermoplastic sheet materials, including acrylics, cellulosics, butadiene-acrylonitrile-styrene, and rigid vinyls, can be formed by some of these methods.

Advantages and Limitations. Very complex shapes can be formed by these methods. Surface defects which occur in blowing rigid vinyl sheet into a mold may include orange peel resulting from heating too long or at too high temperatures, whitening caused by severe stretching or insufficient heating, and wrinkling if the sheet is drawn too thin, particularly at edges and corners. Transparent vinyl sheet thicker than 0.050 in. is difficult to mold by this method without some optical distortion.

When acrylic sheet is formed in a mold approximately the shape of a natural surface-tension bubble, the articles have fairly good optical homogeneity. Under these conditions, all parts of the sheet come into contact with the mold at about the same time, and thereby mark-off is minimized.

Vacuum drawing into a mold is used more often for forming articles which differ quite radically from surface-tension shapes, but in which mark-off is not objectionable. Very good detail can be had with these methods.

Applications. Large signs, relief maps, wall plaques, display cases, doll faces, and a large variety of other articles are made by these methods.

Methods Employing Compressed Air. The methods employing compressed air are discussed in the following pages.

1. Pressure Blowing in Free Space. Compressed air can be used to form thermoplastic sheet materials in free space, when pressures above 14.5 psi are required.

Description of Process. The preheated sheet is clamped over a pressure head and blown to shape (Fig. 5-44). When the clamping ring is circular, the finished article, if shallow drawn, is a section of a sphere. A square or triangular ring will produce a combination shape, of which the central portion will have a spherical contour. Altering the clamping tools in the third dimension will greatly increase the number of possible shapes that can be made. Alignment charts can be used for estimating pressures required to form hemispheres from general purpose acrylic sheet (Fig. 5-45). For heat-resistant acrylic sheet, these pressures should be multiplied by a factor of 1.8.

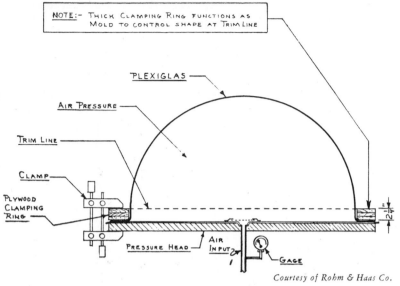

Fig. 5-44

Equipment Required. An air-compressor and storage tank of sufficient capacity to handle the forming equipment are required. Air pressures up to 50 psi have been used, but great care must be taken to make the equipment strong enough to withstand the pressure exerted on large equipment. Such equipment can be very dangerous if not properly designed.

Forming chambers are generally constructed of reinforced steel. Pneumatic or hydraulic cylinders are often used for holding the clamping rings on the sheet during forming.

Materials. Acrylics, cellulosics, vinyls, and butadiene-acrylonitrile-styrene copolymers can be formed by this method.

Advantages and Limitations. Articles having good optical quality can be produced by this method. It has been used to advantage in forming laminated acrylics for aircraft parts, since it is less apt than vacuum forming to produce bubbles at the interface between the acrylic sheet and the polyvinyl butyral interlayer.

The method requires heavy equipment, and is not generally used unless the article cannot be formed as satisfactorily by other methods.

Applications. The large laminated acrylic domes made during the war for B-29 airplanes were formed by this method, as were also other laminated enclosures such as cockpit enclosures for airplanes.

2. Grease-Forming. The use of a lubricant in deep drawing is common in the sheet-metal industry, to prevent sticking of the metal to the die and

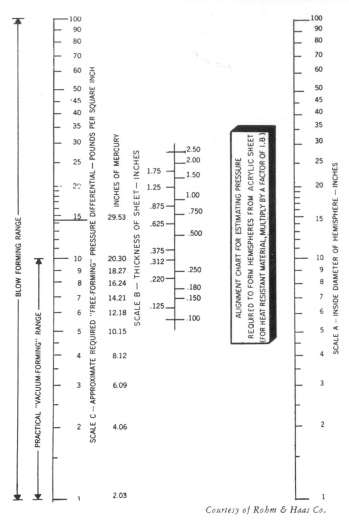

Courtesy of Rohm & Haas Co.

Fig. 5-45

to give a superior distribution of thickness, as well as a better surface. In forming thermoplastics, the grease performs much the same function, and, in addition, helps to prevent mark-off.

Description of Process. Grease-forming may be performed by drawing the thermoplastic sheet material over a male die or by forcing it into a female die by means of a male mold, air pressure or liquid pressure. Vacuum is not generally used in grease-forming, because of the tendency of the grease to bubble under certain conditions.

Forms used in this method should be made of phenolic casting resin with a filler of fibrous glass or shredded asbestos, which will withstand repeated heating and cooling. When a male mold is used, it is covered with a high-quality all-wool felt saturated with grease. The felt prevents the grease from flowing away from the points of high pressure. The felt cover must be carefully conditioned to remove all knots or hard spots. The felt is frequently preconditioned by application of a grease of high graphite content to prevent excessive penetration of the other grease. No pockets of grease should be allowed to accumulate under the felt. Female molds are generally used without the felt cover. During forming, the grease is forced into the felt covering. Entrapped air and excess grease are forced out through vents in the mold. A certain amount of practice and technique is required in order to prevent "grease runs," i.e., optical distortions caused by the running of grease, and consequent variations in pressure and temperature.

In practice, the mold and cover are coated with a layer of grease of the correct type, to a depth of $\frac{1}{16}$ to $\frac{1}{8}$ in. After this has been smoothed to a uniform coating, heat is applied from a bank of infrared lamps or other suitable source until the surface of the grease is hot enough to smoke.

Several types of grease have been used for this operation. One is a petroleum grease of high soap content. Another is based on synthetic polymers, which do not undergo as much change in viscosity with temperature as do the petroleum greases. However, the latter is more difficult to clean from the formed piece. A new type of grease has been developed which is easy to remove by washing the formed articles in water.

The sheet is heated to forming temperatures, which is 300 to 325°F for most work. It is then clamped to the metal flange of the forming pot, and the cover carrying the air line is clamped over the sheet. The sheet is slowly forced into the mold by air pressure.

The sheet can also be stretched over a greased male mold to produce deeply drawn articles with somewhat less unevenness in thickness than is produced when a female mold is used. During the operation, the sheet is cooled by contact with the mold, and this, in combination with friction, resists slippage, so that it is possible to form articles having 300 per cent stretch and with the most deeply drawn section thicker than the sidewalls.

Equipment Required. An air-compressor and an auxiliary tank are required. The construction of the molds is very important. When they are made of a material of high heat capacity, the surface conducts the heat from the sheet so rapidly that it cools and hardens before the forming can be completed, unless the forms and grease are heated to somewhere near the forming temperature of the material. When forms of low heat capacity are used, made, e.g., of wood, thermosetting plastic, or plaster, the heat is not drawn so rapidly from the sheet, and therefore deeper draws can be made. A reinforced cast plaster mold without covering can be used to advantage in many cases. A plaster mold will wear longer if it is kept hot at all times, but it will eventually crack. Expansion and contraction due to temperature change is more harmful to the mold than any forces exerted during forming operations.

Materials. The acrylic sheet materials have been formed to a large extent by this method. It is applicable also to the cellulosic materials.

Advantages and Limitations. Grease forming has great advantages in making it possible to form large parts with compound curvatures to meet critical optical specifications. The grease minimizes mark-off as far as can be expected in methods requiring contact of the hot sheet with a mold. It does not produce as good optical quality as is obtained by forming in free space. The flow of grease causes distortion due to flow lines in the material.

In grease-forming, it is necessary to ensure relatively constant rate of movement of the sheet over the greased surface. Extreme variations in speed will cause distortions in the article. Once the heated sheet has touched the grease form, the operation must be completed without delay or interruption.

Applications. This method has been used to make large aircraft parts such as helicopter noses and some canopies.

Slip Forming. Slip forming is the process of allowing some of the sheet material to slip through the mechanically operated clamping rings during a stretch-forming operation. This principle has been used in the forming of metal articles for many years. Refinements in technique have been adapted to the forming of thermoplastic sheet material in which a predetermined amount of slip through the clamping is allowed. Wrinkles, which tend to form at the clamping ring, limit the amount of material which can be allowed to slip through the ring. When sufficient material has been allowed to slip in, the rings are clamped more tightly together and the draw completed.

Another method of slip forming incorporates the vacuum snapback procedure described previously. In this procedure the material is held under a spring-loaded clamping ring to allow some slippage of the material as vacuum is applied.

Description of Process. One type of mold that has been used for slip forming of butadiene-acrylonitrile-styrene copolymer sheet employs compression springs as the force on the clamping ring (Fig. 5-46). A mold of this type consists basically of a plug, clamping ring, and draw ring. The plug is attached to a plate, which in turn is fastened to the upper force. The clamping ring, with an area cut out to clear the plug, is hung from this plate by means of rods. The compression springs are mounted over these rods between the plate and clamping ring. The plate has clearance holes to allow the rods to travel as the mold is being closed. The draw ring is mounted to the base of the press.

In operation, the heated sheet is placed over the opening in the draw ring, and the plug is pushed through by means of the upper force. With the correct

Courtesy of United States Rubber Co.

Fig. 5-46

spring pressure, the material will slip between the surfaces of the hold-down ring and draw ring.

Another and more successful method of slip forming involves the application of constant pressure on the clamping ring for the full depth of the draw (Fig. 5-47). In this operation, the mold is inverted in relation to molds previously discussed. The draw ring is attached to the upper cylinder or force. The plug is fastened to the bed of the press. The hold-down ring is positioned near the top of the plug and is held by rods extending down through the press bed and resting upon a plate mounted to a force on the bottom of the press bed.

The heated material is positioned over the plug (Fig. 5-48) and draw ring, and the upper force is actuated. The draw ring "wipes" over the plug and pushes the lower cylinder down by means of the rods attached to the clamping ring.

Equipment Required. A press of the proper size, with a force mounted above the press bed, is required. The molds may be constructed of wood, "Masonite," "Micarta," resins, or metal. The method of constant clamping (Fig. 5-49) requires a press with a force or cylinder pushing downward and a lesser force or cylinder mounted on the under side of the press bed pushing upward. The lower force, which serves as a cushion, is connected to a surge

Courtesy of United States Rubber Co.

Fig. 5-47

Courtesy of United States Rubber Co.

Fig. 5-48

tank, which has regulators and valves by which to adjust and maintain any desired pressure throughout its cycle.

In all of these types of molds for slip forming, it has been found ad-

Courtesy of United States Rubber Co.

Fig. 5-49

vantageous to have a button or raised area on each corner of the hold-down ring. This tends to let the sides and ends of the blank slip to a greater degree, while retarding the excess corner material and preventing wrinkling in that area.

Materials. All thermoplastic sheeting can be formed by this method.

Advantages and Limitations. One advantage of slip forming is that it yields articles of more nearly uniform thickness than is obtained by stretch forming. In the case of acrylic parts for airplanes, this means less optical distortion; in the case of a grained or textured-surface sheeting of butadiene-acrylonitrile-styrene copolymer, less distortion of the pattern. Limitations on the depth of the article are imposed by the springs. As the mold is being closed, and the springs subsequently compressed, the pressure on the hold-down ring increases, and when it reaches a point that will not allow the material to slip any farther, there occur a definite mark-off and thinning on the side walls of the article.

Applications. Deep draws or forming operations such as for tote boxes, luggage and decorative posts for bowling alley installations. Medium draws of oval, circular, or rectangular contour, or deep draws where mark-off is not a consideration.

Hydraulic Forming. Hydraulic forming may be a variation of grease forming. But this in its original form did not require a greased mold surface. It was developed at a time when very little was known about the forming of acrylic plastics, and it met the need for compound curved parts with good optical properties.

Description of Process. The basic principle involves heating the material with hot oil, which at the same time is used to force the sheet to the desired contour against a female mold. The surface of the mold is kept cool by circulating water through a jacket. As the heated sheet is forced against the mold surface, the cool surface hardens it so that little mark-off occurs. As soon as the article is nearly formed against the mold surface, cool oil is circulated instead of hot oil, while maintaining the pressure.

There are several possibilities for the future use of modifications of hydraulic forming without the water-jacketed female mold. When combined with grease forming, it might give economies in production, since the transfer of heat from oil to the sheet is much faster than from air.

Equipment Required. The equipment required is relatively expensive, since a supply of both hot and cool oil, pumps, valves, etc., is required, as well as a water-jacketed metal mold to form the outside contour desired.

Materials. Acrylic, cellulosic, and vinyl sheet materials can be formed by this method.

Advantages and Limitations. It is difficult to maintain close tolerances because of irregularity in the extent of springback from piece to piece. This is caused by the cooling of the outside surface of the sheet in contact with the mold while the inner surface is in contact with the hot oil under pressure. When this pressure is relieved, springback of as much as 2 to 3 in. occurs on a large semicircular article.

Applications. The Lockheed Hudson and Lockheed Ventura noses were produced by this method. It has not been used since the war.

"Rotoforming." The "Rotoform" process, developed and patented by Goodyear Aircraft Corporation, is a "free-forming" process in which the hot thermoplastic does not touch a mold except at the attachment areas. Instead of the hydrostatic pressure used in free blowing, centrifugal force produces the draw, and a wide variety of shapes can be obtained by controlling the direction and magnitude of the centrifugal forces.

Description of Process. A heated thermoplastic sheet is clamped to the frame of a jig which can be rotated. The clamping area becomes the final attachment area, and mark-off is thus confined to a band around the edge of the part. The position of the jig with reference to the axis of rotation is varied according to the shape required, but the extent of the draw during the forming operation is controlled by the temperature of the sheet and the speed of rotation.

Equipment Required. The equipment consists of a basic spinning fixture and demountable jigs suited for the particular article to be formed. In general, requirements of ovens are the same as in free blowing or vacuum forming.

Materials. All of the commercially available acrylics have been formed by the "Rotoform" process, including the temperature-resistant grades and laminated acrylic. Other thermoplastic materials could be formed by the process.

Advantages and Limitations. The "Rotoform" process yields articles having the same optical properties that can be obtained in careful free blowing, but also permits the production of a wide variety of shapes, whereas free-blown parts are normally limited to cross sections which are essentially arcs of circles. "Rotoformed" parts can be made with cross sections varying from a circle to

Courtesy of Goodyear Aircraft

Fig. 5-50. A wide variety of enclosure shapes can be obtained by the Rotoform process. From top to bottom; Enclosures illustrated are P-84, FJ-1, BT2D, and F4U4. All are covered with protective coating to better illustrate contours.

a shape that approaches a catenary (Fig. 5-50). Thus this method is most advantageously used where a shape of low frontal area, streamlined, and

Courtesy of Goodyear Aircraft

Fig. 5-51. Rotoform F4U4 Canopy.

nonbulging, is required, without sacrifice of optimum optical properties (Fig. 5-51). A further advantage lies in the fact that the reduction of thickness tends to be more nearly uniform throughout the formed piece. Pieces produced by this method are relatively free from the excessive thinning toward the crest of the bulge of a free-blown piece, and from the local irregularities of thinning which sometimes occur in forming by means of a mold.

Applications. The method has been used to make large canopies and turret enclosures for aircraft. The first canopies made by the process were for the P-84 and later models of the F4U4 airplanes.

Embossing and Swaging. Embossing and swaging of thermoplastic sheet involve displacement of a portion of the hot sheet under pressure to produce a design or decorative effects.

Description of Processes. The types of swaging most generally done on thermoplastic sheet is confined swaging, in which the article is formed from a blank of the same volume. In embossing and swaging, the original thickness of the sheet is practically unaltered. They are essentially molding operations performed on sheet stock.

Various techniques have been used to emboss or swage hot sheet stock. In some cases, the sheet is placed in highly polished male and female dies and the dies are placed in an arbor press or an air-operated press. Such dies may be operated cold or warm.

For some jobs, it is preferable to use a swaging die with an overflow flange to permit simultaneous shaping and trimming.

Embossing can be done also with dies mounted on heated platens in a press. Pressures in the range of 2,000 psi at 285 to 300°F can be used.

Another technique involves the use of a mold, e.g., of reinforced plaster, against which the sheet is embossed by pressure of thick sponge rubber mounted on the top platen of the press.

Equipment Required. Press equipment may be of any type, such as arbor, air or hydraulic. Molds may be constructed of metal or reinforced plaster. Split dies are sometimes used to facilitate removal of articles.

Materials. Acrylic, cellulosic, vinyl, and polyethylene sheet materials can be formed by these methods.

Advantages and Limitations. Sharp indentations in sheet plastics can be produced by embossing and swaging. Combinations of swaging with other methods, such as blowing, can be used to form articles which cannot be produced by swaging alone. Thin-walled articles with compound curvatures also can be produced.

Applications. The many applications of these methods include buttons, watch crystals, signs, lenses, and containers.

Annealing of Formed Articles. Annealing consists of prolonged heating at an elevated temperature followed by slow cooling. The internal stresses and strains, set up during fabrication of the article, are reduced or eliminated by this treatment. This results in a product of greater dimensional stability and greater resistance to crazing. In order to obtain these benefits, it is necessary that the annealing be done after all other fabrication procedures, including polishing, are completed.

Formed articles which are to be cemented will be less subject to stress-solvent crazing if they are annealed before cementing. Annealing after cementing will greatly increase the strength of the cemented joints, as well as improving the articles as mentioned above.

Annealing also lessens the effect of solvent smears and runs which may result from errors in cementing operations. In cases of articles to be subjected to brief exposure to solvents, as in painting, proper annealing will eliminate any tendency toward immediate crazing or cracking. If the exposure to solvent is severe, or such as is known to establish a tendency toward crazing, as in the case of certain paints, the annealing treatment should be given after such exposure.

Cycles of annealing can be worked out in many ways. Some fabricators allow their forming ovens to cool to annealing temperature near the close of the day's work, place the fabricated pieces in the oven and hold them at the annealing temperature for the specified time, then adjust the oven to cool during the night at the specified cooling rate. Other systems involve conveyor belts which carry the fabricated articles through an oven, succeeding sections of which are heated to gradually lower temperatures.

Recommendations of the manufacturer of the raw material will assist in determining the correct annealing temperature for a given material. The correct procedure is to use the maximum temperature that does not produce an objectionable dimensional change in the formed piece. This can be determined only on the basis of experience on a particular formed article. Properly formed articles should withstand the recommended annealing conditions.

If objectionable change occurs, it may indicate that the article has not been properly formed. Forming conditions should be carefully reviewed and revised until the formed pieces will withstand the annealing temperature without undergoing objectionable dimensional change.

After annealing at elevated temperature, the article must be cooled slowly at an even rate. The rate of cooling must be slower for thick sections than for thin sections.

Methods of Forming Thermosetting Plastics

Postforming of Thermosetting Laminates. The term postforming refers to the forming, bending or shaping of fully cured, C-stage, thermoset laminates after heating them to make them flexible and pliable, in suitable molds, jigs or fixtures under relatively low pressure, so that upon cooling and release of pressure the formed piece retains the contour and shape imparted to it while hot, as well as most of its original physical properties.

This method differs from low-pressure molding in that (1) the resin is in stage C instead of stage B, as in low-pressure molding, and (2) the surface finish is that of the precured sheet, whereas in low-pressure molding the surface finish is obtained from the mold. Although thermoplastic resins have also been processed by postforming operations, this discussion will be confined to the thermosetting type, of which phenol-formaldehyde and modified phenol-formaldehyde resins are the most important.

History. Although it has long been known that cured laminated sheets could be formed slightly while still hot and retain the new shape upon cooling, this phenomenon remained unexploited until Mr. William I. Beach, plastics engineer, indicated by his experimental work the commercial potentialities of this process.

Just prior to Pearl Harbor, the emphasis placed upon aircraft production resulted in considerable interest of aircraft manufacturers in components made of plastics. This was due not only to the light weight of these materials or to their specific mechanical or electrical properties, but also to the critical shortage at that time of aluminum, the basic structural material in the aircraft industry.

However, for molding these plastics, of either paper or canvas base, pressures of 1000 psi and more are required, which necessitate molds of alloy steel and heavy-duty presses. Such molds, machined to close tolerances and capable of withstanding these high pressures, are naturally quite expensive. Although these high mold costs are unimportant when the volume of production is large, they are prohibitive when it is small.

Postforming is carried out in cheap molds, generally of wood, plaster of Paris, etc., and within relatively short cycles, since the piece is held under low pressure in the mold only long enough to allow it to cool sufficiently to retain its shape upon release of pressure. The laminating industry has developed combinations of cloth and resin having optimum postforming properties. Also this development has been further extended to the use of a paper base.

Description of Process. Postforming consists of heating the laminate by suitable means to a temperature at which it becomes soft and pliable, inserting it quickly into a cold mold, applying sufficient pressure to form it to the contour desired, and maintaining this pressure until the piece has cooled sufficiently to retain its shape upon removal.

Mention should be made at this time that the physical properties of a formed piece depend primarily on proper cure of the laminates and on selection of the filler.

Proper cure is important because undercuring results in delamination, excessive springback and poor resistance to dimensional changes. Overcured laminates, on the other hand, in general give good performance, although they are somewhat restricted to larger radii of bend and to curved shapes of large area.

Selection of filler can be very important. In the case of fabric-base laminates, the unit elongation of the individual threads is a factor, but the pattern of the weave ultimately determines the stretching characteristics, and the quality of the finish on the resinous surface of the piece.

In heating the material prior to forming, it should be remembered that (1) the lower the forming temperature, the longer the sheet may be exposed to the heat without suffering excessive cure; (2) the higher the temperature, the shorter must be the exposure time, and the greater will be the tendency to blister; (3) the higher the temperature, the greater the softening.

For properly heating the sheets, various methods and equipment have been employed. Hot-air circulating ovens have been successfully used, but are slow in heating the sheet, because of the low rate of heat-transfer, and entail the dangers of blistering the surface even while the inner layers of the laminate remain below forming temperatures, and of hardening the surface to the point of embrittling it, and thereby imposing restriction on the radius to which the sheet can be formed.

Hot oil has one of the highest coefficients of heat-transfer. But a hot oil bath usually introduces other problems. It is messy and a fire hazard. And the pieces formed must afterward be wiped clean.

Baths of molten metal also are used. They provide the highest coefficient of heat-transfer. But the pieces have to be cleaned of frozen metal remaining on them, and this metal may dent the article or the die.

Heated platens are satisfactory for heating sheets of similar thickness, but do not offer sufficient flexibility for heating material in various thicknesses in a production setup.

Infrared ovens offer the most flexibility in operation, because they can be designed to be controllable so that pieces of various thicknesses may be moved at the same velocity and still leave the oven at the same temperature. Pieces are heated uniformly and rapidly.

For heating thicker pieces, high-frequency electrostatic heating is the best method, since the material can be very uniformly heated throughout.

In general, the heating should be as rapid as possible to as high a temperature as practicable. It should require not more than $\frac{1}{2}$ to 1 minute for $\frac{1}{16}$-in. material. Thicker stock will take longer.

Typical temperatures for liquid baths may be 350 to 500°F (temperatures 350 to 420°F are particularly recommended). A test specimen of the material to be used is immersed in the bath until it blisters. Heating time is then set at 85 to 90 per cent of this time—sometimes less, depending on complexity of the shape. A similar procedure is used in heating with infrared lamps.

The simplest way of using infrared lamps (usually 250-watt bulbs with reflectors) is to make up two banks with the bulbs arranged as close together as possible, and to mount these facing each other with an adjustable space of about three inches between the ends of the bulbs. Material heated between these banks should be kept in motion to promote uniformity of heating. If the banks are enclosed in an oven, the spacing may be increased and more nearly uniform heating will result. A more elaborate setup would involve a tunnel with an endless conveyor.

In radiant-heat ovens, the temperature-indicating pyrometers should be set at 450 to 550°F when the radiant bank is 12 in. or more from the stock.

In all methods, the temperature of the apparatus should be kept constant, and control effected by careful regulation of the heating schedule.

Successful forming of properly heated material depends principally on speed of operation; material must be placed in the die and formed in less than $\frac{1}{2}$ min after removal from the source of heat. Hence, arrangement of equipment to save time and motion is very important. The die should be equipped, when possible, with locating pins to ensure quick and proper placement of material in it. Rapid closing of presses will aid in keeping within the time limit. Allowance for springback of the material must sometimes be made in die construction, particularly in making simple bends. Prefabrication of the flat sheet is frequently possible, if provision can be made in the die for locating the cutout precisely. Sufficient pressure to shape the piece is all that is necessary.

Equipment Required. Postforming dies may be constructed of such inexpensive materials as wood, "Masonite," low-melting alloys, cast or laminated plastic, etc.

The fact that no pressure need be applied to these dies, except that necessary to close the die and form the piece, permits great variety in the construction of these molds. Arbor presses, fast-acting hydraulic or pneumatic presses, toggle or cam-acting presses, are all satisfactory. In many instances toggle clamps or dead weights may be used to shape the piece. Heavy equipment and high pressures are definitely not required. However, the design of the mold and the method of applying pressure must be such that the shaping is done quickly.

In making sharp bends, or in any drawing operation, it is preferable that the material around the section involved be partially under lateral compression rather than tension to minimize tearing and crazing.

Materials. The fabrics most commonly used as fillers are Army ducks, twills and herringbone weaves, and single- or double-filled ducks. The resin is usually a simple or modified phenol-formaldehyde. However, aniline-formaldehyde, or a combination of aniline- and phenol-formaldehyde, may be used.

Forming of Allyl-Type Plastics Sheet.   Thermosetting allyl sheet materials can be formed to a limited degree. This limitation results from the cross-linked nature of the material. At elevated temperatures the material is somewhat more flexible and can be formed into moderate simple curvatures. Because the material does not melt or flow at elevated temperatures it is not possible to stretch or draw it into deep compound curvatures. Simple curvatures, however, can be made.

The following tabulation can be used as a guide to the maximum curvatures which can be formed at elevated temperatures with thermosetting allyl sheet materials:

Nominal Thickness	Maximum Radius
(in.)	(in.)
0.060	1.5
0.080	2.0
0.100	2.5
0.125	3.1
0.150	3.8
0.187	4.7
0.220	6.0
0.250	7.5

With certain exceptions based on the limitations of flow of allyl sheet resin, the same methods of forming may be used for these materials as have been described for thermoplastic sheets. The sheet is heated in an oven or with infrared radiation to a temperature of 215 to 225°F. This will require 10 to 30 minutes, depending upon the thickness of the sheet and the efficiency of the means of heating. It is then transferred to the forming dies or jigs, where a slight positive pressure is applied to make the sheet conform to the desired shape. The sheet is allowed to cool in the mold. Upon removal from the mold a little springback toward the original flat shape may occur, depending upon the temperature. In order to compensate for this, molds having slightly exaggerated curvatures may be used. The amount of correction to be provided will depend upon the size, shape and thickness of the article.

(With the allyl resins, direct casting methods may be used to produce articles of simple and compound curvatures having maximum dimensional stability at elevated temperatures; see Chapter 7.)

6. Reinforced Plastics

Scope

The reinforced-plastics industry, given impetus by World War II, has continued to grow steadily. Today the various manufacturing processes involved permit the fabrication of many items previously made of metal or wood, and the manufacture of structural items which were too large for fabrication from other plastics. It has permitted the manufacture of these large items with relatively low mold investment.

Because of the youthfulness of the industry, specific design data, such as those available for most metals, are meager. Partial information along these lines has been gathered by manufacturers of reinforced plastics, by suppliers of raw materials and by government agencies. These sources of information should be utilized to their fullest extent by the fabricator.

Molding of reinforced plastics, one of the newer activities of the plastics industry, involves the combination of glass fibers with thermosetting resins, notably the polyesters. Other resins, such as phenolics, epoxies, silicones, diallyl phthalates and furanes, also are used in reinforced plastics. This chapter discusses the methods of molding and forming structures of reinforced plastics. It will be observed that the processor of reinforced plastics brings together the resin and the reinforcing material, whereas the molder of the more conventional plastics receives his material already compounded. It will be noted also that the unit pressures employed in the molding and forming of reinforced plastics are considerably lower than the conventional pressures of high-pressure molding.

Commercially produced applications of reinforced plastics are shown in Figs. 6-1 through 6-6.

Activities in molding of reinforced plastics have grown rapidly. The many ramifications of the reinforced-plastics industry cannot be covered completely within the space of this chapter. It is recommended that the interested reader refer to the publications of The Society of the Plastics Industry, which reproduce in full the technical papers presented at the annual meetings of the Reinforced Plastics Division of SPI.

History

It has been recognized by the plastics industry for many years that the good physical characteristics of many of its products were due to the rein-

Courtesy of Zenith Plastics Co.

Fig. 6-1. Lower radome of Lockheed radar-search Constellation.

forcing character of various materials, some of which were added as finely divided fillers and others introduced as laminae. Although conventional molding materials and equipment were ample for producing a great variety of articles from plastics, three general exceptions presented difficulties: items too large for conventional molding presses, items so limited in production that the costs of conventional tooling were prohibitive, and parts that required great mechanical strength and rigidity for structural applications.

The low-pressure molding methods of the rubber industry, involving air or steam pressure against distensible bags, have for many years permitted the molding of large contoured shapes without excessive unit pressures. These

Courtesy of Chevrolet

Fig. 6-2. The Chevrolet Corvette.

Courtesy of Winner Manufacturing Co., Inc.

Fig. 6-3. A 12-foot reinforced-plastics boat.

methods* were successfully adapted to the forming of aircraft components of resin-treated plywood during the late 1930's and the early years of World War II. However, even though such techniques are still effectively

Courtesy of Alsynite Co. of America

Fig. 6-4. Corrugated panel installation.

---
* These were described more fully in the first edition of the SPI Handbook (1947, Chapter 2, Section VII). (This edition is now out of print.)

*Molded by Zenith Plastics Co. for the
Herman Miller Furniture Co.*

Fig. 6-5. The Charles Eames arm chair.

employed, subsequent developments in molding of reinforced plastics, since
World War II, have followed other directions. The later methods have turned
to mated molds, utilizing experience gained in high-pressure molding. Also

Courtesy of Apex Electrical Manufacturing Co.

Fig. 6-6. Inner basket of automatic washer.

contributing to this development have been methods of felting contoured shapes, permitting rapid layup of glass fibers in complex shapes, ready for introduction into molds. These refinements have enabled the molding of reinforced plastics to evolve from experimental limited production into a large-scale production enterprise.

Materials for reinforced plastics stem from many sources. Their merits may be more clearly established by examining the more significant ones in the following paragraphs. The resin binders are briefly treated first, followed by the reinforcing materials.

Resin Binder Materials

Polyester Resins. Special unsaturated alkyd resins in combination with a low-viscosity monomer such as styrene or diallyl phthalate provide the polyester resins used by the reinforced-plastics industry. In conjunction with organic peroxide catalysts (such as benzoyl peroxide) and promoters (such as cobalt naphthenate) the resins are converted from a liquid state to a solid state either with or without the application of external heat, depending upon the catalyst and catalyst-promoter system used. Polyester resins, being 100 per cent reactive, do not release by-products during cure; consequently, in molding operations, low pressures may be utilized and breathing of molds is not necessary.

The resins differ in many respects, particularly in viscosity, speed of gelling and curing, degree of reactivity, and content of inhibitor. The cured products may differ in hardness and flexibility. Improved temperature-resistance is now realized through introduction of triallyl cyanurate into the polyester system.

Phenolic Resins. Phenolic resins, better known in high-pressure molding systems, have emerged as an important material in reinforced plastics, particularly in components requiring good performance at temperatures higher than possible with polyesters. Their electrical properties are not as satisfactory as those of polyesters, but some phenolic components show excellent mechanical strength at temperatures as high as 400 to 500°F.

In this country phenolics have been developed in conjunction with glass cloth as reinforcement. In Great Britain phenolics are used with asbestos fibers with considerable success in the aircraft industry.

Epoxy Resins. The newest members of the reinforced-plastics industry, epoxy resins, are notable for their remarkable adhesion to glass and to metal. Epoxy resins are prepared for use by the addition of polyamine hardeners or the anhydrides of dibasic acids, and will cure without the formation of objectionable byproducts. Their edgewise compressive strength, a measure of resistance to delamination, is highest of all resins. Although epoxy resin laminates have been limited to use at low and moderate temperatures, modifications with phenolic resins and with new catalysts, such as M-phenylene diamine, are increasing their service temperatures.

Furanes. The furane resins have found significant application in reinforced plastics, particularly in the construction of large chemical storage and processing tanks. They are reinforced with either woven glass fabrics or asbestos fibers, and may be cured at room temperatures. Furane resins also bond well to phenolics and polyesters, and may be used as protective coatings on chemical equipment made of other reinforced plastics.

Silicones. Although the initial strength of reinforced structures based on silicones is not so high as those of other reinforced plastics, they suffer much less loss in strength at elevated temperatures (500 to 600°F). This excellent resistance to high temperature, and other good properties, make them very useful for certain applications.

Reinforcing Materials

Glass Fibers. The fibrous filler may be used in the forms of cloth, mat, roving, yarn, and chopped strands (used both for conventional fabrication and in the preparation of preforms). At the present time, glass mat and glass cloth are the most commonly used. Glass mat is prepared with either of two principal types of binder present: (1) a highly soluble binder, which is used in low-temperature curing operations such as the open-mold method, and where very low pressures are involved; (2) a binder of low solubility which is generally used where higher temperatures and higher pressures are involved, such as with matched metal molds. Choice of the type will depend upon the type of fabrication.

Many types of woven glass fabrics, available from glass suppliers and weavers, are used in reinforced plastics. The types and weaves are very numerous, and the fabricator is urged to ask his supplier for complete details. For military requirements glass fabrics with special finishes ("Garan" and "Volan," for example) will protect the strength of the laminate against exposure to boiling water or highly humid atmospheres.

Another form of fabrication is the use of glass-filled polyester molding compounds, which make less difficult the molding of items having nonuniform wall thickness or irregular sections. Also they offer the convenience of obviating the necessity of handling separately the reinforcing material and the resin. Their mechanical properties tend to be slightly inferior to those of items made by conventional techniques.

Glass-Fiber Preforms. One of the newest methods of preparing preforms of reinforcing glass fibers eliminates the hand tailoring of complex shapes. Utilizing equipment similar to that used for preforming felt hats, this speedy, economical method involves assembling glass fibers on a perforated metal screen. The fibers, chopped to 2-in. lengths, are drawn to the shaped screen by vacuum. To assist the felting, a small amount of resinous binder is mixed with the fibers as they are drawn to the screen. This technique provides an economical method of preparing diverse shapes. With suitable baffles and shields, variable wall thicknesses are developed.

The finished preforms are removed from the screen and are either stored or placed into matched metal dies for molding. The resin is added to the mold. By proper predistribution of fibers, a uniformly strong article may be prepared.

Fillers. In conjunction with the usual combination of resin and glass, some fabricators may also find it to their advantage to incorporate certain inert fillers in the resin mixture prior to molding. Fillers can perform several functions, some of which are as follows:

(1) improve surface appearance of the molded item;

(2) reduce porosity;

(3) improve the wet strength of the molded item;

(4) reduce development of exothermic heat;

(5) reduce crazing and shrinkage;

(6) reduce cost (although not directly in proportion to the amount of filler used);

(7) improve moisture-stability.

Fillers should be tested for their compatibility and satisfactory behavior in conjunction with the resin. Certain fillers tend to inhibit the cure of the resin.

The fillers which can be utilized in molding of reinforced plastics are of various types. The choice depends to a great extent upon the requirements of the particular fabricator. Such fillers as calcium carbonate, mica, silica, asbestos, talc and clay have all been used with success in conjunction with polyester resins. Two important factors in the selection of a filler are pH and particle size.

Methods of the Reinforced Plastics Industry

Contact Layup. This method is best adapted to relatively small production of items of large area. In cases where only one or a very few pieces are to be made, the molds may be made of wood, plaster or reinforced plastic. Either male or female molds may be used. For more permanent molds, shaped sheet-metal forms may be utilized. Where porous materials such as wood, plaster or reinforced plastic are used, the surface should first be sealed with a lacquer-based material or any similar material which is inert to the action of the polyester resin itself. Several coats of this material may be necessary in order to seal the pores completely and prevent sticking in the mold. After the lacquer is completely dry, a parting agent is applied over the lacquer film to facilitate release of the molded piece from the mold.

The first layer of reinforcement is now laid in place. More resin is then applied to the reinforcing material, and the air is removed, by a hand roller or by dabbing with the end of a paint brush. Successive laminations are then made by applying further plies of reinforcement and saturating each with resin.

After a sufficient number of layers have been built up, the resin is allowed to cure, and the piece is then removed from the mold. Generally an afterbake or post-cure at low temperature is given. This basic process is one of the simplest of those in common practice in the industry. The ratio of resin to glass is generally high, however, and consequently the strength of the article may be lower than that obtained by other techniques where the ratio of glass to resin is higher. Objects made by the contact-molding process include boats, large tanks, and fume hoods.

The technique has both advantages and disadvantages:

advantages

(1) low cost of molds;

(2) ease of reinforcing sections subjected to high stress;

(3) unlimited size of piece to be fabricated;

(4) thorough wetting of the glass fibers.

disadvantages

(1) nonuniformity in wall thickness;

(2) finish on one side only;

(3) long cycles of cure;

(4) difficulty in removing entrapped air;

(5) fairly large proportion of waste.

In connection with this technique of contact layup, a procedure commonly known as "gel coating" is sometimes used in order to provide a permanently colored surface which will hide the pattern of the reinforcing fiber. This is done by applying to the mold, by spray or brush, a highly filled catalyzed resin which cures at low temperature. This is allowed to air cure, and then the reinforced structure is built up as above. This procedure provides a fine surface finish, but it should be used with caution, since the rather heavy surface layer may show a tendency to craze and check under exposure to weather or under severe impact or thermal shock.

Vacuum-Bag Molding. In this process, molds of the same material as those described earlier may be employed, prepared in a similar manner, and made airtight. Again, an overlay or gel coat may be used if desired. After having allowed this overlay to gel, the mat or fabric is laid in place and the resin is applied by either painting or spraying. In certain applications, it is even advantageous to use mat or fabric which has been prewet with resin before laying it in place. After the impregnated fabric has been positioned, a flexible film bag (often polyvinyl alcohol) is placed over the entire mold and is sealed around its entire edge. The bag is clamped in place and the air is drawn out through a number of ports around the outside of the molding. So-called "bleeder strips," which consist of perforated cellophane with rolled muslin on top, are placed directly on the glass fiber and plastic and under the film, to promote removal of air from the layup. These bleeder strips terminate at the vacuum ports. The air is worked out of the layup by various mechanical means. Once the air is removed, the whole assembly is rolled into an oven for cure; or in certain cases, heat is applied to the mold itself. A room-temperature catalyst system may be utilized, but presents the risk of premature cure of the resin, since the removal of air sometimes takes longer than expected.

Examples of reinforced-plastic items which have been made by this process are aircraft components, automobile-body components and initial prototypes for production operations.

The advantages of the process are:

(1) that it is faster than contact layup;

(2) that the uniformity of the product is more easily controlled;

(3) that the tooling is relatively cheap.

Its disadvantages are:

(1) that (as in contact layup) the surface is good on only one side;

(2) that it is not well suited to articles having deep draws or sharp corners;

(3) that it entails some waste;

(4) that it usually necessitates finishing.

Expanded-Bag or Rubber-Bag Method. This technique generally employs molds of cast aluminum or cast steel or molds of sheet metal (provided sufficient supporting structure is provided to resist the pressures, of the order of 50 psi). Very often a source of heat is attached to the under surface of the mold. The procedure is essentially the same as that for vacuum-bag molding except that a rubber bag is employed. A protective film, such as polyvinyl alcohol, should be laid over the reinforced plastic to protect the rubber bag from deterioration by contact with the resin. After the resin and fibrous glass have been laid up, the rubber bag is positioned over the layup and inflated. Air or steam pressure is introduced inside the bag, thus pressing it against the layup, forcing the air out of the layup, and pressing the layup firmly against the mold.

The advantage of this technique is in low cost of the mold. Its disadvantages are the same as those of vacuum-bag molding.

Items which have been fabricated by this method include helmets and helmet-liners, small reinforced-plastic cases and small radomes.

Vacuum-Injection Process. In this process molds are prepared in the same manner as those previously mentioned, except that airtight male and female molds are required, designed so that the space between the two is the wall thickness of the object to be molded. This cavity is filled with reinforcing material and this material is impregnated by resin drawn in by vacuum from a trough which surrounds the male mold. The resin has been catalyzed for cure at room temperature, and after the impregnation the entire setup is held under vacuum until cure is complete.

This process has the advantages of providing a good finish on both sides of the molded piece, and of being relatively neat and less wasteful. Its disadvantages are the low glass content attainable; the inability to ascertain the progress of impregnation, which results quite often in dry spots and nonuniform cross-sections; and the greater cost of the mold.

Typical items of reinforced plastics made by this method are boats, electrical assemblies (in which delicate equipment may be embedded) and any type of tank or vessel where leakage is a problem.

Matched-Metal Molding. This technique lends itself to volume fabrication of reinforced-plastic items. The molds are more costly than for the techniques described above, but pieces molded by this process are stronger since they will have a higher ratio of glass to resin. Pressures of from 50 to 200 psi are conventionally utilized, but higher pressures may be used. The length of time a piece must remain in the mold is governed by such factors as the temperature, the thickness and size of the piece, the resin selected, and the catalyst-promoter system involved. In general articles are produced by this technique with extremely short cycles of cure (i.e., 2 to 3 min) and consequently are much more likely to be competitive with similar items fabricated from other materials. The molds for this technique are machined metal male and female tools operated in hydraulic presses. If proper techniques are utilized and if proper molds are used, very little refinishing is necessary.

Choice of material for the mold depends on such factors as volume of production, shape of the molded article, and surface desired. Steel, "Kirksite," aluminum and "Meehanite" cast iron have been used successfully. "Kirksite" can be used only under low temperature and pressures and for short production runs. Aluminum allows the use of higher temperatures and pressures and can be utilized in longer production runs. However, molds of both "Kirksite" and aluminum tend to accumulate surface scum, and hence to require frequent cleaning if the finish is to be maintained. Steel molds are generally favored for long production runs. They can be polished to high mirror finishes, and even chrome-plated, to improve this finish and the release of the molded pieces.

Preform Molding. Preform molding is usually associated with matched-metal molding. The preparation of the preforms has been described above. This technique is the one most widely used in the industry for large-volume production of reinforced-plastic components. If tooling is properly designed, the articles may be molded so that they come from the mold trimmed, with cutouts, attach holes, etc., molded in, and requiring no finishing other than possibly a burring operation.

Assembly

It is frequently necessary to join reinforced-plastic parts. Bonds may be made by mechanical means or by adhesives, depending upon the nature of · the structure involved.

Mechanical Means. Rivets or screws may be used, with due consideration to the following:

(1) Rivets or screws of diameter greater than $\frac{3}{16}$ in. should be avoided.

(2) Rivets of the soft aluminum type are to be preferred.

(3) In areas where joints are to be made, extra strength should be provided by increasing the thickness.

(4) Rivets should be so inserted that they are not under constant stress.

For joining with bolts, the limit of $\frac{3}{16}$-in. diameter also applies. The holes should be bored accurately, since the structure does not have enough ductility to compensate for unequal loads on adjacent bolts.

Adhesives. Lap joints are successfully made with resins as adhesives. Before such joining is attempted, it is important that parting agents be removed and that the surface be sanded to expose some of the glass fibers. In general, high-viscosity polyester or epoxy resins are recommended as the adhesives.

Summary

In addition to the processes and materials described in the foregoing pages, new processes and materials appear on the horizon almost daily.

For this reason the reinforced-plastics industry is currently one of the most technically difficult industries of our time. Processes such as extrusion, injection molding and transfer molding, which have not been mentioned herein, are already in early production at this writing. Consequently the molder of reinforced plastics has all the problems peculiar to all other phases of the plastics industry as well as the ones unique to this particular phase.

It is also worthy of note that although prototype items and short production runs can be produced on rather inexpensive tooling, the reinforced plastics industry, in final analysis, is exactly like any other, in that the quality and economy of the product depends primarily on the adequacy of tooling and capital equipment. Therefore anyone engaged in or considering entry into this field should plan accordingly, if his enterprise is to progress from a manual-arts shop to full industrial stature.

7. Casting

History

About 1906 Dr. Leo H. Baekeland announced the first feasible process for the manufacture of a synthetic resin by the condensation of phenol with formaldehyde. The syrupy liquid which resulted from condensation was processed in a number of different ways to transform it into finished articles of infusible phenolic plastic. One of the processes employed was that of casting in molds made of either glass or lead. These early cast phenolic resins were, however, limited in usefulness because of limitations in size of piece, and a troublesome tendency to crack and discolor with age. It was not until 20 years later that phenolic resins of a new type were produced specifically for casting. Those improved materials were not only suitable for use in large pieces but also were found to be substantially free from cracking in service. They were also available in colors much lighter and considerably more stable than those previously available.

In about 1934 the acrylic plastics were added to the materials previously available for casting. Because of their remarkable clarity and good mechanical properties they were used almost universally for airplane enclosures during World War II. The materials of this type are readily cast as sheets, rods or tubes with excellent finish from the mold, but they are not practical for casting into complex shapes. These materials may, however, be shaped by bending or forming while hot, and when cooled will retain their new shape; thus it is possible to make a curved window from a flat sheet, or a pretzel-shaped part from a strip. During the postwar period these materials have been used very extensively in the construction of illuminated signs, store fronts, and skylights, and as corrugated glazing. These materials will "pipe" light and are available in fluorescent colors, which extend their usefulness in the construction of advertising devices.

During World War II several new types of cast plastics were added to the products of the industry. The most important of these is the unsaturated polyester, principally used as the bond in laminated structures, but also adaptable to casting. These materials were used originally, because of their superior hardness and scratch-resistance, in the formation of canopies of night fighter planes, but also have been produced since the war in highly flexible form (approaching the elastomers in texture) as well as in intermediate flexibilities. They are currently being used for potting a wide variety of electronic components required for the Defense Program, and the allyl alcohol polyesters are being used in cast lenses for range-finders, gun sights, etc.

The hot-melt compounds, which may be considered members of the family of cast plastics, came into prominence during World War II, chiefly in the form of potting compounds for electrical insulation and for use in drop-forge equipment used in the shaping of aluminum aircraft parts. The early compounds of this type were based upon either ethyl cellulose or cellulose acetate butyrate plastics, whereas some of the later compounds have been based on a polyamide-type resin.

During the postwar period several other hot-melt types have been added and are finding extensive use as potting compounds, as well as in the manufacture of coated papers and fabrics. Most of these compounds are based upon ethyl cellulose, cellulose acetate butyrate, polyethylene, butyl methacrylate, polyamide resins, or mixtures of these.

The most recent addition to the castable plastics is a series of condensation polymers of epichlorhydrin and bis-phenol. These resins, known as ethoxylene or epoxy materials, are very outstanding in their properties, their superiority being due in large measure to the fact that they do not shrink appreciably during curing. Castings containing large embedded inserts (such as electronic circuits) may be made without cracking, and several flexible epoxy compounds are now available for casting around inserts made of glass, or other delicate components such as diodes. These materials have good dielectric strength and excellent volume resistivity. They are resistant to both acids and alkalies over a wide range of concentrations, and are inert to most chemicals except the ketones and chlorinated materials.

Methods

The phenolic resins suitable for casting are syrupy in nature, whereas the acrylics are limpid liquids (but are usually thickened to a syrup, by partial polymerization, before being cast). The polyesters and epoxy materials range from liquids to semisolids.

The phenolics may be solidified in a suitable mold through the addition of a chemically active hardener or by subjecting them to carefully controlled heating for a suitable time (ranging from 2 hours to 10 days). This curing can be done in a closed vessel or autoclave under pressure or in standard baking ovens (Fig. 7-1). The latter are greatly preferred as providing the cheaper process, with less severe limitation of the size of the casting.

Some of the polyesters can be cured catalytically without the application of heat, but most of them are preferably baked in a closed mold to prevent surface softness due to the inhibiting effect of contact with air.

A few epoxy compounds require the application of some heat for curing, but most of the active materials of this type are cured by the addition of a chemical hardener. They may be cured in open molds, since air does not inhibit their cure. A release agent or protective coating on the surface of the

Fig. 7-1

Fig. 7-2

mold is sometimes necessary, depending upon the chemistry of the plastic and the material of the mold.

Commercially, the cast acrylics are available as sheets, rods, and tubes. Sheets are cast in cells comprising sheets of plate glass. Rods can be machined from sheets, or cast in molds made from untapered aluminum tubes, from which they are released by the difference of shrinkage when cooled. Tubes are cast in a rotating horizontally-mounted aluminum tube, in which the liquid monomer is gradually converted into a uniform layer of resin. (Sheets, rods, and tubes of acrylics are now made also by extrusion of molding powders.)

Molds

The mold in which a liquid casting material is formed into a solid cast shape is simply a container shaped to the contour of the piece to be formed, with due allowance for shrinkage. The choice between the various types of molds is based on the chemical makeup of the plastic and the size and contour of the article to be made. The most important types of molds are as follows:

Draw Molds. First, a tapered steel dipping arbor or mandrel is machined to the dimensions of the finished casting and attached to a funnel plate and handle. The mandrel is dipped into molten lead, which coats the steel, freezes on removal from the pot, and is stripped from the mandrel as an open lead mold (Fig. 7-2). It is obvious that no undercut can be cast by this method. Flutes, scallops, beads and other features of design may be incorporated in the castings, but they must run in the direction in which the castings are removed from the mold. Taper is necessary in order to break the vacuum and reduce friction so that the casting can be removed from the mold. A large percentage of phenolic castings are cured in molds of this type.

The molds are almost invariably damaged during the removal of the castings and are salvaged by returning them to the melting pot.

Because of the taper and because the castings are forcibly removed from the molds, the walls of the castings must have adequate thickness (Fig. 7-3). For large radio cabinets, boxes, long tubes, plates and similar items, the walls of the castings must be at least $\frac{3}{16}$ in. thick. For small tubes, small boxes and other articles which can be readily removed from the molds, a $\frac{5}{32}$-in. wall is required. In unusually small castings, such as hollow bottle closures, finger rings, etc., $\frac{1}{8}$-in. wall will suffice.

Split Molds. These are two-piece molds closed at all points except for the gate into which the liquid resin is poured. Undercuts may be incorporated into articles produced in split molds, so long as they do not prevent release from the separate parts of the mold.

In this case, die-casting machines are employed in the production of the lead molds, the machines making one half of the mold at a time, each of which interlocks with the back of the opposite half of the adjacent mold.

The successive sections are clamped together, liquid resin is poured in

Fig. 7-3

through the gates, and the material is cured in the usual manner. Walls cannot be less than $3/16$ in. thick, and articles smaller than ten to the pound cannot ordinarily be produced economically.

Cored Molds. To obtain hemispherical hollow-castings, pilasters with compound curves, and large castings with decorative faces, cored molds are used. A dipping arbor is made to the outside shape and dimensions of the finished piece. A lead mold is made on this arbor. A metal core having outside shape and dimensions representing the inside shape and dimensions of the desired cast piece is fitted against the lead mold to form a cell into which the liquid resin is poured. When the material has been cured, the core is removed and the casting drawn from the lead mold.

Although this method permits a considerable latitude in designing, it is not recommended for units smaller than 4 x 4 x 4 in. because in smaller articles the operating costs per pound are prohibitive. The cores may be used for an indefinitely large production. The molds require no taper. The walls of the castings can be of any thickness above $3/16$ in.

An important fact to remember in the treatment of phenolic resins is that walls can be made as thick as is required for strength without fear of under-curing, defective castings or distortion. Moreover, there is virtually no limit on the size of the casting; housings 20 in. square and 12 in. deep are now included in regular production. Pilasters as long as 36 in. and having a periphery of 18 in. are likewise made in regular production.

Mold shrinkage must be allowed for accurately in castings of this size if satisfactory dimensional accuracy is to be attained. In fastening cast phenolic pieces to the other materials necessary in manufacturing a finished product, oversized holes should be drilled in order to compensate for differences in shrinkage. Where extremely long pieces, such as pilasters, are involved, the castings should be fastened at either the top or the bottom, only, and should ride in grooves along the sides so that they may be free to expand and contract with changes in temperature, and to shrink with age. Fastening at both ends, and thus preventing such changes in length, will permit the development of stresses which will result in cracking.

Flexible Molds. The model to be reproduced may be of porcelain, wood, metal or other nonporous material. Upon it is built up a flexible mold, about $\frac{1}{8}$ in. thick, by application of successive coats of a latex of rubber, or of an elastomeric plastic, by dipping or brushing. The mold is cut in two along a convenient parting line and a shell of plaster of Paris is cast around it to hold it in shape. The shell is parted along the same line, and provided with dowels to align the two parts, and with an opening for the introduction of the liquid resin into the cavity of the mold. The result is a plaster mold lined with the flexible material.

After pouring and curing the resin, the two halves of the mold are separated and the flexible mold stripped from the casting. A fairly good surface is obtained, which can readily be brought to a high luster.

Most of the polyester casting resins cannot be cast in this type of mold since they have some solvent action on the flexible material, and thus adhere to it. The epoxy material may be cured in molds of this type. Figure 7-4 shows a variable-pitch helix, together with the plastisol mold in which it is cast.

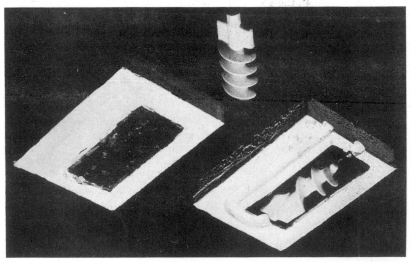

Official United States Navy Photograph

Fig. 7-4

Plaster Molds. During the period when military aircraft were undergoing frequent modifications and improvements, complete redesign of forming dies, drill jigs, stretch presses and similar machine tools was necessary. The cast phenolic resins were found suitable for making these articles. When undercuts are involved, the flexible-mold technique is used, but in most cases no undercut is required, and plain plaster-of-Paris molds are used, without the flexible lining.

To make the plaster mold, successive coatings of the plaster are spread over the master pattern until a strong usable mold is obtained. The inside surface of the mold is coated with a parting compound and the liquid phenolic resins are poured directly into the mold. The castings come from the mold with a smooth, semipolished surface and are ready for finishing to the final shape required.

Methods of Fabrication

The finishing of articles cast to shape, such as radio cabinets, brush backs and juke-box components, consists of removal of the flash, cutting of any required openings which cannot be readily formed by casting, and finally ashing and polishing of the fully shaped piece. Articles which are not cast to shape may be machined from rods, sheets, tubes and profile castings (Fig. 7-5). The cast acrylics, phenolics and epoxies can be machined quite readily, much the same as wood or metal, and with substantially the same tools and

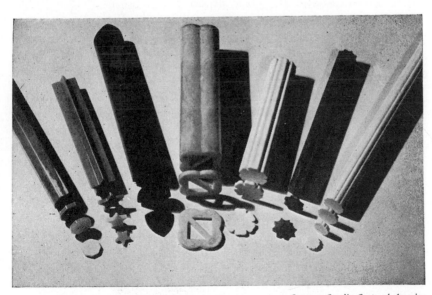

Courtesy Catalin Corp. of America

Fig. 7-5

equipment. Slicing operations may be performed with a band saw, an abrasive cutoff wheel, or specialized equipment.

The ashing of the shaped articles to remove tool marks is done with a cloth wheel and wet pumice and the final polishing is done with a dry, untreated soft buffing wheel. Many small simple pieces, such as dice and poker chips, are finished by tumbling.

During the period since World War II, "heat bending" has been developed as a means of forming the acrylics into complex shapes. A strip of material of proper size and shape is heated to 250°F in a warm-up oven and then bent and formed to the desired shape. Upon cooling, it retains the shape into which it has been formed, e.g., as a decorative piece or component of some assembly such as a dresser set or picture frame.

Another relatively recent development in fabrication is the use of "solvent welding" in the fabrication of acrylic plastics. Instead of using an adhesive or cement to join the parts of an assembly such as a jewelry box, a "welding" solvent is used. The surfaces moistened are softened sufficiently to cause immediate and tenacious adhesion between the assembled parts.

Outstanding Characteristics

All of the cast plastics have the advantage of low mold cost, which makes small runs practicable. Large pieces and thick sections are likewise practicable, since the molds are cheap and the auxiliary equipment, such as baking ovens, relatively inexpensive. Each type of cast plastic has its own outstanding property or characteristics which sets it apart from other plastics, summarized as follows:

The cast phenolics are the cheapest and most versatile of the cast materials. Being heat-setting, rather than thermoplastic, they do not soften when subjected to elevated temperatures. They are tough and resilient and have high compressive strength. If formulated for maximum chemical resistance, they are very waterproof, and resistant to all common reagents except alkalies and strong acids.

The acrylics are outstanding in their crystal clarity, permanence of color, weather-resistance and ease of fabrication.

The cast polyesters are outstanding in chemical resistance, and are obtainable over a wide range of hardness. The hardest product of this series is suitable for use in eyeglass lenses and watch crystals, whereas the most flexible is elastomeric in character. All are heat-stable, and available in a wide range of stable colors.

The various hot-melt compounds which have attained commercial importance are outstanding in toughness. The epoxies are unique in their lack of shrinkage, and excellent in chemical resistance and in volume resistivity. They are color-stable and may be dyed or pigmented to any desired color except the light pastel shades.

Typical Uses

The piece shown in Fig. 7-6 is a voltage-divider made from an epoxy casting compound chosen because of its low shrinkage around the large insert embedded in it, and because of its great resistance to dielectric breakdown. Figure 7-7 shows a high-voltage transformer, the windings of which are embedded in an epoxy casting compound. These pieces are typical of hundreds

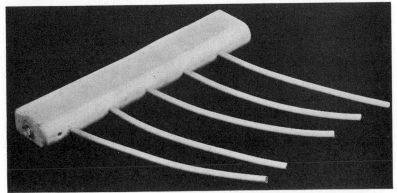

Official United States Navy Photograph

Fig. 7-6

Official United States Navy Photograph

Fig. 7-7

of electronic components which are being cast in epoxy or polyester compounds, depending upon the service requirements.

There are approximately 100 custom fabricators who supply articles machined from cast plastic rods, sheets and tubes, and there are literally thousands of different pieces produced. Buttons, buckles, bracelets, dominoes, chess men, poker chips, beads, knobs, handles and bushings are typical examples. In addition there are hundreds of different pieces fabricated from rough castings approximating the shape of the part to be made. Radio cabinets, juke boxes, pilasters, brush backs, clock cases, cutlery handles, and cigarette- and cigar-holders are representative pieces made in this way.

There is also a sizable hobby-craft market for several of the cast plastics, particularly the acrylics and phenolics. Sheets, rods and tubes are purchased by home crafters and shaped into an endless variety of products ranging from jewelry boxes to lamp bases, paperweights and carved pieces.

8. Tooling with Plastics

Introduction

In the great expansion of the aircraft industry during World War II, the need for rapidly produced and inexpensive production tools led to the investigation of plastics for these applications.

As contrasted with conventional metals, plastics offer the possibility of fabricating tools directly from master die models. With plastics the construction of shrink patterns and the subsequent time-consuming hand barbering of metal tool surfaces are eliminated. Plaster and plaster technology have helped greatly by making available economical and rapidly built molds.

In many instances plastic tools are a distinct improvement over older types constructed of wood and/or metal.

General Considerations

Tooling with plastics means the utilization of plastics in the construction of tools for the fabrication of metal, wood, glass, plastics, etc.

The forming of metals by means of plastic tools is of great interest to the aircraft, automobile, appliance and allied industries because of the high cost of metal tools. In general, plastic tooling has been limited to relatively short production runs. However, a number of cases have been reported of long runs in an initial draw die where the severity of drawing was not too great. In most of these instances the plastic die was only the initial draw die; steel dies used for the further drawing take care of inaccuracies in the initial drawing, resulting from wear of the plastic die.

The use of steel inserts and proper maintenance help to extend the life of plastic tools.

The aircraft industry, which has been the principal user of plastic forming tools, has found them practicable for producing formed components from steel and aluminum, utilizing the drop hammer, hydropress, and stretch press. While their production requirements are relatively low, the complex contours of some of the pieces made, and the difficult forming properties of some of the metals involved, have proved beyond reasonable doubt the feasibility of using plastics in this application.

The automobile companies use plastic forming tools for temporary tooling (tools quickly obtained to meet production deadlines until regular steel tools can be obtained). These tools are operated on regular production equipment, usually the double-action draw-die press. Because of high production rates and fast draw, the forming of steel imposes severe wear on the die; hence, proper lubrication of metal and die is necessary.

There are many other types of tools which may be advantageously constructed of plastics, including duplicate or permanent master die models, check fixtures, assembly fixtures, and drill jigs. These tools, when made of plastics, are more stable than when made of wood, and can be copied from the original die model without the hand shaping of tool surfaces.

Courtesy of Chrysler Automotive Body Div.

Fig. 8-1. Draw-die set, of polyester resin, and prototype rear-fender shield of 0.030-in. stainless steel.

Another application in the automotive industry and similar mass-producing industries is in prototype tools which provide an economical way to "prove" costlier steel tools (Fig. 8-1).

The allied industries are alert to the possibilities of cheaper forming tools and are having notable success in adapting plastics to their own fields.

When plastics are to be used for tooling, it is necessary to consider, in every individual case, the nature of the plastics, and the function and design of the tool.

The construction of plastic tools is restricted, for reasons of economy, to methods of duplication which do not require high pressures, i.e., casting, laminating, and molding under very low pressure.

Because the resins used for tooling are relatively new and diversified, charts of physical properties are not included in this chapter. However, a description of the various types of tools and their basic material requirements will be given, followed by a discussion of the materials and processes available today for production of plastic tools.

Tools Made from Plastics

It is not practicable to formulate strict rules or instructions for the construction of tools from plastics, because the techniques are still in an early stage of development, and because each tool requires individual consideration in design. A brief description of various types of tools which may be made from plastics, together with basic property requirements, is given for the purpose of illustration.

Courtesy of Grumman Aircraft

Fig. 8-2. A plastic stretch die for forming aircraft part. Resin: Rezolin, Inc.

Stretch Dies (Fig. 8-2). These are male-sectioned dies over which sheet metal is formed by gripping it on its edges and pulling or stretching it until the shape of the die is reproduced in the metal sheet. Prime requirements for plastics used in this application are accuracy of duplication and compressive and cohesive strength.

Hydropress Dies. The term "hydropress forming" has been applied to a technique in which a thick rubber pad is substituted for one component of the die. A male die, or a shallow female die, is held upon a fixed base,

Courtesy of Chrysler Automotive Body Div.

Fig. 8-3. Polyester die, and aircraft part formed by hydropress method.

and sheet metal is shaped against this die by hydraulic pressure from above, transmitted through the rubber pad (Fig. 8-3). Plastics used in dies for this process must meet the requirements just mentioned for stretch dies.

Courtesy of Warren Plastics and Engineering, Inc.

Fig. 8-4. Phenolic draw die, showing weldment and cast-iron draw ring.

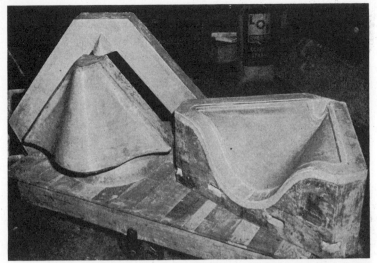

Courtesy of Chrysler Automotive Body Div.

Fig. 8-5. Draw-die set of polyester resin for an aircraft part, showing cavity, punch and ring.

Draw Dies (Figs. 8-4, 8-5 and 8-6). These tools are used to form sheet metal into contoured shapes. They are run in double- or triple-action presses, by conventional draw-die techniques.

Plastics used for such applications must have compressive and cohesive strength in addition to good resistance to wear, and accuracy of duplication.

Drop-Hammer Dies. These dies are used in a drop-hammer press to cold-forge sheet metal into the required shape. The base holds the lower part of the die (cavity). The upper part (punch) is dropped or rammed into the cavity. Several different combinations of metal and plastics have been successfully used for this operation. Hot-melt cellulosic formulations are taking the place of the much heavier cast lead and other metals. These cellulosic hot-melt materials are thermoplastic; dimensional accuracy of the plastic die is created by striking the plug in the cavity.

Hammer Forms (Fig. 8-7). Hammer forms are shapes over which sheet-metal parts are formed and fitted by hand. Impact, compressive and cohesive strength are the most important requirements for this application.

Die Models and Checking Fixtures (Fig. 8-8). Die models and checking fixtures are master shapes used to control dimensions of tools and assembled parts produced in these tools. The primary requirements for this application are ease and accuracy of duplication, and dimensional stability.

Mockups. Mockups are models of a proposed construction and are

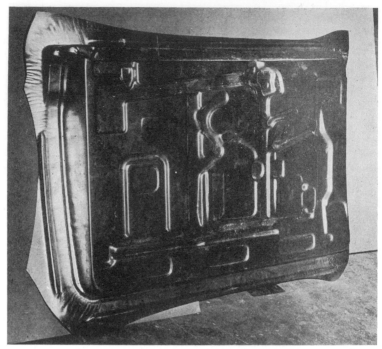

Courtesy of Chrysler Automotive Body Div.

Fig. 8-6. Interior steel door panel, formed in a polyester draw die.

generally nonfunctional, i.e., they are produced mainly for approval of appearance or for engineering study. Ease of duplication and structural stability are required. High dimensional accuracy is desirable, but may often be sacrificed in favor of general ease of working the finished plastics.

Assembly Fixtures (Fig. 8-9). These structures serve for clamping various machined or formed metal parts for final assembly. For accurate assembly, structural rigidity and dimensional accuracy are required. The former is provided by a basic structure of metal; the latter by contoured locating pads of plastics, formed against master models. For this use, the plastic must provide accuracy of duplication, stability of dimensions, and abrasion-resistance.

Holding and Locating Pads. These pads serve to hold partially formed steel parts for additional operations such as piercing and flanging. The pads are not subjected to heavy working loads, and plastics are adequate for this use. Accuracy of duplication is the main requirement.

Drill Jigs, Trim and Routing Fixtures (Fig. 8-10). These tools demand, as a rule, light rigid structures which must accurately support drill

Courtesy of Chrysler Automotive Body Div.

Fig. 8-7. Hammer form, of polyester resin, for flanging an aluminum aircraft part.

Courtesy of Ren-ite Plastics, Inc.

Fig. 8-8. Die model for left front fender, constructed of laminated epoxy resin. Resin: Ren-ite Plastics, Inc.

Courtesy of Ren-ite Plastics, Inc.

Fig. 8-9. Hood-assembly fixture comprising a cast-iron base faced with laminated epoxy resin. Resin: Ren-ite Plastics, Inc.

bushings and trim edges. Metals are generally required for the basic structure, although reinforced laminates are satisfactory, provided they are cor-

Courtesy of Chrysler Automotive Body Div.

Fig. 8-10. Routing fixture of laminated plastic, for an aircraft part.

Courtesy of Plastic Tool Company of America

Fig. 8-11. Foundry master pattern, and match plates made of cast phenolic resin (cope half). Resin: Rezolin, Inc.

rectly designed. Accuracy of duplication and high structural strength are required of plastics for this application.

Foundry Patterns (Fig. 8-11). Foundry patterns are used to make cavities and cores of foundry sand into which metals are cast. Accuracy of duplication and abrasion-resistance are the main requirements.

Miscellaneous. There are many other applications for plastics in tooling, such as dies for vacuum-forming plastics; low-temperature bag molds; layup molds for laminating polyesters; forming jigs, etc. These tools, of specialized nature, are not described here.

Resins for Tooling

The following materials are currently used in the construction of plastic tools. Other new types and formulations are in the process of development.

Phenolic Resins. Today's phenolic casting resins are chemically engineered to overcome their natural shrinkage on curing. Their relative accuracy of duplication and ease of casting, in conjunction with fair to good abrasion-resistance and compressive strength, account for their popularity. The corrosive action of acids used as curing catalysts must be taken into account.

Polyester Resins. Polyester resins with proper reinforcements, predominantly glass fibers, are finding increasing use. Laminated, mat-reinforced or random fiber-filled, these structures have great strength and tough-

ness, especially in thinner sections. Their resistance to wear and erosion adds
to their growing use.

Epoxy Resins. The epoxy resins are entering the tooling field as new and
promising materials. They are 100 per cent reactive and possess favorable
shrinkage characteristics. Their inherent adhesiveness toward glass fibers is
excellent. The exothermic heat developed in curing epoxy resins is apt to
constitute a handicap at times.

Ethyl Cellulose. Hot-melt compounds of ethyl cellulose have become
available in several formulations as another tooling material. Tools may be
produced by pouring of the melted material from special equipment. Worn
or damaged tools of these materials can be reclaimed by remelting and re-
casting, with corresponding saving in cost.

Methods for Producing Plastic Tools

Casting. *Cold Pouring.* Phenolics, polyesters and epoxy resins are
handled by this technique, commonly referred to as casting. These materials
should be handled in strict accordance with the manufacturers' recommendations, as to storage, measuring, mixing (fillers, types and amounts of catalyst),
containers, pouring, curing and aging. When these resins are brought out of
cold storage, sufficient time should be allowed for them to reach room temperature, and correspondingly lower viscosity, before measuring and mixing
them.

The final resin mix as well as the mold are "cold," or at approximately
room temperature, at the time of pouring. The cure is initiated by the action
of the catalyst upon the resin, which causes an exothermic reaction. Further
cure is then achieved by placing the mold in a recirculating hot-air oven.
The details of the technique of cure should be as recommended by the manufacturer of the material.

Cast tools properly prepared are relatively dimensionally stable, and
preferable to many other materials because of their lower sensitivity to
changes in humidity and temperature. Further improvements in materials
and techniques may be expected from the manufacturers of these materials.

Hot Pouring. A method applicable predominantly to some epoxy resin
formulations is hot pouring. The material is softened by heating, poured hot,
and cured by baking at elevated temperatures. Such a process will obviously
introduce some thermal distortion of the mold. It must be ascertained whether
this distortion, as reflected in the dimensions of the finished piece, will allow
the latter to meet required tolerances.

Hot Melt. Some cellulosic formulations are cast from hot melts, which
harden on cooling. There is no chemical reaction or cure with its accompanying shrinkage. Dimensional accuracy is attained by striking the plug in the
cavity.

Laminating. *Contact Lay-Up.* The materials used for tooling by this process are glass-fiber-reinforced polyester and epoxy compounds. Woven glass-fiber cloth is generally used in preference to mat. The parts are laid up in molds at room temperature and allowed to cure without pressure. Heat for curing is generated by the exothermic reaction of the catalyzed resin. A postcure is frequently necessary.

Low-Pressure Laminating. Higher percentages of glass fibers can be incorporated if the cure is carried out under pressure. For this purpose the so-called vacuum-bag technique is used extensively. The entire lay-up, consisting of the mold and the uncured laminate, is slipped into a bag of flexible sheet material (e.g., polyethylene, polyvinyl butyral or polyvinyl alcohol). A vacuum is then applied within the bag. Wrinkling and entrapment of air must be avoided.

Molding under Low Pressures. Mixtures of roving or chopped strands of glass fiber with polyester resins can be molded economically in molds of wood or plaster with simple reinforcements. Molding pressure must be chosen correspondingly and, as a rule, will be kept well below 100 psi. Pneumatic or hydraulic presses with follow-up are used. The exothermic reaction furnishes heat for curing in most cases.

9. Embedding

Introduction

In this chapter will be described briefly some techniques used for embedding of solid objects in blocks of plastic.

Procedures not within the scope of this chapter include the conventional embedment of inserts in the molding of electrical and mechanical components, the processes of lamination of cloth, paper, etc., with plastics, and the coating of objects with plastic.

For purposes of preservation, display, and study, objects are embedded in transparent plastic, through which they can be clearly seen. For electrical and other industrial purposes, the plastic used is frequently opaque.

Attempts to embed objects were first made with phenolic casting resins, but did not reach commercial success because of the discoloration and cracking of the resins then available. Later, a European firm offered a syrup of partially polymerized urea-formaldehyde resin for this purpose, and this likewise failed to gain commercial use, because the blocks of resin made from it frequently broke spontaneously into pieces as they aged.

Probably the first material successfully used for the purpose was methyl methacrylate resin, and perhaps the first public recognition of the utility of embedment came with a display of horticultural and entomological specimens embedded by the United States Department of Agriculture for purposes of preservation, display and instruction.

The techniques of using methacrylate monomers for embedment were further developed by the Department of Agriculture, and subsequently by commercial firms.

At a later date, other resin-forming monomers came into use.

Methods of Embedding

All of the preceding techniques depended upon the pouring of a liquid around the specimen, and the subsequent solidification of the liquid. This technique has been extended to other materials, and also other techniques have been developed, so that procedures now available include:

(1) The casting and polymerizing of polymerizable liquids:
    (a) methacrylate monomers, particularly methyl methacrylate
    (b) polyester resin monomers
    (c) epoxy resin liquids

    (2) Pouring of resins in molten condition, followed by solidification

    (3) Embedment in mixture of acrylic monomer and polymer, followed by polymerization

    (4) Compression molding of polymer, particularly methyl methacrylate polymer.

Procedure 1(a), when applicable, gives the most attractive results, but is the most troublesome and expensive.

Embedment by procedure 1(b) is easier because the reaction of polymerization can be conducted at lower temperature and proceeds more rapidly. But the appearance of the resulting block is not equal to that of a block of methyl methacrylate.

Method (2) is simple and rapid, but restricted obviously to embedment of specimens which will tolerate the temperature of the molten resin. And the viscous nature of the molten resin may cause some difficulty with the entrapment of air bubbles.

Method (4), developed primarily for commercial embedment of metallic specimens, has been refined and improved to such a point that it is now applied to the embedment of delicate and relatively fragile objects such as fishing flies. The appearance of the block made by this method is in general very slightly inferior to that of a block made directly from monomer by method 1(a), since molding powder does not have the perfect transparency of cast polymer.

Materials Suitable for Embedment

In general, metallic objects can be embedded without difficulty, unless a complicated shape results in entrapment of air. But objects containing copper (and perhaps some other metals, similarly) tend to inhibit polymerization of methyl methacrylate.

Likewise other inorganic materials—rocks, minerals, and the like—cause little trouble.

Organic materials, and particularly biological specimens, are likely to offer difficulties. Frequently they are too fragile, or too heat-sensitive to be handled by any but the process of casting in a polymerizable liquid, and even in that process they may not be manageable.

In processes involving polymerization, it is customary to use a catalyst to promote the polymerization, but the catalyst, being a peroxide, may cause bleaching of a colored organic specimen. If, on the other hand, catalyst is omitted, the progress of polymerization is slower, and it may be impeded by inhibiting substances leached out of the specimen.

Another difficulty with some specimens of organic nature, e.g., botanical specimens, is the solubility of natural coloring ingredients of the specimen in the monomer, which may cause the whole block to be tinted.

But more important problems arise from mechanical fragility, from sensitivity to heat, and from moisture content.

In processes involving polymerization of methyl methacrylate, the conversion from monomer to polymer involves a volumetric shrinkage of about 20 per cent, and this may cause distortion or destruction of a delicate specimen. In processes involving pouring a viscous liquid, also, the specimen may be broken or distorted. In embedment by molding, the pressure tends to crush compressible objects such as fur and cotton.

The restriction upon temperature will be obvious with some objects. From this standpoint, process 1 (b) may be the best choice, since it offers some media which can be hardened at moderate temperatures. Process 1 (a) is applicable at moderate temperatures, but only at great sacrifice of speed of hardening.

Porous objects, whether inorganic or organic, require precautions to rid them of air, since the air contained in them tends to escape during the embedment, and to mar the block of resin. Application of vacuum to a closed vessel, after submersion of the piece in monomer or thickened monomer, may serve to draw the air out of the specimen.

Another difficulty arises with porous thin objects, such as paper and the petals of flowers, which owe their normal appearance of opacity to the considerable difference in refractive index between the cellulose of their structure and the air or water within their pores. When this air or water is displaced by resin, which has a much higher refractive index, their opacity is greatly impaired; a piece of white paper, or a white sweet-pea, embedded in methyl methacrylate resin becomes almost invisible. This difficulty is largely overcome in embedment by molding.

Another prime difficulty is the adverse effect of moisture or gross water content of the specimen, which will cause the block of resin to be cloudy. To avoid this, various means may be used for dehydrating the specimen, but they are troublesome and not always effective.

The possibility of these various difficulties with organic specimens makes it impossible to lay down any general rules which will be applicable, without skepticism and actual trial, to any specific material or object.

Dehydration. With materials which will tolerate being washed, rinsed and dried in an oven (perhaps up to an hour or more at 90°C), there is no problem.

The difficulty arises with organic materials which contain water and which will not tolerate drying by heat—which become brittle or discolored before the moisture can be removed.

Some objects in this category will tolerate the classical method of dehydration involving submersion to equilibrium in successive baths of increasing strength of ethyl alcohol, from 35 per cent or less up to absolute, or the simpler method of dipping into absolute alcohol and drying in a vacuum desiccator. But others will not: many botanical specimens will be hopelessly embrittled by the alcohol treatment; a white gardenia will turn brown in 30 per cent alcohol; and some specimens will have their color extracted by the alcohol.

Some biological and surgical specimens are amenable to a process of dehydration of more recent origin, involving first a freezing and then a sublimation of the ice in vacuo.

Details of such processes are to be found in biological and medical literature. and in publications of suppliers of embedding materials.

Resins Used for Embedding

Cast Acrylic Monomer. The monomer used is usually methyl methacrylate, which yields a rigid resin, but other members of the acrylic group are sometimes used, alone or in admixture with methyl methacrylate, to yield less rigid castings (such as may be required for sectioning).

The monomer is a colorless limpid liquid. It is shipped in stabilized or inhibited condition, to prevent polymerization in transit and storage. Before it is used, the inhibitor (usually hydroquinone) must be removed by extraction, or by distillation of the monomer, according to instructions available from its manufacturer.

To promote polymerization, a catalyst is added. Usually this is benzoyl peroxide, which is normally supplied in combination with inert substances to reduce its hazard. The amount added is usually 0.05 to 0.2 per cent of benzoyl peroxide content.

To shorten the procedure, and to reduce somewhat the shrinkage of polymerization (which in addition to distorting a fragile specimen may tend to cause the casting to shrink away from the containing vessel), it is customary to use a partially polymerized monomer. This is syrupy rather than mobile, and the degree of partial polymerization must be carefully restricted so that the syrup will not be so viscous as to cause trouble with entrapment of air.

To prepare the syrup, the uninhibited catalyzed monomer, in a container fitted with a loosely fitting cover (or, better, with a tight cover carrying a reflux condenser), is heated by hot water or steam, until the desired thickening is effected. This may require a few minutes, or an hour or more. Preferably the container is of glass, so that any boiling of the monomer can be seen, and checked by cooling, lest the exothermic reaction of polymerization go out of control. The partially polymerized syrup is then chilled, and stored in a closed container at about 40°F.

The mold or container may be a glass jar for each item embedded; the container is then broken after the embedment is completed. But in commercial production the mold may take the form of a permanent trough, in which successive items are set in position, to be separated, upon completion of the embedment, by sawing of the resulting strip of resin. If the mold is porous, it must be coated with a mold-release agent which is not soluble in the monomer.

For the actual embedment, the first step is the production, in the mold or container, of a base layer. Various heights can be achieved either by many additional layers or by using as the foundation, instead, a block of cast resin, which will fuse with the monomer.

The amount of syrup poured must allow for a volumetric shrinkage of about 20 per cent; since polymerization usually develops from the bottom up, this shrinkage takes place in the vertical dimension only. The pouring should be carefully done, to minimize entrapment of air, and any bubbles which do not spontaneously rise should be worked out. Then the container is warmed, preferably in a water bath at about 113°F for 40 to 50 hr.

Now, syrup is poured on the foundation layer and the object to be embedded is carefully placed in position. Great care must be exercised throughout, and especially at this point, to avoid dust and dirt. Air conditioning for quantity production is advised. Exposure of this tacky layer to a dusty atmosphere, especially during loading of complex embedments, results in a dirty layer, commercially unacceptable.

The softening effect of the syrup on the base helps to anchor the object. This layer of syrup is polymerized, as above, and successive further layers if required.

If the object floats in syrup, the first layer poured with the object on the base must be thin enough not to lift it out of contact with the base.

The depth of a layer of syrup must usually not exceed 0.5 in. in order to permit escape of the heat of polymerization which, in too thick a layer, will build up and cause bubbling. The limit on thickness will be greater, the lower the temperature of the heating bath and the lower the percentage of catalyst.

When the whole block has been built up to the desired thickness, and approximately fully polymerized, a heat treatment of several hours at about 212°F may be desirable, to ensure completion of polymerization and thereby to stabilize the dimensions. This can be done, however, only if the embedded object will not be damaged by such a temperature.

The block is now cooled very gradually to room temperature, and tapped or shaken out of the mold, or eased out with a scalpel. Removal from the mold may be facilitated by coating the mold with a lubricant insoluble in the syrup.

The block is now shaped on a lathe or milling machine to desired dimensions, and polished by the usual procedure of buffing.

The casting shown in Fig. 9-1, for displaying the components of a modern desk-type dial telephone, was made by the foregoing procedure. Other applications have included embedments of surgical exhibits (e.g., a series of sections of a skull), and of botanical and entomological specimens.

As indicated above, the prime limitation on rate of production by this procedure is the necessity of restricting either the operating temperature or the thickness of layer polymerized at one time (or both), in order to avoid overheating and bubbling.

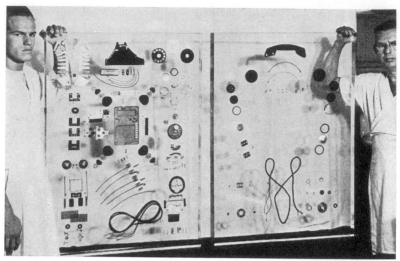

Courtesy of Vernon Benshoff Co.

Fig. 9-1

For some purposes, it is feasible to reduce this restriction by conducting the polymerization under pressures above atmospheric, which will restrain the bubbling. This, however, involves the use of an autoclave and a more complicated setup, and has been relatively little used.

On the other hand, temperatures lower than those suggested above may be required for some heat-sensitive specimens.

Any process of casting acrylic resins requires close chemical control, to steer between ruinously slow operation and loss of yields through bubbling.

Cast Polyesters. Polyester liquids offer the advantages of tolerating some moisture in the objects embedded and of requiring less close control of the polymerization, but the resulting resins lack the full transparency of cast acrylics, and tend to discolor with age.

Various polyester resin monomers are obtainable, with specific instructions for use.

Catalysts are usually added, to hasten polymerization, and temperatures for curing range from about 65 to about 140°F. The time required to polymerize ranges from an hour up to several days. The general precautions against overheating described for acrylics apply to polyesters, but less strictly.

Molds are conveniently of glass or polished aluminum, from which the blocks of resin are easily tapped out. Molds of some other materials may require coating with a release agent. To make blocks with undercuts, flexible molds may be used.

The general procedure is as described above for acrylic syrup, including care to avoid entrapment of air, and very slow cooling of the block. If the surface of the block exposed to air fails to harden fully, it may be machined off, or may be given a coating of catalyzed monomer which is covered with a piece of glass until it polymerizes to give a hard finished surface.

For embedment in polyesters, biological specimens may be dehydrated as described above, but can frequently be used without dehydration. One procedure involves (1) dipping in absolute alcohol, (2) drying in a vacuum desiccator, (3) coating with uncatalyzed polyester, (4) coating with catalyzed uninhibited polyester, (5) embedding.

The preservation and display of biological specimens by embedment in polyesters has been found useful in studies in biology, medicine, etc. As an extension of this procedure, casts of circulatory and respiratory systems are made by injection of vinyl resin, appropriately colored; the casts are then freed of tissue by digestion with alkali; and they are then embedded in polyester.

An industrial use of embedment in polyester resin is the "potting" of electrical coils, tubes, etc., to protect them from mechanical damage, and in some cases to provide electrical insulation.

The resin may be of rigid, semirigid or flexible type. The components are heated for about 4 hr at 250°F under a 20-mm vacuum, and cooled in a desiccator. They are then positioned in molds coated with mold-release greases, and components and molds are heated to about 100°F. Then polyester liquid with a suitable amount of catalyst (e.g., 1.0 per cent of benzoyl peroxide) is poured into the molds. They are held in a vacuum of 30 mm for 20 to 60 min, according to size, to draw out all air and thus effect complete impregnation. The polyester is then polymerized by heat (2 to 3 hr at 240°F is usual, but large sections should be started at somewhat lower temperatures, e.g., 200°F for 1 to 2 hr, and then finished by a final cure of 2 to 3 hr at 250°F.)

The choice and dosage of catalyst must be made to avoid too-rapid polymerization, with excesses of temperature resulting from the exothermicity of the reaction of polymerization. For some applications, a more moderate catalyst is recommended, such as tertiary butyl hydroperoxide (0.5 per cent for thin sections, 0.1 per cent for thick sections).

Epoxy Resins. These resins are available in both liquid and solid forms. They are hardened, after pouring, by action of a catalyst. They are used for embedding resistors and other electrical circuits, which thus become hermetically sealed in solid blocks of resin.

The liquid type is mixed with catalyst and then poured and cured in 3 to 6 hr, at room temperature. It is particularly useful for embedding objects which will not tolerate heat. The solid type is liquefied by heat and then poured. It is cured in 4 to 8 hr at 250°F. Both types are stated to contain no volatiles, and to shrink very little during the cure. Care must be taken, of course, to entrap no air bubbles, and to fill the mold completely.

With these resins, embedments of predetermined shape can be made in disposable molds injection-molded of nylon.

Monomer-Polymer Techniques

Instead of mobile monomer or syrupy partially polymerized monomer, use can be made of mixtures of acrylic polymer (tiny spherical beads) and monomer. Such a mixture may take the form of a slurry, used before the solvent action of the monomer gels the polymer, but more usually used is the doughy mass resulting from more or less thorough kneading as the solvent action takes effect.

Strips of this dough are used to support and cover the object to be embedded, and then the assembly is pressed or coined to the desired shape, and the dough is converted to hard resin by heat. This process, like those utilizing acrylic syrup, involves shrinkage and the need for precautions against heat of reaction, but to a smaller degree because a larger proportion of the mass has already been polymerized before the start of the process. The resulting resin is slightly inferior in transparency. Dough molding is especially susceptible to dust.

Embedment by Molding

This involves the use of polymer powder, and no liquid. The polymer is supplied in the form of tiny beads, smaller than granulated sugar, and ready for use.

The molds are generally positive compression molds of floating-core or landed type, with clearances of 0.003 to 0.005 in. to prevent jamming of the force by polymer adhering to the walls. This clearance of course results in flash; flash would be avoided by a technique of transfer molding, but that has not been perfected for this application. The molds are usually of standard steel or beryllium-copper, preferably chromium-plated after being polished.

The powder is loaded by hand with a scoop, with care to remove any visible contamination by means of tweezers. First a layer is placed and levelled to serve as support for the object to be embedded. A simple locating jig can be used to make a cavity in the top of the layer of powder, to hold the object. The jig is guided down by the sides of the mold, and its penetration into the mold is controlled either by stops which strike the upper surface of the mold or by fingers which pass through the powder and strike the floor of the cavity; these fingers should be slender (generally about 0.063 to 0.125 in. in diameter) so that they will displace little powder and so that the powder will flow back into the holes which they leave when withdrawn.

After the object has been thus properly positioned on the first layer of powder, a final layer is poured into the mold, with care not to displace the object. Then the mass is molded by compression technique.

The compression ratio of these powders ranges from about 1.5:1 to 1.8:1, and allowance of no less than this should be made in designing the mold and in calculating the depths of the layers of powder. Generally a cavity for a block 3 × 3 × 1 in. can be loaded, the specimen included, and the force closed over it, in a matter of a minute or so. This speed, together with the fact that there is no tacky exposed layer, has the advantage of keeping out dust and the appearance of layers common to embedments made in monomer.

Where the real art in embedment in acrylic monomer castings is in controlling the polymerization and directing the shrinkage to where it will do the least harm, the corresponding art of embedment by molding is in the closely controlled administration of heat and pressure to the mold, avoiding movement and crushing of the object embedded. Conventional calculations of pressure to area of piece are used, with modification according to the type of embedment. Pressures may be as little as 200 psi, for straight positive moldings of about 1 sq in., to as much as 500 psi or more for moldings of good size or with compound contours requiring filling. Extremely close control of temperature is required, ranging from just under 300°F for softer materials up to 500°F for harder types.

The molded piece must be adequately cooled in the mold, and this should be done in the press; efforts to save press time by cooling the mold in a clamp result in failure, because of the lack of followup of pressure as the system shrinks.

For economy in equipment and operation, the molded piece should be removed from the mold as soon as possible, but pieces removed too hot, with surface temperatures above 250°F, are subject to gassing from release of internal pressure. On the other hand, too much chilling in the mold not only prolongs the cycle unduly but yields pieces which are subject to crazing by internal strains. Annealing, after molding, at about 145°F is helpful, but close attention to molding temperatures and pressures is of greater importance.

Because of the problems of avoiding displacement of embedded objects by flow of the powder, multiple-cavity molds are seldom used. However, as many as 20 cavities have been made for small cuff-link and tie bar jewels in which fishing flies and other small objects are embedded. The largest mold thus far used produces a block 8 × 4 × 4 in. in which an entire bottle, cap, and label are embedded. In sizes such as this latter it is far more practical to cast, but the compelling factor in this case was to show the label, without the "wet" appearance which the casting process would have given the paper label.

If the powder used is properly clean, this process yields clean blocks of resin, for the rapidity with which the mold can be filled and closed minimizes exposure to contamination. There is no exothermic reaction, no gross shrinkage to distort dimensions, and comparatively little sinking. Pieces of complex shape can be produced directly, without subsequent machining.

The process has certain limitations. While it is possible to make large blocks, the long time required to heat through thick masses makes the process uneconomical of press time. Thus, embedment by molding is generally used for large quantity production of sizes up to one pound. The process is not

Courtesy of Creative Plastics Corp.

Fig. 9-2

applicable to embedding materials which will be crushed by pressure, e.g., fur or cotton. And the transparency of a block molded from powder does not quite equal that of a cast block when sections are about 1 in. thick or more; in thinner sections, the difference cannot be distinguished.

Extensive use of compound radii (see Fig. 9-2) tends to magnify embedment and to bring out internal "lighting" of acrylic, making the embedment almost seem illuminated.

As in other processes of embedment, moisture, grease or oil will cause unsightly clouding or "halos."

The process is applicable to the embedment not only of nonfragile materials such as metal but also of brittle materials such as glass, as in the pocket level shown in Fig. 9-2. In this article a glass level vial is embedded in acrylic resin. To make larger sizes of levels comparable embedded vial inserts are in turn mounted in an injection-molded housing of heat-resistant, high-impact polystyrene.

10. Vinyl Dispersions

Historical

The ordinary methods of utilizing high-polymer resins require either a solution of the resin in large quantities of relatively expensive solvents or the use of expensive, heavy-duty equipment to manipulate the resin in a molten state. Dispersions are the outgrowth of many years of search to circumvent these limitations. In the first practical technique it was discovered that resins of high molecular weight and high vinyl chloride content could be ground in organic media to form stable dispersions provided the suspending phase contained enough polar liquids to have some solvating action on the resin, but not enough actually to dissolve it. A technique for utilizing this in cloth-coating was introduced in this country in 1943, on the basis of work done by the Union Carbide and Carbon Corporation fellowship at Mellon Institute. In the meantime, an emulsion-polymerized resin especially suited for the dispersion technique was developed. With the commercial introduction of this resin by Carbide & Carbon Chemicals Co. in 1944, vinyl dispersions entered a period of rapid growth. Their significance was recognized by the plastics industry with the award of the John Wesley Hyatt Medal in 1950 to Mr. G. M. Powell for their development.

Notable progress in the field of vinyl dispersions occurred in 1947 with the commercial introduction, by the B. F. Goodrich Chemical Company, of a plastisol-type resin permitting the preparation of dispersions containing no volatile ingredient by a simple stir-in technique. With the use of such plastisol resins, practical ratios of resin to plasticizer common in other methods of processing vinyls are possible in nonvolatile systems.

Dispersions of the paste type were developed somewhat earlier and independently in both Germany and England.

The advantage in cost in favor of dispersion coatings has permitted them virtually to supplant the solution-coating of cloth and to compete with calendering in the lower-gauge coatings. The technique is widely used for the preparation of coated paper and film, especially of the highly decorated lightweight variety. Molded and dipped articles prepared from dispersions compete with conventional high-pressure-molded products, as a consequence of lower equipment costs.

Definitions

Vinyl dispersions are suspensions of resin in nonaqueous liquids which do not dissolve the resin at ordinary temperatures. If the liquid phase consists only of plasticizer, the dispersion is termed a *plastisol* or, less frequently, *paste,* following the German terminology; if the dispersing liquid contains volatile components, the dispersion is termed an *organosol.* Plastisols may be converted to organosols by thinning with volatile liquids.

Resins Used

The resins used for dispersions are polymers of vinyl chloride, or copolymers in which vinyl chloride is the predominant constituent. These are prepared by emulsion polymerization to attain the small particle size and spherical shape most desirable for good flow properties. The commercial resins range in particle size from 0.02 to 2 microns in diameter (Figs. 10-1 and 10-2). The smaller sizes are preferred in organosols because they exhibit less tendency

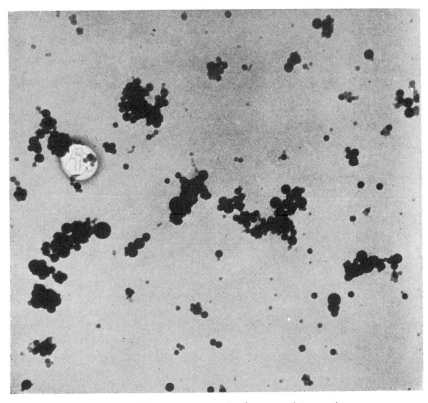

Fig. 10-1. Electron micrograph of organosol-type resin.

to settle, whereas the larger particles are favored for plastisols in that greater fluidity and better viscosity-stability are obtained with equivalent proportions of plasticizer.

Resins for organosols are most conveniently furnished as agglomerates of the individual particles. These require milling to form smooth dispersions. Plastisol resins capable of dispersion by stirring only are available at a slight premium in price.

Preparation of Dispersions

Since organosols contain volatile ingredients, they are usually prepared in closed equipment such as pebble and ball mills. Plastisols are generally prepared in paste-mixers and are sometimes refined by passage through a roller mill. Pigments, fillers, stabilizers and lubricants, if needed, may be dispersed along with the resin, or they may be added at a later stage, usually as a dispersion in the plasticizer.

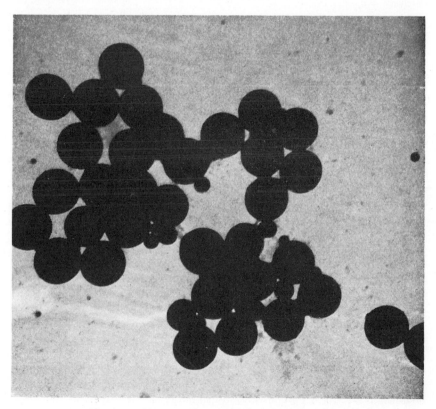

Fig. 10-2. Electron micrograph of plastisol-type resin.

Methods of Use

Organosols are applied by spreader or roller coaters, by dipping or by spraying. The release of solvent is rapid, and heavy coatings can be applied with little danger of blistering. To convert the organosol to a usable film, the volatiles are evaporated and the resin particles are fused together by heat. Preferably these two steps are combined, because the increased solubility of the resin in the hot liquids aids in the fusion. A temperature of 300 to 350°F is required to produce a film of maximum strength. A long bake at lower temperatures cannot be substituted for the required temperature.

Organosols are used for coating cloth, paper, wire and many other surfaces. They are used to prepare dipped articles and unsupported films.

Plastisols are dispersions in which the plasticizer is the sole dispersing medium, and fluid coatings can be made which have no volatile ingredients. A plastisol is converted to a tough, rubbery film by heating to 300 to 350°F. Plastisols are used in much the same way as organosols for knife coating and dip coating. They are also used for low-pressure molding of elastomeric articles.

Formulation

Organosols and plastisols are easy to make, but optimum results are obtained only with definite and often narrow ranges of composition. The formulation must be studied carefully, because the viscosity and stability depend upon careful control of the wetting and swelling of the resin.

Organosols. The liquid components of organosols are classified into two types, dispersants and diluents. Dispersants are polar compounds which form strong attachments to the resin, aiding in wetting and dispersing it. Plasticizers and volatile components such as esters, ketones, glycol ethers, etc., are typical dispersants. Diluents are usually aromatic or aliphatic hydrocarbons. They are used to balance and modify the wetting and swelling characteristics of the dispersants and to lower the cost and the viscosity of the liquid medium. Some diluents, such as the aromatic hydrocarbons, swell the dispersed resin particles. This aids the fusion of the resin and is especially desirable in organosols of low plasticizer content. On the other hand, swelling of the resin raises the viscosity of the dispersion, and thus restricts the solids content which can be used without exceeding practical limits of viscosity. A blend of aromatic and aliphatic diluents is often preferable.

The preferred composition of the liquid phase of an organosol is determined by a study of viscosity as a function of composition. Various pebble-mill grinds are made, in which the ratio of dispersant to diluent is systematically varied, and the viscosity of each of these grinds is measured. The viscosity will pass through a minimum as the ratio of dispersant to diluent is changed, as shown in Fig. 10-3. Formulations just slightly richer in dispersant than those corresponding to the minimum viscosity are the most economical and most satisfactory for general use. Formulations containing less dispersant tend to agglomerate, and to exhibit false body, and then are less stable on aging. On the other hand, formulations with excess dispersant are subject to more swelling of the resin, and their viscosities may increase slowly on storage.

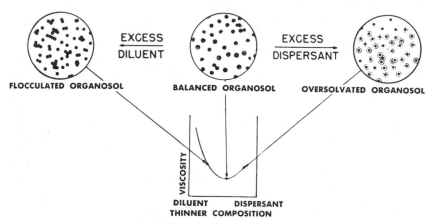

Fig. 10-3. Effect of thinner balance on organosols.

Organosols are quite complex colloidal systems. As such, they cannot be duplicated with the same facility as can true solutions. They differ from solutions in that the resin is dispersed as individual particles in the suspending liquid, and not dissolved. The individual molecules of resin remain in a tightly coiled state. They do not present as large a surface to the dispersing liquid as do the same resin molecules in the extended state found in solutions; thereby they do not absorb or immobilize so large a portion of the liquid. In the coiled state there is less intertangling and interference with the motion of other molecules. Resins which will not form fluid solutions above 15 per cent resin content in the best of known solvents can be used in proportions as high as 40 to 60 per cent to produce spreadable dispersions of comparable viscosity. Thus by deferring solution until the resin particles are in the desired position, the viscosity problems associated with high-polymer solutions are avoided.

The variation in viscosity with change in the proportions of dispersant and diluent suggests that surface-adsorption effects come into play. It is considered significant that those compounds which have very little true solvent action on the resin at room temperature seem to make the most satisfactory dispersants. More active solvents are less satisfactory, producing sharper minima in viscosity-composition curves and tending to cause more rapid increase in viscosity on aging. The molecular structure of these better dispersants is suggestive of the balance between lyophilic and lyophobic groups which is needed in surface-active agents. In other words, a good dispersant should have a solvating group capable of adsorption on the surface of the resin, and non-solvating groups sufficient to prevent excessive penetration and swelling of the resin particle.

Plastisols. There are two basic requirements in the formulation of any plastisol. It must have satisfactory flow properties for the intended method of application and it must give the desired end properties after fusion. Both are influenced by the kind and amount of ingredients present and also by the processing techniques employed.

Vinyl plastisols, being dispersions in plasticizer of vinyl resin particles plus other ingredients such as fillers and colors, differ greatly in consistency. On the whole, they do not behave like Newtonian liquids, because they are crowded systems and because, as in organosols, the liquid phase always exerts some solvating effect on the resin, even at room temperature. Whatever method is to be used in applying a plastisol — spreading, dipping, molding, or spraying — its flow properties are vital to its successful deposition. For example, a plastisol which is quite dilatant would be generally unsuited for application by spreading. The choice of resin is important to the flow properties. Resins of large particle size, such as the usual stir-in type, generally result in lower viscosities in a given plastisol formulation. Mixtures of resins are often utilized, to take advantage of the separate properties of each. For example, a mixture of vinyl resins of two particle sizes, large and small, will usually result in a plastisol of lower viscosity and less dilatancy than if all the resin was of the finer particle size. The reason for this is that the mixture of particle sizes requires less plasticizer to fill the voids between the particles.

The initial viscosity of a plastisol is largely dependent on the viscosity of the plasticizer itself. Low-viscosity plasticizers result in low-viscosity plastisols, and vice versa. On aging, the tendency of the plasticizer to solvate or swell the resin particles at room temperature is dominant, and the viscosity of the plastisol rises accordingly.

The addition of a filler to a plastisol increases its viscosity because the plasticizer required to wet the filler is no longer available to contribute to the fluidity of the dispersion. For this reason, fillers (and pigments also) should be chosen with some consideration for their plasticizer-absorption values. Fillers, stabilizers, and other solid ingredients are usually added in the form of preground dispersions. In some cases, where it appears desirable to grind the entire formulation, they may be added dry in the mixing operation.

ORGANOSOLS

Plasticizers, Dispersants and Diluents

The selection of the dispersants and diluents in organosols is an important factor in the performance of the formulation. The dispersant is a polar compound which has some solvent action on the resin. It is adsorbed on the surface of the resin and perhaps penetrates the resin particle to some extent. The adsorbed layer probably prevents flocculation of the resin particles, by keeping them apart. There seems to be an optimum balance between the solvent and non-solvent groups that makes for a good dispersant. A good resin-solvent, such as methyl isobutyl ketone, is a poorer dispersant than diisobutyl ketone, which is a poor resin-solvent at ordinary temperatures. It is believed that the diisobutyl ketone wets the resin better and swells it less.

The better plasticizers for the vinyl chloride resins are the preferred dispersants. Good compatibility coupled with only moderate solvent power at ordinary temperatures seems to be the criterion for the wide usefulness of a plasticizer with vinyl chloride resins, and the same balance of properties makes for good ability as dispersant. The plasticizers are generally better dispersants than the volatile solvents. Fig. 10-4 shows the effect of replacement of methyl isobutyl ketone by di-2-ethyl hexyl phthalate (DOP). Viscosity is reduced and the viscosity minima are broadened.

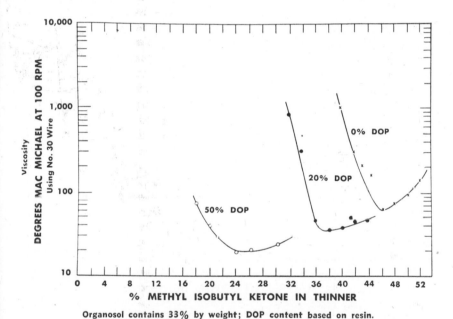

Organosol contains 33% by weight; DOP content based on resin.

Fig. 10-4. Effect on organosol of replacing volatile dispersant with plasticizer.

In compositions containing 30 parts or more of plasticizer per hundred parts of resin, the plasticizer usually serves as the sole dispersant. The balance between dispersant and diluent is then obtained by varying the proportion of aromatic and aliphatic hydrocarbons in the diluent. Fig. 10-5 compares the performance of plasticizers in organosols made with one resin. While the actual viscosity levels and the proportion of xylene in the diluent vary with the resin used, the plasticizers exhibit the same performance with other vinyl chloride

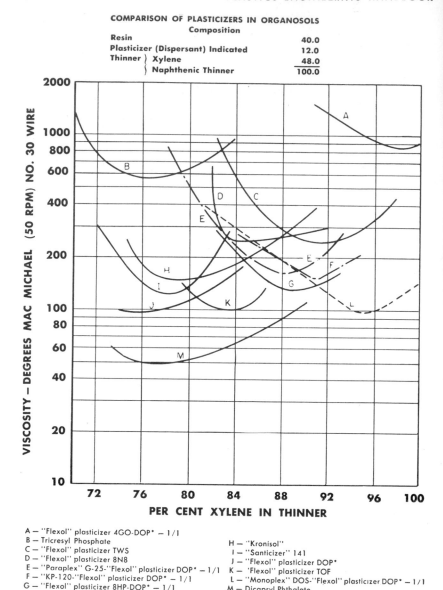

COMPARISON OF PLASTICIZERS IN ORGANOSOLS
Composition

Resin	40.0
Plasticizer (Dispersant) Indicated	12.0
Thinner ⟩ Xylene	48.0
⟨ Naphthenic Thinner	100.0

A — "Flexol" plasticizer 4GO-DOP* — 1/1
B — Tricresyl Phosphate
C — "Flexol" plasticizer TWS
D — "Flexol" plasticizer 8N8
E — "Paraplex" G-25-"Flexol" plasticizer DOP* — 1/1
F — "KP-120-"Flexol" plasticizer DOP* — 1/1
G — "Flexol" plasticizer 8HP-DOP* — 1/1

H — "Kronisol"
I — "Santicizer" 141
J — "Flexol" plasticizer DOP*
K — "Flexol" plasticizer TOF
L — "Monoplex" DOS-"Flexol" plasticizer DOP* — 1/1
M — Dicapryl Phthalate

* Di-2-ethylhexyl phthalate

Fig. 10-5. Comparison of plasticizers in organosols.

dispersion resins. In practice, the type and the amount of plasticizer to be used in the formulations are determined by the ultimate use to which the film is destined, and the organosol formulation is modified to suit the plasticizer.

Volatile dispersants are used where the organosol is formulated with low plasticizer content, either to obtain a film of low flexibility or to obtain a stable dispersion of low resin content. Volatile dispersants are frequently used in compositions containing resinous plasticizers because these are often deficient in dispersing and fusing ability. Since volatile dispersants must remain behind in the film after the evaporation of the diluent in order to assist in the fusion, slow-evaporating compounds are used. High-boiling ketones such as diisobutyl ketone and trimethyl nonanone are preferred for dispersing and fusing ability. High-boiling esters such as 2-ethylhexyl acetate and "Cellosolve" acetate have also been used. Glycol esters are sometimes preferred because they impart less residual odor.

The diluents used in organosols are generally aliphatic or aromatic hydrocarbons, but in some instances alcohols have been used. It is important that the materials chosen have the proper evaporation rate for the particular application. The evaporation should not be so rapid that the organosol dries before it can be applied or spread. On the other hand, in the case of compositions of low plasticizer content, the diluent should evaporate faster than the dispersant. In high-speed fusion of organosol films, it is necessary to have most of the diluent out of the film before the resin reaches the high-temperature zone, in order to avoid blistering.

The viscosity of organosols is markedly affected by the balance between aromatic and aliphatic hydrocarbons in the diluent. Aromatic hydrocarbons such as xylene have a swelling action on the resin. They require only small additions of dispersant to convert them to balanced organosol thinners. The aromatic diluents are particularly well suited to the preparation of organosols of low plasticizer content. They aid fusion and develop films of better clarity, but the resin content must be kept low and there is more shrinkage of the film during drying and fusion.

Aliphatic diluents have little solvating and swelling action on resins of vinyl chloride type, and hence can be used in making organosols of relatively low viscosity or high solids content. They require almost an equal volume of dispersant to convert them to balanced thinners, and are therefore preferred in compositions of high plasticizer content and for diluting plastisols. The naphthenic type of hydrocarbon is preferred to the straight-chain type. The viscosities of organosols made with various commercial diluents are compared in Figs. 10-6 and 10-7.

In practice, blends of aromatic and aliphatic diluents are widely used to obtain a proper balance of dispersant and diluent.

The actual dispersant-diluent balance required for minimum viscosity, as well as the shape of the viscosity-composition curve, varies with the resin that is used. Table 10-1 describes the composition and particle size of several dispersion resins which are compared in organosols in Fig. 10-8.

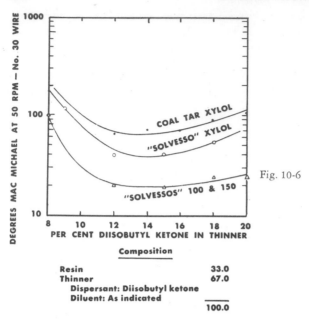

Fig. 10-6

Composition

Resin	33.0
Thinner	67.0
Dispersant: Diisobutyl ketone	
Diluent: As indicated	
	100.0

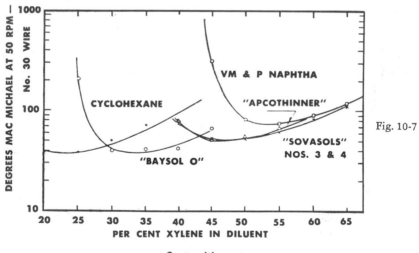

Fig. 10-7

Composition

Resin		40.0
Thinner		
Dispersant:Diisobutyl ketone		24.0
Diluent:		36.0
Xylene	As indicated	
Balance	As indicated	
		100.0

Organosol viscosity-composition diagrams.

TABLE 10-1

Resin Code	% Vinyl Chloride	Specific Viscosity	Ultimate Particle Size (microns) *		
			lower range	most probable	upper limit
1	99+	0.25	0.2	0.3	0.7
2	97	0.24	0.1	0.8	1.3
3	96	0.29	0.05	0.12	0.6
4	91	0.26	0.05	0.10	0.4
5	99+	0.30	0.1	0.75	0.8
6	95	0.20	0.08	0.15	0.6

* Particle size determined from electron micrographs.

Methods of Varying Viscosity

Organosols are prepared in ball, pebble or roller mills at a viscosity most suitable for proper grinding. This is seldom the proper consistency for application; hence the dispersion must be thinned or, occasionally, thickened.

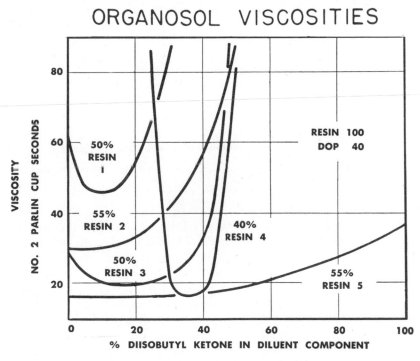

Fig. 10-8. Influence of (a) composition of resin, (b) particle size, (c) ratio of dispersant to diluent upon viscosity of organosol.

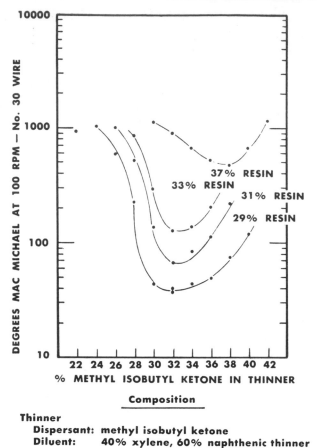

Fig. 10-9. Effect of resin concentration on viscosity in the same thinner composition.

Thinning is readily accomplished with a balanced organosol thinner. This means in the case of plasticized compositions that the diluting thinner must contain sufficient volatile dispersant to be equivalent to the plasticizer and any volatile dispersant in the original composition. In effect a balanced thinner for grinding an unplasticized organosol is suitable for diluting any organosol. This means that thinners made with aromatic diluents should contain 10 to 15 per cent of volatile dispersant, while those made with aliphatic diluents should contain approximately 50 per cent of dispersant.

Where thickening is required, low-boiling active solvents, such as methyl ethyl ketone, are carefully stirred into the dispersion. There is an immediate thinning, followed by a thickening action which may proceed for several days.

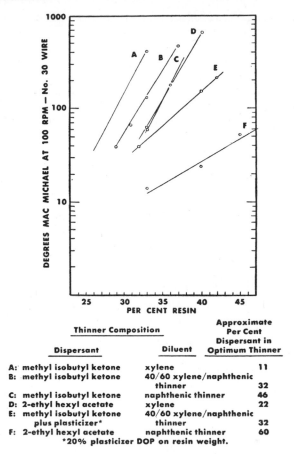

Thinner Composition		Approximate Per Cent Dispersant in Optimum Thinner
Dispersant	Diluent	
A: methyl isobutyl ketone	xylene	11
B: methyl isobutyl ketone	40/60 xylene/naphthenic thinner	32
C: methyl isobutyl ketone	naphthenic thinner	46
D: 2-ethyl hexyl acetate	xylene	22
E: methyl isobutyl ketone plus plasticizer*	40/60 xylene/naphthenic thinner	32
F: 2-ethyl hexyl acetate	naphthenic thinner	60
*20% plasticizer DOP on resin weight.		

Fig. 10-10   Effect of resin concentration on viscosity in various thinner compositions.

Occasionally compatible resins are dissolved in the solvent to hasten the thickening process and to impart more cohesion to the dispersion.

Effect of Solids Content

The viscosity and the flow characteristics of an organosol are controlled not only by the thinner formulation (dispersant-diluent balance), but also by the resin content of the organosol. Fig. 10-9 shows the viscosities of several series of organosols which differ only in resin content. The curves shift to higher viscosities as the resin content is increased, so that a composition containing 37 per cent of resin is so viscous that only slight breakdown occurs in the mills. In the grindable range — under 35 per cent of resin for this system — the

Plasticizer DOP	35
Xylene	26
Naphthenic thinner	39
	100

**Measurements made on
removal from mill.**

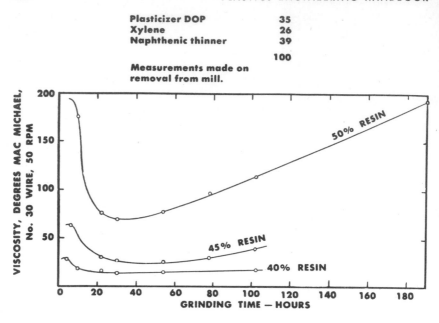

**Measurements made after
4 weeks storage.**

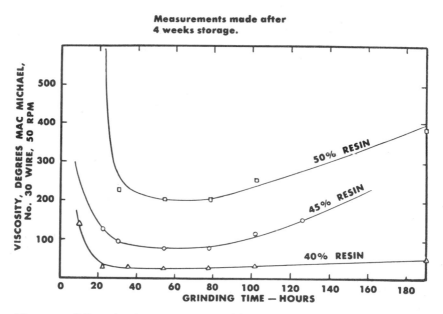

Fig. 10-11. Effect of resin content on rate of grinding and effect of grinding time on viscosity and on stability of viscosity.

dispersant-diluent ratio for minimum viscosity is almost constant. Data for the viscosity of organosols as a function of the resin content are shown in Fig. 10-10, covering the range satisfactorily explored by using laboratory pebble mills. By the gradual addition of resin as the grinds progress, even higher ultimate solids content can be obtained at usable viscosities. The logarithmic increase of viscosity with increase in resin content is the same as that normally found with solutions and dispersions. The viscosity values used correspond to the optimum formulating points. The slopes of the curves differ for various types of organosols, and they may be taken as measures of the degree to which the resin is swelled by the thinner.

The slope of these lines may be used for estimating the viscosity of diluted organosols and for reformulating to different solids content. However, these values represent the viscosities of the dispersed systems as discharged from the mills. The final viscosity of an organosol may not be excessively high from theoretical projections of these curves, but the initial viscosity of the undispersed mix may be too high to permit effective grinding.

Organosols formulated at higher resin contents require longer time for grinding, as shown in Fig. 10-11. Moreover the viscosity and the viscosity-stability are critical functions of the grinding time, as shown in this figure.

The formulation of organosols of the highest possible resin content is not recommended. High solids content can be used only if the solvation of the resin is kept at a minimum. This introduces difficulties in the final fusion of the resin particles during baking. The quality of the dispersion is poorer because of the lesser amount of grinding which can be obtained, and the problem of control is more critical because high-solids formulations magnify even minor differences between batches of raw materials. On the other hand, an organosol which does not require storage can be prepared by the addition of volatile thinners to a plastisol, thereby securing the highest possible solids content consistent with satisfactory flow properties.

Stabilizers and Lubricants

Under the influence of heat, vinyl chloride polymers release hydrogen chloride. This leaves double bonds in the polymer chain. These double bonds develop color in the resin and offer a point for attack by oxygen, which causes degradation and embrittlement of the resin. The rate of breakdown of the resin is accelerated by traces of certain metals such as iron and zinc, especially in the presence of hydrogen chloride. This acid appears to increase the development of color by causing the migration of the double bonds to a conjugated position, where the color is intensified.

Stabilization against heat is effected by the addition of compounds capable of reacting with hydrogen chloride as it is formed, to prevent the development of an acid condition in the resin. Inorganic oxides, salts of inorganic bases with weak acids, complex organometallic compounds and various glycidyl compounds are widely used as stabilizers. Lead compounds, such as pigments and soaps, are especially useful as stabilizers because the lead chloride formed in the process of stabilization does not detract from the water-resistance of the compounds. While clear compounds can be prepared from lead soaps, they lose their clarity after absorbing acid. Hence for clear compounds organic stabilizers are chosen, even though they are usually less efficient than the inorganic stabilizer. Alkali-metal salts of the complex phosphates are effective stabilizers in the presence of iron, but often suffer from poor water-resistance.

In addition to the function of absorbing hydrogen chloride, certain compounds act as color-stabilizers for the resin by addition to the double bond. Maleic acid is typical of a class of compounds that add to conjugated double bonds to break the conjugation and eliminate the color. Organic compounds which produce free radicals, and also certain oxidation catalysts, act as color-stabilizers, supposedly by addition to the double bonds or elimination of them by oxidation.

Light-stabilizers are required for films that do not contain enough pigment to render them opaque to ultraviolet light. The stabilizing problem here is closely related to that encountered in the heat-stabilization of films, although oxidation appears to play a more important role. Most heat-stabilizers have some light-stabilizing effect, but the polyphosphates are especially effective in films prepared from dispersions. Antioxidants often have a stabilizing effect. Ultraviolet-absorbers such as the salicylates exert some stabilizing action, but as a class they are relatively poor light-stabilizers in dispersions.

The amount and type of stabilizer required for dispersions varies with the resin, the plasticizer, the pigments, the conditions of fusing and the conditions of exposure. In every instance careful attention must be paid to the proper choice of stabilizers, and they should be tested under the actual conditions of use.

Dispersions used for cloth-coatings which are to be embossed and for plastisols which are to be molded sometimes require release agents in the formulation. Small proportions of lead soaps used as stabilizers are often sufficient for this purpose. Free fatty acids, incompatible plasticizers and silicone oils have often been used as lubricants to prevent adhesion to metallic surfaces. The problem is seldom as troublesome as that of choosing lubricating compounds for hot processing.

Pigmentation

The majority of the uses of organosol and plastisol require pigmentation. Pigments serve three functions, namely, decoration, stabilization and loading. Whereas the most emphasis is usually placed on the decorative feature, the other two properties are important and should be given consideration in selecting pigments or combinations of pigments for use in vinyl dispersions.

The decorative aspect need not be considered from a technical viewpoint beyond the limitations imposed on the selection of particular pigments by their behavior when combined with vinyl resins. Although there are many pigments which should not be used in organosols or plastisols, the list of satisfactory colors is adequate to provide substantially any shade which decorative requirements may impose.

The function of pigments as stabilizers is largely a consequence of their actinic screening qualities. In most instances this should be regarded as a protection added to that of the stabilizers, which act as acid-acceptors. Pigments lessen the work of the stabilizers by reducing the degree of breakdown of resin by ultraviolet light.

It is not necessary to elaborate on the use of pigments purely to load the film. Many end uses require the incorporation of mineral fillers to produce specific physical properties. In other instances, loading of the film may be desirable for purely economic reasons at some sacrifice of the best properties of the film. Thus pigments, both organic and inorganic, play an important role in manufacture of organosols and plastisols.

Pigments can be dispersed directly in the organosol or plastisol during its manufacture, or dispersed separately in an appropriate vehicle, for subsequent addition to the dispersed clear base. The ultimate requirement in any case is a uniform dispersion of discrete particles of pigment homogeneously distributed throughout the product in its finished form. The procedure to be followed will depend largely upon the grinding characteristics of the ingredients, upon the variety of colored dispersions to be made, and upon the quantities to be produced.

Direct grinding or dispersion of pigments in organosols and plastisols is not as common as the alternative method of preparing a separate color concentrate. This is largely a matter of convenience and inventory control, in that base materials remain much more versatile with respect to a variety of uses when held in this form. If, however, a standard item is being manufactured, in large volume, and not subject to frequent change, it becomes convenient to incorporate the pigment in the original dispersion during its maufacture. There is no particular problem involved in such direct manufacture other than a difference between the times required to disperse the organosol or plastisol itself, and to effect complete dispersion of the pigment or pigments involved. If, for example, the dispersion of the organosol or plastisol by itself requires only 6 or 8 hours, but it is necessary to grind the pigment for 20 hours or more to achieve complete dispersion and full development of color, it would not be efficient to grind them together. On the other hand, where the time cycles are closely related, direct grinding together will be advantageous.

There is an additional advantage, beyond inventory-control and versatility, to be gained from separate manufacture of color paste. When the proportion of pigment in the formulation is small, it does not become thoroughly dispersed when ground in admixture with the resin, and thus does not develop its full color. In such a formulation, and particularly if the pigment is an expensive one, it is more economical and effective to disperse the pigment separately.

The dispersion of pigments and fillers as concentrated color pastes is done usually in heavy-duty dough-type mixers or on three-roll mills. The latter, in combination with a pony or change-can mixer for preliminary mixing of dry color and vehicles, comprises a very satisfactory production unit. Such equipment is well adapted to small batches or to an output of several thousand pounds per 8-hour shift. The ease of dispersion of materials of this type is highly dependent on formulation, which may influence considerably the proportion of pigment required to produce the desired color. For example, the choice of proper grinding media may make the difference between incorporating 50 parts or 75 parts titanium dioxide in a color paste.

Color pastes for use with plastisols should be dispersions in a completely non-volatile vehicle. Such pastes can be used with organosols also, but with the latter it is acceptable also to employ a vehicle containing some volatile constituents. Color pastes of this latter type have the advantage of introducing color with a minimum of plasticizer, and thus impose less limitation on formulation of the clear base dispersion.

There are of course optimum amounts of pigments and fillers which any particular film, coating or molded item should contain. This quantity is usually expressed as a ratio of pigment to binder (resin plus plasticizer). This should be thought of as a volume relationship rather than weight. Variations in density lead to unreliable conclusions if a weight ratio is used. Up to a certain volume, pigments and fillers contribute to the life of a film. Beyond this volume they begin to weaken the film and shorten its useful life. The volume of pigment best suited to any particular purpose must be determined experimentally. Once determined, it should be maintained, even though the pigment or pigment combination is changed. For unsupported opaque films this value is usually 5 to 10 per cent; for coated upholstery fabrics, 15 to 20 per cent. For molded products, the value would depend entirely on end use and quality required.

There is nothing to be gained by including more coloring material than necessary to produce complete hiding, or maximum strength of shade. In the case of a tinctorially strong pigment or one having a high opacity, this optimum amount may occupy less than the desired pigment volume. In such instances, fillers are employed to make up the difference.

Certain precautions must be taken in choosing pigments for use with vinyl chloride resins. Iron and zinc pigments are avoided because they accelerate thermal degradation of the resins. Lead pigments in general work well, because they exert a definite heat-stabilizing action. In compositions of low opacity to ultraviolet light, certain pigments must be avoided, because they accelerate degradation of the resin, which causes the film to become tacky. In compositions containing oil-type and glycol-ether plasticizers, pigments which catalyze oxidation must be avoided, since they would cause rancidity.

Table 10-2 includes those coloring pigments and fillers which are most generally used in vinyl compositions, but their suitability for any particular application must be determined experimentally.

TABLE 10-2

Color	Type	Heat-stability	Light-stability	Remarks
reds	cadmium reds	good	good	dull color
	toluidine toners	good	good	bad bleeders
	"Indanthrene" reds	good	good	fast, bright
	"BON" reds	good	good	fast, bright
	pigment scarlet	fair	fair	slight bleeder
yellows	"Hansa" yellows	good	good	bad bleeders
	chrome yellows	good	fair	
	cadmium yellows	good	good	
	strontium chromate	good	good	poor strength
	benzidines	good	good	transparent, bleeders
oranges	chrome oranges	good	fair	
	molybdate oranges	good	fair	bright
	cadmium oranges	good	good	bright
blues	"Indanthrene" blues	good	good	bright, strong
	phthalocyanine	good	good	bright, strong
maroons or violets	"BON" maroon	fair	fair	hard to disperse
	thioindigo maroon	good	good	
greens	phthalocyanine	good	good	strong, transparent
	chromic oxide	good	good	strong, opaque
blacks	carbon blacks			excellent
	lampblacks			excellent
whites	titanium dioxide			excellent
	antimony dioxide			good for flame-resistance
	basic carbonate white lead			good stabilizer
	basic white lead sulphate			good stabilizer
misc.	blue basic lead sulphate			satisfactory, have
	litharge			stabilizing action
	red lead			
	powdered lead			
	aluminum powder			excellent
fillers	calcium carbonate			good, has stabilizing action
	mica			extenders
	barytes			in pigmented
	silicas			dispersions
	china clay			

Methods of Manufacture

Whereas many mechanical means have been considered, and the search continues, no more economical or efficient means has yet been found for the grinding of organosols than the ball mill. Both porcelain and steel mills are used with equal success, though for several reasons these two types should not be considered as interchangeable. Steel mills will do a more efficient dispersion job, and consequently lend themselves to shorter production cycles, but with them it is impossible to avoid some color contamination. This may be quite pronounced if only occasional batches are made in a steel mill, or may be very slight, after the first one or two batches, if continuous use is made of the mill. Vinyl compounds must be stabilized against iron when steel equipment is used, to prevent undesirable breakdown of the resin.

A mill lined with porcelain or buhrstone does not cause discoloration, and obviates the necessity of stabilizing the organosol specifically against iron. But longer grinding cycles will usually be required in this type, as a consequence of the lower density of the porcelain balls or flint pebbles in comparison with that of steel balls.

General experience has indicated the desirability of having a water cooling system as an integral part of the mill. This is true whether steel or porcelain is used. The viscosity of the finished product will vary over a wide range, depending on the temperature of the batch during grinding. For uniform results it is necessary to control the temperature of the batch, and for any given formulation there exists a maximum temperature above which bodying to an undesirable degree may be expected, as a result of solvation of the particles of resin.

For compositions of the general range of from 70 to 80 per cent total solids, and of normal plasticizer content, there is usually no specific advantage to be gained by loading the mill in installments. Most organosol formulations can be charged *in toto* and will be ground or dispersed to a stable uniform finished product.

There are, however, instances when it is desirable or necessary to charge only a portion of the batch, and to hold out some of the ingredients for addition after the dry ingredients of the first portion have been wetted. Such procedure is indicated when a resin of poor wetting qualities is being used; when the total solids is substantially above 80 per cent; or when the plasticizer content is abnormally low. This procedure is used only when the ratio of dry solids to liquids is high, and the physical wetting of the mass is not easily accomplished by other means.

The optimum charge in the manufacture of organosols is the same as for any other product to be ground in a given mill. Overloading rapidly decreases the efficiency of the mill and results in a poor dispersion and lengthened time cycles. Undercharge of balls or pebbles leads to the same result. Undercharging the mill may result in undue scoring of the mill, and may cause discoloration, even in a porcelain mill. If the proper factors of charge for both balls and batch are not known it is best to consult the producer of the mill for this information.

Depending on a number of factors, principally the degree of dispersion required, the liquid stability of the organosol, and the formulation, time cycles may range from 5 to 40 hr. Shorter cycles would in most instances not produce complete solvation, and the need of longer cycles may indicate improper formulation.

The term "grinding" is rather commonly used in a sense which does not fit the usual definition of the word. Dispersion would be a more apt term, as in no instance is it the objective of this operation to reduce particle size (Fig. 10-12). The shearing action of the mill serves merely to reduce agglomerates to their ultimate unit size and to wet each individual particle with the vehicle or dispersion medium. Since the end result depends, in the case of a ball mill, on shear forces applied over a large surface area, it becomes obvious that proper attention to formulation and mill charge is quite important. Too much material in the mill with respect to its charge of balls, or a liquid too thin or completely lacking in tack, reduces the effectiveness of surface shearing action and results in inefficient dispersing action.

UNGROUND RESIN   SOLVATED RESIN   ORGANOSOL

Fig. 10-12. Preparation of organosols. The mildly fused resin aggregates are broken apart and dispersed as minute, discrete particles in a suspending medium.

Whereas the ball mill is most commonly used, since it lends itself to economical large-batch operation, and is furthermore a closed system which avoids solvent losses, there are production requirements to which the three-roll mill is well adapted. This mill, common in the printing-ink and paint industries, is ideally suited to the fine dispersion of comparatively small batches. Depending on the ease of dispersion or the degree of fineness desired, the material may be fed through the mill more than once.

A three-roll mill tends to screen out large particles, which accumulate between the back rolls and also on the ends. By removing such material from the ends and regrinding it, the entire charge can be reduced to a uniform consistency. If a sizable portion of the batch has required such treatment, a mix to blend after milling is required. This condition is more apt to occur in the dispersion of organosols and plastisols on a three-roll mill than with color pastes or printing inks for which such a mill is commonly used.

One important requirement in the use of the three-roll mill is a thorough premixing of the batch. The more thoroughly wetted the resin component is before milling, the less tendency for hold-back, with consequent saving in milling time.

A disadvantage of the three-roll mill is loss of volatile components. For this reason it is considered more suited to the grinding of plastisols than of organosols. If the composition permits, the resin and plasticizer components may be ground without the volatile components, or with a minimum amount, followed by dilution after dispersion. This, however, involves the cost of an extra operation; for reasons of economy, consideration should be given to the use of a ball mill.

Storage and Aging Characteristics

Organosols are not permanently affected by low temperature, and may be stored outdoors under any conditions if necessary. They are, however, affected by elevated temperatures, and storage at temperatures above 100°F may result in an undesirable increase in body. This condition will be more or less severe, depending upon the particular formulation.

If the composition is under-solvated, the change may be negligible. If the reverse condition exists, the change may render the dispersion unsuitable for use. This increase in body is non-reversible, but may sometimes be corrected by addition of thinners.

Organosols containing fillers, if not properly compounded, may undergo a similar increase in body, irrespective of storage conditions. This is often a thixotropic effect, which can be reversed by agitation. In other instances addition of thinner as well as agitation may be required.

If the organosol is required to stand for any considerable time before use, careful attention must be given to the proper balance between resin, plasticizers, and volatile components. When all these are brought into proper relationship, the product should show relatively little change over a period of a year or more, unless subjected to conditions of hot storage for too long a time.

Fusion of Organosols

The fusion of organosols involves evaporation of the volatile components and solution of the vinyl resin in the plasticizer. For this last step a high temperature is required, and it is essential that the resin and plasticizer reach a temperature of 300 to 350°F if the maximum tensile strength of the film is to be realized.

Organosols may be dried and baked on a faster schedule than solution coatings because the organosols release solvent more rapidly (Fig. 10-13). Since the dispersants and some of the diluents exert considerable solvent action on the resin at elevated temperatures, organosol coatings should be heated as rapidly as possible, consistent with freedom from blistering, so as to utilize the increased solvent action of the thinner to aid in the fusion. This is especially helpful in the formation of films from organosols of low plasticizer content.

WET ORGANOSOL FILM   DRY UNFUSED FILM   FUSED FILM

Fig. 10-13. Fusion of organosols. While drying and fusing are shown as separate steps for simplicity in exposition, these two operations overlap in actual practice.

The speed of the bake must be determined by experiment, and it will be found to depend on the thickness of the film, the type of formulation and the size, shape and composition of the article being coated. Very light coatings (e.g., less than 0.001 in.) may be subjected to temperatures of 350°F while still wet; heavier coatings must be heated more slowly. Coatings of low plasticizer content require critical attention to baking schedules. Often the use of high-boiling thinners is necessary to obtain good fusion.

While it is preferable to bake the film in a continuous single operation, it is possible to bake in two steps. The coating is first set at 225 to 300°F, and finally fused at 300 to 375°F. If the coating is too slow in reaching the gelling temperature, cracks may occur; if it reaches a high temperature too rapidly, blistering, pinholes and shrinking of the film may be encountered.

Ovens for fusing the film are designed to utilize one or more of the standard methods of heating:

1. convection   3. infrared ray
2. direct contact   4. high-frequency radiation

The temperature required is above that normally available with steam; therefore other heat-transfer media, such as hot oil or "Dowtherm," are usually used to heat the air in the oven. A reasonable proportion of the air must be removed continuously to prevent the development of explosive concentrations of vapor in the oven. Whichever of the above methods is used, one basic fact must be kept in mind. The complete mass of the material, which includes the fabric or film-carrier, must be heated rapidly to the fluxing temperature. The time necessary is affected by the conductivity and the specific heat of the total mass of the material. For example, a four-mil film cast on paper may be fluxed at 360°F in 40 seconds; the same film on a glass plate might take 10 minutes. If infrared is used, then color as well as mass must be considered. To obtain vinyl film of best quality from organosol by fluxing, the time must be kept to a minimum at an optimum temperature. The temperature and time may be varied by selection of plasticizers and resins used.

PLASTISOLS

Types of Resin for Plastisols

Depending upon the manner in which they are dispersed, plastisol resins are classified as stir-in and grinding types. Basically, both types are emulsion-polymerized vinyl chloride resins.

Stir-in resins, as the name implies, are dispersed by merely stirring with plasticizer to form a fluid plastisol. The resin particles, approximating one micron in diameter, are only loosely agglomerated during recovery in the manufacturing process. They may be redispersed in the plasticizer with a minimum amount of work. The shearing action of a high-speed stirrer or pony mixer is sufficient to wet the particles and yield a fluid dispersion. The comparatively larger particle size of stir-in resins permits the preparation of plastisols at a lower plasticizer ratio, because there is relatively less surface area for the adsorption of plasticizer. Thus, plastisols can be made at resin-to-plasticizer ratios as low as 100:50. Such plastisols are generally characterized by a high viscosity and dilatancy, but in certain instances these properties are desirable. Once the plastisol has been made, it may be thinned, if necessary, with additional plasticizer for high-speed spreading, or with volatile diluents to form organosols.

The grinding-type plastisol resins require more shearing for dispersion. In such resin, the individual particle size is smaller than in the stir-in resins, but the particles are more tightly agglomerated. Hence, more work must be expended in separating the particles. This is accomplished by making a premix of resin and plasticizer with desired pigments, etc., in a pony mixer, and grinding on a roller mill. Resin-plasticizer ratios around 100:70 are required to attain the same consistency as is obtained with stir-in resins at 100:50. Equal parts of resin and plasticizer are required to attain adequate fluidity for most applications.

Many factors must be considered in the choice of the type of resin for each application, and often blends of both types of resin are to be preferred. The stir-in resins are indicated where low plasticizer-resin ratios are required. Less equipment is required for the preparation of plastisols with these resins. On the other hand, stir-in resins command a premium in price which approximates the added cost of dispersion. The tensile and tear strength of films is dependent upon the particle size of the resin, especially at the lower range of fusion temperatures; the finer particles give the stronger films (Fig. 10-14). If agglomerates of fine particles have not been broken down by adequate grinding, the effect on the strength of the film is the same as that of coarse particles.

Plasticizers for Plastisols

Since plastisols are dispersions of vinyl resins, pigments, stabilizers, etc., in plasticizers, it is evident that the role of the plasticizer is quite important in determining the flow properties of the dispersion. In addition, the proper-

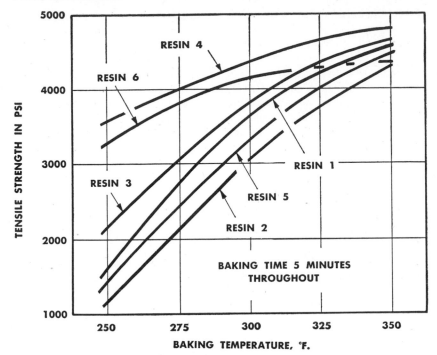

Fig. 10-14. Effect of particle size and baking temperature on strength of film. The resins are those described in Table 10-1.

ties of the finished product in regard to flexibility, toughness, and resistance to embrittlement upon exposure are also related to the amount and kind of plasticizer used.

Generally speaking, plasticizers are divided into two classes, the monomeric and the resinous types. The monomeric type is typified by such compounds as the phthalate esters, di-2-ethylhexyl, dicapryl, etc.; the phosphate esters, tricresyl, trioctyl, etc.; adipate esters; sebacate esters; and others. These compounds are high-boiling liquids of relatively low viscosity. Resinous plasticizers are compatible resins, usually of the linear polyester type. Their use is indicated where migration and extraction of the plasticizer must be avoided. Resinous plasticizers seldom have sufficient fluidity to be used as the sole dispersing medium. Likewise, their ability to dissolve the resin at the fusing temperature is often inadequate to produce films of the highest strength. For these reasons, one frequently finds blends of resinous and monomeric plasticizers in plastisols.

While plasticizers must be chosen with regard to the properties desired in the final product, a further requisite for their use in plastisols is that the plasticizer have little solvent action on the resin at room temperature, but good solvency at elevated temperatures. The lack of solvent action at room temperature is of primary importance in the preparation of plastisols which are to be stored prior to use; if solvent action takes place during storage it may cause an excessive increase in viscosity. Low-viscosity plasticizers are to be preferred in order to obtain low-viscosity plastisols. There is good correlation between viscosities of plasticizer and plastisol measured at low shear rates (Fig. 10-15). Exceptions are found when the plasticizer is a strong solvent at room temperature. At high shear rates, wetting phenomena, dilatancy and thixotropy complicate the correlation.

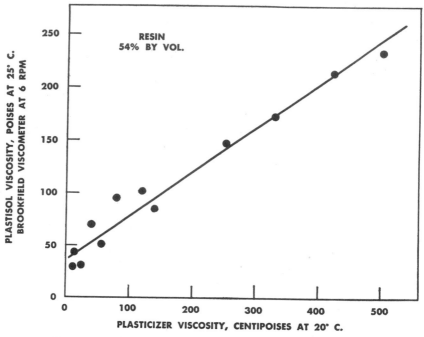

Fig. 10-15. Effect of viscosity of plasticizer on viscosity of plastisol.

Blending of nonsolvent incompatible plasticizers with the compatible plasticizers in plastisols improves the viscosity-stability of plastisols, in much the same way as blends of diluents with dispersants yield more stable organosols.

Methods of Varying the Viscosity of Plastisols

The flow properties of plastisols are largely determined by the amount and type of plasticizer present in the original paste. High viscosity and cohesion are sometimes desired for extrusion coating. These are obtained by the use of resinous plasticizers in the formulation, or by dissolving some of the more soluble vinyl or acrylic resins in the plasticizer. These modified plastisols have superior viscosity-stability. Thinning of plastisols with plasticizers is readily done, but this has the drawback of changing the resin-plasticizer ratio and often radically changing the properties of the fused article. Where it is necessary to keep the product as a plastisol and yet reduce the viscosity, it is usually desirable to reformulate to utilize plasticizers of low plasticizing efficiency. More often one thins a plastisol with volatile solvent, converting it into an organosol. Since the volatile solvents are much less viscous than plasticizers, radical reduction of viscosities is obtained by very slight thinning. When thinning is less than 10 per cent by volume, aliphatic diluents may be used without exceeding the optimum diluent-dispersant ratio. This thinning should be accompanied by careful stirring, to prevent local flocculation of the resin. Aromatic diluents are to be avoided, in that the excessive swelling of the resin which these cause may lead to gelation.

When considerable thinning is required to reduce a plastisol to coating viscosity, it is preferable to use a balanced organosol thinner. Dispersants which do not cause much swelling of the resin are often used alone for thinning plastisols. The glycol ethers are widely used for this purpose.

Stabilizers and Lubricants

See Stabilizers and Lubricants, page 261.

Pigmentation

See Pigmentation, page 262.

Methods of Manufacture of Plastisols

The equipment and technique employed in efficiently compounding relatively stable dispersions are determined to a large extent by the characteristics of the resins and other components, and by the properties of the compositions which they produce. Other factors which influence the course of manufacture are the temperature of the dispersion during compounding, and the state, manner and order in which the components are introduced. In many instances, desirable fluid properties not easily obtainable by direct compounding can be imparted to a specific plastisol formulation, with a minimum of manufacturing effort, by simple mixing of two or more completely compounded plastisols whose combined composition is that of the specific plastisol.

The introduction of stabilizers, pigments and fillers is usually best carried out by use of previously compounded bases of these materials. The choice of these components must be made with considerable care since, while normally used in only minor amounts, many of them have as much influence on the rheological characteristics of the resultant plastisol as do the major components, i.e., the resin and plasticizer blends.

The major problem involved in compounding many plastisols centers around the incorporation of the vinyl resin. The specific type of resin employed frequently determines the equipment and procedure necessary to manufacture the plastisol most economically. For all practical purposes, the various vinyl dispersion resins available on the market today can be classified in two groups — one consisting of those resins which are rather highly agglomerated and which require considerable input of energy to effect de-agglomeration or dispersion; the other consisting of the more recently developed resins which require very little work to produce highly dispersed systems. For brevity, the first group in this chapter will be referred to as the grinding-type resins; the other, as stir-in type resins.

The equipment usually employed with the grinding-type resins are pony mixers, dough mixers, ball mills and three-roll mills. With the stir-in type, simple mixers are adequate, when predispersed solid stabilizers, fillers or pigments are used, but sometimes ball mills or three-roll mills are employed.

In compounding plastisols in any equipment, and particularly when grinding-type resin is used and the dispersing times are extended, it is very important that the temperature of the plastisol mass be kept as low as possible. Here again, the maximum safe temperature of operation is dependent upon the specific formulation but, as a general rule, temperatures over 90°F are to be avoided in order to prevent extensive solvation of the resin by the plasticizer. Water-cooled equipment is very effective in eliminating this source of trouble. When ball mills are employed, steel balls should be avoided because of the deleterious effects of iron on the vinyl resin. In mills having flint or porcelain pebbles, the rapidity and degree of the dispersion of the resin are greatly influenced by the load charge. In a number of cases, very rapid dispersion can be obtained when the levels of plastisol and pebbles are nearly equal. In many instances even moderate overcharging prolongs the milling time so much that the economic advantage of the increased volume is far outweighed. As a general rule, it is good practice to disperse the vinyl resins to the desired degree in the smallest possible amount of liquid, and then to reduce the resultant highly viscous mass with the remainder of the liquid plasticizer. The grinding-type resins lend themselves admirably to this technique, except when the plastisol compositions are highly dilatant. In grinding these resins, the amounts of plasticizer that can be withheld during the dispersion are generally less than in the case of the stir-in resins. By withholding plasticizer, some plastisol formulations with both types of resin can be dispersed by slow tumbling, rolling or slow agitation of the highly viscous mass.

Another method of manufacture, particularly suited to the grinding-type resin, involves the dry grinding of the resin in a ball mill before the addition of the plasticizer. This method permits the incorporation of higher amounts of grinding resin than is possible by conventional ball-milling of the resin in the plasticizers, because of the volume packing effect that dry grinding has on the resin. The dry-grinding technique usually results in plastisols of lower viscosity which, however, are not well dispersed systems and which cannot well be stored, because the resin settles out. In a number of instances dry grinding raises the temperature of the resin far beyond the safe limit, and thus instability of viscosity is often found in plastisols compounded in this manner.

Typical manufacturing procedures for the preparation of several types of plastisol are briefly outlined below.

Low-viscosity (10,000 cp or less) plastisols from stir-in resins: All of the non-grinding resin is added to one-third to two-thirds of the plasticizer in a pony, dough- or similar mixer, and mixed until a thoroughly smooth and homogeneous mass is attained, taking care to avoid mass temperatures over 90°F by water cooling or periodic breaks in the mixing. During or after the mixing, the stabilizers, pigments, and fillers are added as well-dispersed bases or concentrated solutions, and thoroughly mixed into the mass. The plastisol is then diluted with the remainder of the plasticizer by several small additions (rather than one large) during the final mixing. The product can then be evacuated if desired, and passed through a fine screen or gauze to remove extraneous matter before use or packaging. The highly viscous mass may be passed through a three-roll mill before dilution with the remaining plasticizer, to effect more thorough dispersion and thus develop certain desired flow characteristics. These plastisols can also be prepared in a ball mill by adding all the components and rolling for comparatively short periods, usually less than one hour.

Low-viscosity plastisols from grinding-type resins: Some plastisols formulated with grinding-type resin can be prepared by loading all of the resin, plasticizer, etc., into a ball mill, to the proper grinding level, and rolling to the desired degree of dispersion. Many of these plastisols, although of low viscosities when ultimately compounded, pass through a stage of high viscosity which necessitates prolonged grinding before the viscosity is reduced. In such cases, the use of the three-roll mill is recommended. Enough of the plasticizer is added to all of the resin in a pony mixer to produce, after 15 to 30 minutes of mixing, a rather putty-like mass which is then passed once or several times through the three-roll mill. The remaining plasticizer, etc., can then be mixed in, and de-aeration and filtering carried out if desired.

Intermediate-viscosity (10,000 to 50,000 cp) plastisols from stir-in resins: These can be prepared in much the same fashion as the lower-viscosity materials, i.e., by use of conventional mixing equipment. Although ball mills can be employed for the lower-viscosity materials, as already indicated, they are not recommended for these higher-viscosity dispersions because of the difficulty encountered in their removal from the mill. Thorough dispersion of these materials is best effected, if necessary, by use of the three-roll mill, if pronounced dilatancy is not encountered. Should this condition exist, extended dispersion is best effected by prolonging the simple mixing operation at safe temperatures.

Intermediate-viscosity plastisols from grinding-type resins: In practically all cases these materials are best prepared on a three-roll mill in the fashion indicated above.

High-viscosity plastisols, from either grinding or stir-in resins: The high viscosity of these products may be due to either very high content of vinyl resin, high viscosity of plasticizer (*per se* or because of use of secondary resins dissolved in them) or combinations of these. Well-dispersed systems of this type are difficult to prepare, because the heat generated during the compounding with conventional equipment causes rapid solvation and gelation of the resin, with consequent partial or complete loss of fluidity of the plastisol. The slow tumbling technique, mentioned earlier in this section, in which the resin is added in small portions to the plasticizer and other components, has been found effective in several cases. Mulling equipment such as the Simpson mixer has been used in the manufacture of plastisols of very high viscosity.

Storage and Aging Characteristics

The storage of unfused plastisols does not present any serious problem so long as their nature is kept in mind. Although the vinyl resin in these compositions is quite stable under normal atmospheric conditions, it is, however, susceptible to various degrees of decomposition (depending on the other components of the system) when in direct contact with certain metals, coatings, etc. Uncoated steel and galvanized containers should not be used for storage or shipping, since iron and zinc initiate and catalyze the decomposition of the vinyl resin. In some instances, dark-colored and black plastisols can be packaged and shipped in uncoated steel drums, provided the storage period does not exceed several weeks. Glass, aluminum, tin plate, and certain wooden, paper and fibreboard containers can be used quite safely, as well as steel containers lined with proper coatings (such as baked phenolics). In choosing the container for a plastisol, the chemical and physical properties of the latter should be considered, since softening or solution of the container lining, or chemical attack of the metal by the liquid components of the plastisol, may introduce extraneous foreign matter or discolor the product. Of course, care should be taken to ensure that containers are dry and clean before packaging.

The maximum safe storage temperature for these materials depends upon the specific compound. Although some plastisols can be safely stored at temperatures of 90 to 100°F, most should not be stored above 80°F for long periods of time. It is best to avoid sunlight, radiators, heaters, steam pipes, etc., in the storage area.

The aging characteristics of plastisols are variable. Depending upon the ultimate application of the plastisol, compositions of relatively poor viscosity-stability may be quite satisfactory if they can be used comparatively soon after manufacture. However, in most cases good viscosity-stability is a prime requisite. Properly formulated and compounded plastisols have been aged for several years without any detectable deterioration in the form of decomposition, phase-separation, discoloration, etc. These materials also exhibited good viscosity-stabilities, some maintaining their original viscosities and others showing increases of only about 10 per cent over the original values. However, generally speaking, the viscosity of a plastisol does increase with its age. Often this is a true rise in viscosity due to the inherent instability of the particular plastisol composition and/or improper mode of compounding, and it is generally attributed to the solvating action of the fluid medium upon the resin particles. In some instances increases in viscosity of aged plastisols are largely apparent rather than true increases, being really manifestations of their non-Newtonian nature. Settling out of resin is sometimes encountered in plastisols after prolonged aging. Very often minor changes in the formulation and/or compounding technique are found to be effective in eliminating this deficiency, which is usually attributed to insufficient solvation of the dispersed resin particles.

De-aeration of Plastisols

Since most plastisols are relatively viscous fluids, air entrapped in them during the course of manufacture generally escapes very slowly, if at all, and therefore, for most applications, it is necessary to de-aerate them. The need for de-aeration, however, is related to the end use. For example, thin coatings on fabric or embossed fabric coatings normally do not require de-aeration.

It should be noted that retention of air is by no means determined by viscosity alone; other specific properties of the plastisol, such as surface and interfacial tension, have definite influences on the degree to which air becomes occluded, and the ease with which it dissipates. More directly, the specific type of vinyl resin, the plasticizer and other components of the dispersion system, and also the mode of manufacture, frequently determine the ease of entrapment and release of air. Some plastisols, because of their inherent nature and the technique employed in the compounding, do not require anything more than short storage (hours to several days) for spontaneous de-aeration. Where de-aeration is necessary, this operation can be carried out in several ways.

For establishments of modest means, or in the case where the plastisols produced are specialty items and the volume does not warrant investment in equipment, there are several simple ways of carrying out reasonably effective de-aeration. In certain cases the incorporation of very small amounts of surface-active agents is effective in accelerating release of air to a point where storage alone produces substantially air-free material. Also, either alone or in conjunction with the preceding method, draining the plastisol onto a broad inclined plate in order to increase the exposed surface area is found to effect de-aeration in a number of instances. It is obvious that methods such as these are rather limited in their scope. Generally they are found effective in removing large occluded air bubbles (of diameter 1 mm and up), but of no value in removing finely dispersed air.

Subjecting the plastisol to a vacuum constitutes the most obvious approach. In its simplest form, this involves confining the material in a closed chamber which is then evacuated to a pressure of several mm of mercury, and allowing it to stand until the air has been brought to the surface; the time depends upon

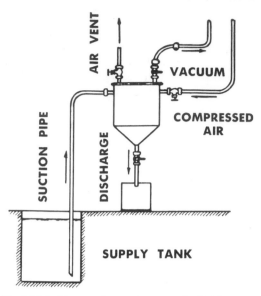

Fig. 10-16. Vacuum de-aeration setup for PVC pastes.

the specific plastisol (Fig. 10-16). Although repeated evacuations can thus ensure substantially air-free materials, it is found in actual practice that the
efficiency of this essentially static method can be greatly increased by mechanical
agitation of the plastisol while under vacuum. In plant practice, plastisols
compounded on a three-roll mill can be evacuated in a closed tank which can
be rolled or rocked, or which is equipped with an agitator. Materials manufactured in a pebble mill can be evacuated while in the mill, either during or
after the compounding. In the latter case, it is considered the better practice
to evacuate the mill completely, allow it to stand idle for 10 to 20 min,
roll for 1 to 2 min, and repeat these steps several times. Some plastisol
compositions are extremely resistant to de-aeration in a tank or pebble mill.
For these types a more efficient method of evacuating plastisols compounded
in the pebble mill or in an internal mixer is by an inversion of the preceding
de-aeration technique; that is, instead of permitting air to become dispersed
throughout the mass and then encountering great difficulty in its removal, the
air can be excluded throughout the whole course of compounding. This is
attained by thorough evacuation of the dry vinyl resin, pigment, etc., and
the introduction of the fluid components by means of the vacuum. With care
in maintaining good vacuum throughout the whole course of the mixing and
dispersing, good results can be obtained. Another method, which can be used
regardless of the method of compounding, consists of pulling the plastisol
down into an evacuated chamber in such a manner as to increase greatly the
area of fluid exposed to the reduced pressure. Such devices can be used as
perforated shower heads, screens or shallow inverted cones immediately at the

point of entry of the plastisol into the evacuated chamber. A modification of this method, which greatly increases the speed and efficiency of de-aeration, involves the use of centrifugal force in conjunction with vacuum (Fig. 10-17). The principles involved with the centrifuge are the same as in allowing the plastisol to flow under vacuum, but the volume and speed of handling are considerably greater. In this method, the plastisol is pumped or drawn into the apex of a conical centrifuge basket which is under high vacuum, and forced toward its periphery in a thin film along the wall of the cone. The separating forces produced are many times greater than gravity, and are limited only by the need to avoid separation of the resin, pigment, etc., from the liquid vehicle.

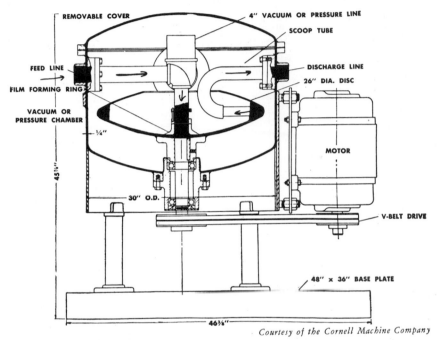

Courtesy of the Cornell Machine Company

Fig. 10-17. Machine for de-aeration by centrifugal action under vacuum.

Fusion of Plastisols

A plastisol, to be converted to usable form, i.e., to a solid state, must be heated to a point where the plasticizer and resin fuse into a single phase (disregarding pigments, fillers, etc.). What occurs during this process is a mutual solution of the resin and plasticizer. Thus the characteristics of both the resin and the plasticizer determine the minimum temperature at which a single phase is produced. Generally, temperatures in the range of 300 to 375°F are required to obtain the ultimate desired properties of the product. Some plastisols can be adequately fused even as low as 250°F; others may require temperatures near 400°F. Although the duration of the bake is of importance, particularly to ensure that the entire cross-section of the film reaches adequate temperature, it is the temperature which the plastisol reaches that is the most significant factor in proper fusion (Fig. 10-18). Once the average plastisol film reaches the optimum fusion temperature, for example 350°F, fusion and solution of the resin in the plasticizer proceeds at a rather rapid pace. The time for heat-transfer depends on the thickness of the film. For thin films, a few seconds at the fusion temperature is often sufficient; for heavier films, several minutes may suffice; but, in the case of 100-200-mil films, the time may be as long as 15 to 30 minutes unless dielectric heating is economical. Higher oven temperatures may be utilized to speed heat-transfer. Prolongation of the time of bake at temperatures below the fusion temperature of the material is not effective in producing a film of the optimum properties (Fig. 10-14, page 271). Baking at too high temperatures is inadvisable, since decomposition, sagging, run-off, and discoloration may develop.

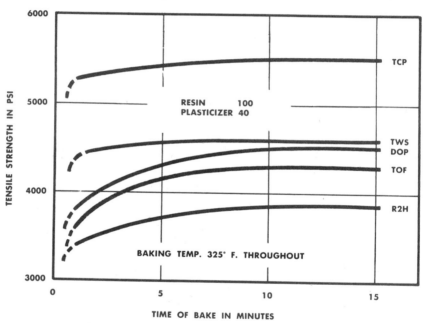

Fig. 10-18. Effect of baking time on strength of films.

The equipment used for the heat source will be dependent upon economic factors, type of product being coated or manufactured, etc. Gas- or oil-fired or electrically-heated ovens, infrared lamps, radiant-type heating equipment or hot liquid baths can be used. The ovens used should have adequate circulation of air to remove the small proportion of plasticizer volatilized during fusion. Cool spots in the oven should be avoided to prevent condensation and dripping of the plasticizer onto the product being manufactured.

LOW-TEMPERATURE-FUSING PLASTISOLS

Although most plastisols require temperatures of at least 300°F for complete fusion, there are also available certain special plastisols which may be fused at temperatures as low as 185°F. These materials do not have the same physical properties as those obtained from dispersions fused at the high temperatures generally used. Plastisols of this type find application for uses in which they must be fused in contact with plaster or special fabrics, or certain thermoplastics which cannot be subjected to temperatures above 200°F. The availability of these plastisols with low fusion temperatures also makes it easier for factories with low-temperature oven facilities (less than 250°F) to convert from rubber to plastisols.

EXPANDED PLASTISOLS

Various expanded or cellular plastisols are commercially available, involving several different methods of expansion, and substantial differences in density.

Those of lightest weight are expanded, by as much as 1000 per cent, by

Courtesy of Bayshore Industries, Inc.

Fig. 10-19. Expanded plastisols.

application of heat to a closed mold containing the dispersion used with a very powerful blowing agent. Production molds for this process may have to withstand pressures above 20,000 psi and are therefore limited to simple geometric shapes, which may later be die-cut or shaped to a desired form.

It is possible also to expand plastisols by incorporating salts which evolve gas at the fusion temperature of the plastisol. These do not require closed molds, but do reach the same degree of expansion.

Expanded plastisols of higher density are made from a specially compounded dispersion by use of a simple and inexpensive foaming apparatus. An expansion of approximately 350 per cent is obtained. Since expansion takes place at the point of discharge from a foaming vessel, rather than during fusion, the material may be poured into and fused in open molds, by techniques similar to cavity-molding of ordinary plastisols. Intricate shapes and minute detail are readily attainable.

Constant efforts are being made to develop a technique by which to combine the low density of the first type with the production advantages of the latter type.

Fig. 10-19 shows typical applications of expanded plastisols.

PLASTIGELS

Plastisols to which certain gelling agents have been added to produce a thickening effect are called "plastigels."

Preparation of Plastigels

The preparation of plastigels from vinyl dispersion resins involves only a minor modification of the familiar plastisol techniques. The plastisols used for making plastigels are prepared in the conventional manner. The additional step is the conversion of the plastisol to a plastigel by the addition of a gelling agent in a dough or pony mixer. Gelling agents which have been found effective are metallic soaps such as aluminum stearate, silica aerogels, and organophilic bentonites.

Viscosity of Plastigels

Freshly prepared plastigels are more mobile than those which have aged undisturbed for several hours. This is a decided advantage since less power is required to mix plastigels of high ultimate consistency. This change in consistency is thixotropic in nature; hence the mobility may be regained by subsequent agitation.

Methods of Use

Equipment unsuited for manufacturing vinyl-resin-base materials by hot processing techniques, because of lack of power, now may be suitable for handling plastigels. For example, plastigels can be used in many low-pressure calendering operations, such as those used in the production of linoleum, which were unsuited for handling vinyl resins by hot processing techniques. Plastigels may be embossed, extruded, calendered, molded or stamped at room temperatures with relatively low-pressure equipment. This may be advantageous to users who do not have conventional equipment for high pressure and hot processing of plastic products. Further, designing of dies is facilitated since there is little distortion in the extruded shapes. Compounds suitable for hand modeling have been made in an unlimited variety of colors and in a wide range of hardness.

Plastigels may be thinned, if necessary, with diluents for knife, spreader or roller coating. After mild drying, required to evaporate the diluent, the plastigels regain their original properties. Thus, coated products may be rolled, embossed or otherwise handled before fusion. The control over the flow which is obtained with plastigels makes it possible to coat open-weave cloth or porous surfaces without excessive penetration.

Dipping of heavy but uniform films is facilitated with plastigels since it is not necessary to preheat the object to prevent sagging and dripping.

Excess material, whether it be of incorrect dimensions or color, or that squeezed from a mold, may be reused before fusing.

Plastigels retain detail after forming and then fuse without measurable distortion. Fusion temperatures are between 300 and 375°F.

APPLICATIONS OF VINYL DISPERSIONS

Spread-coating

Coating of Paper. *Scope.* Vinyl resins have been used in one form or another as coatings for paper since their inception, to impart chemical inertness, abrasion resistance, water resistance, etc. Conversely, it is frequently desirable to modify the properties of vinyl film by the presence of a paper backing, so as to achieve lower cost, better dimensional stability, dead fold, or ease of application to other surfaces. While the combination of vinyl and paper may be effected by lamination, frictioning or calendering of a solvent-free compound, or by a solution or dispersion of the resin, the latter in either water or organic medium, only organic dispersions are considered here.

The uses for a vinyl-coated paper or a paper-backed film are manifold. The field of decoration offers limitless applications in publishing, novelties, home-decoration and furniture. Many uses suggest themselves for coverings where the greater base strength of cloth-backed vinyl is not needed, or where a thin coating of vinyl on paper serves as well as a heavier sheet of vinyl alone. The decorative solid colors, prints or embossed surface effects and the inherent properties of the vinyl film are combined in a form especially suitable for the decoration of large surfaces. Among the foremost in this field are floor- and wall-coverings, and these applications have been in commercial production for several years. More expendable decorative products for the home, such as place mats, table covers and shelf coverings, are also available in combinations of paper and vinyl. This use would seem capable of expansion to the covering of surfaces of factory-finished items for specific uses, wherein the paper would simplify the application of vinyl films to inexpensive structural materials, such as plywood and various composition panels. A host of uses on smaller items suggest themselves.

Containers for food-packaging have been made from vinyl-coated papers, although in this use they have been overshadowed to a great extent by polyethylene. Better abrasion-resistance, elastic recovery and heat-sealing properties are inherently more possible in vinyl compounds than in polyethylene.

Formulation. Dispersion compounds may be made in widely differing compositions. At the present time the variety of resins suitable for dispersions is not large, but more are becoming available. In general, specific properties are obtainable by formulation for the desired end use in the same way as for unsupported film or cloth-coatings, and the technique of application for coating paper does not impose any severe limitations.

Several varieties of resin are available, which require some variation in the technique of conversion to a usable coating. Some require milling and others require only simple mixing. Not only are the application properties — chiefly rheological — affected by the content and type of plasticizer, but the final film as well. As a result, to obtain the desired finished properties, and independently to control the application properties, it is sometimes necessary to include a portion of volatile solvent. To this extent the classification plastisol borders on or overlaps organosol.

Partly because of inherent differences in the resins themselves and partly because of the differences which can be introduced to some extent by volatile solvents, some selection of desired final results is possible by the choice of one or the other system. The production of a plastisol depends at least partly upon the poor solubility or swelling of the resin at room temperature in the properly formulated liquid phase. As a result, it tends to lose this liquid component when in contact with an absorptive surface. For this reason, plastisols tend to strike through a paper more readily than do organosols. This effect is also partly due to the almost complete lack of "set" until heated, as compared to an organosol, which tends to lose mobility as soon as coated, through partial loss of the volatile portion. An organosol, therefore, is more easily kept on the surface of the sheet. This distinction, and rheological differences of the wet coatings, also exert an influence on the tendency to lift fibers from the surface of some types of papers.

It should be borne in mind that these differences are all subject to considerable control by formulation, and by techniques of application and fusing. Likewise, these can be used for obtaining various end properties. For example, the penetration by plastisols, properly controlled, can be turned to advantage in securing improved adhesion.

For obtaining vinyl coatings on papers, dispersions possess a tremendous advantage over a calendered, frictioned or laminated film for a majority of uses, because of the comparative simplicity of their manufacture by relatively inexpensive equipment. Some sacrifice in latitude of formulation exists, in comparison with calendered film, because of the necessity of using only those plasticizers which do not adversely affect the coating operation by causing instability of viscosity through excessive solvent action. However, this restriction does not seriously limit their use.

Plastisols possess the important advantage of providing unlimited thickness of film without the complications of increasingly slow evaporation of solvent as thickness increases. In effect, this means that solvent-removal imposes no restriction on speed of production. Where harder films are required and/or lower viscosities are needed, the presence of some needed volatile thinner, of course, reduces this advantage. At the other extreme, it is sometimes difficult, by some methods of coating, to get sufficiently thin films from plastisols.

Any discussion of specific formulations for particular end uses is beyond the scope of this article, and highly technical. It should be mentioned, however, that the essential raw materials for dispersion-coating of paper are practically identical with those of coatings for application on other surfaces, or for free films.

The essential ingredients are resin, plasticizer and stabilizer. To these, in the case of organosols, are added volatile thinners. In both cases pigments, fillers, dyes and, occasionally, miscellaneous other materials (such as limited proportions of waxes or other resins) may be added. Next to the resin, the greatest influence on the finished film is exerted by the plasticizer, both quantity and type or types. The choice of the proper compounding materials enables the formulator to obtain the best compromise for the application in question, with regard to tensile strength, elongation, hardness, flexibility (at the desired temperature or temperature range), flammability, resistance to solvent or water, extractability, heat-stability, light-stability, color, opacity, electrical properties, etc., and of course economy. Indirectly affecting the film but in most cases nearly as important are the properties of viscosity (type and degree), viscosity-stability, and drying or fusing characteristics. The latter is so much faster than with most film-forming materials that the variations are relatively minor, but they are still of some importance. These application properties also are subject to control by formulation.

Application. Application of an organic coating resolves itself principally into a method of applying a smooth wet film of a uniform controlled thickness to the web of paper. The ideal coating machine would perform this function with little attention from the operator, with preset and reproducible adjustments, irrespective of web speed, viscosity of coating or thickness of web; without damage or defects from occasional foreign matter in the coatings. It would embody a reservoir containing a minimum quantity of coating; would involve little or no adjustment or change for varying widths, and would be easily cleaned. Dispersion coatings have a few characteristics which emphasize the importance of certain of these machine features. As these coatings are not true solutions, they are not capable of being filtered to the same degree as true-solution coating materials. This increases the need for a machine which minimizes the damage caused from particles lodging in the metering clearances.

Some organosol formulations will air-dry to a powdery residue of no film strength, which is a source of trouble by causing streaks. A small reservoir is of help in reducing this trouble. Most dispersion coatings are of a film thickness which rules out certain types of coating devices which apply very thin films, such as engraved rolls. The flow characteristics and rapid set of many dispersion formulas make it desirable that the applied film be initially as level as possible. Since roll changes and many intangible factors frequently make changes of speed or stops unavoidable, it is highly desirable that film thickness be independent of speed.

On a nonabsorbing surface, the thickness of the fused coating is determined by the thickness of the layer of dispersion which is deposited. With plastisols, since they contain no volatile ingredient, the thickness of the fused coating will be essentially the same as that of the layer of dispersion, except to the extent that some minor percentage of the plasticizer is driven off by the heat of the fusing oven. With organosols, the relation between thickness of layer deposited and thickness of fused coating can be calculated as the ratio of the total volume to the volume of nonvolatile ingredients. On an absorbing surface, however, such a calculation is invalidated to the extent that the dispersion enters the paper, and correction must be made on the basis of trial or experience.

For most applications the reverse-roll coater probably most dependably approaches the requirements discussed (Figs. 10-20, a, b and c). In common with calenders and any other device which attempts to maintain a uniform gap under varying hydraulic pressures (as influenced by gap, speed and viscosity), the problem increases tremendously with increase in the width of the web and hence in the length of the rolls. Crowning of rolls is only an approach to the solution, for a specific set of conditions. More precision in adjustments is also desirable. The high turbulence in the reservoir caused by high differential surface speeds is unavoidable, but undesirable, in that it causes occlusion of air and limits the viscosities which may be used. Undoubtedly refinements in design for this type of coater will continue, and will diminish some present difficulties.

Knife coaters are far simpler in design, and meet many requirements, but offer considerably less control of thickness in the face of changes in viscosity and particularly in speed (Figs. 10-21, 10-22, 10-23, 10-24). The lower web-strength of paper, as contrasted with fabrics, rules out in most cases the type of spreader in which pressure of the knife against the web is secured solely by tension on the web. It is usually necessary to employ a drum, roll, stationary bed or blanket backing.

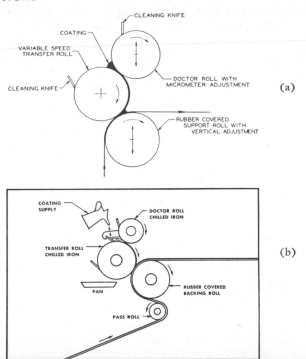

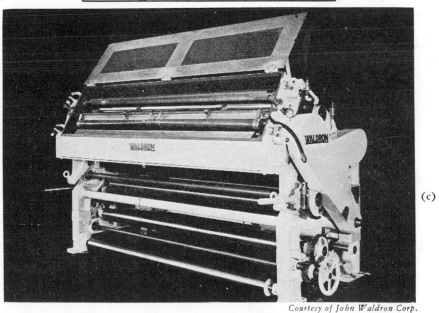

Courtesy of John Waldron Corp.

Fig. 10-20 (a, b and c). Reverse-roll coater.

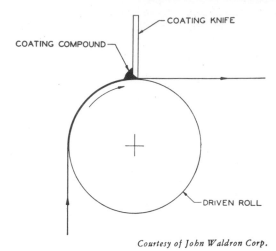

Courtesy of John Waldron Corp.

Fig. 10-21. Knife-over-roll coating head.

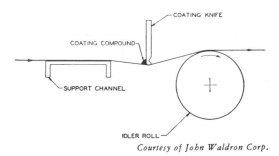

Courtesy of John Waldron Corp.

Fig. 10-22. Floating doctor knife.

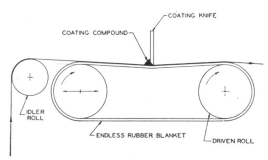

Courtesy of John Waldron Corp.

Fig. 10-23. Continuous-blanket knife coater.

The air-knife coater possesses an important advantage in not having a positive clearance which can become blocked by foreign particles, which result in streaks; this is an inherent difficulty present in all knife coaters with positive backing. On the other hand, the loss of volatile material in the surplus material removed by the air knife presents a difficulty.

Dip-coating, depending solely upon the viscosity of the coating liquid and the speed of the web, with no mechanical metering, should be adaptable in many cases.

A valuable adjunct to coating-control would be an accurate, nondestructive, continuously indicating or recording wet-film gauge. Gauges based on the absorption of beta rays from a radioactive source, recently introduced, may prove the answer to this requirement. The coater of the future might well be coupled to such a device, to maintain thickness automatically.

Problems of applying coatings can usually be approached from two angles, mechanical design to accommodate the physical properties of the coating liquids, and formulation of the coating liquid to meet the mechanical

Courtesy of Frank W. Egan Co.

Fig. 10-24. Continuous-blanket knife coater.

limitations of the machine. Auxiliary equipment is important, and must be properly integrated with the coater itself.

This always involves unwind and rewind stands, and may include smoothing calenders, embossers, cooling drums, web-steering devices, tension-controls, trimmers, slitters, predriers, static-eliminators and many other machines for special purposes or special products. In the simplest form of coating line, uniform control of tension is desirable; it becomes imperative where several operations are conducted in series. Direct-current drives, properly synchronized, are the most common solution. Hydraulic rewinds and variable-speed transmissions are adequate for many operations (Figs. 10-25, 10-26, 10-27).

Fusion. After application of a wet film, the second phase in the production of a coated paper involves the conversion of this deposit into a continuous solid film. In the case of vinyl dispersions this is purely a physical change, brought about by the heat, which activates the plasticizer as a solvent for the dispersed vinyl particles, and effects gelation of the mass. In the case of organosols, evaporation of the volatile thinners must take place, preferably preceding the actual fusion, but not necessarily as a distinctly separate process. Fusion is often erroneously called curing; the latter term is more properly applied to compositions which undergo a chemical change, such as vulcanization, oxidation or polymerization.

Convection Ovens. The rapidity of the conversion of film from liquid to solid, involving a few minutes at most, makes possible the use of the simplest form of web-drier, a straight-pass tunnel oven. In its simplest form this is

Courtesy of Industrial Ovens, Inc.

Fig. 10-26. Reverse-roll coater and fusing oven for organosols or plastisols.

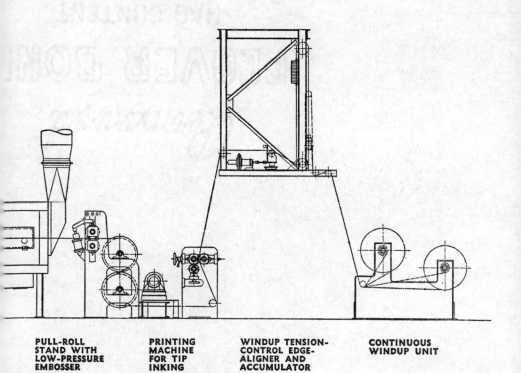

PULL-ROLL STAND WITH LOW-PRESSURE EMBOSSER

PRINTING MACHINE FOR TIP INKING

WINDUP TENSION-CONTROL EDGE-ALIGNER AND ACCUMULATOR

CONTINUOUS WINDUP UNIT

Fig. 10-27. Paper-coater.

a heated tunnel. When web strength is sufficient, no conveyor is needed, except as a simplified threading device. Fusion of the resin requires final temperatures of 300 to 375°F, and such temperature must be provided, at least at the outgoing end. To achieve these temperatures by steam-heating is difficult because of the pressures required. Oil-fired heat-exchangers are commonly used. "Dowtherm" or hot-oil systems are alternatives.

Unless plastisols are used exclusively, provision must be made for sufficient exhaust to remove solvents. A good margin of safety below lower explosive limits is provided by exhausting 10,000 cubic feet of air (measured at room temperature) per gallon of solvent entering the oven. In designing the fans, consideration must be given to the actual exhaust temperatures. Volatile content of the coatings, speeds, film weight and widths all influence the quantity evaporated. Uniform distribution of the fresh heated replacement air, and uniform removal from all portions of the oven, are essential. This is usually accomplished by plenum chambers paralleling the web, either above or below or both. Zoning of the oven into three or more sections maintained at different temperatures is almost essential when solvents are present, in order to remove the solvent gradually, and then ultimately to bring the film to fusion temperature. Too high an air temperature at the entering end results in a flashing off of the solvent, which causes bubbles or blisters. Less air need be exhausted from the fusion sections, thereby permitting the economies of recirculation, but actual tests for solvent content in the oven may be necessary to establish safe conditions. It is of course essential that temperatures be accurately controlled.

Radiant Heat. The fusion of a plastisol is simplified by the almost total absence of explosion hazard and the lack of need for gradual heating for removal of solvent. This makes possible the use of radiant and conducted heat, which provide better heat-transfer. Infrared or radiant heat may be generated from incandescent bulbs, heater strips or "black heat" glass-cloth panels, or gas-fired units. A considerable shortening of time, and therefore of length of fusion section, is possible by this method. Radiant heat may, also, of course, be used as an adjunct to convection ovens, where they are necessary for removal of solvent.

General Construction and Precautions. It is obvious that the properties of a vinyl-coated paper may be influenced by the properties of the paper as well as by those of the vinyl, or may be modified in other ways. The adhesion of vinyls to paper involves little or no chemical affinity; it depends almost entirely upon a mechanical keying into the paper fibers. For this reason adhesion to a dense paper, or one which is repellent to organic liquids, is relatively difficult to achieve. One approach is the use of primer coats of resins having better adhesion or penetration into the surface, to which the dispersion vinyls will subsequently adhere. Vinyl latices, solution-grade vinyls and a limited number of resins of other types can be used, provided they are carefully chosen.

Papers themselves may be modified, as by saturation with resins or elastomers for improvement in internal strength, tensile strength, stiffness, etc.

Depending partly upon the density of the paper, the high temperatures and perhaps poor affinity of the vinyls for the paper makes moisture in the paper something of a problem. It is desirable to use paper of the lowest possible moisture content, and this may in some cases require pre-drying.

Products. Typical coated-paper products are shown in Figs. 10-28, 10-29, 10-30.

Fabric-Coating with Vinyl Dispersions. The exceptional physical qualities of vinyl resins have made them very desirable as coating materials for fabrics. Vinyl-coated fabrics have countless uses, such as upholstery, raincoats, automobile seat-covers, baby pants, awnings, etc. A large proportion of these products are coated by use of organosols or plastisols.

The cost of vinyl solution coatings, made from resins of the highest molecular weight, was almost prohibitive, because of the low solids content attainable and the expensive solvents required. With the development of dispersion resins, organosols and plastisols have largely replaced solution coatings, both of vinyl and of other resins.

Formulations of these dispersions will not be discussed here, as this phase of the subject has been covered in the discussion on coating paper. In general, the same types of formulation apply here, with the possible exception of the viscosity range. It is usually desirable to have a rather high viscosity for application on cloth, unless penetration is desired. For impregnation of the cloth, the dispersion should have a low viscosity.

The reason for the use of materials of higher viscosity is that the majority of cloth-coaters apply the compounds with a knife coating-head, and it is desirable to have a compound which will form a rolling bank in front of the knife. Low-viscosity materials will not form a proper bank, will run off the edges, and tend to penetrate the cloth. Both organosols and plastisols are widely used for coating cloth; the choice depends upon the equipment available. Many cloth-coaters favor organosols because they have large numbers of coating machines in their shops and find it impracticable to have a fusing unit attached to each machine. Organosol coatings can be spread, dried solvent-free, gelled, and rolled up, to be fused at a later time. While plastisols may be applied by this technique, they must be fused directly after coating, because until fused they remain fluid, and therefore cannot be rolled up.

In coating fabrics with low-viscosity dispersions, it is seldom necessary to use a prime coat. Some fabrics made of synthetic fibers are exceptions to this, since comparatively poor adhesion is obtained between them and vinyl coatings, but this use of primer is required only when the coating is to be applied to one side. If both sides of the fabric made of synthetic fibers are to be coated, interlocking of the coats of vinyl dispersion can be accomplished by penetration, and in that way mechanical adhesion can be secured without the use of a primer.

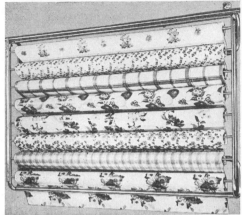

Fig. 10-28. Vinyl-coated paper.

Courtesy of The Munising Paper Co.

Courtesy of Paulsboro Manufacturing Co.   *Courtesy of Paulsboro Manufacturing Co.*

Fig. 10-29. Vinyl-coated floor-covering.   Fig. 10-30. Vinyl-coated floor-covering.

With high-viscosity dispersion coatings, it is nearly always necessary to use a primer, not necessarily from the standpoint of adhesion, but because they tend to flow under heat before they gel and thus become absorbed into the fabric, rather than lying on the surface. This observation does not apply to dispersions of the plastigel type (i.e., plastisols of high yield value).

Other methods of coating dispersions on fabric are in use, such as immersion for two-side coating, reverse-roll coating, etc., many of which are covered in more detail in the discussion on paper-coating.

Typical coated-fabric products are shown in Figs. 10-31, 10-32, 10-33, 10-34.

Coating of Aluminum Foil with Vinyl Dispersions. Organosols and plastisols have found increasing utility in coating moisture-vapor-barrier materials such as aluminum foil. This application serves a multiple purpose. It improves the tear strength and puncture strength of the foil, makes the foil

Fig. 10-31. Safety clothing.

Courtesy of Standard Safety Equipment Co.

Fig. 10-32. Plastisol-coated cloth.

Courtesy of L. E. Carpenter Co.

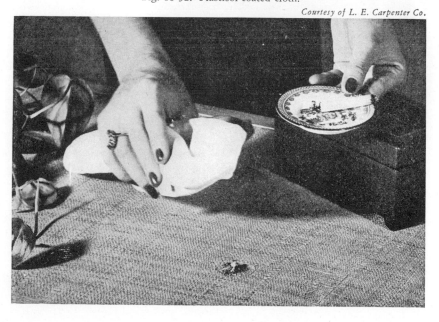

Fig. 10-33. Printed cloth coated with organosol.

Courtesy of M. J. Fassler & Co., Inc.

Fig. 10-34. Venetian-blind tape.

Manufactured by Hunter-Douglas Corp.

heat-sealable, and provides protection against moisture vapor in case of failure of the foil.

The procedure for coating foil is identical with that described for casting film (see the following section). In this case, however, it is necessary to achieve firm adhesion between the foil and the film, either by using a primer coat having adhesion to both foil and film, or by compounding the dispersion in such a manner that its adhesion to aluminum is secure.

Coating with vinyl dispersions is the most practicable and cheapest method for applying vinyl films of from 1.5 mils to 6 mils to foil.

Casting Film from Vinyl Dispersions

In certain cases it is advantageous to manufacture unsupported film by casting plastisols or organosols. Because of their greater versatility as regards formulation, organosols have been used for this purpose to a much greater extent than plastisols.

A few specific examples in which production of film by this method may be considered advantageous over calendering are:

1. manufacture of uniform film one to two mils in thickness;
2. production of high-quality light-gauge printed films;
3. production of stress-free films, which will not be distorted by heat;
4. production of various surface effects on this film, i.e., printing or embossing (see p. 328).

Any equipment designed for coating a material in the form of a web can be used for casting film. It is necessary only to provide that the film shall not adhere to the web, or carrier, in order that it may be stripped from it when fused. The machines most commonly used are the knife coater and the reverse-roll coater. The greatest amount of cast film, by far, has been produced on the reverse-roll coater, which will cast a reasonably uniform film despite small irregularities in and on the carrier.

The dispersion is prepared by conventional means to provide the properties desired in the end product. The viscosity is adjusted to the most efficient operation of the coating machine. On a reverse-roll coater, viscosities should be of the order of 1000 cp. The knife coater usually requires a slightly higher consistency. Coatings which exhibit considerable dilatancy at the coating speeds must be avoided.

Because organosols lose solvent fairly rapidly and tend to form dry, hard particles, it is usually wise to try to maintain a closed system from the storage reservoir to and including the coating head. A recirculation system containing a straining device is also essential in connection with this operation.

The casting surface or carrier is one of the most important parts of the equipment for casting film. The carrier may be an endless belt of stainless steel, heavy aluminum foil, or various grades of treated kraft paper of high tensile strength. Paper, being the cheapest, is probably the most widely used means of carrying the cast film.

Many of the larger paper companies have developed suitable treated papers. The paper must necessarily be strong, must be able to stand temperatures up to 400°F for short periods, must not have too high a moisture content, and above all must release the film easily when the two are finally separated. A good casting paper may be reused 5 to 7 times.

The casting operation itself requires, as mentioned above, a coating head, a carrier, a drying and fusing oven, cooling rolls, a stripping device and a rewind.

The carrier is coated with the required thickness of dispersion, calculated on the basis of the solids content of the dispersion, to yield a fused film of the desired thickness. Allowance is usually made, however, for shrinkage due to loss of plasticizer in fusing, particularly in the case of organosols. The wet film on the carrier is conveyed into a zoned oven which has a first zone temperature of 175 to 225°F, with circulating air to evaporate volatile solvents. In subsequent zones the temperature rises gradually to 400 to 425°F, at which temperature the fusion takes place. The fused film is carried through multiple cooling rolls, and subsequently is separated from the carrier. Two rolls are made on the rewind, one of cast unsupported film, and one of carrier paper. If an endless belt is used, then the film is separated from it and rolled up after cooling.

When a plastisol is used, it is not necessary to zone the oven, as the material can be brought directly to the fusing temperature from the coating head.

The majority of film being produced at present is decorated by printing. Cast film may be printed in two ways. One method is to leave the film on the carrier paper, print the design, dry, cool, and strip. The common method, however, is to print the carrier paper first with a design which is a mirror image of the design desired on the film, by using special inks formulated for easy release from the paper. Film is cast upon the printed carrier. When the film is stripped, the print is stripped with it, leaving the carrier clean for reuse. The printed design itself is fused into the film. This method of manufacturing printed film gives the most faithful reproduction, and the best register.

Application of Dispersions by Dip-coating

One of the major advantages of vinyl dispersions over most other coating compositions is their unique adaptability to the relatively rapid and economical deposition of heavy layers of a decorative, highly chemically resistant, and physically tough coating. They can be applied by comparatively simple dipping operations to irregular and intricately shaped objects which are non-porous, and dimensionally stable up to the fusion temperature.

Dip-Coating with Organosols. As already mentioned, the ratio of the thickness of the fused coating (on a nonabsorbing surface) to the thickness of the wet coating will be the same as the ratio of the volume of nonvolatiles in the organosol to the total volume of the organosol. Wet coatings deposited by a single dip will range in thickness from a few tenths of a mil to as much as 15 mils. Heavier fused coatings can be produced by multiple dipping, with complete or incomplete drying and fusion of intermediate dips. The manner of applying the coating will depend on the nature of the organosol used.

In the dip-coating of continuous lengths of papers, fabrics, filaments, hoses, tubing, etc., the thickness of the coating deposited can be controlled by mechanical devices such as blades, gaskets, etc., by adjustments of the fluid characteristics of the organosol, and by the rate of passage of the object through it. In the case of the coating of single units rather than continuous lengths, the rate and manner of withdrawal of the object from the fluid organosol, determined to a considerable extent by the shape and size of the former and the flow properties of the latter, are of prime importance. While organosols of nearly Newtonian flow characteristics may be used, generally thixotropic compositions are employed for dip applications. With these, rather rapid withdrawal rates may be employed and very little draining occurs.

Dip-Coating with Plastisols. An outstanding advantage of plastisols over organosols lies in the fact, already indicated, that thicknesses of coatings obtainable with the former do not have the limitations imposed by volatile ingredients. Plastisol coatings are generally softer and more resilient than organosol coatings. When wet plastisol films are fused, the shrinkage is comparatively small.

By a single cold dip, plastisol coatings ranging from a fraction of a mil to 60 mils can be deposited. In cold dipping, the thickness of the film deposited is directly determined by the flow characteristics (rheological properties) of the dispersion. For those plastisols which are substantially Newtonian in their flow properties, cold dipping and appropriate draining will generally deposit relatively thin films of the order of one to several mils per dip. On the other hand, extremely thixotropic plastisols, or those having pseudoplastic flow, will deposit, with proper technique, much heavier coatings.

The technique of hot dipping in plastisols takes direct advantage of the effect of heat in developing the solvent action of the plasticizer, and provides a means of depositing relatively thick coatings. The object to be coated is heated, and immersed while hot into the plastisol. The heat given off by the object will partially set a definite increment or thickness of coating on the object. On withdrawing, that portion of the coating that has been so set will not drain off. Single hot dips frequently can deposit coatings up to $\frac{1}{8}$ or $\frac{1}{4}$ in., and heavier coatings are feasible by multiple hot-dips, with partial fusion of each intermediate coat.

In hot dipping, a number of factors have a direct bearing upon the thickness of coating deposited; for any specific plastisol the following considerations have been found to be very important:

1. the mass and shape (ratio of area to volume), not only of the whole object, but also of the sections of it;

2. the temperature of the object at the instant of dipping;

3. the specific heat and specific gravity of the material(s) from which the object is made;

4. the temperature of the plastisol at the time of dipping;

5. the specific heat and specific gravity of the plastisol;

6. the duration of the hot dip;

7. the effect of baking temperatures on the flow characteristics of the plastisol.

Other things being equal, the thickness of the coating set by the heat of the object dipped will be greatest when the ratio of mass to surface area is greatest, since thus a maximum of heat to set the plastisol is available per unit of area. Thus, under given conditions, thicker coatings can be deposited on objects of simple shape (sphere, cube, etc.) than on those of intricate shape.

It is obvious that the higher the temperature at the instant of dipping, the greater the thickness of coating deposited. If all of the other listed factors are held constant, controlling the temperature of the object at the instant of dipping is probably the easiest method of controlling the thickness deposited.

It is also obvious that the specific heat of the object being dipped is an important factor in the thickness of the coating deposited. The tendency of objects of low specific heat to produce relatively thin coatings by this method can be overcome by altering other factors which influence the thickness.

Prolongation of the time of immersion also will increase the thickness deposited, although, depending upon the flow characteristics of the plastisol, it may prolong the time required for draining before fusion can be undertaken. The excess plastisol adhering to the plastisol set by the hot dip will, in the case of plastisols having nearly Newtonian flow characteristics, continue to drain for a considerable time, while in the case of thixotropic or pseudoplastic plastisols little or no draining will occur, depending upon the degree of thixotropy or pseudoplasticity.

The temperature of the plastisol itself immediately prior to the hot-dipping has a very pronounced effect on the thickness deposited. Here the higher the temperature of the plastisol, the greater the thickness deposited. As mentioned previously, plastisols should not be maintained at temperatures above 90°F for a long time; therefore, little can be accomplished in raising the temperature of the plastisol above this safe storage temperature. However, within the normal ambient temperature range of 65 to 90°F the thickness deposited by hot-dip technique varies in the order of one mil per degree, for certain plastisols. Successive hot-dipping of objects in a tank of plastisol over the course of several hours will raise the temperature of the plastisol, and progressively heavier thicknesses will be deposited. It is therefore advisable to maintain the plastisol at a temperature which gives optimum thickness, by means of cooling coils or jackets, and to provide slow mechanical agitation to maintain uniformity of temperature.

Finally, the flow characteristics, or rather their change with change in temperature, may have a significant effect on the appearance and thickness of the fused coating. If the partially set film of plastisol undergoes a marked reduction in viscosity during baking, sagging will result, with local thinning of the deposit, or irregular surface appearance.

Technique of Dip-Coating. The technique used in dipping depends upon the flow characteristics of the dispersion used. Dispersions of nearly Newtonian flow properties are used for the application of relatively thin films. With such dispersions, controlled rates of withdrawal are required for deposition of uniform thickness. Usually, withdrawal rates of 4 to 12 in. per minute are employed. For the deposition of thick films by cold-dip technique, dispersions of highly thixotropic or pseudoplastic flow are required, and in these cases rates of withdrawal are relatively unimportant. The hot-dip technique lends itself primarily to plastisols and not to organosols, because of the volatile vehicles present in the latter.

When sufficient thickness cannot be obtained in a single dip, multiple dips may be used. With organosols the volatilization of the diluent sets the coating sufficiently to permit a subsequent dipping. With plastisols the coating should be partially fused, at temperatures usually ranging from 225 to 300°F, before the application of the subsequent coat. Full fusion of each coat is permissible but, in such cases, a longer baking or a higher temperature in the fusion of the final coat is necessary to ensure a perfect bond between successive coats. Separation, or delamination, of successive coats is likely to occur when each coat is fully fused, because of the relatively low thermal conductivity of the fused dispersion. To prevent this, sufficient heat must be applied so that the interface of each coat reaches its fusion temperature. The final temperature required depends upon the characteristics of the dispersion employed, the size of the object coated, and the thickness of the coating.

Coatings of vinyl dispersions have very poor adhesion to metal surfaces; hence, if the coating must be bonded to the surface, the use of special priming coats is necessary. In addition to having good adhesion to the substrate, the applied primer film must have a certain degree of compatibility with the ultimate fused vinyl dispersion, but if the primer blends too readily with the dispersion it will be absorbed during fusion, and its value as a bond with the metal surface will be lost.

Primers are compounded from mixtures of resins, and are sold under proprietary designations. No single class of resins can be claimed to have all the properties required. Primers are applied by any of the customary methods, i.e., dip, spray, roller-coating, etc. Specific primers may be air-dried or baked before the application of the vinyl dispersion.

As in any other process of coating, the surface to be coated must be thoroughly cleaned, with special treatments if required, in order to enhance the adhesion.

Fig. 10-35. Electroplating racks being dipped in vinyl plastisol at the F. D. Pace Co.

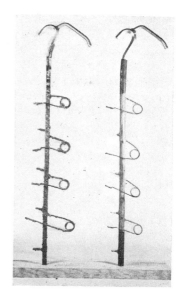

Fig. 10-36. Two racks which have been in lead-plating service, in contact with 27 oz. NaOH per gallon of solution at 120°F. The rack on the left illustrates a solvent solution type of rack-coating after two weeks service. The rack on the right represents a vinyl plastisol after eight months service.

Under optimum conditions, bond strengths of 50 to 80 pounds per linear in. can be expected.

Typical Application of Plastisol Dip-Coatings. *Rack-coatings.* Plastisols were introduced to the plating industry as rack-coatings about 1945, and have largely supplanted all other types of coatings, such as rubber insulation, resin solution coatings, tapes, etc. For this application they must have the following characteristics:

Chemical Resistance:

    a. must withstand intermittent or continuous immersion in dilute and concentrated acids and alkalies, at both room and elevated temperatures, for long periods of time;

    b. must withstand plating solutions (such as oxidizing conditions found in a chromium-plating bath);

    c. must not undergo even minor degradation which may contaminate or poison the plating solutions;

Physical Properties:

    a. toughness, resiliency, and retention of these properties when used in plating solutions;

    b. resistance to rapid changes of temperature;

Adhesion:

    a. good initial adhesion to metal rack, and retention of this adhesion in service;

Ease of Application:

    a. applicability by dipping, preferably with equipment normally available in plating shops.

The application normally consists of dip-coating with primer, preheating the rack to about 350°F, hot-dipping in the plastisol, and final fusing (Figs. 10-35, 10-36).

Glove-Coatings. Plastisols were first used in place of rubber as a coating for industrial gloves about 1946. Because of the much shorter time required to harden the coating, and the greater wear-resistance, plastisols are now used to coat most of the industrial fabric gloves today. In this application, the gloves are usually supported on a metal form, and are coated by dipping, drained from 10 to 30 min, and baked at 300 to 375°F for 10 to 20 min. The overall coating time, therefore, ranges from 20 to 60 min, as compared with the several hours required for vulcanizing rubber-coated gloves. The flow characteristics of the plastisol required for glove-coating are largely governed by the weight or mesh of the fabric, and the thickness of coating desired. When specific resistance to chemicals is required, plastisols can be formulated

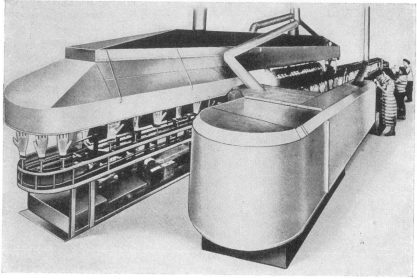

Courtesy of Sarjanian Glove Co.

Fig. 10-37. Automatic glove-coating machine.

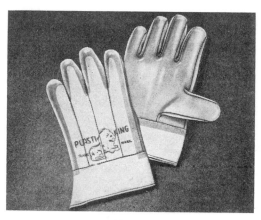

Fig. 10-38. Plastisol-coated gloves.

Courtesy of Sarjanian Glove Co.

Fig. 10-39. Vinyl-plastisol-covered glove.

Courtesy of Hood Rubber Co., A Division of The B. F. Goodrich Co.

to meet a wide range of conditions. By dip-coating the fabricated glove, all seams are filled and a continuous film, impervious to most liquids, envelops the fabric (Figs. 10-37, 10-38, 10-39).

Wire Goods. Probably one of the best known examples of coated wire goods is the dish-drainer basket (see Fig. 10-40). In this application vinyl dispersions, particularly organosols, have largely supplanted rubber coatings. The organosol coating exhibits outstanding resistance to abrasion, soap and detergents, and eliminates the "gumming" experienced with former coatings.

The organosols used for coating wire goods are highly thixotropic and deposit, in a single dip application, films of 40 to 60 mils. The rate of withdrawal is quite rapid, and little or no draining is required. Baking is carried out in large conveyor-type ovens, with low-temperature stages to drive off the volatiles before final fusion.

Plastisols can also be formulated which by slow dipping methods will not drip or flow appreciably when subjected to the fusing operation (see Fig. 10-41).

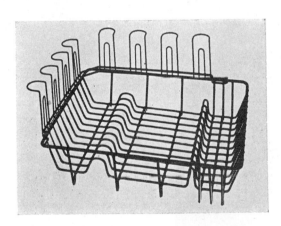

Fig. 10-40. Organosol-coated wire dish-drainer basket.

Courtesy of Artistic Wire Products Co.

Strippable Coatings and Dip-Molding. The foregoing examples all involve the application of dip coatings to surfaces of articles made of metal, fabric, wood, plastic, glass, etc. In most of these cases adequate adhesion of the coating can be obtained only by the use of a primer, by the slight shrinkage of the coating, or by a combination of both. By omitting these steps, however, the lack of adhesion between the coatings and the objects may be used to good advantage, in applying strippable coatings and in dip-molding.

Strippable coatings are sometimes used for masking, when it is desired to paint, plate, or otherwise coat only part of an object. They may be used also

Fig. 10-41. Soap dish
coated with plastisol.

Courtesy of American Anode, Inc.

as protection against rust and other damage to parts or assemblies during shipment and storage.

Dip-molding involves the manufacture of hollow objects, such as unsupported gloves and overshoes (Fig. 10-42), by stripping them from dipping
molds. A mold-release agent may sometimes be required, to facilitate stripping.
A very wide range of articles can be made in this manner.

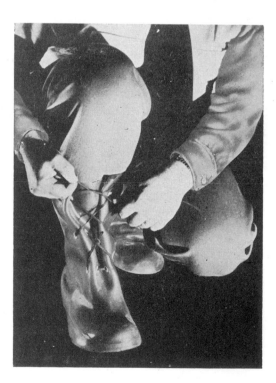

Fig. 10-42. Decontamination
boots made from plastisol.

Courtesy of American Anode, Inc.

Miscellaneous. Plastisol dip-coatings are also being applied to such widely varied articles as tool-handles, lamp-sockets, bobby pins, brackets, electrical assemblies, etc. Mass-produced articles may be dip-coated automatically by placing them on conveyors with special mandrels or holding fixtures, and passing them through the preheating, dipping, fusing and cooling stages under such accurately controlled conditions that defective parts are held to an absolute minimum. Provisions may also be made for automatic removal of completed articles from holding fixtures. Figs. 10-43, 10-44, 10-45, 10-46, 10-47.

Slush-Molding of Vinyl Plastisols

Slush-molding of vinyl plastisols to produce hollow flexible articles offers a number of advantages. Such articles can be produced in inexpensive molds. If large quantities are desired, duplicate molds can be readily made, and the molding equipment is comparatively simple.

The first real impetus to slush-molding of plastisols came with the realization of its applicability to the doll industry. Slush-molded plastisol arms and legs for dolls were found superior in feel, texture, color-retention and washability to doll parts made of latex, such as had already been on the market for many years. Molding of certain doll parts from rubber has always had a number of drawbacks. In order to mold rubber parts, complete redesign is often necessary so that the piece can be removed from the mold and core. With slush-molding, design changes necessitated in rubber because of reverse undercuts are entirely eliminated. Also, many items that are technically impossible to manufacture in rubber, or uneconomical because of cost, are now entirely feasible in vinyl by the slush-molding process. Articles which formerly could not be made of rubber because of low-temperature crystallization can now be manufactured from plastisols formulated to serve at temperatures —70 to 160°F.

Briefly stated, slush-molding consists of producing the desired thickness of coating on the inside wall of a mold, fusing, and then removing the finished article from the mold without distortion or tearing.

Molds. Slush-molding makes it possible to produce quickly and economically a finished plastic sample of an engineer's or designer's brainchild, and thus gives an opportunity to try out new ideas by means of sample pieces made quickly and inexpensively. Such sample pieces can be submitted to prospective customers for approval or change of design.

The first step in making a mold is the preparation of a drawing of the desired item by an artist familiar with slush-molding work. Then a model is made which is transferred into wax. Now the first mold is made, by electroforming over the wax model, the first layer being silver, the second nickel, and the third copper. The electroforming is carried out until the total thickness of the mold is approximately $\frac{1}{16}$ in. After the electroforming is completed

Courtesy of Stemco Corporation

Fig. 10-43. Ramset tool: the safety shield is coated with a plastisol.

Courtesy of United Chromium, Inc.

Fig. 10-44. Grain-mash conveyor scoop coated with a plastisol.

Courtesy of United Chromium, Inc.

Fig. 10-45. Speedometer cables coated with a plastisol.

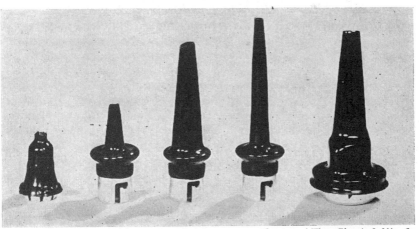

Courtesy of Watts Electric & Mfg. Co.

Fig. 10-46. Plastisol-dipped sockets.

Courtesy of Watts Electric & Mfg. Co.

Fig. 10-47. Over-all view of plastisol dipping operation.

the wax is melted out. The cost of manufacturing these molds is very low, actually being less than 1 per cent of the cost of manufacturing a comparable machined steel mold for high-pressure molding. For additional molds, a number of vinyl slush-molded parts are produced from the initial mold, and on these the moldmaker electroforms duplicate molds which are identical with the original.

Factors in Plastisol Formulations. The plastisol used in a given slush-molding job will depend on three factors:

1. the molder's technique and equipment;

2. variations in shape, size and wall thickness of the article;

3. physical properties required in the finished article, such as color, flexibility at various temperatures, grease-resistance, electrical characteristics, etc.

For slush-molding, viscosities from 1000 to 20,000 centipoises have been used.

Typical Methods of Manufacturing Vinyl Slush-Moldings. There are many different designs of slush-molding machinery. The design will depend on the end product. The methods of slush-molding are being constantly improved and mechanized. Two typical examples are described below.

Method No. 1. The molds are placed on a conveyor belt having positions for as many molds as desired. The vinyl plastisol is poured into a mold until it is filled to the top (Fig. 10-48). This mold, on the conveyor belt, is carried through an oven where temperatures between 210 and 600°F gel the plastisol next to the wall of the mold. The thickness of this gelled plastisol at a given oven temperature is determined by several factors, such as the thickness of the metal wall of the mold, the length of time the mold is in the oven, and the gelling characteristics of the plastisol used. The mold is now turned upside down, and the plastisol remaining in liquid form is dumped out, while the semi-fused material next to the wall remains in place (Fig. 10-49). The mold is then carried to the second oven, where the coating is completely fused (Fig. 10-50). Passage through a cooling chamber cools the mold sufficiently to permit removal of the finished piece by blowing it out with compressed air or collapsing it with vacuum. Whichever system is used, the article is easily and quickly removed.

In the second oven it is advisable to provide a cam arrangement which slowly revolves the molds so that an even fusing is obtained. In an oven designed with two open ends this is essential, because all the oven heat does not follow a uniform pattern, tending to dissipate from the ends of the oven. By rotating the mold, an even temperature is maintained on all sides of the mold.

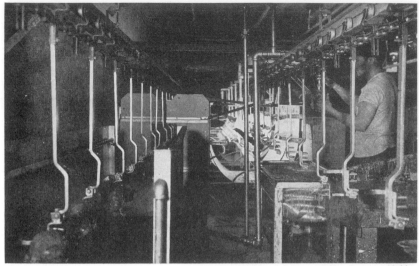

Courtesy of Imperial Crown & Toy Corp. — Molders
and E. B. Blue Co. — Equipment Manufacturers

Fig. 10-48. Plastisol slush molding of doll parts. Filling operation on conveyor line.

Fig. 10-49. Plastisol slush molding
of doll parts. Gelling by infrared
lamps and dumping of excess plastisol.

Courtesy of Imperial Crown & Toy Corp.,
Molders, and E. B. Blue Co.,
Equipment Manufacturers

Fig. 10-50. Plastisol slush molding of doll
parts. Slush moldings entering fusion oven.

Courtesy of Imperial Crown & Toy Corp. — Molders
and E. B. Blue Co. — Equipment Manufacturers

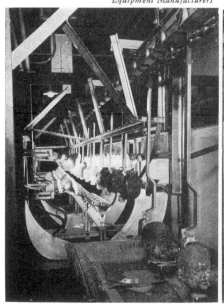

The accompanying sketch (Fig. 10-51) shows a typical conveyorized slush-molding system which operates continuously, the empty molds being returned to the mold-filling operator. The two tanks of material shown must be arranged so that they can be removed quickly and reversed in position; when the first tank is empty, the second is inserted in its place. Such a machine should have a variable drive, so that the operator can adjust the speed for different molding conditions. Likewise, the ovens should be thermostatically controlled, and individually controllable water jets should be provided in the cooling chamber. For a small molded object the water should be cut down; for a larger object, which requires more cooling, the water jets are opened wider.

Compressed air and vacuum equipment serves to remove the articles from the molds. Relatively simple articles can be blown out by compressed air; if the article is difficult to remove, a vacuum will collapse the material from the mold walls.

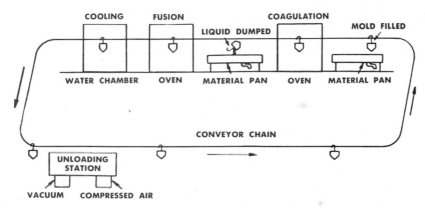

Fig. 10-51 Schematic diagram of a conveyorized slush-molding set-up. Variable-speed chain drive, oven thermostats, and cooling-water controls are desirable.

Method No. 2. Another variation of slush-molding is used today, but to a lesser extent than the foregoing. The operator fills the mold with plastisol and immediately inverts it, draining it into a container directly below the conveyor belt. The mold then travels upside-down on the conveyor line, while continually draining. By the time the inverted mold reaches the first oven there is a very thin unfused film of plastisol lining the mold. Its travel through the first oven gives this only a partial fusion. The mold is removed by the second operator, who fills it up again with plastisol, dumping the excess into a second container, and the mold, in inverted position, continues on the conveyor line. The mold now enters the final fusing oven, and then a water chamber, where it is cooled prior to final removal.

While this method is a little faster than the first, the need of close control of temperature and cycles prohibit its use unless the operators are extremely skilled, and can continuously maintain the speed of the operation, filling, dumping, etc. But if the slush-molding machine is designed and built to provide the necessary close control, the second method is preferred.

Typical slush-molded articles are shown in Figs. 10-52, 10-53 and 10-54.

Molding Techniques and Advantages. The thickness of the molded article depends on four factors: first, the gelling ability of the plastisol; second, the thickness of the mold; third, the temperature of the oven; and fourth, the time the mold is left in the oven for gelling to occur.

Temperature in the fusing oven can vary anywhere from 350 to 600°F, depending on the total quantity of molds and plastisol being run through the oven at a given time. The molder must determine how many pounds of plastisol and how many pounds of molds go through the oven in an hour; then the oven temperature must be set accordingly. A miscalculation will result in underfused or overfused articles.

The physical qualities of slush-molded plastisols are such that it is possible to do exceptionally accurate work. Because the material is not fused under pressure, it exhibits very little shrinkage when molded. Colors are almost unlimited. Articles made from plastisol can be cemented and heat-sealed. Slush-molded vinyl articles, when properly formulated, are unaffected by many acids and alkalies, and a wide range of solvents. They are good on aging and resist sunlight. The molded article can be flexed at least as much as most rubber compounds. It can be made to have excellent electrical insulating properties, and also not support combustion.

Cavity-Molding of Plastisols

Another method of molding plastisols is the use of cavity molds, either open or closed. This method has many applications where close tolerances are required on both outside and inside dimensions. Heavy sections, even several inches thick, can be molded with comparative ease by this method.

Mold Design and Methods of Filling. Open molds may be made in any necessary number of pieces, as long as they fit together tightly. Since the top of the mold is open, the top of the article is necessarily a flat surface.

Closed molds may be made of many parts, which are either clamped or bolted together, or held tightly together in a press. To fill a closed mold, the best method is to use a gun of "Alemite" type, connected to the mold. In order to eliminate air pockets, small bleeder holes must be located in correct positions in the mold, so that all the air is pushed out, and the cavity completely filled with the plastisol. After filling, certain of these bleeders, and the inlet, may have to be shut off or plugged, so that the plastisol will not run out. And also, because during heating in the mold the viscosity of some plastisols becomes very low, before they start to gel.

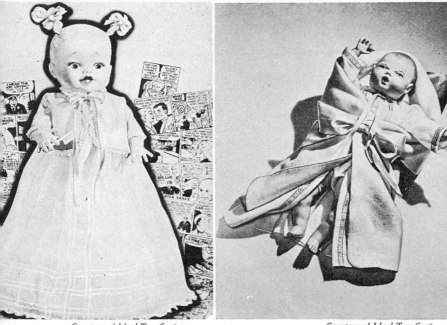

Fig. 10-52. Doll made from
slush-molded parts.

Fig. 10-53. Doll made from
slush-molded parts.

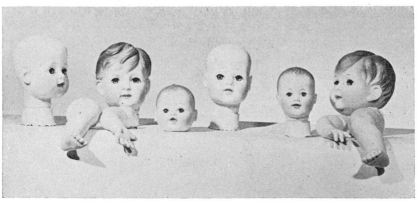

Fig. 10-54. Movable-eye heads and doll parts.

Molds may be made of any suitable metal, preferably chrome-plated steel, or anodized aluminum.

If it is desired (and in some cases it may be necessary) to have a completely tight mold, it must be remembered that the plastisol in the mold will expand on heating and that high pressures will develop. In these cases mold-design and engineering must be carefully analyzed, to prevent bursting of molds.

A well de-aerated plastisol should be used in all cases.

In open molds care should be taken in filling, so that no air is entrapped. In a closed mold the pumping device should not force air into the evacuated plastisol. The plastisol should fill the cavity, leaving no entrapped air in the mold. Also all bleeders should be discharging plastisol, as indication that the cavity has been filled.

Fusing. Two general methods of fusing are used. The first method is merely to heat the mold up to about 325°F (this is the temperature of the mold as measured by a contact pyrometer). Thicknesses up to one inch have been fused this way. For thicker sections it is sometimes necessary to heat the mold to about 325°F and maintain it here long enough for the plastisol to be fused all the way through. The length of time at 325°F to ensure complete fusion must be determined by trial.

A second method is to heat the closed mold in a press. A big advantage of this method is the rapid transfer of heat from the platens of the press to the closed mold. Experiments have shown that fusing times have been cut to one-quarter by this method. Another advantage is that clamps or bolts for holding the mold together may not be necessary, if the mold can be held together by the pressure of the platens of the press.

During the fusing, the plastisol expands. Open molds will overflow if filled too full. In a closed mold, if the bleeders are left open plastisol will be pushed out by the pressure developed in the mold. This plastisol should be caught as long as it is fluid, and can be used again. When the temperature of the mold gets high enough, the plastisol exuding at the bleeder holes will gel and fuse. This will stop the flow from the bleeders, and a small pressure will build up in the closed mold.

Removal from the Mold. The molds should be cooled promptly and may, if desired, be immersed in water. The cooled plastisol can easily be stripped from the mold. No mold-release agent is needed. Care should be taken that the molds are perfectly dry before refilling.

In the case of molds in a press, the heated platens can be cooled with circulating water or cold oil, and the mold thus cooled. But the best method is to cool the mold directly, since it must be cooled anyway, whereas cooling the platens makes it necessary to reheat them for the next mold. Figs. 10-55, 10-56, 10-57, 10-58.

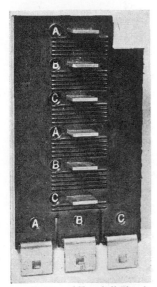

Courtesy of Trumbull Electric,
Department of General Electric Co.

Fig. 10-55. Plastisol-encased busbars.

Courtesy of Trumbull Electric,
Department of General Electric Co.

Fig. 10-56. Installation of plastisol-coated busbars in Trumbullite load center.

Injection Molding of Plastisols

Plastisols may be injection-molded directly, but not with standard equipment. Ordinary injection-molding compounds are solid solutions of resin in plasticizer, with the pigments, stabilizers and lubricants thoroughly dispersed therein. A plastisol is not a solution of vinyl resin in the plasticizer; it is merely a dispersion and does not become a solution until it is fused by heat.

An attempt to mold plastisols directly in conventional injection-molding machines encounters four difficulties:

1. Since a normal plastisol is a fairly viscous liquid, the feeding of a correct amount into the loading gate of the injection-molding machine is so slow and inaccurate as to be not practicable.

2. It is necessary first to effect a nearly complete fusion of the plastisol in the cylinder of the injection-molding machine, and time is required for this step. With normal injection-molding compounds, this step is not required.

Fig. 10-57. Stanley "Magic Carpet" — molded from plastisol. This "carpet" contains electrical activating equipment for opening doors.

Fig. 10-58. Installation of "Magic Carpet" doors.

3. When a plastisol is used directly in the injection-molding machine, the dwells are long and the cycle slow.

4. Plastisols being liquid, the fit of the plunger and screw must be very exact and tight; otherwise the plastisol will squirt out, and pressures cannot be controlled.

For these reasons, the injection molding of plastisols is done in two stages. The plastisol is partially fused, and then granulated, before being fed into the injection-molding machine.

The plastisol, compounded correctly for injection molding, is first partially fused to a point at which (when cool) it is a friable solid, i.e., in extruded form, and cool, it can be rather easily broken by stretching. This fusing can be done in a longscrew extruder, which provides time for forming a partial solution of the resin in the plasticizer. The heated die at the outlet of the extruder finishes the gelation of the plastisol. The extruded and partially cured plastisol is then cooled on a moving belt, and broken into granules.

Exact temperatures for this extrusion cannot be specified, as various compounds require different temperatures to partially fuse them to the condition of friability. It is important to avoid full fusion of the plastisol in the extruder, for then higher temperatures will be needed to soften the material in the cylinder of the injection machine, and there will be risk of breakdown of the resin, with evolution of hydrogen chloride and consequent corrosion of the machine and mold.

With the partially fused and granulated plastisol, a standard injection-molding machine can be used, provided that the interior surfaces of the machine and the mold are chrome-plated or made of corrosion-resistant alloy.

Temperatures required for injection molding of granulated plastisol cannot be specified exactly, since formulations differ greatly, and these differences necessitate variations in the temperatures, and also the pressures, required in the injection-molding machine.

The specific advantages in the use of granulated plastisol for injection molding are (1) that compounds of very low durometer readings may be produced by this method (compounds with durometer readings as low as 20 have been produced with excellent results) ; and (2) that small runs of special colors or formulations may be made (this is a definite advantage over the conventional method of producing standard vinyl injection-molding compounds) (Fig. 10-59).

On the other hand, this technique cannot be used to produce molded articles of high durometer reading, and in very large production also it probably cannot compete in cost with the use of standard injection-molding compounds.

Extrusion of Plastisols

Plastisols may be extruded as a means of producing finished goods, or as a means of preparing partially fused material for molding.

Courtesy of The U. S. Department of Defense
Molded by The George S. Scott Manufacturing Co.

Fig. 10-59. Magazine cap.

The extrusion of plastisols, although it is not a new art, has recently been recognized as the ideal way of easily producing elastomeric vinyl formulations of low durometer reading. Because these plastisols are fused under pressure and in a confined space, volatile plasticizers may be used, whose loss by the conventional method would seriously affect the product. It is possible to produce materials of extremely low durometer readings, which could not be processed by the conventional two-roll mill because of adhesion to the rolls.

It can be stated that almost any type of extruder, from the old rubber type to the present-day hot-melt type, will extrude a plastisol, but the important factors are quantity of production and uniformity of output. The screw in an extrusion machine is nothing more than an inefficient high-pressure pump, in which the friction between the cylinder wall and the root surfaces of the screw creates the forward driving force. As can be seen, a fluid plastisol will offer no resistance. It is, therefore, desirable that a machine be used in which the screw is at least twice as long as those normally used in the extrusion of elastomeric products from molding powder. Since plastisols in a partly fused or a gelled state are "hot short," they offer little resistance to action of the screw forcing them forward. Therefore, it is possible to increase the screw speed of such machines to at least triple what is normally used for conventional extrusions. If the extruder is being used as a step in the compounding of a plastisol, rather than in producing a finished product, it is desirable that the plastisol be extruded incompletely fused, so that the final fusion can take place in an injection- or compression-molding machine.

The method of feeding the plastisol to the extruder will depend upon its viscosity. It is desirable that the machine have a large opening or throat for high-viscosity materials, so that they may flow into the hopper at a rate which will maintain a reservoir of material, and avoid the entrapment of air or surging of the material. If, on the other hand, the material is of low viscosity, it is desirable to suspend the drum of plastisol over the machine, and pipe it to the hopper, with suitable gaskets to prevent leaking. The ideal plan is to place a drum of plastisol on a floor above the machine, and feed it through a pipe not less than $2\frac{1}{2}$ in. in diameter. It is possible to attach a cover to the drum and inject a safe amount of air to increase the flow of the plastisols from the drum.

In a $2\frac{1}{2}$-in. extruder, the optimum conditions are obtained when the temperature of the cylinder does not rise over 300°F, and that of the die not over 320°F. In this operation, when a rod die approximately 4 in. in length with a $\frac{1}{4}$-in. hole is used, and a screw speed of 60 revolutions per minute, 40 lb per hour is extruded. Under these conditions, the consumption of power is very low. It is necessary to have a sufficient back pressure at the extrusion end, in either the head or the die, in order to prevent the plastisol from passing through the machine too readily, and thus arriving at the die in a semiliquid form. It has been found that a reasonable back pressure is necessary to provide uniform extrusion.

The screw used for this operation should not have deep flights, because, unless the screw is heated, all the heat necessary to fuse the material must come from the outside of the cylinder. This causes rapid fusing of the material on the outside of the screw, while the material at the base of the threads remains still fluid. This condition causes considerable surging, since the material in the screw revolves without leaving the machine. When fused down to the root of the threads, it will gush out until the screw is empty, and then the cycle will be repeated. To prevent surging, the screw may be heated by insertion of a 500 to 1,000-watt cartridge heater in the end of the screw. The screw should be fairly shallow; in fact, the depth can be as little as $\frac{3}{16}$ in. and still give excellent results.

If the extruder is used as a means of processing prior to granulation, the take-off apparatus can be very simple. The rod, as it leaves the die, may pass over a series of rolls for a sufficient distance to cool it so that it can be granulated without binding together. It then can be passed over a pulley and dropped into the hopper of a granulating machine, thus making the operation continuous from the plastisol in the barrel to the finished granules. If the plastisol is to be extruded into a finished product, the conventional method of take-off, such as conveyors, capstans, etc., can be used. A typical extruded article is shown in Fig. 10-60.

The advantage of plastisols over conventional molding powders in extrusion lies in the production of formulations of low durometer reading. Extrusion of such formulations gives results more uniform than can be obtained from a mill.

Plastisols are advantageous also in extruding delicate shapes, because their fluidity permits the use of low pressures.

Types of machine and designs of screws must be selected by the individual extruder, to meet his specific requirements.

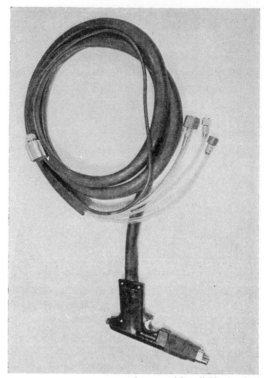

Courtesy of Jessall Plastics, Inc.

Fig. 10-60. Extruded plastisol tubing for the protection of electric welding leads.

Coating of Wire, Various Filaments, and Woven Cords

Formulation. In formulating a coating for wire, the first thing to be considered is the requirements of the end use. Thus coatings on wire for electrical use should have good dielectric strength and insulation resistance, both wet and dry, good heat-resistance, and good stability. Coatings on blasting wire need only moderate dielectric strength, but must have very good abrasion-resistance and low-temperature flexibility. These two examples show the importance of selecting the proper ingredients for the vinyl dispersion to meet the requirements of the job.

To meet varied requirements, the nonvolatile ingredients of the vinyl dispersion must be carefully selected and tested. It will be found that the various dispersion resins differ considerably in their electrical properties.

Plasticizers must be carefully chosen and blended to give the properties desired. Often this must be a compromise, e.g., those plasticizers which give low-temperature flexibility are usually poor in electrical properties. Pigments very often impair electrical properties. A general rule is to use the smallest amount needed to give the required color. Some pigments are especially bad, and must be avoided. Where cost is of sufficient importance, up to 20 per cent of a carefully selected filler may be used. Stabilizers are among the most critical ingredients in the compound, and must be carefully checked. They can, if properly selected, give good resistance to heat and light, and at the same time improve the electrical properties of the vinyl dispersion.

The formulation of dispersion coatings for cord, thread, rope, filaments, etc., follow the same general principles as those for wire-coatings; in other words, one must formulate to meet the requirements of flexibility, drape, penetration, adhesion, etc.

Application. The procedure is very important, since even the most satisfactory material may fail if the wire or rope is coated unevenly. Thus a formulation that meets all requirements in a uniform 8-mil covering will not meet the same requirements if it has 12 mils on one side and 4 mils on the other. The following three methods, if properly used, give an even coating all around.

Method Using No Die. The wire or line is passed vertically through the organosol or plastisol, the viscosity of which is so adjusted as to give a uniform pickup of desired thickness, with no runbacks. A runback occurs if the wire or line is passing too fast through the coating material, or if the viscosity of this material is too high. In either case, there is too great an initial pickup of material, and this tends to flow back down the wire, causing an uneven coating. This method is generally suitable for dispersions of relatively very low viscosity. The maximum pickup that can be obtained without runbacks is ordinarily quite low; to produce thick coatings, this method generally requires a series of passes.

Floating-die Method. In this method, the die is loosely held in place and thus allowed a certain amount of freedom to move from side to side. The theory is that the die will center itself around any slight bend or imperfection. The limiting factor in this case (as in the preceding method) is the viscosity of the organosol or plastisol. If it is too heavy, the material will pile up under the die, and restrict the freedom of movement of the die. The dispersion must, therefore, be thin enough to flow freely off the die, with only very slight accumulation.

Set-die Method. The die is rigidly set and centered around the wire or line. The wire or line to be coated must be held sufficiently taut so that all bends or imperfections are straightened out before it enters the die. Although this method will work for wide ranges of viscosities, it is particularly suitable for viscous organosols or plastisols, and thus will provide a heavier coat per pass in certain instances.

Fusion. Fusing is dependent upon speed of travel, length of oven or tower, temperature of oven or tower, and thickness of coating. One or more of these may be changed to meet particular requirements, since they are interdependent. For example, if it is desired to increase the speed one may increase the temperature of the tower, make the tower longer, or reduce the thickness of the coating. Thus there is a wide range of possibilities from which to choose. Figs. 10-61, 10-62.

Handling of Organosols. Since organosols contain thinner, which must be volatilized, the temperature must be raised, fast enough to prevent cracking, yet slowly enough to prevent blistering. Mud-cracking occurs if the organosol is kept too long at too low a temperature; the thinner escapes before the dispersion begins to gel, and thus there is nothing left to hold the coating together. Blistering occurs if the organosol reaches a high temperature too soon; the outside layer of the coating fuses before most of the thinner has a chance to escape, and the entrapped thinner, unable to escape, causes blisters. The ideal condition, therefore, lies somewhere between these two extremes. After the organosol has had sufficient solvent removed and the film is partially gelled, so that there are no cracks, it can be passed into the section of the tower where complete fusion occurs.

When using organosols, it should be remembered that there are volatile and flammable solvents which might cause a fire if the tower is not properly

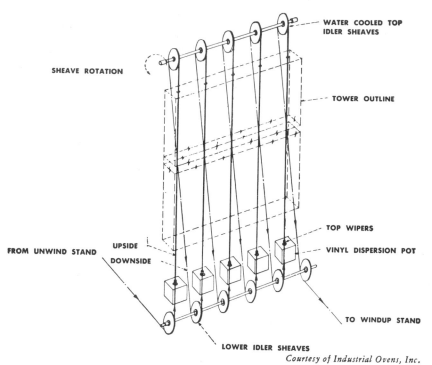

Courtesy of Industrial Ovens, Inc.

Fig. 10-61. Schematic drawing of coating equipment for wire or other filaments.

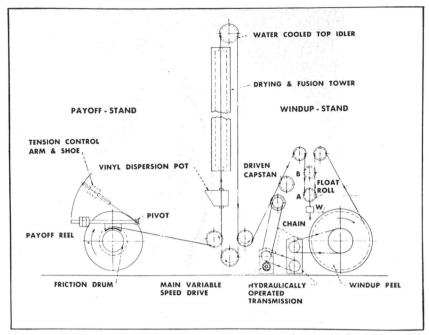

WATER COOLED TOP IDLER

DRYING & FUSION TOWER

PAYOFF - STAND

WINDUP - STAND

TENSION CONTROL
ARM & SHOE

VINYL DISPERSION POT

DRIVEN
CAPSTAN

B

FLOAT
ROLL

A

W.

PIVOT

CHAIN

PAYOFF REEL

FRICTION DRUM

MAIN VARIABLE
SPEED DRIVE

HYDRAULICALLY
OPERATED
TRANSMISSION

WINDUP PEEL

Courtesy of Industrial Ovens, Inc.

Fig. 10-62. Schematic drawing of coating equipment for wire or other filaments.

ventilated with a sufficient amount of air to carry these solvents away and keep the mixture below the explosive limit.

In practice, the maximum film thickness obtainable from organosols is 2 to 6 mils per wet coat.

Handling of Plastisols. Plastisols, since they contain no volatile ingredient, offer no problem of blistering or of hazard of explosion. It is merely necessary to apply enough heat to the film in order to fuse it completely. This may be done by electric strip heaters, induction heaters, heaters using gas or superheated steam, or infrared lamps.

Spraying

Almost any organosol or plastisol may be sprayed. But, because of the usually high viscosities of these materials, it may be necessary to use the spray equipment specially designed for very heavy sound-deadeners, roofing compounds, auto-underbody coatings, etc. The best type of spray gun for these materials is one in which the air strikes the organosol or plastisol inside the nozzle—in other words, an "internal atomization" nozzle. A small volume of air is used in the gun, and a pressure tank is used to force the dispersion to the nozzle of the gun. Spray guns of conventional type, such as those customarily

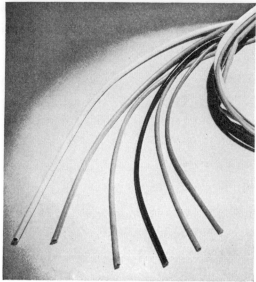

Courtesy of Bentley, Harris Manufacturing Co.

Fig. 10-63. Plastisol-coated glass-fiber tubing.

used for lacquers and enamels, are not suited for spraying organosols or plastisols, except those of very low viscosity.

Formulations which are to be sprayed must be compounded so as to possess low viscosity, freedom from dilatancy, and more or less yield value.

Organosols. As these materials contain volatiles, they can be further thinned with proper thinners so that they can be handled by spray equipment of a particular type.

Without a proper primer, organosols have poor adhesion to most smooth surfaces. A coating of properly formulated organosol can be deposited to a dry thickness of 1.5 mils. If the coating is then heated for a short time at about 200°F, most of the volatiles are removed, preventing the coating from mud-cracking. Another spray coat of the organosol can then be applied, and the process repeated until the desired thickness is reached. After the last bake at 200°F, a final fusion at 300 to 375°F is required. This eliminates the last traces of volatile material, and fuses the successive coats into a homogeneous tough film.

Because of the rapid evaporation of some of the volatile thinners, organosols properly formulated and correctly sprayed will not sag. However, they do not flow out well. Therefore, they should be buffed with a lamb's-wool wheel after partial fusion. Otherwise they will show marked orange peel.

Plastisols. By careful formulation, i.e., by proper choice of dispersion resins and plasticizers, low-viscosity plastisols can be made which can be handled easily by normal spray equipment with an "internal atomization" gun.

One of the major advantages of plastisols is the absence of highly volatile components. This means that if they can be sprayed as is, one deposits a film of 100 per cent solids. (The plasticizer is not a solid material, but because it becomes part of the ultimate fused coat it is counted, along with resin, pigment, and other solid ingredients, as part of the "solids"). Often it is desirable to thin plastisols slightly, to obtain lower viscosities for spraying. When the amount of thinner added is as little as 5 per cent, the fire risks and risk of blistering encountered with organosols are usually avoided.

Plastisols, like organosols, have little, if any, adhesion to smooth surfaces. If adhesion is required, a suitable primer should be used.

Most plastisols applied to a smooth cold surface continue to flow. If the parts are preheated, the plastisol will gel and not run, unless an excessive amount is applied. The temperature of the surface being sprayed, its heat capacity, and its conductivity will determine the amount of plastisol which can be gelled on the article without sags or runs. Coatings of 10 to 30 mils can be so applied. Fusion of the coating should then be carried out at 300 to 375°F. Certain formulations, when fused, have a tendency to become fluid again or melt. This can be overcome by reformulation.

In certain applications where it is desired to apply very heavy coats, and where appearance is of minor importance, a plastisol may be formulated which has high viscosity, over 20,000 centipoises, and no flow. For spraying this, equipment of the type used for spraying roofing compounds or auto undercoatings is used. Coatings of 60 to 80 mils can be applied. They are sprayed on cold-primed metal, and they must be so formulated that when fused they will not run or sag.

Inks

Organosols. *Machine Printing.* Organosols, properly pigmented, may be applied to a web by intaglio printing, with subsequent drying and fusing. Since the dispersion has relatively large particle size, it is necessary to use an engraved cylinder of proper depth of cell and screen size to avoid clogging, with resultant misprints or streaks. For this reason, pantograph or milled cylinders should be used, rather than photoengravings. In addition to application of decorative effects, a milled cylinder is an ideal means for application of a clear topcoat to unsupported heavy-gauge film or vinyl-coated fabrics.

Screen Printing. Requirements for screen printing are such that heavier-bodied inks may be used. In screen printing also there is less concern with particle size. Screens used must be constructed to resist solvents, and need not be painted with caustic resist, since the printing vehicles and colors are substantially neutral and will not attack the masking emulsion. Organosol inks lend themselves readily to screen printing, requiring only normal drying and subsequent fusion to ensure a good bond and abrasion-resistance. When these are applied to certain surfaces, it is necessary to modify the formulation, or to use primers to obtain adhesion.

Plastisols. Plastisols may be adapted to screen printing, but care must be taken in formulation to provide a sufficiently fluid body, and at the same time to avoid excessive tack or pull, which would interfere with good wiping action of the squeegee.

The requirements of machine printing are such that plastisols are not recommended, except for special effects. The body characteristics of many plastisols do not provide good working properties in a printing machine, and poor flow will usually result in a very sharp definition of applied print. Interesting effects in raised printing may be obtained by this means, but for general printing requirements organosols will usually provide a more satisfactory result. By proper formulation, dispersion inks can be adapted to other types of printing.

EMBOSSING OF VINYL-DISPERSION FILMS

The embossing of vinyl-dispersion films may be accomplished in several ways, whether they be cast films or films coated on a supporting base such as cloth, paper or foil.

Cast Films

There are three well-known methods of securing an embossed design on a cast film.

1. If the carrier upon which the vinyl dispersion is cast has a design embossed on it, the cast film will conform to this design, and when stripped from the carrier will show a faithful reproduction of that design.

2. A cast film after being stripped from the carrier may be embossed by the usual hot-calender method. However, great care must be exercised in control of the temperature and pressure, since otherwise the impression of the embossing design may be either too weak or so deeply cut as to destroy the strength of the film.

3. This is identical with (2) except that the film is left on the carrier. After embossing, the film is stripped from the carrier.

Of these three methods, (1) is preferred, because the film is fused into the embossed design. In the other two methods it is not possible to emboss with as finely defined design, nor does the embossing stay in as well. In the third method, the carrier is embossed, as well as the cast film, and this makes the carrier unsuited for further use in casting flat film.

Films Coated on a Carrier which is an Integral Part of the Finished Product

Three methods are in general used for embossing cloth, paper, etc., which have been coated with vinyl dispersions. Methods (1) and (2) apply to both organosol and plastisol coatings, while (3) is used only with an organosol.

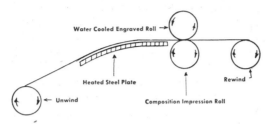

Fig. 10-64. Schematic drawing of cold embossing.

Courtesy of Industrial Ovens, Inc.

Fig. 10-65. Cold embosser.

(1) is similar to (3) above, except that the carrier, being an integral part of the finished article, is naturally not stripped after the embossing.

(2) The coated material is completely fused in the conventional manner. There are now two ways of embossing, depending on the manufacturer's setup: First — When the coated material comes out of the hot (fusion) end of the oven, the vinyl dispersion is soft and plastic. It is immediately run through a cold light-weight embossing calender, and the soft and hot vinyl coating is molded into the embossing design. It is then chilled and set. In this manner, a fine embossing is produced, which by quick chilling is retained permanently.

Second — If embossing is not practicable at the completion of the fusion, the coated material can be cooled and rolled up. Then, when desired, it can be embossed by being rapidly heated to a point at which the vinyl coating is soft and plastic (say 350°F), and then run through the chilled calender. One of the best methods of rapidly heating the coated material is to pass it rapidly over a chrome-plated steel plate having a slightly convex profile. This convex surface forces the coated material, under tension, to be in intimate contact with the chrome-plated surface at all points. The chrome-plated steel plate can be heated by flame, electric resistance, etc. The temperature should be high, about 500 to 700°F, and one end of the plate should be very close to the nip of embossing rolls (Figs. 10-64, 10-65). Mechanical means should be included, to lift the coated materials from the surface of the heated plate in case the operation stops, and also to drop it back on the plate the instant the material begins its travel again. The reason for this is that if the coated carrier stays on the plate at its high surface temperature for more than a few seconds, either it will catch fire or at least the vinyl coating will be discolored and decompose.

This method (2) is the best in many respects, and with variations is very widely used.

(3) In the case of organosols, when most of the thinner has been removed and the organosol has been partially gelled, the coated carrier is run through a standard roller embosser. The embossed material is then fused in the regular manner.

GLOSSARY

absorption . . . . The penetration into the mass of one substance by another.

acid-acceptor . . . . . . A compound which acts as a stabilizer by chemically combining with acid, which may be initially present in minute quantities in a vinyl resin, or which may be formed by the decomposition of the resin.

adsorption . . . . A concentration of a substance at a surface or interface.

aliphatic hydrocarbons . . Petroleum products derived from a paraffin-base crude oil, and sometimes called *straight-chain hydrocarbons*.

ambient temperature . . . Temperature of the medium surrounding an object.

apparent viscosity . . . . Viscosity which is apparent at a given shear rate.

aromatic hydrocarbon . . . An organic compound having a closed carbon-atom ring and characterized by or derived from a benzene nucleus.

centipoise . . . . A unit of viscosity, conveniently and approximately defined as the viscosity of water at room temperature. The following table of approximate viscosities at room temperature may be useful for rough comparisons:

liquid	viscosity in centipoises
water	1
kerosene	10
motor oil SAE 10	100
castor oil; glycerine	1,000
corn syrup	10,000
molasses	100,000

conjugated double bonds . Alternate double bonds occurring in a carbon chain.

dead fold . . . . A fold which does not spontaneously unfold.

dielectric heating . . . . Method of heating a material between metallic plates and thereby subjecting it to a strong electrostatic field produced by high-frequency voltage; the heat is developed within the material rather than being brought to it from the outside, and hence the material is heated more uniformly throughout.

dilatant (adj.) . . . . . A dilatant fluid, or *inverted pseudoplastic,* is one whose apparent viscosity increases instantaneously with increasing rate of shear; i.e., the act of stirring creates instantly an increase in resistance to stirring.

diluent . . . . A liquid component of an organosol, that part which has little or no solvating action on the resin, its purpose being to modify the action of the dispersant.

dispersant . . . . A liquid component of an organosol, that part which has a solvating or peptizing action on the resin, so as to aid in dispersing and suspending it.

dispersion . . . . As used here, a dispersion is a suspension of finely divided vinyl resin particles in a non-aqueous liquid.

durometer . . . . Refers to the hardness of a substance measured with a Shore Durometer Hardness Meter.

elastomeric . . . . Rubberlike

false body . . . . The deceptively high apparent viscosity of a pseudoplastic fluid at a low rate of shear.

fusion . . . . As used here, the intimate blending of plasticizer and resin under the influence of heat, a mutual solution being effected.

fusion temperature . . . . The temperature at which fusion occurs; also called *fluxing temperature.*

gelation . . . . Gel formation in the early stages of fusion.

grinding-type resin . . . A vinyl resin which requires grinding to effect dispersion in plastisols or organosols.

hot-short . . . . Inelastic, nonstretchable and easily broken by tension, when hot.

lyophilic . . . . Having affinity for the dispersing medium.

lyophobic . . . . Not having affinity for the dispersing medium.

micron . . . . A unit of measure, 1×10^{-6} meter; i.e., one millionth of a meter, or about 0.00004 in.

mud-cracking . . . . . . Cracking resembling that which occurs in a pool of mud as it dries.

naphthenic type of
  hydrocarbon . . . . . Cycloparaffins.

Newtonian . . . . Newtonian liquids are perfect liquids; i.e., the rate of flow is directly proportional to the force applied. The viscosity is independent of the rate of shear, and there is no yield value in Newtonian flow.

orange peel . . . . A lack of smoothness of surface, giving an appearance resembling the skin of an orange.

organosol . . . . A vinyl dispersion, the liquid phase of which is non-aqueous and contains volatile liquids.

plastic (adj.) . . . . . . Subject to flow only when the force applied exceeds a definite minimum value, corresponding to the yield point of the material.

plasticizer . . . . A substance added to a plastic material to soften it or otherwise modify its properties.

plastigel . . . . A plastisol exhibiting gel-like flow properties; one having an effective yield value.

plastisol . . . . A vinyl dispersion in which the liquid phase consists solely of a plasticizer.

plenum chamber . . . . . This is a means of distributing heated air uniformly against a web which is passing through an oven. One face of the chamber parallels the web and contains closely-spaced perforations or nozzles through which air is directed upon the web.

polar . . . . A liquid is said to be polar when the electrical charges of its molecules are so placed as to make the molecules subject to influence of an electrical field. As a result, polar liquids are in general more readily adsorbed than the non-polar.

polymer . . . . A product of the successive addition of many relatively small molecules (monomers).

pseudoplastic (adj.) . . . A pseudoplastic fluid is one whose apparent viscosity or consistency decreases instantaneously with increase in rate of shear; i.e., an initial relatively high resistance to stirring decreases abruptly as the rate of stirring is increased.

rheological (adj.) . . . . Refers to rheology, the science of deformation and flow of matter.

solvation . . . . The process of swelling, gelling, or solution of a resin by a solvent or plasticizer as a result of mutual attraction.

solvency . . . . Solvent action, or strength of solvent action.
stir-in resin . . . . . . A vinyl resin which does not require grinding to effect dispersion in a plastisol or an organosol.

straight-chain hydrocarbons . . . . . See *aliphatic hydrocarbons.*

thixotropic (adj.) . . . . A thixotropic fluid is one whose apparent viscosity decreases with time, to some constant value at any constant rate of shear; i.e., its apparent viscosity can be gradually decreased, to that limit, by stirring; when stirring is discontinued, the apparent viscosity increases gradually back to the original value.

viscosity . . . . The resistance of a fluid to flow.

web . . . . A textile fabric, paper, or a thin metal sheet of continuous length handled in roll form as contrasted with the same material cut into sheets.

yield value . . . . The force which must be applied to a plastic to initiate flow, also called *yield stress*.

11. Laminated Products*

Foreword

Laminated thermosetting products are broadly classified as sheets, rods, and tubes. They are widely used in the electrical industry.

This chapter, furnished through the courtesy of the National Electrical Manufacturers Association, is divided into four parts and contains excerpts from NEMA standards, as follows:

1. NEMA Standards for Laminated Thermosetting Products, Publication No. LP1-1951, September 1951.

2. Recommended Practice for Fabricating Laminated Plastics, Publication No. 45-107, December 1945.

3 & 4. NEMA Standards and Recommended Practices for Fabricating and Applying Laminated Thermosetting Decorative Sheets, Publication No. LP2-1951, June 1951.

Portions of the NEMA standards which have been omitted from this chapter are indicated by the headings of the omitted parts. The complete NEMA standards may be obtained at a nominal cost by writing to the National Electrical Manufacturers Association, 155 E. 44th St., New York 17, N. Y.

The NEMA standards† have been developed through consultation among manufacturers, users, and national engineering societies. They represent practical and economical methods.

The standards cover description of grades, sizes and variations; physical and electrical properties; and test methods. The fabrication section covers cutting; punching; drill-press operations; screw-machine operations; lathe operations; threading; milling and gear cutting; marking; sanding and grinding; and finishing.

1. Excerpts from NEMA Standards for Laminated Thermosetting Products

The term "thermosetting" has been adopted to provide a broad basis for the inclusion of thermosetting resins, such as phenolic, melamine and silicone.

---

* Reproduced by special permission of The National Electrical Manufacturers Association —Laminated Products Section.

† See page 398 for information on the purpose of NEMA Standards, their classification and status as set forth in certain clauses of the NEMA By-Laws.

LP1-1.01   General Description of Laminated Thermosetting Products

Laminated thermosetting products consist essentially of fibrous sheet materials, such as cellulose paper, asbestos paper, cotton fabric or mat, asbestos fabric or mat, wood veneer, nylon fabric, glass fabric, etc., which are impregnated or coated with a thermosetting resin binder and consolidated under high temperature and pressure into hard solid products of high mechanical strength.

The principal resins used in laminated thermosetting products are the phenolics. These are made by the chemical combination and partial polymerization of formaldehyde and phenolic bodies, such as phenols, cresols or cresylic acid, under carefully controlled conditions. Another class of thermosetting resins includes the melamine resins. These are made by the chemical combination and partial polymerization of formaldehyde with melamine and with urea or urea derivatives or combinations. Copolymers of two or more of these resins may also be used. Still another class of thermosetting resins includes the silicones. These are generally alkylphenyl silicone copolymers made by the condensation of hydrolytic products of organosilicon chlorides.

These resins are dissolved in alcohol, alcohol-water or other suitable solvents to form varnish solutions with which the fibrous sheet materials may be impregnated or coated.

After impregnation and drying, the material is cut into sheets which are stacked together between metal pressing plates and pressed under high temperatures and pressures to form laminated thermosetting sheets. During this operation, the resin passes from a fusible soluble stage into one which is practically infusible and insoluble. Temperatures in the neighborhood of 270 to 350°F (approximately 132 to 180°C) are commonly employed. For the silicone resins, temperatures up to 500°F may be required. Molding pressures of approximately 1000 to 2500 psi are common.

With certain resins and certain types of fibrous sheet materials, it may. be possible to produce satisfactory laminated sheets at much lower pressures.

When the material has been heated for a period sufficient to bring about this change in state (so-called "thermosetting"), the presses are cooled and the finished sheets removed.

Tubes are formed by rolling the impregnating sheet material upon mandrels between heated pressure rolls and then either oven-baking or pressing the material in a heated mold until the curing or setting of the resin into the infusible form is completed.

Molded rods are composed of laminations of impregnated sheet material which have been molded in cylindrical molds under high temperature and pressure and then ground to size.

NOTE—Machined Rods—Rods machined from sheets are also made. In these rods, the laminations are parallel chords of a circular cross-section. In general, their properties conform to the grade of sheet stock from which they are cut. This type of rod is low in flexural strength when stress is applied perpendicular to the lamination.

Molded shapes are composed of impregnated sheet materials which have been cut into various sizes and shapes to fit the contours of a mold and molded under heat and pressure. In special cases, depending upon the design of the piece, some macerated material is used in combination with impregnated sheet materials. The requirements of these standards, particularly with regard to mechanical properties, should not be considered as applying to molded shapes, except for rectangular and square tubes, since the properties of such shapes will depend to a considerable extent upon the design of the piece.

Authorized Engineering Information 1-23-1951.

LP1-1.02   Grades and Standardization

While the properties of laminated thermosetting materials can be varied within quite a large range by varying the sheet fillers, the binders or manufacturing processes, it has been found that a reasonable number of grades or classes will suffice for most applications.

A description of the chief characteristics of the grades of laminated thermosetting products and the various forms available is contained in the following standards. Unless otherwise specified, a phenolic resin binder is used.

Authorized Engineering Information 4-12-1946.

LP1-1.02A   Classification of Insulating Materials

For details refer to NEMA Publication No. LP1-1951.

LP1-1.03   Paper-base Grades
GRADE X

Sheets—Primarily intended for mechanical applications where electrical properties are of secondary importance. Should be used with discretion when high-humidity conditions are encountered. Not equal to fabric-base grades in impact strength.

Rolled Tubes—Good punching and fair machining qualities. Low power factor and high dielectric strength under relatively dry conditions.

Rods and Molded Tubes—This grade is not recommended in these forms.

GRADE P

Sheets—Primarily intended for punching hot. More flexible and not as strong as Grade X. Intermediate between Grades X and XX in moisture-resistance and electrical properties. With good punching practice*, sheets having a thickness up to and including $\frac{1}{16}$ in. may be punched cold. When heated to between 120 and 140°C, sheets having a thickness up to and including $\frac{1}{8}$ in. can be punched.

Tubes and Rods—This grade is not recommended in these forms.

---

* See *NEMA Recommended Practice for Fabricating Laminated Plastics,* Publication No. 45-107.

GRADE PC

Sheets—Primarily intended for cold punching and shearing. More flexible and higher cold flow but lower in flexural strength than Grade P. With good punching practice, this grade can be punched up to and including $\frac{1}{8}$ in. in thickness at a room temperature of approximately 23°C. In general, at the same temperature and with a sharp power squaring shear, sheets up to $\frac{3}{32}$ in. in thickness can be sheared in $1\frac{1}{2}$ in. wide strips in both the lengthwise and crosswise directions without developing surface cracks.

Tubes and Rods—This grade is not recommended in these forms.

GRADE XX

Sheets—Suitable for usual electrical applications. Good machinability.

Rolled Tubes—Good machining, punching and threading qualities. Not as strong mechanically as Grade X rolled tubes but better in moisture-resistance. Better for low dielectric losses, particularly on exposure to high humidity.

Molded Tubes—Better in moisture-resistance than Grade XX rolled tubes. Good machining and good electrical properties, except in thin walls where the dielectric strength may be low at the molded seams.

Rods—Characteristics are similar to those for sheets except as limited by inherent differences in construction and shape.

GRADE XXP

Sheets—Better than Grade XX in electrical and moisture-resisting properties and more suitable for hot punching. Intermediate between Grades P and XX in punching and cold-flow characteristics.

Tubes and Rods—This grade is not recommended in these forms.

GRADE XXX

Sheets—Suitable for radio-frequency work, for high-humidity applications and with minimum cold-flow characteristics.

Molded Tubes and Rods—Characteristics are similar to those for sheets except as limited by inherent differences in construction and shape.

Rolled Tubes—No standards developed for this grade in this form.

GRADE XXXP

Sheets—Better in electrical properties than Grade XXX and more suitable for hot punching. Intermediate between Grades XXP and XX in punching characteristics. This grade is recommended for applications requiring high insulation resistance and low dielectric losses under severe humidity conditions.

Tubes and Rods—This grade is not recommended in these forms.

GRADE ES-1

Sheets Only—Suitable for engraving as nameplates, etc. Made with black or gray surfaces and white opaque core (usually melamine binder).

GRADE ES-2

Sheets Only—Similar in application to Grade ES-1 but made with a white subcore and black core (usually phenolic binder) to obtain toughness when made in thick sheets.

GRADE ES-3

Sheets Only—Similar in application to Grade ES-1 but made with white or gray surfaces and black core.

Authorized Engineering Information 1-23-1951.

LP1-1.04   Fabric-base Grades

GRADE C

Sheets—Made from cotton fabric weighing over 4 ounces per square yard and having a count of not more than 72 threads per in. in the filler direction nor more than a total of 140 threads per in. in both the warp and filler directions as determined from an inspection of the laminated sheet. A strong, tough material suitable for gears and other applications requiring high impact strength. The heavier the fabric base used the higher will be the impact strength, but the rougher the machined edge; consequently, there may be several subgrades in this class adapted for various sizes of gears and types of mechanical service. This grade does not have controlled electrical properties and its use for electrical applications is not recommended.

Rolled Tubes—Made from a cotton fabric with the same weight and thread-count limits as for sheets of this grade.

Molded Tubes—No standards developed for this grade in this form.

Rods—Made from a cotton fabric with the same weight and thread-count limits as for sheets of this grade. In general, characteristics are the same as those for sheets except as limited by inherent differences in construction and shape.

GRADE CE

Sheets—Made from a cotton fabric with the same weight and thread-count limits as for Grade C. Suitable for electrical applications requiring greater toughness than provided by Grade XX or for mechanical applications requiring greater resistance to moisture than provided by Grade C. This grade is not recommended for primary insulation* for electrical applications involving commercial power frequencies at voltages in excess of 600 volts.

Rolled Tubes—No standards developed for this grade in this form.

Molded Tubes—Made from a cotton fabric with the same weight and

---

* "Primary insulation" means insulation which is in direct contact with terminals, conductors or other current-carrying members. Laminated insulation used for its mechanical or thermal properties, such as armature slot wedges, spacers, structural members, switchboard panels where terminals have separate insulation, etc., is not considered "primary insulation."

thread-count limits as for Grade C. Suitable for use where a tough, dense, fabric-base material having good mechanical properties and good resistance to moisture is required.

This grade is not recommended for primary insulation* for electrical applications involving commercial power frequencies at voltages in excess of 600 volts.

Dielectric strength may be low at molded seams, especially in thin walls.

Rods—Characteristics are the same as for molded tubes except as limited by inherent differences in construction and shape.

GRADE L

Sheets—Made from cotton fabric weighing 4 ounces or less per square yard. The minimum thread count in any ply is 72 threads per in. in the filler direction and a total of 140 threads per in. in both the warp and filler directions as determined from an inspection of the laminated sheet. For purposes of identification, the surface sheets have a minimum thread count of 80 threads per in. in each of the warp and filler directions. This grade is suitable for small gears and other fine machining applications, particularly in thicknesses under 1/2 in. Not quite so tough as Grade C. This grade does not have controlled electrical properties and its use for electrical applications is not recommended.

Rolled Tubes—No standards developed for this grade in this form.

Molded Tubes—Made from fine-weave cotton fabric weighing 4 ounces or less per square yard. The minimum thread count in any ply is 72 threads per in. in the filler direction and a total of 140 threads per in. in both the warp and filler directions as determined from an inspection of the molded tube. Has high density and good moisture resistance. Primarily suitable for mechanical applications where finer machined appearance is required than is secured with Grade CE molded tube or where tougher material is required than Grade LE molded tube. This grade does not have controlled electrical properties and its use for electrical applications is not recommended.

Rods—Made from a cotton fabric with the same weight and thread-count limits as for molded tubes of this grade. In general, characteristics are similar to those for molded tubes except as limited by inherent differences in construction and shape.

GRADE LE

Sheets—Made from a cotton fabric having the same weight and thread-count limits as Grade L sheet. Suitable for electrical applications requiring greater toughness than provided by Grade XX. Better in machining properties and appearance than Grade CE, and available in thinner sizes. Good in moisture resistance. This grade is not recommended for primary insulation* for electrical applications involving commercial power frequencies at voltages in excess of 600 volts.

Rolled Tubes—Made from a cotton fabric having the same weight and thread-count limits as Grade L molded tubes. Suitable for use where the seams of a molded tube may be objectionable and where the application requires good machining qualities, together with fair electrical and good mechanical properties. This grade is not recommended for primary insulation* for electrical applications involving commercial power frequencies at voltages in excess of 600 volts.

Molded Tubes—Made from a fine-weave cotton fabric having the same weight and thread-count limits as Grade L molded tubes. Has excellent machining and moisture-resisting characteristics. For use in restricted electrical applications where a tougher material than Grade XX tube is required at some sacrifice of electrical properties. Dielectric strength may be low at molded seams, especially in thin walls. Better electrically than Grade CE molded, but not quite as tough. This grade is not recommended for primary insulation* for electrical applications involving commercial power frequencies at voltages in excess of 600 volts.

Rods—Made from a cotton fabric with the same weight and thread-count limits as for molded tubes of this grade. In general, characteristics are similar to those for molded tubes except as limited by inherent differences in construction and shape.

Authorized Engineering Information 1-23-1951.

LP1-1.05   Asbestos-base Grades

GRADE A

Sheets—Asbestos paper base. More resistant to flame and slightly more resistant to heat than cellulosic laminated grades because of high inorganic content. Not recommended for primary insulation* for electrical applications involving commercial power frequencies at voltages in excess of 250 volts. Small dimensional changes when exposed to moisture.

Rolled and Molded Tubes—Characteristics are similar to those for sheets except as limited by inherent differences in construction and shape.

Rods—This grade is not recommended in this form.

GRADE AA

Sheets—Asbestos fabric base. More resistant to heat and stronger and

---

* "Primary insulation" means insulation which is in direct contact with terminals, conductors or other current-carrying members. Laminated insulation used for its mechanical or thermal properties, such as armature slot wedges, spacers, structural members, switchboard panels where terminals have separate insulation, etc., is not considered "primary insulation."

tougher than Grade A. Not recommended for primary insulation for electrical applications at any voltage. Small dimensional changes when exposed to moisture.

Rolled and Molded Tubes—Characteristics are similar to those for sheets except as limited by inherent differences in construction and shape.

Rods—This grade is not recommended in this form.

Authorized Engineering Information 1-23-1951.

LP1-1.06   Glass-base Grades

GRADE G-1

Sheets—Staple-fiber-type glass cloth. General-purpose, heat-resistant grade. Higher impact strength than cotton-fabric-base grades. Good dielectric loss properties and insulation resistance under dry conditions. Dielectric strength perpendicular to laminations low in thin sheets. Good dimensional stability.

Tubes and Rods—This grade is not recommended in these forms.

GRADE G-2

Sheets—Staple-fiber-type glass cloth. Electrical and heat-resistant grade. Good electrical properties under high humidity conditions. Mechanically it is the weakest of the glass-base grades. Lower in dielectric losses than other glass-base grades excepting silicone. Good dimensional stability.

Tubes and Rods—This grade is not recommended in these forms.

GRADE G-3

Sheets—Continuous-filament-type glass cloth. General-purpose grade. High impact and flexural strength. Bonding strength is the poorest of the glass-base grades. Good electrical properties under dry conditions. Dielectric strength perpendicular to laminations is good. Good dimensional stability.

Rolled Tubes—Characteristics are similar to those for sheets except as limited by inherent differences in construction and shape.

Molded Tubes—This grade is not recommended in this form.

Rods—Characteristics are similar to those for sheets except as limited by inherent differences in construction and shape. Mold seams are weak points mechanically and electrically.

GRADE G-5

Sheets—Continuous-filament-type glass fabric with melamine resin binder. Highest mechanical strength and hardest laminated grade. Good flame resistance; second only to silicone laminates in heat and arc resistance. Excellent electrical properties under dry conditions. Low insulation resistance under high humidities. Good dimensional stability.

Rolled Tubes—Characteristics are similar to those for sheets except as limited by inherent differences in construction and shape. Especially high internal bursting strength.

Molded Tubes—This grade is not recommended in this form.

Rods—Characteristics are similar to those for sheets except as limited by inherent differences in construction and shape. Mold seams are weak points mechanically and electrically.

GRADE G-6

Sheets—Staple-fiber-type glass cloth with silicone resin binder. Extremely good dielectric loss and insulation resistance properties under dry conditions and good electrical properties under humid conditions, although the percentage of change from dry to humid conditions is high. Dielectric strength perpendicular to laminations is low. Excellent heat and arc resistance. Second only to Grade G-5 in flame resistance. Good impact strength. Other mechanical properties are fair. Good dimensional stability. Meets AIEE requirements for Class H insulation with a tentative maximum hot-spot temperature of 180°C.

Tubes and Rods—No standards developed for this grade in these forms.

GRADE G-7

Sheets—Continuous-filament-type glass cloth with silicone resin binder. Extremely good dielectric loss and insulation resistance properties under dry conditions and good electrical properties under humid conditions, although the percentage of change from dry to humid conditions is high. Excellent heat and arc resistance. Second only to Grade G-5 in flame resistance. Good impact and flexural strength. Bonding strength slightly lower than for Grade G-6. Dielectric strength perpendicular to laminations is the best of the silicone grades. Meets AIEE requirements for Class H insulation with a tentative maximum hot-spot temperature of 180°C.

Tubes and Rods—No standards developed for this grade in these forms.

Authorized Engineering Information 1-23-1951.

LP1-1.07   Nylon-base Grade

GRADE N-1

Sheets—Nylon cloth base with phenolic resin binder. Excellent electrical properties under high humidity conditions. Good impact strength, but subject to flow or creep, especially at temperatures higher than normal.

Rods and Tubes—No standards developed for this grade in these forms.

Authorized Engineering Information 1-23-1951.

LP1-1.08   Applications

Considered on the basis of strength-weight ratio, laminated phenolic is one of the strongest materials known. With a density for cellulose-base grades of approximately 1.35, only half that of aluminum, the mechanical grades find large application in the aircraft and other structural fields.

Because of their high strength, resilience, good wearing and quiet running qualities, gears cut from either laminated phenolic plate or molded blanks are used in thousands of industrial applications ranging from the tiny gears in electric clocks to 8- to 10-in. face gears in rolling mills.

The high strength, excellent resistance to moisture and heat, and good electrical properties of laminated phenolic, combined with the fact that it is readily machined, account for its use in large volumes in all branches of the electrical industry.

The resistance of laminated phenolic to corrosion makes it suitable for many applications in the various chemical industries, particularly where organic solvents, organic acids in any concentration or dilute inorganic acids are encountered. In general, laminated phenolic is not suitable for use in alkaline media, although certain grades are more resistant to alkalies than others and are used for special applications in dilute alkaline solutions.

The ES paper-base grades with both melamine and phenolic binders are primarily used for engraving applications such as nameplates, where white letters on a black background or black letters on a white or gray background are desired.

The glass-base phenolic materials are used for motor insulation and in other applications where high strength and good electrical properties are required even at fairly high temperatures. The glass-base melamine materials are used primarily for their high mechanical strength and resistance to arc and flame. They are particularly suitable for power equipment in marine application.

The glass-base silicone materials are resistant to high temperatures up to 400°F and have especially low dielectric losses. These grades extend the upper temperature range of laminated material to a new high.

Nylon-base laminates are suitable for application in the electronic and high-frequency fields and provide superior insulation resistance under high humidities. Their high flow or creep, particularly under hot conditions, requires special handling and design considerations.

Authorized Engineering Information 1-23-1951.

FORMS, COLORS AND FINISHES

LP1-2.00   Quality and Workmanship

The laminated materials shall be uniform in quality*. Sheets shall be

---

* In general, most of the grades can be drilled, tapped, sawed and machined. Grades X, P, PC, A, G-7, and N-1 are not recommended for drilling and tapping parallel with laminations. Grade XXX, CE and LE are best suited to these operations.

NEMA Standard 3-11-1954.

free from blisters, wrinkles or cracks, and reasonably free from other small defects, such as scratches, dents, heat marks, etc. All tubes shall be free from blisters, pronounced mandrel scores and loose layers, and reasonably free from resin pockets, voids and heat marks. Rolled tubes shall be free from wrinkles. Molded tubes shall be substantially free from seam cracks. Rods shall be free from blisters and substantially free from mold seam cracks, voids and resin pockets.

LP1-2.01   Standard Forms of Laminated Thermosetting Materials

For details refer to NEMA Publication No. LP1-1951.

LP1-2.02   Standard Colors—Sheets, Tubes and Rods

For details refer to NEMA Publication No. LP1-1951.

LP1-2.03   Standard Finishes—Sheets, Tubes and Rods

For details refer to NEMA Publication No. LP1-1951.

STANDARDS FOR DIMENSIONS AND TOLERANCES SHEETS, TUBES AND RODS

LP1-3.01   Tolerances for Warp or Twist (Sheets, Tubes and Rods)

For details refer to NEMA Publication No. LP1-1951.

Sheets

LP1-3.02   Tolerances for Warp or Twist

See LP1-3.01.

LP1-3.02A   Standard Sizes* and Tolerances in Length and Width†

The tolerances in length and width of manufacturers' standard size sheets shall be plus or minus one inch from the manufacturers' standard.

---

* Due to variation in sizes of press equipment, there is considerable variation in the lengths, and widths of manufacturers' standard size sheets. For most of the NEMA grades these standard sizes range between 36 and 50 in. in width and between 36 and 96 in. in length. Certain grades are sometimes supplied in standard sizes ranging from 24 to 36 in. in width and from 24 to 96 in. in length.

† For tolerances in length and width of cut pieces (sheets) see Standard LP1-3.06.

NEMA Standard 9-17-1953.

LP1-3.03   Range of Thickness

The range of thickness of laminated thermosetting sheets shall be:

Grade	Standard Thickness Range (In.)		Grade	Standard Thickness Range (In.)	
	Minimum	Maximum		Minimum	Maximum
X	0.010	2	C	$\frac{1}{32}$	10
P	0.010	$\frac{1}{4}$	CE	$\frac{1}{32}$	2
PC	$\frac{1}{32}$	$\frac{1}{4}$	L	0.010	2
XX	0.010	2	LE	0.015	2
XXP	0.015	$\frac{1}{4}$	A	0.025	2
XXX	0.015	2	AA	$\frac{1}{16}$	2
XXXP	0.015	$\frac{1}{4}$	G-1 and G-2	$\frac{1}{32}$	2
ES-1	$\frac{3}{64}$	0.084	G-3	0.010	2
ES-2	0.085	$\frac{1}{4}$	G-5	0.010	$3\frac{1}{2}$
ES-3	$\frac{3}{64}$	$\frac{1}{4}$	G-6	$\frac{1}{16}$	2
			G-7 and N-1	0.010	1

NEMA Standard 1-23-1951.

LP1-3.04   Tolerances in Thickness

For details refer to NEMA Publication No. LP1-1951.

LP1-3.05   Permissible Variations in Thickness of Component Parts of Engraving Stock Grades

For details refer to NEMA Publication No. LP1-1951.

LP1-3.06   Tolerances in Length and Width of Cut Pieces

For details refer to NEMA Publication No. LP1-1951.

Round Tubes

LP1-3.07   Tolerances for Warp or Twist

See LP1-3.01.

LP1-3.08   Range of Sizes

The range of sizes of round laminated thermosetting tubes, including inside and outside diameters and wall thicknesses, shall be:

A. ROLLED TUBES

	Standard Sizes (In.)						Maximum Ratio of Wall Thickness to Inside
	Inside Diameter		Outside Diameter		Wall Thickness		
Grade	Minimum	Maximum	Minimum	Maximum	Minimum	Maximum*	Diameter†
X	$\frac{1}{8}$	48	0.145	49$\frac{1}{2}$	0.010	$\frac{3}{4}$	$\frac{1}{4}$
XX	$\frac{1}{8}$	48	0.145	50	0.010	1	$\frac{1}{2}$
XXX	$\frac{1}{4}$	8	$\frac{5}{16}$	10	$\frac{1}{32}$	1	$\frac{1}{2}$
C	$\frac{3}{8}$	48	$\frac{1}{2}$	50	$\frac{1}{16}$	2	$\frac{1}{2}$
CE	none	none	none	none	none	none	....
L	none	none	none	none	none	none	....
LE	$\frac{3}{16}$	48	$\frac{1}{4}$	50	$\frac{1}{32}$	1	$\frac{1}{2}$
A	$\frac{5}{16}$	48	$\frac{7}{16}$	49	$\frac{1}{16}$	$\frac{1}{2}$	$\frac{1}{4}$
AA	....	....	....	....	....	....	....
G-3	$\frac{1}{4}$	48	$\frac{9}{32}$	50	$\frac{1}{64}$	1	$\frac{1}{2}$
G-5	$\frac{1}{8}$	48	$\frac{5}{32}$	50	$\frac{1}{64}$	1	$\frac{1}{2}$

All dimensions given in inches.

* Tubes having a wall thickness greater than $\frac{1}{2}$ in. can show checks and/or cracks between the laminations on machined or sawed edges.

† "Maximum ratio of wall thickness to inside diameter" means that, for any size of tube, the standard wall thickness shall not be greater than $\frac{1}{4}$ or $\frac{1}{2}$ of the inside diameter, whichever value applies. For example, the maximum wall thickness of Grade X rolled tube with a $\frac{1}{8}$-in. inside diameter is $\frac{1}{32}$ in., with a $\frac{1}{4}$-in. inside diameter it is $\frac{1}{16}$ in., with a 1-in. inside diameter it is $\frac{1}{4}$ in. and with a 3-in. inside diameter and above it is $\frac{3}{4}$ in.

B. Molded Tubes

		Standard Sizes (In.)					
	Inside Diameter		Outside Diameter		Wall Thickness		Maximum Ratio of Wall Thickness to Inside Diameter†
Grade	Minimum	Maximum	Minimum	Maximum	Minimum	Maximum*	
X	....	....	....	....	....	....	....
XX	$\frac{1}{8}$	$3\frac{7}{8}$	$\frac{1}{4}$	4	$\frac{1}{16}$	1	$\frac{1}{2}$
XXX	$\frac{1}{8}$	$3\frac{7}{8}$	$\frac{1}{4}$	4	$\frac{1}{16}$	1	$\frac{1}{2}$
C	none	none	none	none	none	none	....
CE	$\frac{1}{4}$	$3\frac{7}{8}$	$\frac{3}{8}$	4	$\frac{1}{16}$	1	$\frac{1}{2}$
L	$\frac{1}{8}$	$3\frac{7}{8}$	$\frac{3}{16}$	4	$\frac{1}{32}$	1	$\frac{1}{2}$
LE	$\frac{1}{8}$	$3\frac{7}{8}$	$\frac{3}{16}$	4	$\frac{1}{32}$	1	$\frac{1}{2}$
A	$\frac{5}{16}$	$3\frac{7}{8}$	$\frac{7}{16}$	4	$\frac{1}{16}$	$\frac{1}{2}$	$\frac{1}{4}$
AA	$\frac{3}{8}$	$3\frac{3}{4}$	$\frac{5}{8}$	4	$\frac{1}{8}$	1	$\frac{1}{2}$
G-3	....	....	....	....	....	....	....
G-5	....	....	....	....	....	....	....

All dimensions given in inches.

* Tubes having a wall thickness greater than $\frac{1}{2}$ in. can show checks and/or cracks between the laminations on machined or sawed edges.

† "Maximum ratio of wall thickness to inside diameter" means that, for any size of tube, the standard wall thickness shall not be greater than $\frac{1}{4}$ or $\frac{1}{2}$ of the inside diameter, whichever value applies. For example, the maximum wall thickness of Grade X rolled tube with a $\frac{1}{8}$-in. inside diameter is $\frac{1}{32}$ in., with a $\frac{1}{4}$-in. inside diameter it is $\frac{1}{16}$ in., with a 1-in. inside diameter it is $\frac{1}{4}$ in. and with a 3-in. inside diameter and above it is $\frac{3}{4}$ in.

NEMA Standard 1-23-1951.

LP1-3.09　Steps in Inside and Outside Diameters

For details refer to NEMA Publication No. LP1-1951.

LP1-3.10　Tolerances in Inside and Outside Diameters

For details refer to NEMA Publication No. LP1-1951.

LP1-3.11　Tolerances in Wall Thickness (Round Rolled Tubes)

For details refer to NEMA Publication No. LP1-1951.

LP1-3.12　Tolerances in Wall Thickness (Round Molded Tubes)

For details refer to NEMA Publication No. LP1-1951.

LP1-3.13　Tolerances in Length of Circular Sawed Pieces (Round Tubes)

For details refer to NEMA Publication No. LP1-1951.

Square and Rectangular Molded Tubes

LP1-3.14   Tolerances for Warp or Twist

See LP1-3.01.

LP1-3.15   Range of Sizes*

The range of sizes of square and rectangular molded phenolic tubes, including the inside and outside dimensions and wall thickness, shall be:

| | Standard Sizes (In.) | | | | | |
| | Inside Dimension | | Outside Dimension | | Wall Thickness | |
Grade	Minimum	Maximum	Minimum	Maximum	Minimum	Maximum†
X	$\frac{3}{16}$	$3\frac{29}{32}$	$\frac{9}{32}$	4	$\frac{3}{64}$	$\frac{1}{2}$
XX	$\frac{3}{16}$	$3\frac{29}{32}$	$\frac{9}{32}$	4	$\frac{3}{64}$	$\frac{1}{2}$
XXX	$\frac{3}{16}$	$3\frac{29}{32}$	$\frac{9}{32}$	4	$\frac{3}{64}$	$\frac{1}{2}$
CE	$\frac{3}{8}$	$3\frac{7}{8}$	$\frac{1}{2}$	4	$\frac{1}{16}$	$\frac{1}{2}$
L	$\frac{1}{4}$	$3\frac{29}{32}$	$1\frac{1}{32}$	4	$\frac{3}{64}$	$\frac{1}{2}$
LE	$\frac{1}{4}$	3	$1\frac{1}{32}$	4	$\frac{3}{64}$	$\frac{1}{2}$
A	$\frac{1}{4}$	$3\frac{7}{8}$	$1\frac{1}{32}$	4	$\frac{1}{16}$	$\frac{1}{2}$
AA	$\frac{1}{2}$	$3\frac{3}{4}$	$\frac{3}{4}$	4	$\frac{1}{8}$	$\frac{1}{2}$

* Manufacturer's lengths of tubes vary from 18 to 24 in. in small outside dimensions and from 30 to 48 in. in large dimensions.

† Tubes having a wall thickness greater than $\frac{1}{2}$ of the minimum inside dimension are not recommended for many applications.

NEMA Standard 4-12-1946.

LP1-3.16   Tolerances in Inside and Outside Dimensions

For details refer to NEMA Publication No. LP1-1951.

LP1-3.17   Tolerances in Wall Thickness

For details refer to NEMA Publication No. LP1-1951.

LP1-3.18   Tolerances in Length of Circular Sawed Pieces

For details refer to NEMA Publication No. LP1-1951.

Rods

LP1-3.19   Tolerances for Warp or Twist

See LP1-3.01.

LP1-3.20 Range of Outside Diameters

The range of outside diameters of laminated thermosetting rods shall be:

Grade	Outside Diameter (In.)	
	Minimum	Maximum
XX*	1/8	2
XXX*	1/8	2
C	1/4	4
CE	1/4	4
L	3/16	4
LE	3/16	4
G-3	1/4	2
G-5	1/4	2

* Molded rods in these grades having a diameter greater than 1 in. can show checks and/or cracks between the laminations on machined or sawed edges.

NEMA Standard 1-23-1951.

LP1-3.21 Tolerances in Outside Diameters

For details refer to NEMA Publication No. LP1-1951.

LP1-3.22 Tolerances in Length of Circular Sawed Pieces

For details refer to NEMA Publication No. LP1-1951.

STANDARDS FOR PHYSICAL AND ELECTRICAL PROPERTIES

LP1-4.01 Values

The values given in LP1-4.05 to LP1-4.18, inclusive, designate minimum or maximum standards. These values represent the average for the number of specimens specified for the particular test under the given conditions and serve as the basis for determining whether or not the requirements of this standard have been met.

For example, if the minimum flexural strength of a sheet having a certain thickness is specified as 15,000 psi in the lengthwise direction, then the average value for 4 specimens cut from a sheet in the stronger of the two directions must meet this limit if the sheet is to meet the requirements of these standards.

Authorized Engineering Information 1-23-1951.

LP1-4.02   Variation in Properties with Form

Because of differences in shape, structure and method of manufacture, physical tests, electrical tests and properties will not be the same for sheets, tubes and rods of the same grade.

Authorized Engineering Information 4-12-1946.

LP1-4.03   Factor of Safety

As with other structural and insulating materials, good engineering practice demands an adequate factor of safety. Based on the standard properties of the various grades of sheets, tubes and rods, a minimum factor of safety of 4 for mechanical strength and 6 for dielectric strength is recommended.

Authorized Engineering Information 4-12-1946.

LP1-4.04   Standards Set for Certain Properties Only

In the interest of simplifying matters for both the consumer and the manufacturer, standards for any one grade are set only for those properties which have proven susceptible to manufacturing control and which are essential to the major applications of the grade. For example, both manufacturers and consumers of timing and rolling mill gears are interested in the mechanical and not in the electrical properties of such gears. In fact, good electrical properties cannot be obtained without some sacrifice in mechanical strength. Furthermore, the best electrical properties can only be obtained with a considerable loss in mechanical properties, particularly in toughness or impact strength.

Authorized Engineering Information 4-12-1946.

Sheets

LP1-4.05   Minimum Flexural Strength

The minimum flexural strength of laminated thermosetting sheets, measured flatwise, shall be:

MINIMUM FLEXURAL STRENGTH, MEASURED FLATWISE, PSI — CONDITION A
(See LP1-5.03)

| | | Thickness (In.) | | |
| | | $\frac{1}{8}$ | | 1 and Over |
Grade	Lengthwise	Crosswise	Lengthwise	Crosswise
X	25,000	22,000	22,000	19,000
P	14,000	12,000	....	....
PC	12,000	10,000	....	....
XX	15,000	14,000	13,500	12,500
XXP	14,000	12,000	....	....
XXX	13,500	11,800	12,000	10,600
XXXP	12,000	10,500	....	....
ES-1	....	....	....	....
ES-2	13,500	13,500	....	....
ES-3	13,500	13,500	....	....
C	17,000	16,000	14,400	14,400
CE	17,000	14,000	15,300	12,600
L	15,000	14,000	14,400	13,500
LE	15,000	13,500	13,500	12,000
A	13,000	11,000	12,000	10,000
AA	18,000	16,000	13,500	11,700
G-1	22,000	18,000	18,000	14,500
G-2	20,000	16,000	16,000	12,500
G-3	20,000	18,000	17,000	15,300
G-5	44,000	38,000	31,200	28,500
G-6	18,000	16,000	14,000	11,000
G-7	20,000	18,000	14,400	11,700
N-1	10,000	9,500	8,000	7,500

NOTE—For intermediate thicknesses, the values given for the next smaller thickness shall apply. For other thicknesses, refer to NEMA Publication No. LP1-1951.

NEMA Standard 1-23-1951.

LP1-4.06   Minimum Impact and Bonding Strength

The minimum impact strength in the edgewise direction and the minimum bonding strength of laminated thermosetting sheets shall be:

Grade	Minimum Izod Impact Strength, Ft-lb/1-in. Notch, Condition E-48/50†, for Sheets Having a Thickness from 1/32 in. up to the Maximum Thickness for the Grade but Not Exceeding 2 in.		Minimum Bonding Strength, lb, for Sheets Having a Thickness from ½ in. up to the Maximum Thickness for the Grade but Not Exceeding 2 in.‡	
	Lengthwise	Crosswise	Condition A†	Condition D-48/50†
X	0.55	0.50	700	400
P	0.50	0.45	....	....
PC	0.60	0.55	....	....
XX	0.40	0.35	800	600
XXP	0.45	0.40	....	....
XXX	0.40	0.35	950	700
XXXP	0.35	0.30	....	....
ES-1	0.25	0.22	....	....
ES-2	0.25	0.22	....	....
ES-3	0.25	0.22	....	....
C	2.10	1.90	1800	1600
CE	1.60	1.40	1800	1600
L	1.35	1.10	1600	1500
LE	1.25	1.00	1600	1500
A	0.60	0.60	700	600
AA	3.60	3.00	1800	1600
G-1	5.0	4.0	1000	750
G-2	4.5	3.5	1000	800
G-3	6.5	5.5	850	700
G-5	*	*	1570	1400
G-6	6.0	5.0	800	700
G-7	6.5	5.5	650	550
N-1	3.0**	2.0**	1000	1000

* The minimum impact strength of Grade G-5 sheets shall be:

Thickness (In.)	Minimum Impact Strength Ft-lb/1-in. Notch	
	Lengthwise	Crosswise
1/32 to under 1/8	6.0	5.0
1/8 to under 1/2	7.0	5.5
1/2 to under 2	9.0	6.0

** The impact values for Grade N-1 sheets apply only to thicknesses of 1/8 in. and over.

† See LP1-5.03.

‡ Specimens shall have a nominal thickness of 1/2 in. or shall be machined to 0.500 in., plus or minus 0.005 in., from thicker sheets. Unmachined specimens shall meet the tolerances given for the 1/2-in. thickness of the grade being tested. For thicker sheets, the specimens shall be cut from the center of the cross-section, and approximately equal amounts shall be machined from each surface.

NEMA Standard 3-11-1954.

LP1-4.07   Maximum Water Absorption

The maximum water absorption of laminated thermosetting sheets shall be:

MAXIMUM WATER ABSORPTION, PER CENT — CONDITION D-24/23
FOLLOWING CONDITION E-1/105 (See LP1-5.03)

Grade	Thickness (In.)	
	1/16	1/8
X	6.00	3.30
P	3.60	2.20
PC	5.50	3.00
XX	2.00	1.30
XXP	1.80	1.10
XXX	1.40	0.95
XXXP	1.00	0.75
ES-1	2.50	......
ES-2	......	1.80
ES-3	2.50	1.80
C	4.40	2.50
CE	2.20	1.60
L	2.50	1.60
LE	1.95	1.30
A	1.50	0.95
AA	3.00	2.50
G-1	2.70	2.00
G-2	1.50	0.95
G-3	2.70	2.00
G-5	2.70	2.00
G-6	0.55	0.35
G-7	0.55	0.35
N-1	0.60	0.40

NOTE—For intermediate thicknesses, the values given for the next smaller thickness shall apply. For other thicknesses, refer to NEMA Publication No. LP1-1951.

NEMA Standard 1-23-1951.

LP1-4.08   Minimum Dielectric Strength Parallel to Laminations

Using the step-by-step test*, the minimum dielectric strength parallel to the lamination shall be:

MINIMUM DIELECTRIC STRENGTH PARALLEL TO THE LAMINATIONS, Kv,
USING THE STEP-BY-STEP TEST

Grade	Condition A†		Condition D-48/50†	
	Thickness (In.)		Thickness (In.)	
	1/32 to 1, Inclusive	Over 1 to 2, inclusive	1/32 to 1, Inclusive	Over 1 to 2, Inclusive
X‡	......	......	......	......
P	40.0	......	5.0	......
PC‡	......	......	......	......
XX	40.0	25.0	5.0	3.0
XXP	60.0	......	8.0	......
XXX	50.0	40.0	6.0	4.0
XXXP	60.0	......	15.0	......
ES-1‡	......	......	......	......
ES-2‡	......	......	......	......
ES-3‡	......	......	......	......
C	15.0	10.0	......	......
CE	35.0	25.0	2.5	2.5
L	15.0	10.0	......	......
LE	40.0	30.0	3.0	3.0
A	5.0	......	......	......
AA†		......	......	......
G-1	15.0	10.0	......	......
G-2	30.0	25.0	10.0	......
G-3‡	......	......	......	......
G-5	23.0	15.0	5.0	3.0
G-6	32.0	25.0	15.0	......
G-7	32.0	25.0	15.0	......
N-1	60.0	50.0	40.0	30.0

* See LP1-5.07.
† See LP1-5.03.
‡ These materials are not primarily electrical grades and, therefore, no standards for their electrical properties are contemplated.

NEMA Standard 1-23-1951.

LP1-4.09   Maximum Dielectric Constant and Dissipation Factor

The maximum dielectric constant and dissipation factor for laminated thermosetting sheets shall be:

	Maximum Dielectric Constant at 1 Megacycle*			Maximum Dissipation Factor at 1 Megacycle*		
	Condition A† Thickness (In.) 1/32 to Maximum	Condition D-24/23† Thickness (In.) 1/8	Condition D-48/50† Thickness (In.) 1/8 Only	Condition A† Thickness (In.) 1/32 to Maximum	Condition D-24/23† Thickness (In.) 1/8	Condition D-48/50† Thickness (In.) 1/8 Only
Grade						
XX	5.50	·6.00	....	0.045	0.050	....
XXP	5.00	5.20	5.80	0.040	0.050	0.100
XXX	5.30	5.70	....	0.038	0.045	....
XXXP	4.60	4.80	5.30	0.030	0.035	0.05
LE	5.80	6.00	....	0.055	0.070	....
G-1	6.00	....	....	0.035	....	....
G-2	5.50	5.80	....	0.025	0.080	....
G-5	**	8.00	....	0.020††	0.080	....
G-6	4.50	4.80	....	0.005	0.060	....
G-7	4.20	4.20	....	0.003	0.022	....
N-1	**	3.90	4.00	0.038	0.039	0.045

* Dielectric loss factor = dissipation factor × dielectric constant.

† See LP1-5.03.

** The maximum dielectric constant for Grade G-5 and N-1 sheets shall be:

	Maximum Dielectric Constant at 1 Megacycle—Condition A	
	Thickness (In.)	
Grade	1/32 to 1/8, Inclusive	Over 1/2 to 1, Inclusive
G-5	7.80	8.70
N-1	3.90	4.40

†† For Grade G-5 sheets over 1 in. in thickness, the dissipation factor is 0.025.

NOTE—No dielectric loss value for Grades X, P, PC, ES-1, ES-2, ES-3, C, CE, L, A, AA and G-3 are included because these grades are not suitable for applications where low dielectric loss under radio frequencies is required.

For other thicknesses, refer to NEMA Publication No. LP1-1951.

NEMA Standard 1-23-1951.

LP1-4.10 Minimum Arc Resistance

The minimum arc resistance of laminated thermosetting sheets shall be:

Grade	Minimum Arc Resistance, Seconds, Condition A or Condition D-48/50*, Thickness of ⅛ to 2 In., Inclusive
G-5	180
G-6	180
G-7	180

* See LP1-5.03.

NOTE—No standards contemplated for phenolic grades because of extremely low arc resistance.

NEMA Standard 1-23-1951.

Round Rolled Tubes

LP1-4.11 Maximum Water Absorption

The maximum water absorption of round rolled tubes shall be:

MAXIMUM WATER ABSORPTION, PER CENT

CONDITION D-24/23 FOLLOWING CONDITION E-1/105*

Wall Thickness (In.)	Grade X Inside Diameters (In.)		Grade XX Inside Diameters (In.)		Grade C Inside Diameters ⅜ to 8 In., Inclusive	Grade LE Inside Diameters (In.)		Grade G-5 Inside Diameters ⅛ to 8 In., Inclusive
	⅛ to ½, Inclusive	Over ½ to 8, Inclusive	⅛ to ½, Inclusive	Over ½ to 8, Inclusive		3/16 to ½, Inclusive	Over ½ to 8, Inclusive	
1/16	7.0	5.0	4.0	3.0	5.0	5.0	4.5	4.5
⅛	5.2	4.0	2.5	2.0	3.0	2.5	2.5	3.5

* See LP1-5.03.

NOTE—For intermediate wall thicknesses, the values given for the next smaller thickness shall apply. For other thicknesses, refer to NEMA Publication No. LP1-1951.

NEMA Standard 1-23-1951.

LP1-4.12 Minimum Density and Compressive Strength

The minimum density and compressive strength of round rolled tubes shall be:

Grade	Inside Diameter (In.)	Minimum Density (G/Cu Cm)	Minimum Compressive Strength in the Axial Direction* (Psi)
X	$\frac{1}{8}$ to $\frac{1}{2}$, inclusive	1.10	10,000
	Over $\frac{1}{2}$ to 8, inclusive	1.12	12,000
XX	$\frac{1}{8}$ to $\frac{1}{2}$, inclusive	1.10	11,000
	Over $\frac{1}{2}$ to 8, inclusive	1.12	13,000
C	$\frac{3}{8}$ to 8, inclusive	1.12	12,000
LE	$\frac{3}{16}$ to $\frac{1}{2}$, inclusive	1.12	13,000
	Over $\frac{1}{2}$ to 8, inclusive	1.14	15,000
G-5	$\frac{1}{8}$ to 8, inclusive	1.70	10,000†
		1.70	13,000‡

* The values given for compressive strength apply to wall thicknesses of $\frac{1}{16}$ in. and over and to inside diameters of $\frac{1}{4}$ in. and over.

† This value applies to wall thicknesses of $\frac{1}{16}$ up to $\frac{1}{8}$ in.

‡ This value applies to wall thicknesses of $\frac{1}{8}$ in. and over.

NEMA Standard 1-23-1951.

LP1-4.13 Minimum Dielectric Strength Perpendicular to Laminations

Using the short-time test*, the minimum dielectric strength perpendicular to the laminations shall be:

MINIMUM DIELECTRIC STRENGTH PERPENDICULAR TO THE LAMINATIONS, VOLTS PER MIL, USING THE SHORT-TIME TEST (CONDITION A†)

Grade	Wall Thickness (In.)					
	1/32 to 1/16, Inclusive	Over 1/16 to 1/8, Inclusive	Over 1/8 to 1/4, Inclusive	Over 1/4 to 1/2, Inclusive	Over 1/2 to 3/4, Inclusive	Over 3/4 to 1, Inclusive
X‡	400	290	200	145	120	....
XX	400	290	200	145	120	105
C	No values contemplated					
LE	150**	170	120	85	70	60
G-5	225	160	110	80	65	55

* See LP1-5.07.

† See LP1-5.03.

‡ The dielectric strength of Grade X tubes decreases markedly under humid conditions.

** Low dielectric strength in the thin wall is due to the small number of laminations and to the possibility of overlapping of resin-filled interstices.

NOTE—These dielectric strength values cover sizes ranging from the minimum inside diameter for the grade up to a maximum inside diameter of 8 in.

NEMA Standard 1-23-1951.

Round Molded Tubes

LP1-4.14   Maximum Water Absorption

The maximum water absorption of round molded tubes shall be:

MAXIMUM WATER ABSORPTION, PER CENT
CONDITION D-24/23 FOLLOWING CONDITION E-1/105*

	Wall Thickness (In.)	
Grade	1/16	⅛
XX	2.0	1.6
XXX	1.4	1.1
CE	3.0	2.0
L	3.5	1.8
LE	2.2	1.5

* See LP1-5.03.

NOTE—For intermediate wall thicknesses, the values given for the next smaller thickness shall apply. For other thicknesses, refer to NEMA Publication No. LP1-1951.

NEMA Standard 1-23-1951.

LP1-4.15   Minimum Density and Compressive Strength

The minimum density and compressive strength of round molded tubes shall be:

Grade	Minimum Density* G/Cu Cm	Minimum Compressive Strength in the Axial Direction (Psi)†
XX	1.25	18,000
XXX	1.22	20,000
CE	1.25	19,000
L	1.25	18,000
LE	1.25	19,000

* The densities given apply to all tube sizes.

† The values given for compressive strength apply to wall thicknesses of ⅟₁₆ in. and over and to inside diameters of ¼ in. and over.

NEMA Standard 1-23-1951.

LP1-4.16 Minimum Dielectric Strength Perpendicular to Laminations

Using the short-time test*, the minimum dielectric strength perpendicular to the laminations shall be:

MINIMUM DIELECTRIC STRENGTH PERPENDICULAR TO THE LAMINATIONS, VOLTS PER MIL, USING THE SHORT-TIME TEST (CONDITION A†)

Grade		Wall Thickness (In.)		
	1/16	Over 1/16 to ⅛, Inclusive	Over ⅛ to ¼, Inclusive	Over ¼ to ½, Inclusive
XX	300	220	150	110
XXX	300	220	150	110
CE	**	175	125	90
L‡	......	......	......	...
LE	150††	175	125	90

* See LP1-5.07.

† See LP1-5.03.

‡ There are no values for Grade L since this grade is not manufactured primarily for electrical applications.

** No value is contemplated because of the weakness of the tube at the mold seam.

†† The mold seam has a more pronounced effect on the dielectric strength of tubes having a wall thickness of 1/16 in. than on the dielectric strength of tubes having a wall thickness over 1/16 in.

NEMA Standard 1-23-1951.

Rods

LP1-4.17 Minimum Density, Flexural Strength and Compressive Strength

The minimum density, flexural strength and compressive strength of laminated thermosetting rods under Condition A* shall be:

Grade	Diameter (In.)	Minimum Density, G/Cu Cm	Minimum Flexural Strength† (Psi)	Minimum Compressive Strength in the Axial Direction (Psi)
XX	⅛ to 2, inclusive	1.30	15,000	20,000
XXX	⅛ to 2, inclusive	1.25	13,000	20,000
C	¼ to 2, inclusive	1.28	16,000	19,000
CE	¼ to 2, inclusive	1.26	13,000	20,000
L	3/16 to 2, inclusive	1.28	16,000	19,000
LE	3/16 to 2, inclusive	1.26	12,000	20,000
G-5	¼ to 2, inclusive	1.80	30,000	22,000

* See LP1-5.03.

† These values apply to rods having a diameter of 1 in. and under.

NEMA Standard 1-23-1951.

LP1-4.18   Maximum Water Absorption

The maximum water absorption of laminated thermosetting rods shall be:

MAXIMUM WATER ABSORPTION, PER CENT

CONDITION D-24/23 FOLLOWING CONDITION E-1/105*

Diameter	Grades						
(In.) †	XX	XXX	C	CE	L	LE	G-5
⅛	2.5	1.5	......	......	2.5‡	2.2‡	......
1	1.0	0.75	2.0	1.0	1.2	1.0	3.0

* See LP1-5.03.

† For intermediate diameters under 1 in., the values given for the next smaller diameter shall apply.

‡ These values apply to rods having a diameter of ³⁄₁₆ in.

For other thicknesses, refer to NEMA Publication No. LP 1-1951.

NEMA Standard 1-23-1951.

TESTING STANDARDS

LP1-5.01   Test Methods for Sheets, Tubes and Rods

All test values given in these standards are based on the test methods of the American Society for Testing Materials, unless otherwise specified. In all cases, the value reported shall be the average of the values determined for the number of specimens required by the specific test method. The latest published revisions or changes in the ASTM test methods shall automatically apply. The latest revisions will be found in the book of *ASTM Standards on Non-Metallic Materials—General**, and its annual supplements. The test methods will also be found in the annual handbook of *ASTM Standards on Electrical Insulating Materials* prepared by the Committee D-9.

The test values given in these standards are based upon specimens which have been conditioned as specified in LP1-4.05 to LP1-4.18 which cover the properties of sheets, tubes and rods. The conditioning procedures are described in LP1-5.03. Unless otherwise specified, tests on the conditioned samples shall be made at a room temperature of 25°C, plus or minus 8°C, and under the prevailing laboratory humidities. In case of disputes, tests shall be made under the standard laboratory atmosphere of 23°C, plus or minus 2°C, and 50 per cent, plus or minus 2 per cent, relative humidity.

---

* Copies are available from the American Society for Testing Materials, 1916 Race Street, Philadelphia 3, Pa.

NEMA Standard 1-23-1951.

LP1-5.02   Direction of Material Under Test

In conducting tests, "lengthwise" shall be interpreted to mean that direction of the sheet known to be stronger in flexure. "Crosswise" shall then be that direction of the sheet known to be weaker in flexure and shall be at 90 degrees to the lengthwise direction.

Authorized Engineering Information 1-23-1951.

LP1-5.03   Conditioning Procedures

The conditioning procedures are the same as those included in MIL-P specifications of the military services for laminated thermosetting sheets and are described as follows:

DESIGNATING TYPE OF CONDITIONING

The following letters shall be used to indicate the type of conditioning required:

Condition A—As received; no special conditioning.

Condition C—Humidity conditioning.

Condition D—Immersion conditioning in distilled water.

Condition E—Temperature conditioning.

NOTE—A conditioning letter which is followed by an inferior numeral 1 (for example, D_1) means that a prior temperature conditioning has been carried out.

DESIGNATION

Conditioning procedures shall be designated in accordance with the following:

1. A capital letter indicating the general condition of the specimen to be tested, i.e., as received or conditioned to humidity, immersion or temperature.

2. A number indicating the duration of the conditioning in hours.

3. A number indicating the conditioning temperature in degrees Centigrade.

4. A number indicating the relative humidity whenever the relative humidity is controlled.

The numbers shall be separated from each other by a slant mark and from the capital letter by a dash.

EXAMPLES—

Condition C-96/35/90—Humidity conditioning—96 hr at 35°C and 90 per cent relative humidity.

Condition D-48/50—Immersion conditioning—48 hr in distilled water at 50°C.

Condition E-48/50—Temperature conditioning—48 hr at 50°C.

NOTE—For time, temperature and humidity tolerances, refer to NEMA Publication No. LP1-1951.

NEMA Standard 1-23-1951.

LP1-5.04   Test Method and Number, Size and Condition of Test Specimens (Sheets)

For details refer to NEMA Publication No. LP1-1951.

LP1-5.05   Test Method and Number, Size and Condition of Test Specimens (Tubes)

For details refer to NEMA Publication No. LP1-1951.

LP1-5.06   Test Method and Number, Size and Condition of Test Specimens (Rods)

For details refer to NEMA Publication No. LP1-1951.

LP1-5.07   Special Test Methods or Modifications of Standard Test Methods

A. DIELECTRIC BREAKDOWN PARALLEL TO LAMINATIONS

Specimens—The test specimens shall be 2 $\times$ 3 in. $\times$ the thickness of the sheet. American Standard tapered pins, such as Morse, Brown and Sharpe or Pratt & Whitney, or their equivalent, having a taper of $\frac{1}{4}$ in. per ft, shall be used.

For test specimens having a thickness up to $\frac{1}{2}$ in., inclusive, No. 3 American Standard tapered pins* 3 in. long and having a diameter at the large end of $\frac{7}{32}$ in. shall be used. Drill two $\frac{3}{16}$-in. diameter holes, centrally located, 1 in. apart, center to center, and perpendicular to the faces of the specimen. Ream holes to a sufficient depth to allow the pins to extend approximately $1\frac{1}{2}$ in. from the small end of the hole.

For test specimens having a thickness over $\frac{1}{2}$ in. up to 2 in., inclusive, No. 4 American Standard tapered pins* 4 in. long and having a diameter at the large end of $\frac{1}{4}$ in. shall be used. Drill two $\frac{3}{16}$-in. diameter holes, centrally located, 1 in. apart, center to center, and perpendicular to the faces of the specimen. Ream holes to a sufficient depth to allow the pins to extend approximately 1 in. from the small end of the hole.

* For information on tapered pins, see Kents Mechanical Engineers Handbook, 12th Edition, Design and Production, Page 15-14.

The electrodes shall be inserted after the conditioning of the test specimen. Spheres having a ½-in. diameter, when placed on the extremities of the tapered pins, will decrease the tendency to flashover.

Procedure—Tests shall be made in accordance with the short-time and step-by-step methods given in *ASTM Methods of Testing Sheet and Plate Materials Used in Electrical Insulation,* Designation D-229†, one specimen only being tested for the short-time method in order to establish a basis for initial voltage of the step-by-step test.

B. DIELECTRIC CONSTANT AND DISSIPATION FACTOR (SHEETS)

Specimens—The specimens shall be rectangular samples sawed from sheets. The size of the test specimens shall be in accordance with the following table. The electrodes shall cover both sides of the sheet and shall consist of silver paint sprayed or painted on or of metal foil held in place by a thin layer of petrolatum. When the same specimen is used for Condition A and after immersion in water and when metal foil electrodes are used, the metal foil electrodes are to be removed and petrolatum cleaned off with a suitable solvent before immersion:

Thickness of Sheet (In.)	Size of Test Specimen (In.)
Up to and including ³⁄₆₄	2 x 2
Over ³⁄₆₄ up to ³⁄₃₂, inclusive	3 x 3
Over ³⁄₃₂ up to ¼, inclusive	4 x 4
Over ¼ up to 2, inclusive	4 x 8

Procedure—The test method described in the *ASTM Methods of Test for Power Factor and Dielectric Constant of Electrical Insulating Materials,* Designation D-150†, shall be followed, using a suitable bridge method, namely, impedance-bridge-circuit, resonant-circuit resistance-variation, or resonant-circuit resonant-rise method. Measurements shall be made at a frequency of 1 megacycle.

C. FLEXURAL STRENGTH IN THE FLATWISE DIRECTION—For size of specimens, refer to NEMA Publication No. LP1, 1951.

NEMA Standard 1-23-1951.

---

† Copies are available from the American Society for Testing Materials, 1916 Race Street, Philadelphia 3, Pa.

LP1-5.08   Recommended Control Tests (Sheets)

Where a grade of laminated thermosetting sheets has been found satisfactory for some particular application, the number of tests required to ascertain the uniformity of the product and whether or not it meets these standards may be greatly decreased. For suggested control tests, refer to NEMA Publication No. LP1-1951.

Authorized Engineering Information 1-23-1951.

AUTHORIZED ENGINEERING INFORMATION ON THE PROPERTIES OF SHEETS, TUBES AND RODS

LP1-6.01   Values

The typical values given in this section represent the average values for the specific property taken from a large number of tests on the products of the several laminators for that particular grade and serve only as a general guide in design. These typical values are not intended as standards.

Authorized Engineering Information 1-23-1951.

LP1-6.02   Authorized Engineering Information on Properties of Laminated Thermosetting Sheets

See page 366 and 367 for the text of this standard. The notes to which reference is made in this standard are as follows:

* For typical dielectric values over the full range of sheet thicknesses for a particular grade, see the curves shown in NEMA Publication No. LP1-1951.

† Insulation resistance is tested in accordance with *ASTM Methods of Test for Electrical Resistance of Insulating Materials,* Designation D-257, using specimens 2 in. x 3 in. x the thickness of the sheet, with $\frac{3}{16}$-in. taper-reamed holes spaced on 1-in. centers, and using tapered-pin electrodes, Pratt & Whitney #3 stainless steel, or their equivalent.

‡ Grade N-1—Because of high cold flow of this material, compressive strength cannot be measured accurately. Compressive yield strength flatwise is approximately 20,000 psi.

NOTE I—MIL-P Specifications No. 3115A, 15035A, 15037A and 15047A call for natural color only.

NOTE II—Modulus of elasticity values are determined by measuring the slope of the stress-strain curve at the origin. These values are not too highly significant for materials of as plastic a nature as thermosetting laminates. They become less significant for the softer and more plastic grades such as Grade N-1, nylon base, and the punching grades P, PC, XXP and XXXP.

NOTE III—Cold flow is measured according to *ASTM Methods of Test for Deformation of Plastics Under Load,* Designation D-621, (Method A), using specimens preconditioned for 4 hr at 65°C, conditioned for 68 hr at 35°C and 90 per cent relative humidity, and then tested at 50°C.

NOTE IV—Experience indicates that laminates will give satisfactory service in most applications at these temperatures. Property values will not approach those obtained at room temperature. The detailed effect of elevated temperatures on property values is under investigation.

Authorized Engineering Information 3-11-1954.

LP1-6.02 Authorized Engineering Information on Properties of Laminated Thermosetting Sheets

Typical Values for Condition A (See LP1-5.03) (Based on ASTM Test Methods, Except as Otherwise Noted)

NEMA and ASTM Grades	X	P	PC	XX	XXP	XXX	XXXP	ES-1	ES-2	ES-3	C	CE
Equivalent MIL-P Specification No.				3115A		3115A	3115A				15035A	15035A
MIL-P Type (see Note 1)				PBG		PBE	PBE-P				FBM	FBG
Tensile strength, psi—Lengthwise	20,000	12,000	10,500	16,000	11,000	15,000	12,400	12,000	13,000	15,000	14,200	12,000
Crosswise	16,000	9,000	8,500	13,000	8,500	12,000	9,500	8,500	9,000	12,000	9,500	9,000
Modulus of elasticity in tension (see Note II)—Lengthwise	1,900,000	1,200,000	1,000,000	1,500,000	900,000	1,300,000	1,000,000				1,000,000	900,000
Crosswise	1,400,000	500,000	800,000	1,200,000	700,000	1,000,000	800,000				900,000	800,000
Modulus of elasticity in flexure (see Note II)—Lengthwise	1,800,000	1,200,000	1,000,000	1,400,000	900,000	1,300,000	1,000,000				1,000,000	900,000
Crosswise	1,300,000	900,000	800,000	1,100,000	700,000	1,000,000	700,000				900,000	800,000
Compressive strength, psi—Flatwise	36,000	25,000	22,000	34,000	25,000	32,000	25,000				37,000	39,000
Edgewise	19,000			23,000		25,500					23,500	24,500
Rockwell hardness (M)	M-110	M-95	M-75	M-105	M-100	M-110	M-105	M-118	M-118	M-120	M-103	M-105
Deformation and shrinkage (cold flow at 4000 psi for 1/8-in. thickness, per cent change) (see Note III)				0.90		0.80	0.80					
Dielectric strength* perpendicular to laminations, volts per mil—Short time 1/32 in. thickness	950	900	850	950	950	900	900				no values recommended	
1/16 in. thickness	700	650	600	700	700	650	650	750				500
1/8 in. thickness	500	470	425	500	500	470	470		550			360
Step by step 1/32 in. thickness	700	650	625	700	700	650	650				no values recommended	
1/16 in. thickness	500	450	425	500	500	450	450	550				300
1/8 in. thickness	360	320	290	360	360	320	320		400			220
Insulation resistance†—condition C-96/35/90, megohms				60	500	1,000	20,000					
Density, g/cu cm.	1.36	1.33	1.34	1.34	1.32	1.32	1.30	1.45	1.40	1.38	1.36	1.33
Specific volume, cu in./lb.	20.4	20.8	20.6	20.6	21.0	21.0	21.3	19.1	19.8	20.1	20.4	20.8
Thermal expansion (cm/cm/°C)	2.0×10^{-5} (all grades) →											
Thermal conductivity (cal./sec./cm²/ °C/cm)	7.0×10^{-4} (all grades) →											
Maximum operating temperature, continuous, °F (see Note IV)	225	250	200	250	250	250	250	250	250	250	225	250
AIEE insulation class.	A	A	A	A	A	A	A	A	A	A	A	A
Specific heat.	0.35 to 0.40 (all grades) →											
Effect of acids.	All grades except Grade G-5 are resistant to dilute solutions of most acids.											
Effect of alkalies.	Not recommended for use in alkaline solutions except for Melamine Grade G-5 which is resistant to dilute alkaline solutions.											
Effect of solvents.	Unaffected by most organic solvents except acetone which may soften the punching grade stocks. Benzol and toluol may affect silicone Grades G-6 and G-7.											

See page 365 for notes applying to this table.

(Continued)

TYPICAL VALUES FOR CONDITION A (See LP1-5.03) (Based on ASTM Test Methods, Except as Otherwise Noted)

NEMA and ASTM Grades	L	LE	A	AA (Continued)	G-1	G-2	G-3	G-5	G-6	G-7	N-1
Equivalent MIL-P Specification No. (see Note I)	15035A	15035A						15037A		997A	15047A
MIL-P Type (see Note I)	FBI	FBE						GMG		GSG	NPG
Tensile strength, psi—Lengthwise	14,000	13,500	10,000	12,000	12,500	16,000	23,000	37,000		23,000	8,500
Crosswise	10,000	9,500	8,000	10,000	9,500	11,000	20,000	30,000		18,500	8,000
Modulus of elasticity in tension (see Note II) Lengthwise	1,200,000	1,000,000	2,500,000	1,700,000	1,900,000	1,800,000	2,000,000	2,300,000		1,800,000	400,000
Crosswise	900,000	850,000	1,600,000	1,500,000	1,100,000	1,200,000	1,700,000	2,000,000		1,800,000	400,000
Modulus of elasticity in flexure (see Note II) Lengthwise	1,100,000	1,000,000	2,300,000	1,600,000	1,800,000	1,300,000	1,500,000	1,700,000		1,400,000	600,000
Crosswise	850,000	850,000	1,400,000	1,400,000	1,000,000	1,000,000	1,200,000	1,500,000		1,200,000	500,000
Compressive strength, psi—Flatwise	35,000	37,000	40,000	38,000	50,000	38,000	50,000	70,000	40,000	45,000	‡‡‡
Edgewise	23,500	25,000	17,000	21,000		15,000	17,500	25,000	9,000	14,000	‡‡‡
Rockwell hardness (M)	M-105	M-105	M-111	M-103	M-110	M-105	M-100	M-120	M-95	M-100	M-105
Deformation and shrinkage (cold flow at 4000 psi for 1/8-in. thickness, per cent change) (see Note III)						0.40	0.30	0.30		0.30	
Dielectric strength* perpendicular to laminations, volts per mil — Short time: 1/32 in. thickness	no values recommended	700					750			450	850
1/16 in. thickness		500	225	no values recommended	250	500	700	350	250	400	600
1/8 in. thickness		360	160		200	425	600	260	185	350	450
Step by step: 1/32 in. thickness	no values recommended	450					550			400	650
1/16 in. thickness		300	135		150	360	500	220	220	350	450
1/8 in. thickness		220	95		120	300	450	160	160	250	300
Insulation resistance†—condition C-96/35/90, megohms		30				5,000		100		2,500	50,000
Density, g/cu cm.	1.35	1.33	1.72	1.70	1.66	1.50	1.65	1.90	1.65	1.68	1.15
Specific volume, cu in./lb.	20.5	20.8	16.1	16.3	17.3	18.5	16.8	14.6	16.8	16.5	24.1
Thermal expansion, linear (cm/cm/°C)	2.0×10^{-5}		1.5×10^{-5}			1.8×10^{-5}		12.0×10^{-4}	1.0×10^{-5}		
Thermal conductivity (cal./sec./cm²/°C/cm)	7.0×10^{-4}								7.0×10^{-4}		
Maximum operating temperature, continuous, °F (see Note IV)	225	250	275	275	290	275	290	300	400	400	165
AIEE insulation class.	A	A	B	B	B	B	B	B	H	H	A
Specific heat.	0.35-0.40				0.30			0.26		0.25	0.35-0.40
Effect of acids.											
Effect of alkalies.											
Effect of solvents.											

All grades except Grade G-5 are resistant to dilute solutions of most acids.
Not recommended for use in alkaline solutions except for Melamine Grade G-5 which is resistant to dilute alkaline solutions.
Unaffected by most organic solvents except acetone which may soften the punching grade stocks. Benzol and toluol may affect silicone Grades G-6 and G-7.

See page 365 for notes applying to this table.

**LP1-6.03   Authorized Engineering Information on Properties of
Laminated Thermosetting Tubes and Rods**

TYPICAL VALUES FOR CONDITION A (See LP1-5.03)

Grade	Tensile Strength* (Psi)	Dissipation Factor, 10^6 Cycles	Dielectric Constant, 10^6 Cycles	Specific Heat	Thermal Conductivity‡
ROLLED TUBES					
X	8,500	†	†	....	....
XX	8,000	0.040	5.0	....	....
C	6,000	†	†	....	....
LE	7,000	†	†	....	....
G-5	25,000	0.012	7.0	....	....
MOLDED TUBES					
XX	11,000	0.040	5.5	0.35-0.40	7×10^{-4}
XXX	9,000	0.040	5.3	0.35-0.40	7×10^{-4}
CE	8,500	....	....	0.35-0.40	7×10^{-4}
L	9,000	....	....	0.35-0.40	7×10^{-4}
LE	8,500	....	....	0.35-0.40	7×10^{-4}
MOLDED RODS					
XX	10,000	....	....	0.35-0.40	7×10^{-4}
XXX	9,000	....	....	0.35-0.40	7×10^{-4}
C	9,000	....	....	0.35-0.40	7×10^{-4}
CE	8,000	....	....	0.35-0.40	7×10^{-4}
L	11,000	....	....	0.35-0.40	7×10^{-4}
LE	10,000	....	....	0.35-0.40	7×10^{-4}
G-5	30,000	....	....	0.26	12×10^{-4}

* See *ASTM Methods of Testing Laminated Round Rods Used in Electrical Insulation,*
Publication No. D-349.

† No value recommended.

‡ Cal/sec/cm²/°C/cm.

Authorized Engineering Information 1-23-1951.

2. Recommended Practice for Fabricating Laminated Plastics

Introduction

The machining of laminated plastic products can be accomplished without difficulty when using standard wood- or metal-working machinery. It should be recognized that these materials have certain fundamental properties not common to metals, and, because of these, some modification of metal fabricating practices can be made. Among these properties are: lower shearing strength, which permits high cutting speeds and feeds even on machines of light construction, and greater resiliency, which requires greater clearance and less rake on cutting tools. It must also be recognized that certain machining operations, such as drilling parallel with the laminations or milling at right angles to the laminations, will require additional care due to the laminated structure. In all machining operations on these materials it is extremely important to keep tools sharp.

The following recommendations are offered as a guide. However, departures from many of these recommendations may be made to meet individual requirements.

Cutting Laminated Plastics

Laminated plastics are manufactured in the form of sheets, rods, tubes and special shapes. Generally it is necessary to cut this material into various sizes and shapes prior to final fabrication. Various methods of cutting can be used, depending upon the thickness, grade and desired results.

The following methods are those generally used by the industry. Under normal conditions all cutting is done without lubricants.

Shearing

Equipment: Metal squaring shears—guillotine type.

Capacity: Up to $\frac{1}{8}$ in. in thickness, depending upon the grade of material.

Preparation of Stock: Up to $\frac{1}{16}$ in. thickness in XP material and up to $\frac{1}{8}$ in. thickness in most fabric base grades may be sheared at room temperature (minimum of 50°F). Harder stocks may be sheared by heating from 200 to 280°F, depending on grade and thickness.

Speed: Up to 50 strokes per minute.

Feed: By hand.

Remarks: Shears can be used for angular cutting in addition to straight stripping. When shearing grades and thicknesses that require heating, it is important that heating be done uniformly and that the material be removed from the heating medium as soon as it reaches the required temperature.

Band Sawing

Equipment: Standard woodworking band saw.

Saws: File hard, carbon steel band saw blades, or hardened steel blades with soft backs. Teeth range from 5 to 8 points per in. 18 to 20 gauge, $\frac{1}{4}$ to $\frac{1}{2}$ in. wide for circles. 1 to $1\frac{1}{4}$ in. for straight cutting.

Capacity: Up to 10 in. in thickness.

Speed: Up to 8000 surface feet per minute.

Feed: By hand, depending upon thickness. Feed work into blade as fast as it will cut without forcing the saw.

Remarks: Band sawing is recommended for curved or straight cuts where smooth edges and close tolerances are not required and when cutting material thicker than the normal circular sawing range. Blades should be given a medium set for straight cuts and a heavy set for circular cuts. The amount of set depends upon the radius of cut required. The smaller the radius, the greater the set. Blades must be kept sharp at all times. An automatic band-saw grinding or filing machine is recommended.

Circular Sawing

Equipment: Standard floor or bench circular sawing machines (as used in woodworking industry).

Saws: Hollow ground saws of carbon or high-speed steel, without set, are recommended, $\frac{1}{16}$ to $\frac{1}{8}$ in. thickness and from 4 to 8 teeth per in., depending upon thickness and form of material. Teeth should be ground square with axis for smoothest cutting and should have liberal clearance.

Capacity: Up to 1 in. in thickness where smooth edge and close tolerance is required. Greater thicknesses with special equipment and care.

Speed: Up to 13,000 surface feet per minute.

Feed: By hand. Feed work into blade as fast as it will cut without forcing the saw.

Remarks: For each thickness and for various grades of stock there is an elevation of the saw above the table that will reduce chipping to a minimum. Set saw so that it just protrudes through the work; then adjust upward until smoothest cut is obtained.

Small tubing may be cut by feeding the material straight through the saw. Heavy walled tubing over $\frac{3}{4}$ in. diameter should be "rolled" through the saw to prevent excessive break out.

Sawing is not confined to straight cutting but may also be employed for beveling, notching, grooving, etc. Saws must be kept sharp, and, if carbon or high-speed steel saws are used, sharpening may be necessary after 20 or 30 minutes production. Automatic grinding or filing machines are recommended for sharpening carbon steel and high-speed steel saws.

Abrasive Cutting

Equipment: Standard woodworking circular saw machines or special abrasive cut-off equipment.

Abrasive Wheels: Abrasive wheels $\frac{1}{16}$ in. and heavier in thickness. Diameter range from 6 to 16 in. Abrasive-wheel manufacturer should be consulted as to proper grain sizes, bond strength, diameter and speed for the specified job. A steel centered wheel is recommended for table saws.

Capacity: Up to 2 in. in thickness.

Speed: Up to 12,000 surface feet per minute.

Feed: By hand. Feed work into wheel as rapidly as possible without forcing.

Remarks: All glass base and most asbestos base materials can best be cut by using an abrasive wheel.

The work must be mounted solidly and the cut made without any side-wise movement in order to prevent breakage of the wheel.

Special grits and bonds are available from manufacturers for materials which cannot be satisfactorily cut by the standard wheels. A flood of water on the work and wheel may be used when necessary to prevent over-heating and "loading" of the wheel.

Machines used for dry cutting should be provided with efficient dust collecting equipment.

Punching, Shaving and Broaching

Laminated plastics can be readily punched, shaved and broached, depending upon the thickness and grade of material.

All of these operations are performed without coolant or lubricant. In some cases where heat is required, any of the following methods may be used: hot plate, oven, hot oil or infrared lamps.

Punching

Equipment: Standard power-driven vertical punch presses.

Dies: Progressive, compound and multiple operating dies, including combination blanking and shaving. Dies are practically the same as those for metal with the exception that little clearance is allowed between punch and die and punch and stripper plate. Shrinkage allowances must be taken into consideration when designing tools.

Capacity: Up to $\frac{1}{8}$ in. in thickness.

Preparation of Stock: Some punching grades can be punched cold up to $\frac{3}{32}$ in. thick. Harder grades must be heated in thicknesses from $\frac{1}{32}$ in. up. Do not exceed 250°F.

Speed: 70 to 300 strokes per minute, depending upon size of machine and work.

Feed: Manual, using automatic stops and gauges. When practical, rotary table feeding mechanism with vacuum or mechanical pick-up may be used.

Remarks: Material cannot be punched to extremely close tolerances due to the normal contraction of the material and, also, its thermal contraction when punched hot.

Relatively smooth edges can be obtained when punched hot up to $\frac{1}{16}$ in. thick. Checking occurs over $\frac{1}{16}$ in. Generally speaking, better edges are obtained from fabric base materials.

The degree of heat used when punching depends entirely upon the thickness and grade of material. 120°F is often enough temperature, but in some cases as high as 250°F. is required.

Tools must be kept sharp at all times in order to maintain tolerances and must be given good edges.

Shaving

Equipment: Standard power-driven vertical punch press.

Dies: Any desired shape is worked out in a die block. The cutting edge is then beveled at 45 degrees on the outside of the die. The work is pushed through the shaving die by means of a soft steel or brass plate which does not enter the die.

Capacity: Up to $\frac{3}{4}$ in. thickness.

Preparation of Stock: For thicknesses greater than $\frac{1}{8}$ in. the material is preheated up to 250°F, depending upon grade and thickness. Oil is generally a suitable heating medium.

Speed: Up to 100 strokes per minute.

Feed: By hand or automatic dial feed.

Remarks: When smoother edges are required than obtainable by punching, a shaving operation will generally meet the requirements for finish. For irregular shaped blanks too thick to punch, shaving will give the desired shape accurately and rapidly.

Blanks cut oversize are used. Combination punching, blanking and shaving dies can be used for material up to $\frac{1}{8}$ in. in thickness. These dies are commonly known as "double decker" dies, and the blanked piece is pushed through the shaving cutter on the same stroke by the succeeding blank.

Broaching

Equipment: Hydraulic, motor- or hand-operated broaching machines of the vertical or horizontal type can be used. Broaching may also be done on a standard punch press.

Broaches: Standard broaches with approximately 4 degrees cutting clearance with a slight positive rake. With the exception of this clearance angle, the broach is exactly the same as for brass.

Capacity: Any.

Speed: 30 to 50 feet per minute.

Remarks: Broaches can be used to produce square, hexagonal and other polygonal holes, irregular shapes, keyways, etc. The laminated structure of the material makes it necessary to use a special broaching procedure. When cutting across the laminations, the material must be backed up with a mild steel or brass plate which forms a slide fit with the last cutting tooth on the broach. This is necessary to prevent fraying and breaking out of the edges. When the cutting is done parallel to the laminations, a fixture applying pressure at right angles to the laminations should be used.

The teeth of the broach should be spaced so that, except for the beginning and end of the cut, at least two teeth will be in contact with the material. Ample chip room between the teeth should be provided based upon the depth of the cut per tooth. The pilot pin should be as large as possible and tapered to facilitate rapid operation. A cut of .001 to .005 in. per tooth can be taken with the pitch ranging from 1/4 to 3/4 in., as determined for the material and type of operation.

Drill-Press Operations

A great amount of development work has been done by manufacturers to design drills especially adapted for laminated plastics. These drills are available, and, if recommendations are followed, no difficulties are likely to be encountered. All normal drill-press operations can be performed dry, but in some cases, especially with asbestos or glass base materials, coolants may be used to advantage.

Drilling

Equipment: Standard drilling machines, vertical or horizontal, single, gang or multiples.

Drills: For best results use a standard drill of special design for drilling laminated plastics. This drill is available through all drill manufacturers and will give better results than standard metal drills. The drills are made of high-speed steel and have highly polished flutes.

Capacity: 80 lb and up. Where holes are large enough to use fly-cutters it is usually more economical to do so.

Speed: Up to 400 surface feet per minute.

Feed: Generally by hand. Feel of drilling will denote whether withdrawal of drill is necessary for cleaning flutes.

Remarks: Dubbing the lip of the drill and giving it plenty of clearance will cause it to cut free and will prevent grabbing. Drill should be operated at its highest possible speed without burning and should not be forced into the work. To avoid chipping and grabbing when drilling thin material and tubing, the included angle of the point may be modified to as low as 60°C.

Laminated plastics have a tendency to bind on the drill and to close in when the drill is removed. It is, therefore, advisable to use a drill slightly oversized in order to get the required size hole.

Well-designed drill jigs, clamping the work between top and bottom plates, will insure an accurate and clean job. All holes being drilled should be backed for best results.

Drilling parallel with the laminations should be avoided whenever possible. If drilling must be done in this manner, the work should be held in clamps or drill jig. For drilling holes ¼ in. and larger in glass and asbestos base material, drills which have been designed for cutting metal and which have been tipped with carbide are recommended.

Counterboring and Countersinking

Equipment: Standard drilling machines.

Counterbores and Countersinks: High-speed steel or carbide-tipped conventional counterbores and countersinks. Generally two-lipped tools are used with negative rakes up to 10 degrees.

Capacity: Up to 5 in. diameter.

Speed: Up to 200 surface feet per minute.

Feed: Generally by hand. The initial contact between the tool and the work should be with a light touch in order to break the highly polished surface without cracking.

Remarks: If chattering occurs, a slower speed may prevent this condition, and, if a drill is used as a cutting tool, the breaking of the inner surface of the cutting edge will likewise decrease chatter.

Fly-cutting

Equipment: Standard drilling machines.

Fly Cutters: Generally a single- or two-point cutter held in a cutter bar which is adjustable for various diameters.

Capacity: Up to 6 in. diameter by 1 in. in thickness.

Speed: Up to 400 feet per minute.

Feed: Generally by hand. Care must be taken to prevent digging when approaching the work with a cutter.

Remarks: Fly-cutting is generally employed to cut discs or large holes not practical for drilling. Fly-cutting tools are generally designed so that the center post which holds the cutter bar can be used as a pilot in a previously drilled hole to steady the bar during the cutting operation. Cutting tools must have clearance both in front and inside of the cutting edge.

Screw Machines and Turret Lathes

Under the heading of screw machines there are two types generally used for fabricating laminated plastics; one type being the automatic-screw machine, either single or multiple spindle, and the other the hand-screw machine which primarily has the same functions as the automatic machines, the exception being that the operation of the tools, stock feed, etc., are by hand.

Turret lathes have primarily the same function as screw machines, the exception being that the turret-lathe type of machine is generally larger and intended for the heavier class of work. Chucking work as well as bar feed work can be handled on these machines.

Most screw-machine and turret-lathe work is performed dry, but for deep-hole drilling, threading, etc., a coolant should be used. A satisfactory mixture consists of 60 per cent paraffin oil and 40 per cent kerosene oil.

Deep-hole drilling should be performed by withdrawing the drill from the hole several times. A good practice is not to drill in depth more than three or four times the diameter of the drill without withdrawing it from the hole so that the chips can be cleaned away.

Internal and external threading can be performed with standard threading tools properly ground. Chasers should have a 33-degree chamfer on the lead and a negative rake up to 10 degrees.

Forming and undercutting can successfully be performed, but care must be taken that an extremely fine feed is used, preferably not over .0005 to .001 in. per revolution. Circular and square tools can be used for forming but should not be greater in width than 75 per cent of the diameter of the stock.

Many attachments, fixtures and magazine feeds can be used for this work.

Automatic- and Hand-Screw Machines

Equipment: Standard metal-working machines.

Tools: High-speed steel, carbide-tipped and diamond tools are used with excellent results. Tools are ground approximately the same as for brass.

Capacity: Up to 1 in. for hand-screw machines. Up to 2 in. for automatic-screw machines.

Speed: Hand-screw machines up to 3000 rpm. Automatic-screw machines up to 6000 rpm.

Feed: Any desired, depending upon finish required.

Remarks: Hand- and automatic-screw machines are highly productive and operate the same as for brass except at much higher speeds and feeds. Production from these machines range from 1000 per hr downward, depending upon the job. Laminated phenolic cams are economically used on automatic-screw machines where tool pressures are not too great.

Turret Lathes

Equipment: Standard machine tools.

Tools: High-speed steel and carbide-tipped, ground approximately the same as for brass.

Capacity: Up to 4 in. in diameter.

Speed: Up to 1500 rpm.

Feed: Any desired, depending upon finish required.

Remarks: As a rule these machines are operated at their top speed for most jobs within their capacity. The operations are approximately the same as for brass except at much higher speeds and feeds.

Lathe Operations

Lathe operations are generally performed on two standard types of machine tools: namely, engine lathes and production lathes. On these machines turning, boring, recessing and any other lathe operations can be performed. The engine lathes are either of the bench or heavy-duty-floor type, and these machines can be used for all lathe operations, including thread chasing.

Production lathes are for plain turning and facing, and usually operate at much higher speeds and feeds than the engine lathe.

Lathe work is generally performed dry, but, in the case of internal threading, it is sometimes advisable to use a lubricant.

Lathes

Equipment: Standard machine tools of either the engine or production type, sometimes modified for high spindle speeds.

Tools: High-speed steel, carbide- or diamond-tipped for turning, boring, facing and cutting-off. The tools should be ground from 0 degrees to 10 degrees negative rake for threading and forming.

Capacity: Depending upon size of lathe.

Speed: Up to 4000 surface feet per minute.

Feed: Any desired, depending upon finish required.

Remarks: Generally speaking, lathe operations performed on laminated plastics are about the same as brass with the exception of the surface speed which can be higher.

Fabric base materials can generally be worked with high-speed steel, but for paper, graphite, asbestos and glass base, carbide-tipped tools should be used whenever possible.

Threading — Internal and External

Internal and external threading, as covered by this section, includes recommendations for tapping with a tap and threading with a die. This work may be done manually or on standard threading equipment. High-speed steel taps from .002 to .005 in. oversize should be used if available. A 75 per cent thread with a Class 2 fit is the maximum accuracy obtainable in laminated plastics for either internal or external threading.

Threading of this type can be performed dry, but a coolant is often necessary, especially in deep-hole tapping.

Threading (Tapping and Die Threading)

Equipment: By hand or with standard threading equipment. For tapping, tapping heads or tapping machines. For external die work, any revolving equipment.

Taps and Dies: Standard taps and dies. If possible, taps should be purchased oversize. Taps should be ground with a negative rake from 0 degrees to 10 degrees, depending upon size, pitch and grade of material. Die chaser should have a 33 degree chamfer on the lead and a negative rake up to 10 degrees. For larger sizes, a self-opening die head or collapsible tap will facilitate operations.

Capacity: Up to 2 in.

Speed: Up to 200 feet per minute.

Remarks: Care must be taken to insure the proper chamfer and rake for each job. Experience will teach the operator the proper method of grinding for best results. A slight chamfer around the edge of the hole to be tapped, or on the outside of the diameter of the piece to be externally threaded, will improve the class of the work.

Milling and Gear Cutting

All laminated phenolic materials can be milled. Standard milling cutters may be used on all materials, but for longer life between sharpenings, carbide-tipped cutters are recommended. The cutting speeds recommended are based on carbide-tipped cutters and should be reduced approximately 25 per cent for high-speed steel cutters.

Gears with any standard type of teeth may be cut from laminated phenolic gear material. (Never use tubing or rod.) Whenever the design of the hub will permit, it is good practice to cut gears in multiple, and the last blank should be backed up with some rigid material in order to prevent breaking-out of the last few laminations.

Teeth may be formed by hobbing, shaping or milling.

For all normal operations milling and gear cutting may be done dry.

Milling

Equipment: Standard metal-working machine tools.

Tools: Standard milling cutters with a negative rake from 0 degrees to 10 degrees is recommended. High-speed steel or carbide-tipped.

Capacity: Any.

Speed: Up to 1000 surface feet per minute.

Feed: Up to 20 in. per minute.

Remarks: For fabric cotton base best results can be obtained by operating at the highest spindle speed the cutter will stand with the maximum feed possible to give the desired finish. For paper, graphite, asbestos and glass base materials, carboloy cutters are always recommended, and it is advisable to reduce the spindle speed and increase the feed. For best results almost all types of milling should be done by the (climb) cutting method. This method prevents the edges of the material from being raised, and it also helps to hold the work tightly in the fixture. The chips are also cleaned from in front of the cut, providing longer tool life. Backing plates of hard wood or other suitable materials are recommended when cutting across the laminations.

Gear Cutting

Equipment: Standard metal gear-cutting machines. (Hobbing, shaping and milling.)

Tools: High-speed steel or carbide-tipped tools.

Capacity: Depending upon the capacity of the machine.

Preparation of Stock: Material is sawed, molded, fly cut or turned into suitable blanks.

Speed: Up to 400 surface feet per minute.

Feed: To be determined by finish desired.

Remarks: Gears with any of the standard types of teeth may be cut from laminated gear material. These may be spur-helical, mitre, worm or herringbone gears. Teeth may be formed in blanks by hobbing, shaping or milling, using standard metal gear-cutting machines. The highest speed and feed within the capacity of the machine should be used. If the machine is used consistently for cutting laminated gear material, special gearing may be installed to increase the surface speed of the cutter and the feed mechanism above that commonly used for cutting metal.

In cutting teeth in laminated gear stock, the last blank must be backed up to prevent fraying and breaking of the material as the cutter comes through. The backing plates can be made of hardwood or other suitable materials.

Important: Gears are cut from special laminated gear stock. Laminated rod and tubing are not suitable as a gear material.

Marking

Laminated plastics may be marked by means of engraving, stamping or printing.

Engraving and stamping are recommended for permanence under conditions of severe wear.

Printing is a rapid operation and is satisfactory where rough handling is not encountered.

Engraving

Equipment: Pantograph machines.

Cutters: Single-lip, high-speed steel cutters ground 60 degrees to 90 degrees included angle point. Relieved 2 degrees to 5 degrees at cutting edge.

Capacity: Up to 1½-in. characters.

Speed: 10,000 to 15,000 rpm.

Feed: By hand.

Remarks: The depth of the cut depends upon the width of the character desired. The finished cut should have few cutter marks. Characters are copied from a master held in a copy holder. Engraving machines will give a reduction up to 50-1, and any size character within that ratio to the master can be reproduced. Alphabetical masters are generally used, but on jobs where the entire surface of the panel is to be engraved, a master plate especially made for the whole job can be used if the quantity is sufficient to justify the expense. This master can be two or three times the size of the finished job. Characters may be filled with colored lacquers to be made more readable.

Stamping

Equipment: Standard marking machines with or without roll leaf feed.

Stamps: Hardened steel stamps.

Capacity: Any.

Speed: Depending upon size of work and area of impression.

Remarks: Lettering, serial numbers, trade-marks and decorative effects can be permanently imparted to laminated plastics by pressing a heated hardened steel stamp into the surface. Excellent contrasts may be obtained by filling in with a colored lacquer or by stamping through a thin sheet of pigmented roll leaf.

Automatic roll-leaf presses are recommended when a great number of identical pieces are to be marked. Hand-operated stamping presses which can be satisfactorily used if the quantity of production can be handled, are available.

Temperature and pressure should be determined by visual inspection. Temperature can be from room to 420°F. The pressure applied will be in relation to the depth of impression desired.

Printing

Equipment: Standard printing presses.

Type: Printing plates.

Capacity: Any within size of printing press.

Preparation of Stock: The surface should be cleaned with a suitable solvent.

Remarks: Laminated phenolic sheet material can be printed with various colored inks on hand or power printing presses. After the ink has been thoroughly dried, a coat of protecting lacquer should be applied over the printed section to prevent the ink from rubbing. The protecting lacquer should be baked in order to make it permanent. Rubber hand stamps can be used to print identification marks, serial number, etc., on laminated plastics. Standard stamps may be used with quick-drying permanent ink. An inking pad is generally satisfactory for rubber stamp use.

Rubber stamping or printing on sanded surfaces is not satisfactory.

Sanding and Grinding

Laminated plastics can be sanded on a belt or disc sander where it is necessary to finish shaped surfaces or for roughening prior to gluing.

Grinding may be employed to finish fabricated work to extremely close tolerances.

Sanding

Equipment: Standard belt or disc sanders.

Abrasives: Abrasive belts and discs ranging from 40 to 240 grit depending upon the finish required.

Capacity: Any size within the limits of the machine.

Speed: Up to 2000 surface feet per minute.

Feed: By hand.

Remarks: Sanding may be employed for facing and shaping surfaces, or roughening preparatory to gluing, and for removing burrs and sharp edges from the work.

Grinding

Equipment: Standard or special grinding machines of the type used for metals.

Abrasives: Abrasive wheels varying in coarseness, depending upon desired finish. It is suggested that the recommendations of manufacturers be followed closely.

Capacity: Any within range of the machine.

Speed: Up to 5000 surface feet per minute.

Feed: Depending upon desired finish.

Remarks: Grinding may be employed to finish fabricated work to extremely close tolerance or to insure parallelism of opposite surfaces. The work is generally clamped in a fixture which is moved across the face of the grinding wheel. Double spindle grinders can be used for grinding two opposite parallel surfaces at the same time. In this case, the work is placed in a fixture which is pushed between the wheels. A coolant is generally used when grinding laminated plastics. This tends to prevent the wheel from loading.

Finishing

Included under this heading are burring, tumbling, cleaning and buffing. All or some of these operations are generally necessary to finish a fabricated part. Many methods are used for cleaning and burring the fuzz from machined parts. The most common practice is to use a vertical spindle drill press in the chuck of which is held a shaft containing emery cloth or emery wheels of various sizes and shapes.

Quite often extensive hand work must be done in order to completely remove objectionable burrs and fuzz.

Dirt, burrs and fuzz may be, to a certain extent, removed from pieces by tumbling in standard revolving barrels. Contact between the pieces will remove the burrs to a certain extent and clean away the dirt. Various polishing agents can be used in the drums with different results. This method can also be used to clean the material as well as to give it an oily finish. Saturating a cloth in oil and allowing it to revolve in the drum will be sufficient to put a thin film of oil on the pieces.

Buffing with standard rag buffing wheels will give the material a brilliant finish. The use of rouge will be beneficial in restoring high polish to machined surfaces.

Authorized Engineering Information 7-25-1945.

3. Excerpts from NEMA Standards for Laminated Thermosetting Decorative Sheets

Scope and Introduction

These standards cover laminated thermosetting sheets intended for decorative purposes. The sheets consist essentially of layers of fibrous sheet materials impregnated with thermosetting condensation resins and consolidated under heat and pressure. The resultant product is resistant to staining and has the property of hardness to provide resistance to severe wear.

Sheets are available in a wide variety of colors, decorative designs and surface finishes. Standard thicknesses are from $\frac{1}{16}$ to $\frac{1}{4}$ in., inclusive.

Laminated thermosetting decorative sheets are generally supplied with the back sanded for bonding to plywood or other types of base material. They are used for applications calling for the maintenance of good appearance under hard service. Some of the most common applications are:

1. Counter and table tops for use in restaurants, cafeterias and bars.
2. Sink tops and kitchen work surfaces.
3. Dinette tables.
4. Baseboards.
5. Wainscoting.
6. Wall paneling.

A cigarette-proof grade is made by incorporating a heat-conducting layer under the surface of the sheets. This has the effect of conducting and dissipating the heat from a concentrated source more rapidly.

LP2-1.01   Grades

There are 2 grades of laminated thermosetting decorative sheets:

1. Standard grade.
2. Cigarette-proof grade.

NEMA Standard 8-26-1948.

LP2-1.02   Description of Grades

1. Standard-grade material is material which is highly resistant to heat.
2. Cigarette-proof-grade material is material which is specially constructed to withstand concentrated sources of heat, such as lighted cigarettes.

NEMA Standard 8-26-1948.

LP2-1.03   Ordering Information

Orders for laminated thermosetting decorative sheets should include the following information: grade, quantity, sheet size, thickness, color and finish.

NEMA Standard 8-26-1948.

LP2-1.04 Thicknesses and Tolerances

Laminated thermosetting decorative sheets in standard thicknesses from $\frac{1}{16}$ to $\frac{1}{4}$ in., inclusive, shall have the following tolerances:

Nominal Thickness of Sheets (In.)	Tolerances (In., Plus or Minus)
$\frac{1}{16}$ (0.062)	0.005
$\frac{3}{32}$ (0.094)	0.007
$\frac{1}{8}$ (0.125)	0.008
$\frac{5}{32}$ (0.156)	0.009
$\frac{3}{16}$ (0.188)	0.010
$\frac{7}{32}$ (0.219)	0.011
$\frac{1}{4}$ (0.250)	0.012

NEMA Standard 8-26-1948.

LP2-1.05 Squareness

The length and width of decorative sheets shall be such that a rectangle of the size specified by the manufacturer can be obtained.

NEMA Standard 1-23-1951.

LP2-1.06 Method of Test for Resistance of Surface to Wear

SCOPE

This method of test covers the ability of the surface of laminated thermosetting decorative material to maintain its original design or color under abrasive wear such as may be encountered in service.

A. TEST SPECIMENS

Test specimens shall be $\frac{1}{16}$ in. in thickness. They shall be in the form of a disc having a diameter of $4\frac{1}{16}$ in. and having a hole $\frac{1}{4}$ in. in diameter through the center. Three specimens shall be tested.

B. TEST APPARATUS

The test apparatus shall consist of:

1. A Taber abraser complete with rubber-covered test wheels, sandpaper, zinc standardization disc, and rimmed specimen holder with clamping ring, all of which are supplied by the Taber Instrument Company, North Tonawanda, N. Y. (Catalog No. NE-4010, or its equivalent). The component parts of this apparatus consist of the following:

   1 Main abraser unit (Model E-4010) with two 1000-g auxiliary range weights and two 500-g plugs.

    1 Specimen holder and ring (Catalog No. 100-131) with $4\frac{1}{4}$ in. threaded outside diameter. (This threaded holder provides positive hold-down pressure which is desirable.)

    2 Sets of NEMA wheels (Catalog No. S-32). (See par. C for the preparation of test wheels.)

  100 NEMA sandpaper strips (Catalog No. S-33).

    5 NEMA zinc plates (Catalog No. S-34). These discs are 0.032-in. rolled zinc sheet having a scleroscope hardness of 14-17 and designated as Mix No. 103 by the New Jersey Zinc Company, 160 Front Street, New York, N. Y., or the equivalent.

    1 Brush (Catalog No. S-12).

2. A Y-tube having parallel forks $2^{19}\!\!/_{32}$ in. apart and having an inside diameter of $\frac{1}{4}$ in.

3. A rubber hose, 2 to 4 ft in length and having an inside diameter of $\frac{3}{8}$ in.

4. A source of compressed air at 20 psi.

5. A ring stand and clamp.

6. An analytical balance and weights.

See par. D and E for the preparation of the test rig and the standardization of the abrasive.

C. PREPARATION OF TEST WHEELS

The test wheels which are supplied by the Taber Instrument Company are already prepared for use in tests, except for the application of sandpaper.

Those who prepare their own test wheels should do so in accordance with the following:

From a sheet of NEMA Grade C laminate, machine discs as follows:

1. Thickness—$\frac{1}{2}$ in.

2. Diameter—$1\frac{1}{2}$ in.

3. Center-hole diameter—$\frac{5}{8}$ in., plus $\frac{1}{64}$ in., minus 0 in.

To the periphery of the discs, cement sections of a rubber hose having a width of $\frac{1}{2}$ in., a wall thickness of $\frac{1}{4}$ in., an inside diameter of $1\frac{1}{2}$ in. and a Shore Durometer A hardness of 50-55.

Surface grind the rubber-surfaced discs on center to square the periphery of the wheel to a finished diameter of 2 in., plus 0 in., minus 0.025 in. Dust the rubber surface lightly with zinc stearate and apply one thickness only of a strip of $\frac{1}{2}$-in. wide double-coated (coated both sides) scotch tape or its equivalent to the periphery of the wheel. The ends of the tape should butt as closely as possible.

Apply a $\frac{1}{2}$-in. strip of Behr-Manning 5/0-180A Adalox finishing paper (sandpaper), (cut crosswise to the sheet), or its equivalent, to the outer surface of the tape, making the butt joint carefully and avoiding contamination of the face of the sandpaper.

If sandpaper strips supplied by the Taber Instrument Company are used, remove the backing and apply the sandpaper directly to the wheel.

The outside diameter of the finished wheel should be 2.025 in., plus or minus 0.025 in.

D. Preparation of the Test Rig

Set up the Taber abraser with the 500-g plugs in place. Place the test wheels described in par. C on the test arbor and fasten them in position with the nuts supplied for that purpose. Connect the rubber hose to the air source and insert the base of the Y-tube in the free end of the hose. Clamp the open ends in position one inch from the abrasive wheels and at an angle of 45 degrees from the horizontal so that, when the air is turned on and the wheels are in position, the air blast will be directed at the point where the center of the abrasive surface meets the specimen.

E. Standardization of the Abrasive

Make up test wheels from each lot of sandpaper received. Subject the standard zinc disc to a 500-cycle "run-in" on the abraser.

Clean the zinc disc and clamp it on to the turn-table, using the center hold-down nut and washer and the rimmed specimen holder. Place the abrasive wheels on the surface of the zinc disc, turn on the air and allow the turntable to revolve 500 cycles (see par. F.1). Remove the zinc disc, wipe it clean and weigh it to the nearest 0.001 g.

Using fresh sandpaper, rerun this test for 500 cycles as above and reweigh.

The weight loss should be 0.130 g, plus or minus 0.020 g. If the weight loss is out of this range, run 2 additional tests using fresh paper from the same lot. If the average weight loss for these 3 tests is out of range, the lot of sandpaper being tested should not be used for testing laminates under this method.

A correction factor for each lot of sandpaper shall be calculated as follows:

$$\text{Correction factor} = \frac{\text{Average weight loss of zinc disc}}{0.130}$$

F. Factors Influencing Accuracy of Test*

Three important factors which affect the accuracy of this test are:
1. Standardization of the abrasive in accordance with par. E should be carried out for each lot of abrasive and, additionally, before running each test, because the abrasive paper is subject to change due to the relative humidity of storage conditions. The optimum relative

---

* This portion of the standard has been approved as Authorized Engineering Information.

humidity is 50 per cent but, in any case, excessive temperature and relative humidity of storage conditions should be avoided.

2. Specimens should be clamped flat on the table to ensure contact across the face of the abrading wheels.

3. Sandpaper should be replaced in accordance with par. G.

G. Test Procedure

Clean the surface of the test specimen of all foreign substances with a suitable solvent. Weigh the specimen to the nearest 0.001 g and clamp it on the turntable as described in par. E.

Fasten an unused set of abrasive wheels in position on the test arbor and lower them to the surface of the test specimen. Turn on the air, and start the abraser.

Inspect the specimen for wear every 25 cycles. Replace the sandpaper every 500 cycles and more often if the sandpaper "loads." If the abraded particles cling to the abrasive wheel and resist being blown off, the test is meaningless.

Stop the turntable when wear is observed. The end point of the wear test is defined as follows:

1. Printed patterns—that point at which an appreciable portion of the pattern is erased.

2. Plain colors other than black—that point at which the color layer is first cut through.

3. Black—that point at which a fibrous condition of the surface is first observed.

Remove the test specimen from the abraser, wipe it with a chamois and weigh it. Record the weight loss.

H. Test Results

The wear value (average of 3 tests) shall be the observed number of cycles at the end point of the test times the correction factor.

The rate of wear per 100 cycles shall be calculated as follows:

$$\frac{\text{Weight loss at end point}}{\text{Wear value}} \times 100$$

This rate of wear, in grams per 100 cycles, should not exceed 0.08 for all classes of material. Class 1 laminates are those which have a minimum wear value of 400 cycles. Class 2 laminates are those which have a minimum wear value of 200 cycles.

NEMA Standard 1-23-1951.

LP2-1.07   Method of Test for Resistance of Surface to Boiling Water

A. TEST SPECIMEN

The test specimen shall be approximately 9 in. square in size.

B. TEST APPARATUS

The test apparatus shall consist of:

1. A heat-insulating sheet of wood having a thickness of ¾ in.

2. A flat-bottom round aluminum vessel having a capacity of approximately 1 pint (Fisher Scientific Co., Pittsburgh, Pa., Catalog No. 2-542, No-Bump Solution Evaporator, 600 milliliter, with the bottom sanded flat, or the equivalent).

3. A hot plate or some other source of heat.

4. A clamping jig to hold the laminate flat against the wood sheet.

C. TEST PROCEDURE

Fill the vessel almost completely with water, and heat it until the water is boiling vigorously. Clamp the test specimen to the heat-insulating wood sheet and spill a small amount of boiling water on the surface of the specimen. Set the vessel containing the remainder of the water in the puddle of water on the test specimen and allow it to stand for 20 min. Remove the can and wipe the surface of the test specimen dry. Examine the test specimen for any surface injury, the reflection of light at a high-incidence angle being the best means of examining the specimen.

D. TEST RESULTS

The material shall show no blistering or other discernible surface disturbances.

NEMA Standard 3-16-1950.

LP2-1.08   Method of Test for Resistance of Surface to High Temperature

SCOPE

This method of test covers the resistance of the surface of laminated thermosetting decorative material to high temperature over a local area such as may be encountered in kitchen service.

A. TEST SPECIMEN

The test specimen shall be 9 in. square in size.

B. Test Apparatus

The test apparatus shall consist of:

1. A heat-insulating sheet of wood 9 in. square and having a thickness of ¾ in.

2. A flat-bottom round aluminum vessel having a capacity of approximately 1 pint (Fisher Scientific Co., Pittsburgh, Pa., Catalog No. 2-542, No-Bump Solution Evaporator, 600 milliliter, with the bottom sanded flat, or the equivalent).

3. A hot plate or some other source of heat.

4. Approximately 1 lb of Fisher Bath Wax (Catalog No. 15-532 of the Fisher Scientific Company, Pittsburgh, Pa.) or its equivalent.

5. A clamping jig to hold the laminate flat against the wood sheet.

C. Test Procedure

Fill the vessel almost completely with Fisher Bath Wax and heat it until the temperature of the wax is 180°C, plus or minus 1°C. Clamp the test specimen to the heat-insulating wood sheet and place the vessel of hot wax on the surface of the specimen. Allow it to stand for 20 min and then remove the vessel. Examine the test specimen for any surface injury, the reflection of light at a high-incidence angle being the best means of examining the specimen.

D. Test Results

Satin and dull-finish laminates shall show no blistering or other discernible surface disturbance. High-gloss laminates shall show no blistering but there may be a slight impairment of surface finish.

NEMA Standard 7-23-1953.

LP2-1.09   Method of Test for Resistance of Surface to Cigarette Burns

Scope

This method of test covers the resistance of the surface of laminated thermosetting decorative material to spot heating, such as is comparable to a fast-burning cigarette.

A. Test Specimen

The test specimen shall be 9 in. square in size.

B. Test Apparatus

The test apparatus shall consist of:

1. A heat-insulating sheet of wood 9 in. square and having a thickness of $\frac{3}{4}$ in.

2. A clamping jig to hold the laminate flat against the wood sheet (see NEMA Publication No. LP2-1951).

3. A resistor heating element with silver-soldered copper lead lugs as shown in NEMA Publication No. LP2-1951, mounted as shown in NEMA Publicaiton No. LP2-1951.

4. A draft-excluding enclosure having:

   a. Approximate inside dimensions as follows:
   Width—13 in.
   Length—16 in.
   Height—10 in.

   b. Open bottom, or equally convenient arrangement.
   c. Means for visually inspecting the test specimen while it is under test.

5. A stop watch or some other suitable timer.

6. A radiation calibration block in accordance with Fig. 5 in NEMA Publication No. LP2-1951.

7. A thermocouple potentiometer for determining the temperature with an iron-constantan thermocouple.

8. A suitable spotlight directed on the test area to observe effects.

C. CALIBRATION

Place the heating element on the calibration block, making certain that the unit is located against the guides and is flat against the top of the calibration block. This will locate the heating element directly over the metal disc.

Adjust the height of the heating element so that the distance between the disc and the resistance coil is 0.313 in. plus or minus 0.003 in.

Remove the heating element from the calibration block for a preliminary heating period. Adjust the power input to the heating element to approximately 26 watts and allow the unit to heat for 15 min.

Blacken the metal disc with carbon from the flame of a $5\frac{1}{2}$ standard spermaceti candle (Sargent No. S-14535 or equivalent) mounted vertically and shielded from all drafts. Hold the calibration block so that the disc is half way down in the bright yellow portion of the flame. (Note—avoid the lower or darker portion of the flame as it consists of partially unburned wax which produces an undesirable waxy carbon deposit.) Allow the carbon to deposit on the disc for 30 seconds and then remove calibration block from the flame. Remove the carbon deposit from the Marinite area surrounding the disc.

Replace the heating element over the black disc and cover the assembly to prevent cooling from drafts. Allow 10 min. for the calibration disc to heat up with no temperature being determined.

Remove the heating element without interrupting the power input and allow the calibration disc to cool to 40°C. This establishes equilibrium conditions in the insulating block and the heating circuit.

Replace the heating element on the calibration block having an initial temperature of 40°C and cover the assembly immediately. Measure and record temperatures at 1-minute intervals, starting at 2 min., for a total of 10 min. and plot a curve of temperature versus time. If this calibration curve does not come within the limits of the standard curve (Figure 6, NEMA Standard LP2-1951), adjust the power input as necessary so that the final observed temperatures are within those indicated on the curve (289 to 294°C for the 10-min. reading).

After the necessary adjustments are made, proceed with the test in accordance with par. E.

D. Factors Influencing Accuracy of Test

Four important factors which affect the accuracy of this test are:

1. The voltage stabilizer which shall be accurate within plus or minus 1 per cent.

2. Scales of the ammeter and voltmeter which shall be subdivided into tenths and estimable to hundredths.

3. Accuracy of distance between the calibration disc and the resistance coil (0.313 in., plus or minus 0.003 in.).

4. Accuracy of distance between the surface of the test specimen and the resistance coil (0.313 in., plus or minus 0.003 in.).

E. Test Procedure

Place the test specimen on the surface of the wood backing and clamp both of them in the jig.

With a power input to the heater determined in accordance with par. C, allow the heater to warm for 15 minutes. Clamp the test specimen flat to the insulating wood sheet. Position the heater element on the specimen, starting the timer at this instant, and immediately cover them with the enclosure.

Continue the test until the test specimen fails or for 10 minutes. Failure is evidenced by blistering, charring, permanent discoloration, or crazing. If failure occurs before 10 minutes, note the time of failure.

The results shall be recorded as the average of 3 tests on any one specimen. Individual tests on a specimen shall be made at least 2 in. apart.

F. Test Results

Standard-grade material shall not fail in less than 110 sec.
Cigarette-proof-grade material shall not fail in less than 10 min.

NEMA Standard 9-17-1953.

LP2-1.10 Method of Test for Resistance of Surface to Stains

A. TEST SPECIMEN

The surface finish of the specimen to be tested shall be wet-rubbed with Grade FF pumice or its equivalent just enough to remove the surface gloss and washed with a mild soap or detergent.

B. TEST APPARATUS

The test apparatus shall consist of glass covers, one for each reagent, to prevent evaporation. (Covers suggested are small glass bottles, or watch glasses.)

C. TEST PROCEDURE

Run 2 tests, in parallel, with each of the staining materials listed in par. E. Run one test with the reagent uncovered and the other with the reagent covered to prevent evaporation and to ensure contact of the staining material with the glass and the laminate. Apply the staining materials to the test specimens and allow them to stand for 16 hr at a temperature of 24°C (75°F). At the end of 16 hr, wash the specimen with water and then with a solvent such as ethyl alcohol. One hour after cleaning, examine the material for stains.

NOTE—Reagents should be kept in closed containers to avoid change in concentration.

D. TEST REPORT

The effect of the staining materials listed in par. E shall be reported as:

1. Unaffected—no color change and no appreciable change in surface texture.

2. Superficial—stains which are easily removed by a light application of a mild abrasive, such as "Lava" soap, "Bon Ami," etc.

3. Considerable—stains which are not easily removed or which result in etching.

E. TEST RESULTS

The material shall be unaffected by the following:

1. Gasoline or naphtha.

2. Water.

3. Alcohol (ethyl, methyl and isopropyl).

4. Amyl acetate.

5. Acetone.

6. Carbon tetrachloride.

7. Moth spray (e.g., "Larvex").

8. Fly spray (e.g., "Flit").

9. Household soaps and washing powders.

10. Soapless detergent (e.g., "Dreft").

11. Trisodium-phosphate (e.g., "Oakite").

12. Olive oil.

13. Household ammonia solution (containing 10 per cent ammonia).

14. Citric acid solution (containing 10 per cent citric acid).

15. Coffee.

16. Mustard (paste made of dry mustard).

17. Sodium bisulfite.

18. Wax crayon.

19. 6.6 per cent urea (urine).

20. Shoe polish, liquid or paste.

The material shall be unaffected by the following except for superficial stains which are easily removed by a light application of a mild abrasive such as "Lava" soap or "Bon Ami":

21. Tea.

22. Beet juice.

23. Vinegar.

24. Bluing.

25. Dye (e.g., "Tintex," "Rit," etc.).

26. Ink, washable.

27. Iodine solution (alcohol containing 1 per cent iodine).

28. Mercurochrome solution (water containing 2 per cent mercurochrome).

29. 5 per cent phenol solution in water ("Lysol").

NOTE—It is recommended that the following reagents not be allowed to remain in contact with the decorative material:

30. Hypochlorite bleach (e.g. "Hilex," "Clorox," etc.)
31. Hydrogen peroxide solution in any concentration.
32. Mineral acids (e.g., hydrochloric, sulfuric and nitric acids).
33. Lye solution (containing 1 per cent or 2 per cent lye, e.g. "Draino").
34. Sodium bisulfite (e.g. "Sani Flush").
35. Potassium permanganate in any concentration.
36. Berry juices, such as grape and raspberry.
37. Silver nitrate (1 per cent concentration).
38. Gentian violet in any concentration.
39. Mild silver protein like 20 per cent Argyrol.

LP2-1.11   Method of Test for Color Fastness of Surface to Light

For details refer to NEMA Publication No. LP2-1951.

LP2-1.12   Method of Test for Resistance to Moisture

For details refer to NEMA Publication No. LP2-1951.

LP2-1.13   Method of Test for Dimensional Change

For details refer to NEMA Publication No. LP2-1951.

LP2-1.14   Flexural Strength, Modulus of Elasticity and Deflection at Rupture

Tests for flexural strength, modulus of elasticity and deflection at rupture shall be made flatwise in the with-grain and across-grain directions and shall be made with the face both in tension and in compression. They shall be run on the sheets in the "as received" condition. The span/depth ratio shall be 16 to 1. The methods of test shall be made in accordance with *ASTM Method of Text for Flexural Properties of Plastics (Tentative)*, Publication No. D 790-49T*.

The average flexural strength shall be not less than 15,000 psi.

The average modulus of elasticity shall be not less than 800,000 psi.

The minimum deflection at rupture shall be 0.02 in. for $\frac{1}{16}$-in. material with the face in tension and 0.03 in. for $\frac{1}{16}$-in. material with the face in compression.

NEMA Standard 3-13-1952.

4. NEMA Recommended Practices for Fabricating and Applying Laminated Thermosetting Decorative Sheets

The fabricating of laminated thermosetting decorative sheets can be accomplished without difficulty when using standard woodworking or metalworking machinery with the proper precautions.

The following recommendations are offered as a guide and may be modified to meet individual requirements.

---

* Copies are available from the American Society for Testing Materials, 1916 Race Street, Philadelphia 3, Pa.

LP2-2.01   Recommended Techniques for Applying Laminated Thermosetting Decorative Sheets

A. ASSEMBLY

Laminated decorative material is generally veneered to a plywood core which provides rigidity and a means of attachment to a supporting structure from the back of the assembly. It is recommended that a backing of phenolic laminate at least 0.020 in. in thickness be applied to the back face of the core. This assembly will display less tendency to warp than those made without a backing.

When all edges are to be covered with the laminated decorative material, it is customary to apply the edging first, to dress it flush with the faces of the plywood core and to install oversize face and backing, which can subsequently be dressed flush with the edges. Where metal or plastic edging is to be applied, a groove is routed in the plywood to accept the leg of the T-shaped edging which is held in place by nailing from the back side. In installations of wall paneling where flush joint construction is desired, the edges are routed to accept $\frac{1}{4}$-in. splines, the panels being attached to grounds or furring strips by toe-nailing through the plywood core. All edges should be chamfered.

B. GLUES

Water-resistant rigid-type glues have been found satisfactory for veneering laminated decorative material. Flexible cements are not recommended, because strains induced in the assembly by varying humidity and temperature will cause destruction of the bond.

The choice of glue is based upon the service for which the assembly is intended and upon the veneering facilities which are available. For most applications, there are types of casein-alkaline and urea-formaldehyde glues which are entirely satisfactory from the standpoint of strength of bond, water resistance, pot-life of glue and ability to be veneered cold. Since these glues require several hours under pressure for setting, it is customary to assemble a stack of panels in the press, to clamp them under sufficient pressure to assure uniform contact (about 20 psi) and then to allow them to stand in the clamps for the length of time required to permit setting of the glue. Excessive pressure may lead to surface waviness, while too low a pressure may result in excessively thick glue lines.

In applications where greater water resistance is required, such as drain boards, bars, soda fountains, etc., the resorcinol or phenol-resorcinol glues are desirable. These glues must be mixed with the proper amount of hardener, and steps must be taken to keep the temperature of the mixture low so that satisfactory pot-life of the glue is maintained. These glues can be used at room temperature or, to complete the setting of the glue in a matter of minutes, elevated temperatures may be employed. The use of veneering temperatures above 185°F should be avoided since dirt specks will cause dents in the surface.

C. Cores

Plywood with a face of close-grained wood and with an optimum moisture content is recommended as a core to avoid the reproduction of a pronounced wood grain like that which results from veneering on rotary-cut fir. The bond in the plywood should be water-resistant (urea-bonded) for ordinary service, but the "exterior grade" core (resorcinol-bonded) is desirable for applications where moisture will be prevalent (drain boards, etc.).

D. Waterproofing

In constructions where the core material is exposed and water is encountered, it is recommended that the machined surfaces of the decorative laminates and the plywood core be given a waterproofing treatment prior to the installation of the trim.

Authorized Engineering Information 8-7-1952.

LP2-2.02 Recommended Practices for Fabricating Laminated Thermosetting Decorative Sheets

A. Sawing

To avoid chipping, it is important that the saw feed into the decorative face.

B. Band Sawing

Band sawing is recommended for curved or straight cuts where smooth edges and close tolerances are not required. For smooth edges on curved cuts, it is customary to saw oversize and to finish by filing or sanding.

Equipment

A standard woodworking band saw can be used.

Saws

Eighteen- to 20-gauge carbon-steel band-saw blades or hardened steel blades with soft backs should be used. Teeth range from 16 to 18 points per in. For circular cutting the blade should be $\frac{1}{4}$ to $\frac{1}{2}$ in. wide. For straight cutting the blade should be 1 to $1\frac{3}{4}$ in. wide. Teeth should be given a medium set for straight cuts and a heavy set for circular cuts. The amount of set depends upon the radius of the cut required. Teeth must be kept sharp at all times, preferably with an automatic band-saw grinding or filing machine.

Speed

Speeds up to 8000 ft per minute are satisfactory.

Feed

Feed the work into the blade as fast as it will cut without forcing the saw.

C. Circular Sawing

Circular sawing is recommended where close tolerances and smooth edges on straight cuts are required.

Equipment

Standard floor or bench circular sawing machines like those used in the woodworking industry can be used.

Powered circular hand saws 6 in. in diameter and with 120 to 150 teeth may be used for rough cutting. The teeth of the saw should have a set.

Saws

Hollow-ground or fine-set saws of carbon or high-speed or semi-high-speed steel, $\frac{1}{8}$ to $\frac{3}{32}$ in. in thickness, 10 to 12 in. in diameter, with 126 to 200 teeth, and operated at 3600 rpm are recommended.

Carbon-steel saws should have a Rockwell hardness of not over 40°C. Teeth should be ground square with the axis for smoothest cutting and should have a liberal clearance. Tooth gullets should be well rounded on high- and semi-high-speed steels and cemented-carbide tipped saws.

For continuous service cemented-carbide-tipped saws, 10 to 12 in. in diameter, with 60 to 100 teeth, and operated at 3600 rpm are recommended.

D. Sanding

Portable hand sanders of the disc or belt type, or floor-type belt, disc or spindle sanders, may be used to finish the edges of veneered assemblies. When finishing the edges, care should be taken to direct the sanding operation straight along the edge or at an angle away from the decorative surface.

A hand or belt sander is recommended for finishing the radii after cutting.

The grit for finish sanding can be varied to give the desired smoothness.

E. Drilling

For drilling laminated decorative material, a standard drill with dubbed lip to provide plenty of clearance is recommended. The drill should be ground flat in the flute for a distance of approximately $\frac{3}{32}$ in. back from the cutting edge, with a tolerance up to plus or minus $\frac{3}{16}$ in. for a 1-in. drill. A double-angle drill point has proven successful in preventing break-out on the back side. For production work, drill speeds as high as 16,000 rpm with tungsten-carbide-tipped drills provide excellent work.

Regardless of the diameter of the hole, all material being drilled should be backed with wood to prevent break-out at the bottom of the drilled hole.

For machine drilling (drill press), the diameter of the drill selected should be 0.002 in. larger than the specified diameter of the hole. Straight-shank high-speed twist drills are satisfactory.

For hand work, a brace and bit, regular boring brace bits, or bit stock drills can be used.

Large holes can be cut by using a trepan, circular-band-saw drill, fly cutter or an adjustable wood bit.

F. Routing

Routing may be done, utilizing standard power-driven routers. Carboloy-tipped cutters are recommended.

The speeds recommended are the same as those used in standard wood-working practice.

Authorized Engineering Information 1-23-1951.

LP2-2.03   Field Working of Veneered Assemblies

A. Veneered laminated decorative material may be sawed, planed, routed, filed, drilled, and otherwise worked and fitted in the field. The tools used may be hand or power operated. Since decorative laminates dull tools more rapidly than wood, it is necessary to sharpen tools frequently as dull tools may cause chipping.

B. Several simple rules should be followed in order to produce a sound workmanlike job:

1. Chamfer all exposed edges of decorative laminates by filing to prevent possible damage by chipping. This is not necessary, however, if the edges are to be covered by hardware, pipe collars, metal moldings, frames, etc., and are concealed.

2. Install wall paneling so that the tongue of the spline stays at least $\frac{1}{16}$ in. away from the bottom or back of the groove. This will permit some movement and will tend to prevent warping in the event of expansion and contraction.

3. Seal exposed plywood edges with metal moldings, self-banding of the laminates, waterproofing compounds, etc., where they are exposed to water or continual high humidities. This is particularly applicable to joints in work tops such as counters, bars, sink tops, etc.

4. Avoid making cut-outs in veneered assemblies where the entire core is cut away, leaving nothing supporting the laminate. Cut-outs may be made, but some portion of the plywood should remain as a support.

5. Avoid using splines to join 2 or more sections of horizontal work surfaces. Always seal the plywood edge and dowel together with metal dowel pins, using metal pull-up angles underneath instead of wood batten strips.

6. Avoid making miter joints at 45-degree angles for outside corners of wall paneling, applied edges of tops, etc. A miter joint is particularly vulnerable to damage from sharp blows.

7. Scratches, nicks and gouges which may have resulted from accidental damaging of the laminate should not be sanded.

C. Although any woodworking tool may be used to work decorative laminates, the best results are obtained by using the following particular types of tools:

1. Carpenter's hand saw. (Cross-cut, panel, or cut-off saw with 8 to 12 points, fine set.)

2. Hand plane. (Block or jack plane.)

3. File. (Flat or round, as required, bastard file. For extra fine finishing, use a smooth file.)

4. Chisel. (Beveled-edge wood chisel.)

5. Drill. (Straight-shank, high-speed twist drill. For brace and bit, regular boring brace bits or bit stock drills.)

6. Power-driven circular saw. (For 10-in. diameter tool steel, 126 teeth, 20-degree angle returned at teeth, tapered $\frac{1}{8}$ to $\frac{1}{16}$ in., 5-in. collar, very fine set.)

7. Power driven hand router, 18,000 to 20,000 rpm. (Two-flute, $\frac{1}{2}$ in. in diameter or larger.)

Authorized Engineering Information 1-23-1951.

NEMA STANDARDIZATION

The purpose of NEMA Standards, their classification and status are set forth in certain clauses of the NEMA By-Laws, which are quoted below:

Purpose of Standards

National Electrical Manufacturers Association Standards are adopted in the public interest and are designed to eliminate misunderstandings between the manufacturer and the purchaser and to assist the purchaser in selecting and obtaining the proper product for its particular need. Existence of a National Electrical Manufacturers Association Standard does not in any respect preclude any member or nonmember from manufacturing or selling products not conforming to the standard.

Definition of a Standard

A Standard of the National Electrical Manufacturers Association defines a product, process or procedure with reference to one or more of the following: nomenclature, composition, construction dimensions, tolerances, safety, operating characteristics, performance, quality, rating, testing and the service for which designed.

Classes of Standards

National Electrical Manufacturers Association Standards are of two classes:

1. *NEMA Standard,* which relates to a product commercially standardized and subject to repetitive manufacture, which standard has been approved by at least 90 per cent of the members of the Subdivision eligible to vote thereon;

2. *Suggested Standard for Future Design,* which may not have been regularly applied to a commercial product, but which suggests a sound engineering approach to future development, which standard has been approved by at least two-thirds of the members of the Subdivision eligible to vote thereon.

Authorized Engineering Information

Authorized Engineering Information consists of explanatory data and other engineering information of an informative character not falling within the classification of NEMA Standard or Suggested Standard for Future Design.

Identification of Status

At the end of each standard in this publication appear the words "NEMA Standard" or "Suggested Standard for Future Design" which indicate the status of the standard. These words are followed by a date which indicates when that standard was adopted in its present form by the Association.

The classification "Authorized Engineering Information" is designated similarly.

Section II—Design

12. Design of Molded Articles

Scope

There is no easy solution to the problems encountered in designing molded articles of plastics. The design will often hinge on what is the best process of molding for the piece in question. The selection of the molding process is, in turn, determined by the choice of the molding material best suited to provide the desired physical properties in the finished molded piece. Often the necessity for certain elements in the design, such as thin sections or long delicate inserts, or requirements of exact concentricity or of accuracy of dimensions and working tolerances, make it desirable to use one technique of molding rather than another. The problem is complicated by the facts that there are two types of molding materials in general use, i.e., the thermosetting and the thermoplastic, and three basic methods of molding commonly used, i.e., compression, transfer and injection molding. Frequently in the problem of design it is necessary to put the cart before the horse; we must know which technique is to be employed before the design can be created on paper. Selection of material and technique should be based on careful consideration of all requirements and influencing factors. No one molding process and no one type of plastic can meet all requirements.

The molding of plastics is not a simple operation. It has many complications. For this reason, the correct design of a molded piece is of paramount importance; upon it depends the success of the piece in service. It is the purpose of this chapter to set forth the fundamental principles of design which must be followed in order to achieve both economical production and maximum serviceability.

Basic Principles

To ensure proper design, close cooperation is required between the engineer-draftsman, the tool-builder, the molder, the supplier of raw material and, where styling is a factor, the artist-designer also.

In the creation of the design of a molded article, the following steps should be followed carefully:

1. On the basis of the characteristics required in the finished article, such as mechanical strength, electrical properties, chemical resistance,

dimensional stability, heat-resistance and moisture-absorption, a selection is made of the type and grade of molding material which will best ensure the desired performance in service.

2. The engineer-draftsman lists the fundamentals of the design, taking into consideration all functional requirements, and then makes a mechanical drawing of the piece as a component of the assembly.

3. The artist-designer, using the fundamentals set forth by the engineer-draftsman, incorporates color and form to meet the requirements of styling.

4. The engineer-draftsman, working in close collaboration with the artist-designer, converts the sketches and perspective drawings into accurately dimensioned detailed mechanical drawings of the piece to be produced.

5. A machined model of the piece is produced, preferably from a molded block of the plastic selected. While the physical properties of a machined piece may not always be identical with those of a molded piece, nevertheless it is possible in many instances to conduct accelerated life tests on such a counterpart and thus judge the suitability of the proposed design as well as the physical characteristics of the plastic selected. Thus, costly time-consuming changes in design, remaking of molds, and loss of production may frequently be avoided.

   A model will also enable the prospective user of the piece to see just what it will look like, and to check clearances and possible interferences in assembly with other parts. Also, experience has shown that models usually pay for themselves by showing where material might be saved, and shapes altered, to reduce costs of molds and of production.

6. We are now ready to consider the design of the article from the standpoint of the molding problems involved. What are the problems to be considered in the mold design?

   Chapter 15 covers the subject of design and construction of molds, and the types of molds used in producing articles from both thermosetting and thermoplastic materials. However, one of the most important steps preparatory to the decision on the type of mold to be used is a study of the flow behavior of the plastic selected for the article, during the flowing or formative period in the mold cavity.

   The mechanical, electrical and chemical properties of the molded article depend in part upon the controlled flow of the plastic. A study of the design of the article from the standpoint of the movement of the material in the mold cavity will reveal weaknesses in details of the design, such as poor knitting or welding of the material around protruding core pins and core sections. This is true in both thermoplastic and thermosetting materials.

Consideration must be given to the length of time required to complete the flow, and a study of the path of flow and probable movement of the plastic will reveal ways of providing a streamlined flow.

Care should be given to avoid heavy-sectioned areas which may entrap air, moisture and gas. Control of flow to avoid gas pockets in stagnant areas of mold cavities must receive serious study by the designer of the article, by the designer of the mold, and by the molder.

7. A single-cavity mold is built before proceeding with the construction of the multiple-cavity mold for production. Pieces produced from this experimental single-cavity mold are studied to determine whether proper provision has been made for molding shrinkage, dimensional accuracy, interchangeability in assembly, and serviceability. Generally, it is possible and practicable to design this single-cavity mold so that it may be used as one unit of the multiple-cavity production mold. In operating the single-cavity injection mold, and to get good dimensional reproduction comparisons between the production cavities and the initial test cavity, it is desirable to establish the time delay necessary for the plastic to arrive at the positions to be occupied by the number of cavities to be used in the finished mold. Therefore it is desirable to build the production mold base with all runners cut in place when testing the single cavity. Valuable information is obtained without substantially increasing the cost of the latter. The molder is also able to determine molding costs accurately, on the basis of actual operating cycles.

In any event, the foregoing precautions should be taken to make sure that the product is correctly designed in every detail before proceeding with the construction of the production mold. Experience indicates that all too often, when these precautions are not taken, changes must be made after the molds have been completed and the piece is in production. This involves expensive alterations of the mold, as well as loss of production. The studies made possible through the use of a model and a single-cavity experimental mold do much to avoid this risk.

Shrinkage

The fact must be recognized that each plastic material has certain characteristics which are inherent. Shrinkage, or the contraction that takes place in a molded piece after it has been formed in the mold, comes in this category.

While the problems of shrinkage are of greater concern to the designer of molds than to the designer of molded articles, the fundamentals of shrinkage should be understood by both.

Shrinkage is defined as the difference between corresponding linear dimensions of the mold and of the molded piece, both measurements being made at room temperature. This shrinkage in phenolics generally ranges from 0.001 to 0.015 in. per in., depending upon the type of thermosetting plastic, the material from which the mold is produced, and the conditions under which the piece is molded. Of thermoplastic materials, polyethylene will shrink as much as 0.050 in. per in. and nylon as much as 0.040 in. per in.

Although the shrinkage characteristics of plastics are well recognized and are compensated for, more or less adequately, each time a mold is designed, the data available are insufficient to permit the mold designer to predict accurately the shrinkages that will occur in various sections of a molded piece. One reason for this inadequacy of technical information is the complex nature and overlapping of the causes of shrinkage, which necessitate study of many variables and combinations of variables. However, the causes of shrinkage have been fairly well agreed upon, and it seems safe to say that the amount by which a piece will shrink is dependent upon one or a combination of the following factors:

1. chemical reaction, if any, in the plastic;

2. temperature range over which the plastic cools after its shape has been permanently established in the mold, coupled with its coefficient of thermal expansion;

3. degree to which the material has been compressed during molding.

The first factor is an inherent property of each thermosetting compound and cannot be controlled by the molder or fabricator.

The second is controllable partially by the manufacturer of the material, in that the coefficient of thermal expansion of any plastic is influenced by the characteristics of the resins, fillers, plasticizers, etc., of which it is composed. Since the coefficients of thermal expansion of plastics are greater than those of the metals used for molds, a molded article which exactly fills a mold cavity at an elevated temperature will be smaller than the mold cavity when both have been cooled to room temperature. It is controllable also to some degree by the molder; thus a piece molded from thermosetting resin at 300°F will be slightly larger than another piece molded from the same material in the same mold at 350°F, when both have been cooled to room temperature. However, there are other factors which may alter this relationship. These are discussed below.

The third factor mentioned above is controlled entirely by the molder, and its total effect is the most difficult to predict. In general, the more the material is compressed, the less the shrinkage will be. Under certain conditions the molded piece may actually be larger than the mold cavity in which it was formed. Some of the conditions that may influence the extent to which a molding compound is compressed in the mold are given below:

	Compression Molding	Injection and Transfer Molding
1. Design of piece		
Uniformity of cross-section	X	X
2. Design of mold		
Positive, semipositive, or flash	X	X
Location and size of gates		X
3. Plasticity of material	X	X
4. Manner of loading, i.e., preform or powder . . .	X	
5. Preheating	X	X
6 Temperature of mold	X	X
7. Effective molding pressure	X	X
8. Rate of application of pressure	X	X
9. Degree of cure	X	X

Table 12-1 has been prepared to show the actual amounts of the influence of some of these variables upon the shrinkage of a given piece. Specifically, the variables investigated were molding temperature, pressure, and preheating of a transfer-molded piece. The minimum pressure used with each of the two molding temperatures was that pressure which would just fill the cavity and give a sound molding. The following conclusions for the piece in question are immediately evident:

1. Increase in pressure, causing greater compression of the plastic, reduces shrinkage.

2. Preheating reduces shrinkage.

3. Shrinkage parallel to the direction of flow from the gate is greater than shrinkage across the direction of flow, or, in general, shrinkage increases with increase of flow of material travel in the mold.

4. Shrinkage is not materially affected by change in molding temperature. This may possibly be explained by the fact that at the higher temperature the material was more fluid and hence was compressed to a greater extent by a given pressure, with the result that the expected effect of higher temperature was neutralized. It does appear to be generally true that decreasing the temperature at which the piece is released from the mold, to a temperature below that at which the plastic was molded, results in decrease of shrinkage.

5. Shrinkages in thickness are inconsistent, but probably because of slight variations in the closing of the mold, rather than actual variations in ratio of shrinkage. However, in general, shrinkage appears to be less in the direction of the molding pressure.

Although there may often be conditions which counteract each other, as discussed in (4) above, an attempt is made below to summarize the usual individual effects of the other factors listed, but not discussed, above.

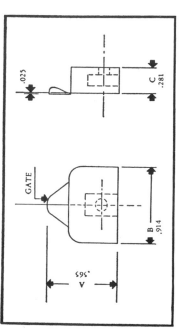

TABLE 12-1. EFFECT OF MOLDING CONDITIONS ON SHRINKAGE OF TRANSFER-MOLDED ARTICLE

Material	Molding Temp. (°F)	Molding Pressure (psi)	Preheat	Shrinkage — in. per in.			Specific Gravity
				A	B	C	
General-purpose phenolic	302	3390	NONE	0.0088	0.0055	0.0049	1.336
	302	6780	NONE	0.0062	0.0049	0.0007	1.330
	302	6780	5′ @ 250° F	0.0035	0.0033	0.0014	1.335
	356	2260	NONE	0.0088	0.0066	0.0068	1.335
	356	3390	NONE	0.0097	0.0055	0.0075	1.336
	356	6780	NONE	0.0079	0.0044	0.0025	1.331
	356	6780	5′ @ 250° F	0.0071	0.0022	0.0035	1.335
			All Above Values Average of 4				
Polystyrene	302	6780	NONE	0.0018	0.0033	0.0035	

1. Design of Piece. Uniformity of cross-section—When a piece has one or two portions considerably heavier in cross-section than the rest, it may be found that, if molding conditions are selected so as to mold the thinner sections properly, the thicker sections will fail to receive an adequate charge of material, or pressure, or cure, and as a result will shrink nonuniformly.

2. Design of Mold. Positive, semipositive or flash (compression molding) ; location and size of gates (injection and transfer molding)— This is closely associated with molding pressure. It must always be remembered that the full calculated molding pressure, which is determined by the size of the ram and the hydraulic line pressure, does not always reach the material in the mold. The pressure in which the molder is interested is that which actually does the work of compressing the plastic in the mold; this may be called the "effective pressure." A positive mold transmits to the material in the cavity practically all of the applied pressure; a flash mold transmits an indeterminate amount, depending upon how quickly the flash over the land sets up. In transfer, plunger and injection molds, undersized gates will restrict the flow of material excessively; also length and diameter of runners as well as the number of shifts in the direction of flow which the plastic must travel before arriving at the cavity gate will reduce the effective pressure considerably.

    In transfer and injection molds, the location of the gate also is important, since this determines the direction of flow of material, the importance of which has been discussed in (3) above.

    Comparing transfer molding and compression molding of the same phenolic material, it will usually be found that the transfer-molded piece will have the less shrinkage.

3. Plasticity of Material. Of the thermosetting materials, the materials of harder flow will usually shrink somewhat less than the softer materials, which have a tendency to flow away under the pressure and to yield a less dense molding.

    Similarly, of the plasticized thermoplastic materials, the harder materials will usually shrink less than softer materials of the same type.

4. Manner of Loading. The use of preforms in compression molding will reduce shrinkage, by facilitating the proper distribution of the charge in the mold cavity, and by precompressing the charge.

5. Rate of Application of Pressure. Determination of the proper rate of application is a matter of experience. In compression molding, closing too rapidly, particularly upon a soft material, will create a "splash" effect in the mold which will produce moldings of low density.

6. Degree of Cure. Inadequately cured thermosetting material will

usually shrink more than the same material properly cured. Thermoplastic articles with heavy sections must be cooled in the mold long enough to avoid excessive shrinkage which may cause internal voids.

When multiple-cavity molds are used, slight variations in shrinkage between pieces from different cavities can be expected, due to small differences in temperature, loading, and pressure from cavity to cavity.

The shrinkage discussed above is that which occurs during and immediately after molding. In addition to this shrinkage, some plastics will shrink an additional amount during aging. This shrinkage during aging is particularly noticeable in the thermosetting materials, and to varying degrees in the cellulose esters, such as cellulose acetate, depending on the type and proportion of the plasticizer used.

Table 12-2 shows the aging shrinkage that occurred in an experimental molding of urea-formaldehyde. In this case, baking for 24 hr at 150°F was considered to be equivalent to one year's normal aging. The articles were allowed to remain at room temperature for about 24 hr before the baking was begun. It will be noticed that the aging shrinkage at the top of the molding was greater than that at the bottom, showing the restraining influence of the two ears in the insert. When tests were made with moldings in which the ears were spaced $\frac{7}{32}$ in. apart, the moldings cracked during the baking test. Consequently, in order to eliminate any possibility of cracking in service, the design was changed as shown in Table 12-2.

Since there are definite limitations on the extent to which the molder can control shrinkage by changes in his technique, the designers of the piece and of the mold must compensate for it in their designs.

Closely related to the problems of the tolerances considered in Standards for Tolerances on Molded Articles are the allowances for molding shrinkage which must be carefully calculated for the particular plastic to be used in a given application. Material-manufacturers provide data for the mold shrinkage of each material they produce. They determine shrinkage figures by molding the material in a standard test mold and calculating the unit mold shrinkage as the difference in linear dimension between the mold at room temperature and the molded piece at room temperature, divided by the dimension of the mold. Thus all such shrinkage data are given as inch per inch of mold dimension. For the convenience of the mold designer, it may be assumed that this is equivalent to the shrinkage, inch per inch of the molded piece. Consequently, for pieces up to 25 in. in length to be produced from materials with a shrinkage of 0.008 in. per in. or less, the mold dimension can be computed by the formula:

$$A = B (1 + S)$$

where A = dimension of mold

B = dimension of molded piece

S = unit shrinkage

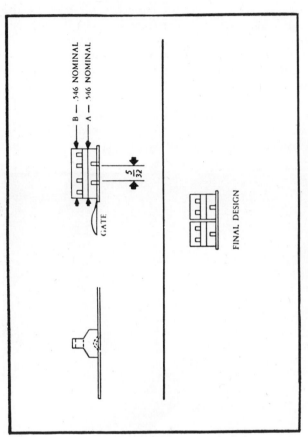

TABLE 12-2. AFTER-MOLD SHRINKAGE OF UREA MOLDING

	Hr Bake @ 150°F	Dimension A	Dimension B
Molding shrinkage (in. per in.)		0.007	0.007
After-mold shrinkage, in addition to molding shrinkage (in. per in. total)	24	0.0022	0.0026
ditto	6	0.0044	0.0055

For the occasional piece larger than 25 in., molded from material of relatively high shrinkage, it is recommended that the following accurate formula be used:

$$A = \frac{B}{1-S}$$

The shrinkage data given by the material-manufacturer are determined from standard test specimens whose shapes are not necessarily representative of the usual commercially molded articles. Therefore the mold-designer must temper his use of manufacturers' shrinkage data with previous experience, and with consideration of the factors influencing shrinkage discussed above.

In designing a mold in which one or more dimensions must be held very accurately, it is better to assume that the prediction of shrinkage will not be exactly correct, and hence construct the mold in such a manner that it can be readily modified after sample pieces have been molded and measured.

This practice was followed in producing the fathometer illustrated in Fig. 12-1. The graduations, used in calculating the depth of letter, were

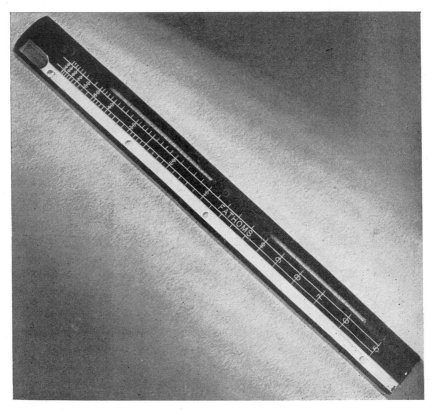

Fig. 12-1

produced by engraving the logarithmic scale directly on the surface of the mold. Only after determining the correct shrinkage value for the material, and compensating for the variations in shrinkage in different parts of the length of the article and under the molding conditions used, was the article held within the required close tolerances.

Nonuniformity of thickness in a molded piece tends to produce unbalanced shrinkage and consequent warpage. As the piece is taken from the mold, the thinner sections cool more rapidly than the heavier, and the heavier sections tend to shrink more than the thin sections, and thus internal stresses are created. In the design of a piece in which adjacent thin and thick sections are necessary, generous fillets should be used, in order that the change from one section to the other shall not be abrupt. The best design is the one in which a uniform wall section is used throughout. On large flat sections, supporting ribs will minimize warpage. Best results are obtained if ribs are placed on both sides of the article, thus overcoming concave warpage which may occur on the unsupported side; this is particularly noticeable if ribs are relatively thin.

In injection-molded thermoplastic materials, shrinkage in heavy sections will usually produce internal voids, or surface shrink marks. These may be avoided by designing thinner wall sections and obtaining necessary stiffness with ribs. Also, large flat surfaces should be made slightly convex, or decorated with engraved or embossed figures to obscure flow marks.

Warping or excessive shrinkage can be avoided by the use of cooling fixtures to maintain inside dimensions and flat surfaces while the article is cooling to room temperature. But there is risk that when the normal shrinkage of the plastic is prevented, by cooling fixtures, or metal inserts, or die members, internal stresses will be set up in the article as it hardens, and cools. When these stresses exceed the strength of the material, the plastic will crack.

Fig. 12-2 illustrates this effect, showing cracks developed by the restraining action of a steel insert. In order to correct this condition, it was necessary to use thin aluminum tubing instead, to take advantage of the relatively high coefficient of expansion of aluminum, which approaches that of plastics, and the ability of the thin tube to yield slightly when the plastic shrinks. Warpage and cracking of this sort is closely associated with design of inserts, and in this connection it is recommended that reference be made to Chapter 14 on Design Standards for Inserts.

Flash Lines

Flash is defined as that portion of the material which flows from or is extruded from the mold during the molding.

The designer must design specifically for molding. For example, it is impracticable to duplicate, by molding, the appearance of a handle which has been fabricated from wood or metal by machining. To design a molded

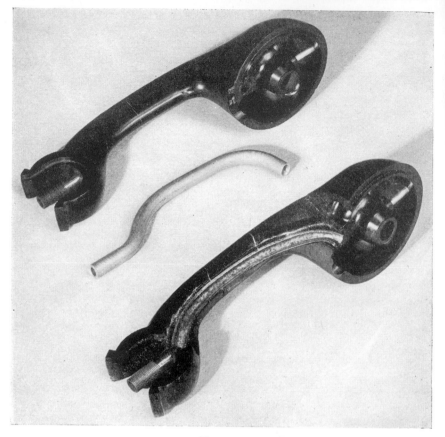

Fig. 12-2

piece of good appearance calls for a knowledge of the molding technique and of mold-construction.

In compression molds, the closing or telescoping of the two parts of the mold results in flow of material into the clearance between these parts. This material is known as flash and occurs at the parting line of the molds. The removal of flash from the article leaves a flash line, which is unavoidable and generally unsightly. The problem of flash lines is one that requires careful consideration by the designer, as the attractiveness of the product may depend to a large degree on a careful location of the flash line where it will not be seen. When a piece is molded in a transfer or injection mold, the problem of flash is greatly simplified, because the mold is already locked in closed position before the plastic enters it.

When flash lines are located improperly, the molded article may be marred either during its removal from the mold or later at the finishing bench, because the design does not permit easy removal of the flash. Articles of irregular shape must, as a rule, be smoothed along the flash line with a hand file, and then polished on a buffing wheel. A design which necessitates such work may impair the appearance of the article and will certainly increase its cost. In compression molding, by arranging flash lines so that they are vertical (Fig. 12-3), or parallel to the movement of the ram (Fig. 12-4), the removal of flash is made easier and cleaner.

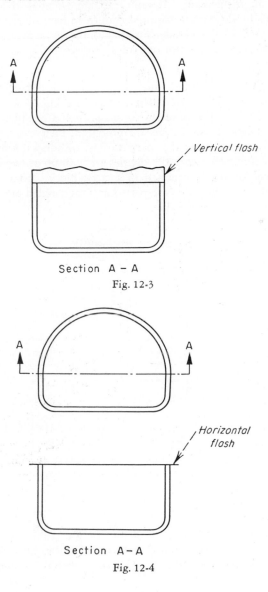

Vertical flash

Section A – A

Fig. 12-3

Horizontal flash

Section A – A

Fig. 12-4

Undercuts

Modern molding practice dictates certain principles of design which should be observed if molded articles are to be produced successfully. Most elementary is the fact that the piece must be easily removed from the mold after it has been formed. This point is frequently overlooked, and many products are designed with undercuts which make it impossible to eject them directly from the mold cavity. If undercuts are essential, then split molds or removable mold sections are required, and these increase the cost of molds and of the molded articles. Undercuts should always be avoided unless mechanical construction or the function of the piece make such a design an absolute necessity.

External Undercuts. When undercuts are located in the outside contours of the piece, they are called external undercuts (see Fig. 12-5). It would be impossible to withdraw a piece of such a shape from a one-piece mold cavity. While many articles of this nature are produced, their cost is considerably higher than that of one designed to permit direct withdrawal from a one-piece cavity. For molding such pieces, the cavities are built up of two or more loose members. These are tightly retained in a chase block. After the piece has been molded, the loose members are parted and the molded piece is removed. A parting or flash line is inevitable.

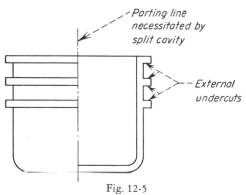

Fig. 12-5

Internal Undercuts. When undercuts occur on the inside contours of the molded piece they are termed internal undercuts (see Fig. 12-6). Such a piece may be removed from the mold cavity, but not from the force plug. The molding of pieces with internal undercuts is considered impracticable and must, therefore, be avoided.

Wall Thickness

Under favorable conditions, the design of wall thickness normally depends upon the selection of the material. Occasionally, however, limitation of space precludes this, and the selection of material becomes predicated

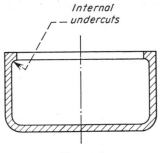

Fig. 12-6

partly upon the wall thickness available. Whichever the path of approach, the determination of wall thickness should be the result of an analysis of the following requirements:

Requirements of Use	Manufacturing Requirements
1. Structure	1. Molding
2. Weight	a. Flow
3. Strength	b. Setting
4. Insulation	c. Ejection
5. Dimensional stability	2. Assembly
	a. Strength
	b. Precision

The foregoing requirements are intimately related. Purely from an economic standpoint, a wall thickness which is too great or too small can affect the design adversely. From the standpoint of all requirements the optimum wall thickness normally will be most economical.

Generally, the most important single influence on wall thickness is structure. In practically every design, one or more structural features which determine size and shape are mandatory. From this starting point, consideration of the remaining listed requirements should develop the best design achievable from the standpoint of wall thickness. The relatively low specific gravity of most plastics is frequently a factor in their selection.

The thickness of wall must be sufficient to give the strength needed, both during manufacture and in service. Occasionally the use of the article involves little need of strength, but still adequate strength must be provided to withstand ejection from the mold and to facilitate assembly operations. In molding both thermoplastic and thermosetting materials, a wall 0.012 in. thick may be adequate for the service, but the piece would be so fragile as to impose very severe complications in molding and assembly. With thermosetting materials, even a thickness of 0.031 in. requires special care in molding and assembly because of structural weakness. A wall thickness of less than 0.062 in. is rarely successful in thermosetting materials, except in very slightly stressed small articles, and 0.125 in. is usually considered a more reliable minimum.

SUGGESTED WALL THICKNESSES OF MOLDED ARTICLES (IN.)

THERMOSETTING	Minimum For Any Article	For Small Articles	Average For Most Articles	Large To Maximum Articles
PHENOLICS				
General-purpose & Flock-filled	0.050	0.062	0.125	0.187 to 1.000
Fabric-filled	0.062	0.125	0.187	0.187 to 0.375
Mineral-filled	0.125	0.125	0.187	0.200 to 1.000
ALKYD				
Glass-filled	0.040	0.093	0.125	0.187 to 0.500
Mineral-filled	0.040	0.125	0.187	0.187 to 0.375
UREAS AND MELAMINES				
Cellulose-filled	0.035	0.062	0.100	0.125 to 0.187
Fabric-filled	0.050	0.125	0.125	0.125 to 0.187
Mineral-filled	0.040	0.093	0.187	0.187 to 0.375
THERMOPLASTIC				
ACRYLICS	0.025	0.035	0.093	0.125 to 0.250
CELLULOSE ACETATE	0.025	0.050	0.075	0.125 to 0.187
CELLULOSE ACETATE BUTYRATE	0.025	0.050	0.075	0.125 to 0.187
ETHYL CELLULOSE	0.035	0.050	0.062	0.093 to 0.125
POLYAMIDE	0.015	0.025	0.060	0.093 to 0.125
POLYETHYLENE	0.035	0.050	0.062	0.093 to 0.125
POLYSTYRENE	0.030	0.050	0.062	0.125 to 0.250
POLYVINYLS	0.093	0.062	0.093	0.125 to 0.250

Consideration of mechanical stresses anticipated in manufacture and service, and a study of the physical properties of the materials to be molded, are the next steps in determining wall thickness.

Frequently either the magnitude of impact stresses is underestimated or designers overlook the relative brittleness of some plastics. Heavy articles, or those housing apparatus which add considerable weight to the assembly, require intelligent distribution of impact stresses by structural design. Adjustment of wall thickness alone, as a means of sustaining such stresses, is not always adequate, and is often not feasible for other reasons. Thicknesses greater than $5/16$ in. are seldom practicable and are usually not economical because of the long time required to transfer the heat to cause setting of the material. Also, any precuring during flow, before full pressure is applied in the closing of the mold, and any nonuniformity of cure resulting from irregularity of penetration of heat, will create variation in density and thus also internal stresses.

An exception is found in certain thermosetting plastics when preheated thermionically. Proper distribution of stress can be achieved best by adjusting the shape or contour of the molded part. Wall thickness and ribs are too frequently relied upon to satisfy this requirement. This applies also to the method of providing adequate lengths of path to meet requirements of electrical or thermal insulation.

If metal inserts are to be molded in or later assembled with tight fits, the coefficient of thermal expansion should not be overlooked (see Table 14-2, p. 480). Many plastics have coefficients from 3 to 12 times that of brass or steel, and radial cracking of the plastic may occur if the wall thickness of the adjacent plastic is inadequate.

The requirements of molding, such as flow, setting and ejection, all influence the choice of wall thickness. Designs most favorable to flow facilitate movement of the plastic at a uniform rate in all directions. In transfer and injection molding, and to a lesser extent in compression molding, holes, inserts and isolated areas of reduced wall thickness constitute obstructions

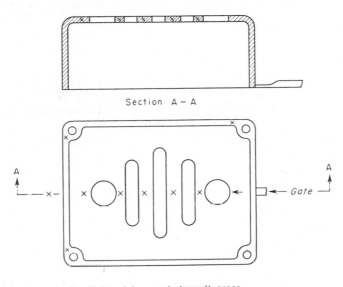

Section A – A

X = Weld points – weak strength areas

Fig. 12-7

which divert the flow of plastic (Fig. 12-7). Since the flow follows the path of least resistance, two or more streams may be formed, and if the obstructions are large the mold may be otherwise completely filled before sufficient back pressure develops to reunite the streams. This delay may permit setting to progress to a stage at which the two advancing fronts of material cannot coalesce and weld properly. Under these circumstances, strength and stability may be impaired. Sometimes, also, obstructions of this sort create the possibility of entrapment of air, if the streams reunite at some distance beyond the obstruction in such a way as to prevent the escape of air from the mold. This usually is manifested by a defective surface at the point of entrapment. In general, uniformity of thickness is highly preferable, and any reduction of thickness should be progressive in the direction of the flow which occurs during the molding.

For either thermoplastic or thermosetting materials, the process of setting is a function of heat-transfer, from or to the mold. Obviously, thin sections set more rapidly than thick ones and, since contraction or shrinkage occurs simultaneously with setting, irregularity in thickness causes irregularity in contraction and creates internal stresses. These will tend to relieve themselves either by forming concave depressions, known as "sink marks," on the thick sections, or by causing warping. This difficulty can frequently be eliminated by coring a thick section so as to divide it into two thin sections, when that is feasible.

Even though ejection of a molded piece may be considered to be solely the responsibility of the mold-designer, the piece must be strong enough to withstand ejection, and wall thickness may be important in this respect.

In assembly, the strength of the molded article, and its precision and fidelity to the design, may be important economic factors, and these can be seriously influenced by wall thickness.

Obviously, thickness should be a compromise based upon all requirements. Usually the ingenuity of the molder will overcome faulty design imposed by the desired appearance of the product. However, when requirements of use are rigid these violations will manifest themselves in breakage, warpage and other failures which frequently could have been eliminated or greatly minimized by proper design.

Taper or Draft

In the design of articles produced from moldable rigid and elastomeric plastics, it is important that consideration be given to the easy removal of the part from the mold cavity. Draft or taper should be provided, both inside and outside. Also, it is important that the surface of the molded piece, and hence that of the mold, particularly on the vertical or tapered walls, be polished to a high luster finish. If the molded piece is straight-sided or vertical, it is necessary to exert a strong pull in order to open the mold, but by the use of taper and a highly polished surface the article is easily released.

In deep-drawn articles, converging tapers assist by creating a wedging or compressing action as the mold is closed, and, in compression molding of thermosetting materials, tapers of this type increase the density of the plastic in the upper sections.

There are no precise calculations or formulas for taper. The amount of taper required will vary with the depth of draw, and common sense will dictate how much. Since a designer should be on the alert to avoid details in design which will obstruct free ejection from the mold, he should provide the most liberal taper which the design will tolerate.

Figure 12-8 is a table of relation of degree of taper per side to the dimension, in inch per inch. It illustrates the effect of taper for various depths of piece. A piece 4 in. in depth can carry a 4-degree taper, or 0.2796 in. per side,

DEGREE TAPER OR DRAFT PER SIDE
ALL VALUES SHOWN IN INCHES

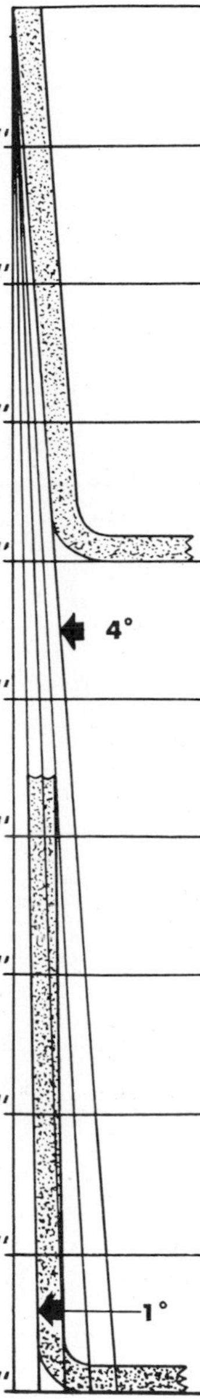

	⅛°	¼°	½°	1°	2°	3°	4°
1"	0.0022	0.0044	0.0087	0.0175	0.0349	0.0524	0.0699
2"	0.0044	0.0088	0.0174	0.0350	0.0698	0.1048	0.1398
3"	0.0066	0.0132	0.0261	0.0525	0.1047	0.1572	0.2097
4"	0.0088	0.0176	0.0348	0.0700	0.1396	0.2096	0.2796
5"	0.0110	0.0220	0.0435	0.0875	0.1745	0.2620	0.3495
6"	0.0132	0.0264	0.0522	0.1050	0.2094	0.3144	0.4194
7"	0.0154	0.0308	0.0609	0.1225	0.2443	0.3668	0.4893
8"	0.0176	0.0352	0.0696	0.1400	0.2792	0.4192	0.5592
9"	0.0198	0.0396	0.0783	0.1575	0.3141	0.4716	0.6291
10"	0.0220	0.0440	0.0870	0.1750	0.3490	0.5240	0.6990

4°

1°

Fig. 12-8

or 0.0699 in. per in. A 4-degree taper may be more than can be used in a deep article. Thus, in a 10-in. piece, it will amount to 0.6990 in. per side.

Common molding practice has proved that for deep articles tapers of less than 1 degree can be used satisfactorily. Tapers as small as 0.001 in. per in. have proved satisfactory for side walls of radio and television cabinets 6 to 24 in. deep.

Courtesy of Molded Products, Division of
Admiral Distributors, Inc.

Fig. 12-9

Tapers combined with round corners and generous fillets and wide-sweeping domed surfaces will do much to improve the appearance and the ease of molding of the majority of pieces, whether by compression, transfer or injection, and whether thermosetting or thermoplastic (see Fig. 12-9).

Radii and Fillets

The principal function of radii and fillets is distribution of stress. Also they facilitate the flow of the plastic and the ejection of the molded article. And frequently a radius on a molded article is essential from the standpoint of diemaking, from the standpoints of machining and of the strength of mold members.

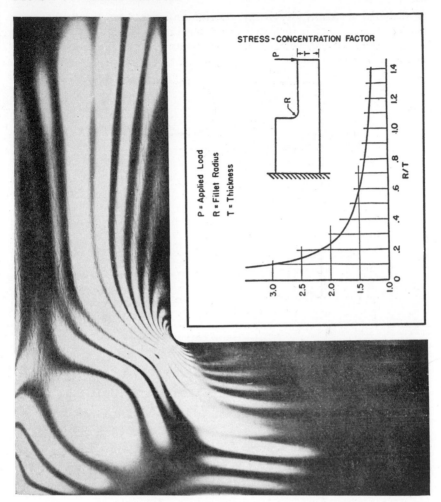

Fig. 12-10

Stresses tend to concentrate at the junction of two sections. An examination of Fig. 12-10 shows the effectiveness of fillets in reducing the concentration of stress. The curve gives an indication of proper radius of fillet to be used with a given wall thickness. From this it will be observed that the concentration of stress builds up very rapidly whenever the radius of the fillet is less than one-quarter of the thickness. Also, it will be noticed that there is little benefit from the use of a radius greater than three-quarters of the wall thickness.

Concentration of stress is further reduced by using a radius on external corners of junctions of sections. Figure 12-11 shows a junction with a radius one-half the thickness. When the exterior corner is sharp the thickness of section at the corner is increased about one-third. Figure 12-12 illustrates a much better design, with an exterior radius one and one-half times the thickness, which maintains a uniform thickness of section.

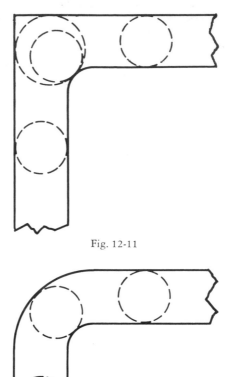

Fig. 12-11

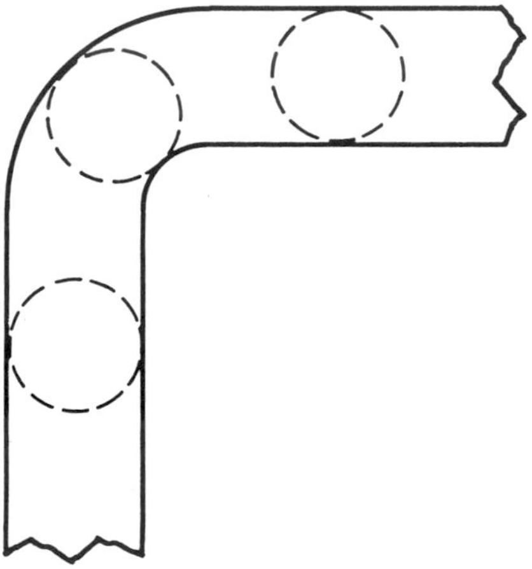

Fig. 12-12

The over-all advantages of radii and fillets in the design of a molded article are several:

1. The molded article is stronger and more nearly free from stress.

2. Elimination of the sharp corner automatically reduces the hazard of cracking as result of notch-sensitivity, and increases the over-all resistance to sudden shock or impact. Elimination of all internal sharp

corners by using a radius of 0.015 in. or $\frac{1}{64}$ in. will greatly improve the strength.

3. The flow behavior of the plastic will be greatly improved. Rounded corners permit uniform, unretarded and less stressed flow of the plastic into all sections of the mold, and will improve the uniformity of density of the molded sections.

4. Mold members, force plugs and cavities will be stronger because there will be less tendency for these parts of the mold to develop internal stresses due to notch-sensitivity created by concentration of stress at sharp corners. Mold parts frequently crack in hardening as result of failure to provide appropriate radii and fillet.

Ribs

The function of ribs is to increase the rigidity and strength of a molded piece without increasing its thickness throughout. Proper use of ribs will usually prevent warpage. In some cases they facilitate flow during molding. Several features in the design of a rib must be carefully considered in order to minimize the internal stresses associated with irregularity in wall thickness. The width of the base of a rib should be less than the thickness of the wall to which it is attached. This can be demonstrated by examination of Fig. 12-13. Ribs of the proportions shown are frequently used in molded articles. However, when the circle R_1 is placed at the junction of the rib and wall, it will be seen that the thickness is increased by about 50 per cent, and this may produce "sink marks" on the surface under normal molding conditions. By reducing the width of the base of the rib to one-half the wall thickness, as shown in Fig. 12-14, the increase in thickness at the junction is made less than 20 per cent. Sink marks are improbable when these proportions are used. To use two or more ribs is better than to increase the height of a single rib more than is shown. When two or more ribs are required, the spacing of centers should not be less than 2A.

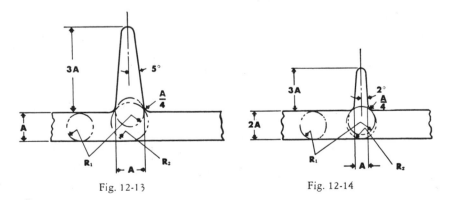

Fig. 12-13   Fig. 12-14

Bosses

Bosses are protruding studs or pads and are used in design for the reinforcement of holes or for mounting an assembly (Fig. 12-15). The same general precautions to be considered in the use of ribs may apply also to the utilization and design of bosses. They should be located in corners wherever practicable and should be small, but the height should not be more than twice the diameter. They should be provided with sufficient draft to ensure easy removal of the piece from the mold. When bosses are used for mounting molded parts, it is usually necessary to grind their top surfaces flat. It is recommended that not more than three bosses be used, in order to avoid the finishing operation necessary to achieve perfect alignment of four or more.

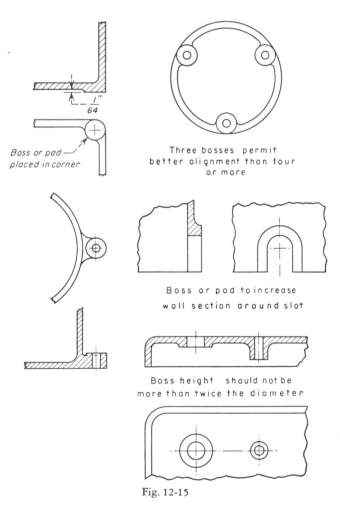

Boss or pad placed in corner

Three bosses permit better alignment than four or more

Boss or pad to increase wall section around slot

Boss height should not be more than twice the diameter

Fig. 12-15

In the design of pieces required to fit on a flat surface, it is often good practice to design an external surface that will project $\frac{1}{64}$ in. beyond the normal face, and is easily sanded or finished to a flat, uniform surface.

Avoid the use of high bosses wherever possible, as they tend to trap gas, which decreases both the density and the strength of this molded section. This is particularly true in straight compression molding and where the boss is formed by the upper half or plunger of the mold.

Ribs may be employed on the sides of the boss to assist the flow of the material. Fillets at the junction of the boss to the wall section are very important.

Holes

For a variety of reasons, holes are often required in a molded piece. They should be designed and located so as to introduce a minimum of weakness and to avoid complication in production. This requires the careful consideration of several factors.

Between successive holes, and between a hole and a side wall, a distance equivalent to the diameter of the hole should be provided. It is always wise to provide as thick a wall section as is practicable, as cracking around holes in assembly is generally traceable to a disregard of this fundamental consideration.

The problem of design is always more complicated when a threaded hole must be used, because of the concentration of stress which causes notch-sensitivity in the region immediately surrounding the hole. Laboratory determinations provide a wealth of evidence indicating that the linear distance between the edge of the hole and the edge of the piece should be three times the diameter of the hole, if the stress at the edge of the hole is to be reduced to a safe working figure. As shown in the section on Bosses, increased boss areas are often used to provide additional strength.

Through Holes. Through holes are usually more useful for assembly than blind holes, and also they are easier to produce. Through holes should be preferred whenever possible, because the mold pins which form the holes can then be supported in both parts of the mold. Through holes may be produced by either a single pin supported at each end or by two pins butted together. The first method is generally considered the better. Where the two-pin method is used, one pin should be slightly larger in diameter than the other to compensate for any misalignment (see Fig. 12-16). The butting ends of the pins should be ground flat, and provisions must be made in the mold assembly for sufficient clearance to avoid upsetting the ends of the pins. While opinion differs regarding the amount required, a clearance of 0.005 in. appears to be considered good practice.

Blind Holes. The designer must remember that a blind hole is formed by a core pin which through necessity can be supported only at one end. Thus

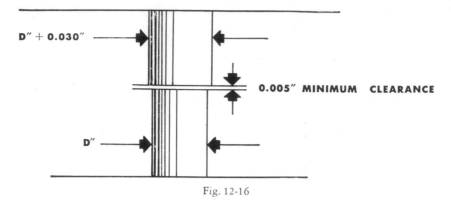

Fig. 12-16

this pin can be distorted, bent or sheared off during the molding operation as a result of the unbalanced pressure exerted by the flow of the plastic. The depth of blind holes, i.e., the length of the core pin, should be limited to twice the diameter of the hole, unless the diameter is $\frac{1}{16}$ in. or less, in which case the length shall not exceed its diameter (see Fig. 12-17).

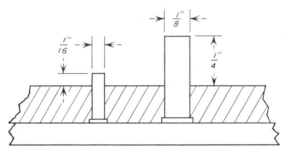

Fig. 12-17

Drilled Holes. Often it will be found less expensive to drill holes after the molding, rather than attempt to mold them, particularly when they must be deep in proportion to their diameter. Broken and bent core pins are an expensive item.

Good manufacturing practice calls for provision of drill jigs for the accurate drillings of molded pieces. Drill jigs will do much to reduce the cost of broken drills and too-frequent resharpening. However, in some instances it is possible to provide spot points on the molded part which can be used to locate the holes, so that jigs are not needed.

Threaded Holes. See discussion of threads, below.

Side Holes. Side holes are difficult to produce and present problems which are not easily solved, because they create undercuts in molded pieces.

Holes which must be molded at right angles to each other necessitate split molds or core pins and therefore are more costly, particularly in compression molding. The core pins, being not parallel to the applied pressure, may be distorted or sheared off, particularly if of small diameter. Also the molding of such holes adds to the time required for molding, in that it is necessary to withdraw these core pins from the molded piece before it can be removed from the cavity. These problems are less serious when transfer or injection methods are used, but there remains the necessity of withdrawing the core pins from the molded piece prior to its removal.

Another problem brought about by the presence of core pins is imperfect welding of the plastic, in the area back of or adjacent to the pin and on the side opposite to the direction of flow. Figure 12-7 illustrates this condition, which will be encountered more frequently in thermoplastic materials, but exists also in pieces made from thermosetting materials in a compression mold.

Molded Threads

The thread profile best suited to molding of both thermosetting and thermoplastic materials is the American National form thread.

The classification of thread fits are as follows:

Class 1. A loose fit for easy assembly.

· Class 2. Used extensively. For interchangeable parts a fit with no play or looseness.

Class 3. Recommended only for semiprecision work where high cost of precision tools and constant checking of tools and parts are warranted. Expensive to maintain.

Class 4. Not recommended for molded or machined threads in plastics. A precision fit for machine tools, dies, aircraft parts, etc.

Threaded Pieces. Under this heading are included pieces in which standard or special threads, male or female, are formed in the molding operation. Threaded holes used for assembly of pieces by means of screws and bolts are ordinarily not formed by molding, and are discussed on p. 431.

External. Articles with molded male, or external, threads can be removed from the mold either by unscrewing the molded article from the mold member (or vice versa), or by splitting the mold so that its parts can be separated at right angles to the axis of the thread. In general, the first method, while it may lengthen the molding cycle, will produce the more accurate thread. The second is faster, but requires great accuracy in matching up the split members of the mold and will leave a parting line which necessitates a finishing operation on the molded piece.

External threads should be started at least $\frac{1}{32}$ in. from the end of the molded piece, and in the case of threaded bosses or studs should not

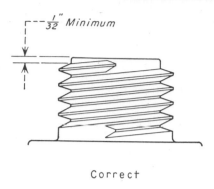

Correct

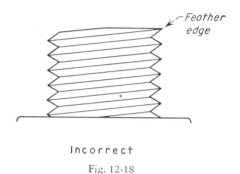

Incorrect

Fig. 12-18

run clear to the face of the main body (see Fig. 12-18). This will eliminate feather edges in the mold at the ends of the threads, which would be impossible to maintain.

Fine threads, 32-pitch or less, should be avoided whenever possible, and especially in fabric-filled material, as the fabric fails to fill out the crest of the thread and leaves a partial thread of pure resin, which is weak. Close-fitting threads, class 2 or more accurate, should be avoided, particularly on plastics having poor dimensional stability, as such threads require very close control of molding shrinkages.

On long threads, also, care must be taken to allow for shrinkage in length. Thus for a 32-pitch thread the mold must be constructed to have 32 threads per 1.008 in. or 1.010 in., depending on the shrinkage of the plastic used.

Internal. Internal threads of American National Standard Profile may be molded by a threaded pin from which the article is unscrewed (Fig. 12-19).

The plastic will shrink around the mold pin, and it is necessary that the thread form on the mold pin be extremely accurate and smooth to permit the two to be separated by unscrewing without chipping or cracking the molded piece. As with external threads, fine threads 32-pitch or less should

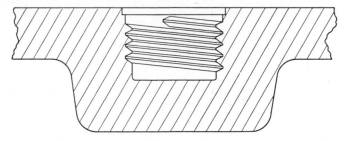

Fig. 12-19

be avoided and the threads should start below the surface of the piece, from a slight counterbore (see Fig. 12-19).

Stripping the molded article by pulling or pushing it directly off the mold pin, with no twisting motion, can be done only with specially designed threads which are well rounded on the resisting side and fairly shallow. The plastic is actually stretched over the threads, and the method is limited to certain types of plastics. Special grades for stripping are made by most of the suppliers of phenolic and urea plastics. Most of the thermoplastic materials can be stripped. This method is confined generally to closures for glass bottles and jars.

Threaded Holes. The threaded holes frequently needed for assembly purposes are ordinarily formed by machine tapping or by use of threaded metal inserts. The machine-tapped hole is more economical to produce than the molded threaded hole or than the use of metal inserts, especially when the hole is not larger than $\frac{3}{16}$ in.

Tapped holes in thermosetting molded articles two and a half times the diameter in length will prove stronger in resistance to stripping than the actual strength of hardened threaded screws. The head of the screw will twist off first.

When screws must be removed and replaced in service, a molded thread will last longer than tapped or machined threads, but still better in this respect are threaded metal inserts. Where a piece requires a large number of threaded holes, metal inserts should be used whenever possible. For data on inserts, see Chapter 14.

Threads molded or tapped in the plastic should not be finer than 32 threads per in.

The hole to be tapped should be drilled slightly larger than that used with metals. The recommended tap-drill sizes are given in Table 12-3. The drilled or molded hole should be slightly countersunk (Fig. 12-20) to avoid chipping at the surface.

The following data on sizes of tap drills for plastics are based on experience with thermosetting plastics. For thermoplastics, use these sizes or one size larger (Table 12-3).

TABLE 12-3. TAP DRILL SIZES FOR PLASTICS

Tap	Drill	Tap	Drill	Tap	Drill	Tap	Drill
F 0 x 80	55	9 x 24	28	16 x 16	3		
1 x 56	1/16	8 x 30	28	16 x 18	7/32		
C 1 x 64	52	C 8 x 32	27	16 x 20	2		
F 1 x 72	51	F 8 x 36	27	17 x 16	1		
2 x 48	49	9 x 28	25	17 x 18	A	N.C.S.	
C 2 x 56	48	9 x 30	24	17 x 20	B	1/4 x 20	5
F 2 x 64	48	9 x 32	24	18 x 16	B	5/16 x 18	G
3 x 40	45	C 10 x 24	22	18 x 18	D	3/8 x 16	O
C 3 x 48	44	10 x 30	19	18 x 20	E	7/16 x 14	3/8
F 3 x 56	43	F 10 x 32	19	19 x 16	E	1/2 x 13	7/16
4 x 32	42	11 x 24	17	19 x 18	F	9/16 x 12	31/64
4 x 36	42	11 x 28	16	19 x 20	G	5/8 x 11	17/32
C 4 x 40	41	11 x 30	16	20 x 16	H	3/4 x 10	21/32
F 4 x 48	40	12 x 20	16	20 x 18	I	7/8 x 9	49/64
5 x 30	37	12 x 22	15	20 x 20	J	1" x 8	7/8
5 x 32	36	C 12 x 24	13	22 x 16	L		
5 x 36	36	F 12 x 28	12	22 x 16	M		
C 5 x 40	34	13 x 20	12	24 x 14	5/16		
F 5 x 44	35	13 x 22	10	24 x 16	O	N.F.S.	
6 x 30	32	13 x 24	9	24 x 18	P	1/4 x 28	2
C 6 x 32	31	14 x 20	6	26 x 14	Q	5/16 x 24	I
6 x 36	31	14 x 22	5	26 x 16	11/32	3/8 x 24	R
F 6 x 40	1/8	14 x 24	4	28 x 14	23/64	7/16 x 20	25/64
7 x 28	1/8	15 x 18	5	28 x 16	U	1/2 x 20	29/64
7 x 30	1/8	15 x 20	4	30 x 14	W	9/16 x 18	33/64
7 x 32	30	15 x 22	3	30 x 16	X	5/8 x 18	37/64
8 x 24	29	15 x 24	7/32			3/4 x 16	11/16
						7/8 x 14	13/16
						1" x 14	15/16

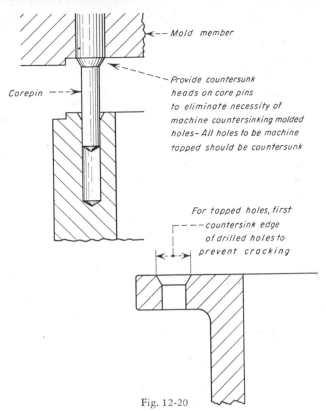

<-- Mold member

Corepin -->

~ Provide countersunk
heads on core pins
to eliminate necessity of
machine countersinking molded
holes - All holes to be machine
tapped should be countersunk

For tapped holes, first
countersink edge
of drilled holes to
prevent cracking

Fig. 12-20

Specification of percentage thread is based upon diameters in small sizes, and upon pitch in larger sizes.

The formula used is:

$$D = T - n \times 2d$$

in which

$D =$ diameter of drill
$T =$ outside diameter of thread or tap
$2d =$ double depth of thread
$n =$ percentage of thread depth desired
(expressed as a decimal)

Percentage depths of threads:

50 per cent below No. 6
60 per cent No. 6 through No. 14
70 per cent No. 15 through No. 30
70 per cent $\frac{1}{4}$ through $\frac{1}{2}$ in. N.C.S.
70 per cent $\frac{1}{4}$ through 1 in. N.F.S.
75 per cent $\frac{9}{16}$ through 1 in. N.C.S.

The "C" before the size shows the Standard N.C.S. size (American National Coarse Thread Series). The "F" shows the Standard N.F.S. size (American National Fine Thread Series).

While ordinary standard taps can be used, they will dull very quickly, especially with thermosetting plastics, and special taps for plastics should be used; these are available from most manufacturers of drills and taps.

A variation of tapping is the use of self-tapping screws, which eliminates the necessity of a threaded hole. Self-tapping screws, as the name implies, cut their own thread when screwed into a straight hole. Drive screws are hammered home, and should be used only as a permanent fastening, as they cannot be removed without great difficulty (see Table 12-4 for hole sizes for self-tapping and drive screws).

TABLE 12-4

SELF-TAPPING SCREWS

Size	O.D. Thread	THERMOSETTING		THERMOPLASTIC	
		Hole	Drill	Hole	Drill
2	.086	.078	47	.078	47
4	.112	.112	37	.093	42
6	.137	.137	30	.120	31
7	.151	.144	27	.128	30
8	.163	.152	24	.144	27
10	.186	.177	16	.169	18
12	.212	.199	8	.191	11
14	.243	.238	A	.221	2

DRIVE SCREWS

Size	O.D. Thread	PLASTICS	
		Hole	Drill
00	.058	.052	55
0	.073	.067	51
2	.098	.086	44
4	.114	.104	37
6	.138	.120	21
7	.152	.136	29
8	.164	.144	27
10	.179	.161	20
12	.209	.191	11
14	.239	.221	2

Molded holes should be formed with a rounded chamfer; drilled holes should be machine-chamfered.

Surface Treatment

The designer should make full use of the many different types of surface treatment to which plastics so readily lend themselves. The possibilities are limited only by the ingenuity of the designer plus the fundamental requirement that the piece must be removed from the mold. They range from mirror-like surfaces to dull satin finish. Surface treatments such as fluting, reeding, stippling, fine straight lines, diamond-knurl cut, leather grain—to mention only a few—may be used to advantage. They tend to conceal surface blemishes which might prove objectionable on a highly lustrous surface.

The appearance of a product is greatly influenced by the surface treatment employed. The designer should be familiar with the problems encountered by the molder. This is particularly true when large flat surfaces with a high lustrous finish are called for. Such surfaces are difficult to produce. The molder must invariably resort to special molding techniques which are both time-consuming and costly. The designer, understanding these problems, can do much to simplify the molder's difficulties through modification of design.

Wide, sweeping curves and domed rather than flat surfaces should be employed. Improved flow and distribution of material, during the molding operation, are thus achieved. In addition the tendency to warp is greatly reduced. As a result the appearance of the molded piece is improved.

Unfortunately there are no simple rules or formulas for solving the problems of surface treatment. What may prove to be a sound solution in one case may not work in another. Each new piece presents its own individual problems. The designer must draw freely upon his ingenuity, but always remember that the molded article must be easily removed from the mold after it has been formed.

The telephone desk-set shown in Fig. 12-21 is a typical example of the pleasing appearance gained by combining wide sweeping curves, domed surfaces and a lustrous finish.

Molded Lettering

Names, monograms, dial numbers, instructional information, and the like, are frequently required on molded articles. The lettering must be applied in such a manner as not to complicate the removal of the article from the mold. This is accomplished by locating it perpendicular to the parting line and providing adequate draft.

While both raised and depressed letters are possible, the method to be used in constructing the mold will dictate which is the more economical.

When the mold is to be made by machining, raised leters on the molded piece will be less costly (see Fig. 12-22). A raised letter on the molded piece is formed by a corresponding depression in the mold, and it is far less costly to engrave or machine the letters into the face of the mold than it is

Courtesy of Bell Telephone Laboratories, Inc.

Fig. 12-21

Fig. 12-22

to form a raised letter on the surface of the mold by cutting away the surrounding metal. On the other hand, if the mold is to be formed by hobbing, then the letters on the molded piece should be depressed, since it is the hob which must be machined. In making the hob, the letters are engraved into its surface. As the hob is sunk into the steel blank to produce the mold cavity, the letters are raised on the surface of the latter. These raised letters on the mold in turn produce depressed letters on the molded piece.

Fig. 12-23

To improve legibility, depressed lettering, filled in with paint (Fig. 12-23) is sometimes required. When hobbing of the whole mold is not practicable, the desired result can generally be accomplished by setting in a hobbed block carrying the lettering. When this insert is treated as a panel and the fin line is concealed by fluting, the appearance is not unpleasant.

13. Standards for Tolerances on Molded Articles

The purpose of this chapter is to indicate the magnitude of practical tolerances on the dimensions of articles molded from a variety of thermosetting and thermoplastic materials, other than laminates.

This information is given in the form of tables based upon data obtained from representative firms in the plastics molding industry by means of a questionnaire. It must be stressed that these tables are not to be construed as offering hard-and-fast rules applicable to all conditions. They can best be used as a basis for establishing standards for individual molded articles by agreement between the purchaser, or his design engineer, and the molder.

The questionnaire was based upon a hypothetical molded article, of which a cross-section is shown in the tables. This is a revised form of the article used for the same purpose in the first edition of the Handbook. It was agreed that the revised shape, closed on the lower side, represents better a typical molded article of today, in view of the progress of the molding industry, in recent years, in producing larger and less simple articles, e.g., radio and television cabinets, closed containers, panels, shelves, etc. The hypothetical article represents a variety of problems of tolerances on diameter, length, depth and thickness.

Tables of tolerances are given for only those materials which have been used widely enough, commercially, to provide significant data. However, the additional experience and information gained since the publication of the first edition of the Handbook have made possible an increase from the 20 tables of tolerances in that edition to 31 in the present edition.

The independent topic of dimensional stability is not covered in this chapter. It is hoped that sufficient information on this subject will be available for a chapter in a subsequent edition.

It should be recognized that extreme accuracy of dimensions in molded articles is expensive to achieve. The closer the tolerances demanded, the greater will be the cost of the molds, because of the precision required, and also the greater will be the operational costs of molding, because of the greater care required to maintain uniformity of conditions. In some cases a further expense arises from the need of using cooling fixtures after the molding.

Dimensional tolerances in a molded article are the allowable variations, plus and minus, from a nominal or mean dimension.

Fine tolerance represents the narrowest possible limits of variation obtainable under close supervision and control of production.

Standard tolerance is that which can be held under average conditions of manufacture.

Coarse tolerance is acceptable when accurate dimensions are not important.

The use of the tables may be illustrated by an example of articles molded from woodflour-filled phenol-formaldehyde. Reference is made to Table 1, which presents standards of tolerances for articles of the typical shape shown, as molded from this material.

Note that the typical article shown in cross-section in the tables may be of round or rectangular or other shape. Thus dimensions *A* and *B* may be diameters or lengths.

	Tolerance (in.) (plus or minus)		
	fine	standard	coarse
In a compression-molded article, if dimension *A* is 3 in., the chart at the top shows the tolerances for *A* to be	0.005	0.007	0.012
If dimension *B* is 1 in., the same chart shows tolerances for *B* as	0.0027	0.0045	0.010
If dimension *C* is 2 in., the tolerances for *C* are	0.004	0.006	0.011
If a dimension is greater than 6 in., the tolerance for 6 in. is to be increased by the amount indicated in the next two lines. For example, if dimension *A* is 10 in., add to the tolerances for 6 in.	0.0085	0.0115	0.015
the further allowance for the additional 4 in.	0.006	0.008	0.010
The tolerances will thus be	0.0145	0.0195	0.025
If dimension *A* is 14 in., we have			
for 6 in.	0.0085	0.0115	0.015
for additional up to 12 in.	0.009	0.012	0.015
for additional beyond 12 in.	0.004	0.006	0.010
Thus the tolerances will be	0.0215	0.0295	0.040
The tolerance on the over-all height *D* must be greater in a multiple-cavity mold than in a single-cavity mold, because of variation in dimensions between cavities, variation in loading, and errors of alignment. Tolerances are shown in the table for both types when *D* is not more than 1 in. When *D* is more than 1 in., an addition must be made. Thus, if *D* in a multiple-cavity mold is 3 in., we have, for the first inch	0.006	0.008	0.010
To these must be added, for the additional 2 in. of depth	0.004	0.010	0.016
The tolerances will be the sums of these, i.e.	0.010	0.018	0.026
If dimension *E* is 0.150 in., i.e., between 0.100 and 0.200, the table shows the tolerances to be	0.003	0.005	0.008
Note, however, that for a compression-molded article having a projected area greater than 20 sq in. these values for *D* and *E* must be increased as indicated in the lower part of the table. Thus, for an article of projected area 26 sq in. the tolerances on *D*, shown above as	0.010	0.018	0.026
become	0.011	0.020	0.029
Similarly the tolerances on *E*, shown above as	0.003	0.005	0.008
become	0.004	0.007	0.011

The wall thickness F is to be held as nearly as possible constant. Complete uniformity in this dimension is impossible to achieve, by reasons of limitations in accuracy of dimensions of the mold, variations in mold shrinkage, and lack of concentricity of mold and punch.

In a well-made mold, the variation in wall thickness F due to lack of concentricity between mold and force will be, as indicated, 0.005 to 0.007 in., plus or minus. This can be reduced by interlocking.

Tolerances on draft are shown as:
    fine $\frac{1}{8}°$
    standard $\frac{1}{4}°$
    coarse $1°$

For articles molded by transfer, jet or injection, the chart at the bottom of the table shows the tolerances for D, when D is not more than 1 in., to be

in single-cavity mold	0.001	0.003	0.005
in multiple-cavity mold	0.003	0.005	0.007

If the depth D is 3 in., these become

in single-cavity mold	0.003	0.005	0.007
in multiple-cavity mold	0.005	0.007	0.009

TABLE 13-1

MATERIAL: WOODFLOUR-FILLED PHENOLIC MATERIALS

Plus or Minus in Thousands of An In.#

Drawing Code		Dimensions (In.)		Fine ±	Standard ±	Coarse ±
A = Diameter or Length		0.000				
B = Diameter or Length		0.500				
C = Depth		1.000				
		2.000				
		3.000				
		4.000				
		5.000				
		6.000				
		6.000 to 12.000 / For each inch over 6.000 add (in.)		0.0015	0.002	0.0025
		Over 12.000 / For each inch over 12.000 add (in.)		0.002	0.003	0.005
HEIGHT	D	Single Cavity 0.000-1.000		0.004	0.006	0.008
		Multiple Cavity 0.000-1.000		0.006	0.008	0.010
		For each inch over 1.000 add (in.)		0.002	0.005	0.008
BOTTOM WALL	E	0.000 to 0.100		0.003	0.005	0.008
		0.100 to 0.200		0.003	0.005	0.008
		0.200 to 0.300		0.003	0.005	0.008

SIDEWALL F DIMENSION ##   Section thickness to be held relatively constant

F Variation in wall thickness due to eccentricity, 0.005–0.007 in. Interlocking reduces this.

DRAFT ALLOWANCE	1/8°	1/4°	1°

DWG. CODE					
D, E	Compression Molded For projected area over 20 sq. in.	Fine	Add 0.001 in. for each additional 10 sq. in.		
		Standard	Add 0.002 in. for each additional 10 sq. in.		
		Coarse	Add 0.003 in. for each additional 10 sq. in.		

Transfer, Jet, or Injection molded Any area

PLUS OR MINUS TOLERANCE IN THOUSANDTHS OF AN IN. (F = Fine; S = Standard; C = Coarse)

	1	2	3	4	5	6	7	8	9	10	11	12	13	14	15	16	17	18	19	20	21	22
Single cavity	F		S		C																	
Multiple cavity			F		S		C															
D — For each inch of depth over 1.000 add (in.)	0.001																					

These tolerances do not apply to screw threads, gear teeth, or fit of mating parts; dimensions in these classifications can generally be held to closer limits. These tolerances do not include allowance for aging characteristics of material.

See introduction to chapter.

TABLE 15-2

MATERIAL: COTTON-FLOCK-FILLED PHENOLIC MATERIALS

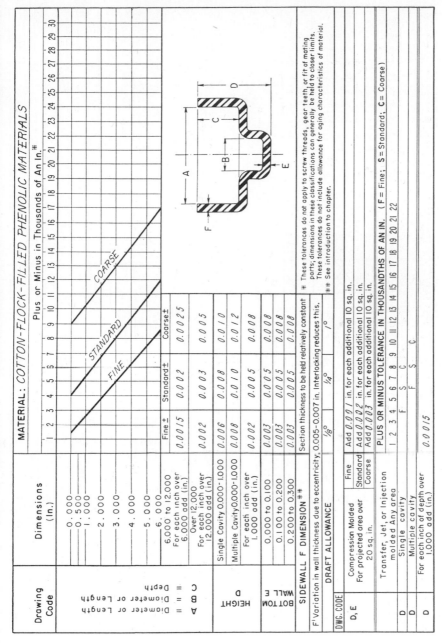

Plus or Minus in Thousands of An In.*

Drawing Code	Dimensions (In.)		Fine±	Standard±	Coarse±
A = Diameter or Length	0.000 0.500 1.000 2.000 3.000 4.000 5.000 6.000				
B = Diameter or Length	6.000 to 12.000		0.0015	0.002	0.0025
C = Depth	For each inch over 6.000 add (in.)		0.002	0.003	0.005
	Over 12.000 For each inch over 12.000 add (in.)		0.006	0.008	0.010
D	Single Cavity 0.000-1.000		0.008	0.010	0.012
	Multiple Cavity 0.000-1.000				
	For each inch over 1.000 add (in.)		0.002	0.005	0.008
HEIGHT	0.000 to 0.100		0.003	0.005	0.008
BOTTOM	0.100 to 0.200		0.003	0.005	0.008
WALL E	0.200 to 0.300		0.003	0.005	0.008

SIDEWALL F DIMENSION ** Section thickness to be held relatively constant

F'Variation in wall thickness due to eccentricity, 0.005–0.007 in. Interlocking reduces this.

DRAFT ALLOWANCE		1/8°	1/4°	1°

DWG. CODE			
D, E	Compression Molded For projected area over 20 sq. in.	Fine	Add 0.001 in. for each additional 10 sq. in.
		Standard	Add 0.002 in. for each additional 10 sq. in.
		Coarse	Add 0.003 in. for each additional 10 sq. in.

	Transfer, Jet, or Injection molded Any area	PLUS OR MINUS TOLERANCE IN THOUSANDTHS OF AN IN. (F = Fine; S = Standard; C = Coarse)
D	Single cavity	F S C
D	Multiple cavity	F S C
D	For each inch of depth over 1.000 add (in.)	0.0015

\# These tolerances do not apply to screw threads, gear teeth, or fit of mating parts; dimensions in these classifications can generally be held to closer limits.

These tolerances do not include allowance for aging characteristics of material.

\#\# See introduction to chapter.

TABLE 13-3

MATERIAL: COTTON-RAG-FILLED PHENOLIC MATERIALS

Drawing Code	Dimensions (In.)		Fine ±	Standard ±	Coarse ±
A = Diameter or Length	0.000 to 6.000	6.000 to 12.000	0.002	0.0025	0.003
B = Diameter or Length	For each inch over 6.000 add (in.)				
C = Depth	Over 12.000 / For each inch over 12.000 add (in.)		0.002	0.003	0.005
D HEIGHT	Single Cavity 0.000-1.000		0.006	0.008	0.010
	Multiple Cavity 0.000-1.000		0.008	0.010	0.012
	For each inch over 1.000 add (in.)		0.002	0.005	0.008
E WALL BOTTOM	0.000 to 0.100		0.004	0.006	0.010
	0.100 to 0.200		0.004	0.006	0.010
	0.200 to 0.300		0.004	0.006	0.010

Plus or Minus in Thousands of An In.#

These tolerances do not apply to screw threads, gear teeth, or fit of mating parts; dimensions in these classifications can generally be held to closer limits. These tolerances do not include allowance for aging characteristics of material.

SIDEWALL F DIMENSION **

Section thickness to be held relatively constant†

F¹ Variation in wall thickness due to eccentricity, 0.005-0.007 in. Interlocking reduces this.

** See introduction to chapter.

DRAFT ALLOWANCE

1/8°   1/4°   1°

DWG. CODE			
D, E	Compression Molded For projected area over 20 sq. in.	Fine	Add 0.001 in. for each additional 10 sq. in.
		Standard	Add 0.002 in. for each additional 10 sq. in.
		Coarse	Add 0.003 in. for each additional 10 sq. in.

Transfer, Jet, or Injection molded Any area

PLUS OR MINUS TOLERANCE IN THOUSANDTHS OF AN IN.   (F = Fine; S = Standard; C = Coarse)

	1	2	3	4	5	6	7	8	9	10	11	12	13	14	15	16	17	18	19	20	21	22
D Single cavity				F	S	C																
D Multiple cavity					F	S	C															
D For each inch of depth over 1.000 add (in.)		0.0015																				

TABLE 13-4

MATERIAL: COTTON-TIRE-CORD-FILLED PHENOLIC MATERIALS

Plus or Minus in Thousands of An In.*

Drawing Code	Dimensions (In.)	Fine ±	Standard ±	Coarse ±
A = Diameter or Length	0.000			
B = Diameter or Length	0.500			
C = Depth	1.000			
	2.000			
	3.000			
	4.000			
	5.000			
	6.000			
	6.000 to 12.000 / For each inch over 6.000 add (in.)	0.0015	0.002	0.0025
	Over 12.000 / For each inch over 12.000 add (in.)	0.002	0.003	0.005
D = HEIGHT	Single Cavity 0.000-1.000	0.008	0.010	0.012
	Multiple Cavity 0.000-1.000	0.010	0.012	0.014
	For each inch over 1.000 add (in.)	0.002	0.005	0.008
E = WALL / BOTTOM	0.000 to 0.100	0.004	0.006	0.009
	0.100 to 0.200	0.004	0.006	0.010
	0.200 to 0.300	0.004	0.006	0.010

(Graph axis: 1 through 30 Thousandths of An In., with diagonal lines labeled COARSE, STANDARD, FINE for dimensions 0.000 through 6.000)

SIDEWALL F DIMENSION Section thickness to be held relatively constant

F' Variation in wall thickness due to eccentricity, 0.005–0.007 in. Interlocking reduces this.

DRAFT ALLOWANCE 1/8° 1/4° 1°

DWG. CODE			
D, E	Compression Molded / For projected area over 20 sq. in.	Fine	Add 0.001 in. for each additional 10 sq. in.
		Standard	Add 0.002 in. for each additional 10 sq. in.
		Coarse	Add 0.003 in. for each additional 10 sq. in.
	Transfer, Jet, or Injection molded Any area		PLUS OR MINUS TOLERANCE IN THOUSANDTHS OF AN IN. (F = Fine; S = Standard; C = Coarse) 1 2 3 4 5 6 7 8 9 10 11 12 13 14 15 16 17 18 19 20 21 22
D	Single cavity		F S C
D	Multiple cavity		F S C
D	For each inch of depth over 1.000 add (in.)		0.0015

* These tolerances do not apply to screw threads, gear teeth, or fit of mating parts; dimensions in these classifications can generally be held to closer limits. These tolerances do not include allowance for aging characteristics of material.

** See introduction to chapter.

TABLE 13-5

MATERIAL: MACERATED-PAPER-FILLED PHENOLIC MATERIALS

Plus or Minus in Thousands of An In.#

Cross-section drawing with dimensions A, B, C, D, E, F.

Drawing Code	Dimensions (In.)	Fine±	Standard±	Coarse±
A = Diameter or Length B = Diameter or Length C = Depth	0.000 0.500 1.000 2.000 3.000 4.000 5.000 6.000			
	6.000 to 12.000	0.002	0.0025	0.003
	For each inch over 6.000 add (in.)	0.002	0.004	0.006
	Over 12.000			
	For each inch over 12.000 add (in.)			
D HEIGHT	Single Cavity 0.000-1.000	0.008	0.010	0.012
	Multiple Cavity 0.000-1.000	0.010	0.012	0.014
	For each inch over 1.000 add (in.)	0.002	0.005	0.008
E BOTTOM WALL	0.000 to 0.100	0.003	0.005	0.008
	0.100 to 0.200	0.003	0.005	0.009
	0.200 to 0.300	0.003	0.006	0.011
SIDEWALL F DIMENSION**	Section thickness to be held relatively constant†			

F¹ Variation in wall thickness due to eccentricity, 0.005-0.007 in. Interlocking reduces this.

DRAFT ALLOWANCE	1/8°	1/4°	1°

DWG. CODE			
D, E	Compression Molded For projected area over 20 sq. in.	Fine	Add 0.001 in. for each additional 10 sq. in.
		Standard	Add 0.002 in. for each additional 10 sq. in.
		Coarse	Add 0.003 in. for each additional 10 sq. in.
	Transfer, Jet, or Injection molded Any area		

PLUS OR MINUS TOLERANCE IN THOUSANDTHS OF AN IN. (F = Fine; S = Standard; C = Coarse)

Scale: 1 2 3 4 5 6 7 8 9 10 11 12 13 14 15 16 17 18 19 20 21 22

DWG. CODE			
D	Single cavity	F S C	
D	Multiple cavity	F S C	
D	For each inch of depth over 1.000 add (in.)	0.0015	

\# These tolerances do not apply to screw threads, gear teeth, or fit of mating parts; dimensions in these classifications can generally be held to closer limits. These tolerances do not include allowance for aging characteristics of material.

\#\# See introduction to chapter.

TABLE 13-6

MATERIAL: SHORT-FIBER-ASBESTOS-FILLED PHENOLIC MATERIALS

Plus or Minus in Thousands of An In.# — chart showing FINE, STANDARD, COARSE diagonal lines against a scale of 1–30.

Drawing Code	Dimensions (In.)		Fine ±	Standard ±	Coarse ±
A = Diameter or Length	0.000–0.500–1.000–2.000–3.000–4.000–5.000–6.000	6,000 to 12,000			
B = Diameter or Length		For each inch over 6,000 add (in.)	0.001	0.0015	0.002
C = Depth		Over 12,000 For each inch over 12,000 add (in.)	0.002	0.003	0.005
D HEIGHT		Single Cavity 0.000-1.000	0.004	0.006	0.008
		Multiple Cavity 0.000-1.000	0.006	0.008	0.010
		For each inch over 1.000 add (in.)	0.002	0.003	0.005
WALL E BOTTOM		0.000 to 0.100	0.003	0.005	0.008
		0.100 to 0.200	0.003	0.005	0.008
		0.200 to 0.300	0.003	0.005	0.008

SIDEWALL F DIMENSION ## Section thickness to be held relatively constant

F'Variation in wall thickness due to eccentricity 0.005-0.007 in. Interlocking reduces this.

DRAFT ALLOWANCE — 1/4° | 1/2° | 1°

DWG. CODE

D, E	Compression Molded For projected area over 20 sq. in.	Fine Add 0.001 in. for each additional 10 sq. in.
		Standard Add 0.002 in. for each additional 10 sq. in.
		Coarse Add 0.003 in. for each additional 10 sq. in.

Transfer, Jet, or Injection molded Any area

PLUS OR MINUS TOLERANCE IN THOUSANDTHS OF AN IN. (F = Fine; S = Standard; C = Coarse)

		1 2 3 4 5 6 7 8 9 10 11 12 13 14 15 16 17 18 19 20 21 22
D	Single cavity	F S C
D	Multiple cavity	F S C
D	For each inch of depth over 1.000 add (in.)	0.001

\# These tolerances do not apply to screw threads, gear teeth, or fit of mating parts; dimensions in these classifications can generally be held to closer limits. These tolerances do not include allowance for aging characteristics of material.

\## See introduction to chapter.

TABLE 13-7

MATERIAL: LONG-FIBER-ASBESTOS-FILLED PHENOLIC MATERIALS

Plus or Minus in Thousands of An In.* (scale 1–30)

Drawing Code	Dimensions (In.)	Fine ±	Standard ±	Coarse ±
A = Diameter or Length B = Diameter or Length C = Depth	0.000 0.500 1.000 2.000 3.000 4.000 5.000 6.000			
	6.000 to 12.000	0.001	0.0015	0.002
	For each inch over 6.000 add (in.)	0.002	0.0035	0.006
	Over 12.000	0.004	0.006	0.008
	For each inch over 12.000 add (in.)	0.006	0.008	0.010
D HEIGHT	Single Cavity 0.000-1.000	0.002	0.006	0.008
	Multiple Cavity 0.000-1.000	0.006	0.008	0.0075
	For each inch over 1.000 add (in.)	0.002	0.005	0.009
E WALL BOTTOM	0.000 to 0.100	0.003	0.005	0.0075
	0.100 to 0.200	0.003	0.0055	0.009
	0.200 to 0.300	0.003	0.0055	0.009
SIDEWALL F DIMENSION ##	Section thickness to be held relatively constant			

F' Variation in wall thickness due to eccentricity, 0.005-0.007 in. Interlocking reduces this.

DRAFT ALLOWANCE	1/4°	1/2°	1°

DWG. CODE			
D, E	Compression Molded For projected area over 20 sq. in.	Fine	Add 0.001 in. for each additional 10 sq. in.
		Standard	Add 0.002 in. for each additional 10 sq. in.
		Coarse	Add 0.003 in. for each additional 10 sq. in.
	Transfer, Jet, or Injection molded Any area		

PLUS OR MINUS TOLERANCE IN THOUSANDTHS OF AN IN. (F = Fine; S = Standard; C = Coarse) (scale 1–22)

		F	S	C
D	Single cavity	F	S	C
D	Multiple cavity	F	S	C
D	For each inch of depth over 1.000 add (in.)	0.001		

* These tolerances do not apply to screw threads, gear teeth, or fit of mating parts; dimensions in these classifications can generally be held to closer limits. These tolerances do not include allowance for aging characteristics of material.

\#\# See introduction to chapter.

TABLE 13-8

MATERIAL: ASBESTOS-WOODFLOUR-FILLED PHENOLIC MATERIALS

Plus or Minus in Thousands of An In.*

Drawing Code		Dimensions (In.)	Fine ±	Standard ±	Coarse ±
A = Diameter or Length		0.000			
B = Diameter or Length		0.500			
C = Depth		1.000			
		2.000			
		3.000			
		4.000			
		5.000			
		6.000			
		6.000 to 12.000 / For each inch over 6.000 add (in.)	0.0015	0.002	0.0025
		Over 12.000 / For each inch over 12.000 add (in.)	0.002	0.003	0.005
D HEIGHT		Single Cavity 0.000-1.000	0.004	0.006	0.008
		Multiple Cavity 0.000-1.000	0.006	0.008	0.010
		For each inch over 1.000 add (in.)	0.002	0.003	0.005
E WALL / BOTTOM		0.000 to 0.100	0.003	0.005	0.008
		0.100 to 0.200	0.003	0.005	0.008
		0.200 to 0.300	0.003	0.005	0.008

SIDEWALL F DIMENSION** Section thickness to be held relatively constant

F'Variation in wall thickness due to eccentricity. 0.005–0.007 in. Interlocking reduces this.

DRAFT ALLOWANCE	1/8°	1/4°	1°

DWG. CODE			
D, E	Compression Molded For projected area over 20 sq. in.	Fine	Add 0.001/in. for each additional 10 sq. in.
		Standard	Add 0.002 in. for each additional 10 sq. in.
		Coarse	Add 0.003 in. for each additional 10 sq. in.

Transfer, Jet, or Injection molded Any area

PLUS OR MINUS TOLERANCE IN THOUSANDTHS OF AN IN. (F = Fine; S = Standard; C = Coarse)

1 2 3 4 5 6 7 8 9 10 11 12 13 14 15 16 17 18 19 20 21 22

D	Single cavity	F S C
D	Multiple cavity	F S C
D	For each inch of depth over 1.000 add (in.)	0.001

* These tolerances do not apply to screw threads, gear teeth, or fit of mating parts; dimensions in these classifications can generally be held to closer limits. These tolerances do not include allowance for aging characteristics of material.

** See introduction to chapter.

TABLE 13-9

MATERIAL: MICA–FILLED PHENOLIC MATERIALS

Drawing Code		Dimensions (In.)	Fine ±	Standard ±	Coarse ±
A = Diameter or Length		0.000			
B = Diameter or Length		0.500			
C = Depth		1.000			
		2.000			
		3.000			
		4.000			
		5.000			
		6.000			
		6.000 to 12.000			
		For each inch over 6.000 add (in.)	0.001	0.0015	0.002
		Over 12.000			
		For each inch over 12.000 add (in.)	0.0015	0.003	0.005
D HEIGHT		Single Cavity 0.000-1.000	0.004	0.006	0.008
		Multiple Cavity 0.000-1.000	0.006	0.008	0.010
		For each inch over 1.000 add (in.)	0.002	0.003	0.004
E BOTTOM WALL		0.000 to 0.100	0.003	0.005	0.008
		0.100 to 0.200	0.003	0.005	0.008
		0.200 to 0.300	0.003	0.005	0.008

SIDEWALL F DIMENSION** — Section thickness to be held relatively constant

F' Variation in wall thickness due to eccentricity, 0.005–0.007 in. Interlocking reduces this.

DRAFT ALLOWANCE: $1/8°$ $1/4°$ $1°$

DWG. CODE		
D, E	Compression Molded For projected area over 20 sq. in.	Fine — Add 0.001 in. for each additional 10 sq. in.
		Standard — Add 0.002 in. for each additional 10 sq. in.
		Coarse — Add 0.003 in. for each additional 10 sq. in.

Transfer, Jet, or Injection molded Any area

	PLUS OR MINUS TOLERANCE IN THOUSANDTHS OF AN IN. (F = Fine; S = Standard; C = Coarse)
	1 2 3 4 5 6 7 8 9 10 11 12 13 14 15 16 17 18 19 20 21 22
D — Single cavity	F S C
D — Multiple cavity	F S C
D — For each inch of depth over 1.000 add (in.)	0.001

Plus or Minus in Thousands of An In.#
1 2 3 4 5 6 7 8 9 10 11 12 13 14 15 16 17 18 19 20 21 22 23 24 25 26 27 28 29 30

COARSE   STANDARD   FINE

These tolerances do not apply to screw threads, gear teeth, or fit of mating parts; dimensions in these classifications can generally be held to closer limits. These tolerances do not include allowance for aging characteristics of material.

** See introduction to chapter.

TABLE 13-10

MATERIAL: UNFILLED PHENOLIC MATERIALS

Plus or Minus in Thousands of An In.[#] — graph with lines labeled COARSE, STANDARD, FINE (scale 1–30).

Drawing Code		Dimensions (In.)	Fine±	Standard±	Coarse±
A = Diameter or Length		0.000			
B = Diameter or Length		0.500			
C = Depth		1.000			
		2.000			
		3.000			
		4.000			
		5.000			
		6.000	0.0015	0.002	0.0025
		6.000 to 12.000 For each inch over 6.000 add (in.)			
		Over 12.000 For each inch over 12.000 add (in.)	0.002	0.0035	0.0055
HEIGHT	D	Single Cavity 0.000–1.000	0.008	0.010	0.012
		Multiple Cavity 0.000–1.000	0.010	0.012	0.014
		For each inch over 1.000 add (in.)	0.002	0.0035	0.005
BOTTOM		0.000 to 0.100	0.0045	0.0065	0.0085
WALL E		0.100 to 0.200	0.0045	0.0065	0.0085
		0.200 to 0.300	0.0045	0.0065	0.0085

SIDEWALL F DIMENSION [##] Section thickness to be held relatively constant

F'Variation in wall thickness due to eccentricity, 0.005–0.007 in. Interlocking reduces this.

DRAFT ALLOWANCE		1/8°	1/4°	1°

DWG. CODE			
D, E	Compression Molded For projected area over 20 sq. in.	Fine	Add 0.001 in. for each additional 10 sq. in.
		Standard	Add 0.002 in. for each additional 10 sq. in.
		Coarse	Add 0.003 in. for each additional 10 sq. in.
	Transfer, Jet, or Injection molded Any area		

PLUS OR MINUS TOLERANCE IN THOUSANDTHS OF AN IN. (F = Fine; S = Standard; C = Coarse)

	1 2 3 4 5 6 7 8 9 10 11 12 13 14 15 16 17 18 19 20 21 22
	F S C
D Single cavity	F S C
D Multiple cavity	F S C
D For each inch of depth over 1.000 add (in.)	0.001

[#] These tolerances do not apply to screw threads, gear teeth, or fit of mating parts; dimensions in these classifications can generally be held to closer limits. These tolerances do not include allowance for aging characteristics of material.

[##] See introduction to chapter.

TABLE 13-11

MATERIAL: *ALPHA-CELLULOSE-FILLED UREA-FORMALDEHYDE MATERIALS*

Plus or Minus in Thousands of An In.#

Drawing Code	Dimensions (In.)		Fine ±	Standard ±	Coarse ±
A = Diameter or Length	0.000				
B = Diameter or Length	0.500				
C = Depth	1.000				
	2.000				
	3.000				
	4.000				
	5.000				
	6.000				
	6.000 to 12.000		0.003	0.0045	0.0065
	For each inch over 6.000 add (in.)				
	Over 12.000				
	For each inch over 12.000 add (in.)				
D HEIGHT	Single Cavity 0.000-1.000		0.0035	0.0055	0.0075
	Multiple Cavity 0.000-1.000		0.005	0.008	0.011
	For each inch over 1.000 add (in.)		0.007	0.010	0.013
			0.003	0.004	0.006
WALL E BOTTOM	0.000 to 0.100		0.0035	0.0055	0.0085
	0.100 to 0.200		0.0035	0.006	0.009
	0.200 to 0.300		0.0035	0.0065	0.0105

SIDEWALL F DIMENSION *#   Section thickness to be held relatively constant

F' Variation in wall thickness due to eccentricity, 0.005-0.007 in. Interlocking reduces this.

DRAFT ALLOWANCE		1/4°	1/2°	1°

Compression Molded For projected area over 20 sq. in.	Fine	Add 0.002 in. for each additional 10 sq. in.
	Standard	Add 0.003 in. for each additional 10 sq. in.
	Coarse	Add 0.004 in. for each additional 10 sq. in.

Transfer, Jet, or Injection molded Any area

DWG. CODE   PLUS OR MINUS TOLERANCE IN THOUSANDTHS OF AN IN.   (F = Fine;   S = Standard;   C = Coarse)

DWG. CODE	1	2	3	4	5	6	7	8	9	10	11	12	13	14	15	16	17	18	19	20	21	22
D, E				F	S	C																
Single cavity D					F	S	C															
Multiple cavity D						F	S	C														
For each inch of depth over 1.000 add (in.) D	0.002																					

\# These tolerances do not apply to screw threads, gear teeth, or fit of mating parts; dimensions in these classifications can generally be held to closer limits. These tolerances do not include allowance for aging characteristics of material.

\#\# See introduction to chapter.

TABLE 13-12

MATERIAL: ELECTRICAL GRADE UREA-FORMALDEHYDE MATERIALS

Drawing Code	Dimensions (In.)		Fine±	Standard±	Coarse±
A = Diameter or Length	0.000				
B = Diameter or Length	0.500				
C = Depth	1.000				
	2.000				
	3.000				
	4.000				
	5.000				
	6.000				
D HEIGHT	6.000 to 12.000	For each inch over 6.000 add (in.)	0.005	0.007	0.009
	Over 12.000	For each inch over 12.000 add (in.)	0.004	0.006	0.009
	Single Cavity 0.000–1.000		0.002	0.005	0.008
	Multiple Cavity 0.000–1.000		0.004	0.006	0.010
	For each inch over 1.000 add (in.)		0.003	0.004	0.004
E WALL BOTTOM	0.000 to 0.100		0.003	0.004	0.008
	0.100 to 0.200		0.003	0.004	0.008
	0.200 to 0.300		0.003	0.004	0.008

SIDEWALL F DIMENSION ## — Section thickness to be held relatively constant

F' Variation in wall thickness due to eccentricity, 0.005–0.007 in. Interlocking reduces this.

DRAFT ALLOWANCE	1/8°	1/4°	1°

DWG. CODE		Fine	Standard	Coarse
D, E	Compression Molded For projected area over 20 sq. in.	Add 0.001/in. for each additional 10 sq. in.	Add 0.002 in. for each additional 10 sq. in.	Add 0.003 in. for each additional 10 sq. in.

Transfer, Jet, or Injection molded Any area

PLUS OR MINUS TOLERANCE IN THOUSANDTHS OF AN IN. (F = Fine; S = Standard; C = Coarse)

	1 2 3 4 5 6 7 8 9 10 11 12 13 14 15 16 17 18 19 20 21 22
D Single cavity	F S C
D Multiple cavity	F S C
D For each inch of depth over 1.000 add (in.)	0.002

\# These tolerances do not apply to screw threads, gear teeth, or fit of mating parts; dimensions in these classifications can generally be held to closer limits. These tolerances do not include allowance for aging characteristics of material.

\#\# See introduction to chapter.

TABLE 13-13

MATERIAL: CELLULOSE-FILLED MELAMINE-FORMALDEHYDE MATERIALS ‡

Graph — Plus or Minus in Thousands of An In.# (horizontal axis 1–30) showing FINE, STANDARD, and COARSE curves. Cross-section drawing of molded part with dimensions A, B, C, D, E, F.

Drawing Code	Dimensions (In.)		Fine ±	Standard ±	Coarse ±
A = Diameter or Length B = Diameter or Length C = Depth	0.000 0.500 1.000 2.000 3.000 4.000 5.000 6.000				
	6,000 to 12,000		0.002	0.003	0.006
	For each inch over 6,000 add (in.)		0.004	0.006	0.007
	Over 12,000				
	For each inch over 12,000 add (in.)				
D HEIGHT	Single Cavity 0.000–1.000		0.004	0.006	0.007
	Multiple Cavity 0.000–1.000		0.0045	0.007	0.0095
	For each inch over 1.000 add (in.)		0.0035	0.006	0.008
WALL E	0.000 to 0.100		0.004	0.005	0.007
BOTTOM	0.100 to 0.200		0.005	0.006	0.008
	0.200 to 0.300		0.005	0.006	0.008

SIDEWALL F DIMENSION** Section thickness to be held relatively constant

F¹ Variation in wall thickness due to eccentricity, 0.005–0.007 in. Interlocking reduces this.

DRAFT ALLOWANCE	¼°	½°	1°

DWG. CODE			
D, E	Compression Molded For projected area over 20 sq. in.	Fine	Add 0.002 in. for each additional 10 sq. in.
		Standard	Add 0.003 in. for each additional 10 sq. in.
		Coarse	Add 0.005 in. for each additional 10 sq. in.
	Transfer, Jet, or Injection molded Any area		

PLUS OR MINUS TOLERANCE IN THOUSANDTHS OF AN IN. (F = Fine; S = Standard; C = Coarse)

	1	2	3	4	5	6	7	8	9	10	11	12	13	14	15	16	17	18	19	20	21	22
D	Single cavity			F	S	C																
D	Multiple cavity				F	S	C															
D	For each inch of depth over 1.000 add (in.) 0.002																					

These tolerances do not apply to screw threads, gear teeth, or fit of mating parts; dimensions in these classifications can generally be held to closer limits. These tolerances do not include allowance for aging characteristics of material.

** See introduction to chapter.

† Tolerances shown are approximate and apply only where material is subjected to less than 50°C after molding.

TABLE 13-14

MATERIAL: ASBESTOS-FILLED MELAMINE-FORMALDEHYDE MATERIALS ‡

Drawing Code	Dimensions (In.)	Fine ±	Standard ±	Coarse ±
A = Diameter or Length	0.000			
B = Diameter or Length	0.500			
C = Depth	1.000			
	2.000			
	3.000			
	4.000			
	5.000			
	6.000			
	6.000 to 12,000	0.004	0.005	0.007
	For each inch over 6,000 add (in.)		0.005	0.008
	Over 12,000			
	For each inch over 12,000 add (in.)	0.004		
D (HEIGHT)	Single Cavity 0.000-1.00C	0.003	0.006	0.010
	Multiple Cavity 0.000-1.00C	0.005	0.008	0.012
	For each inch over 1.000 add (in.)	0.003	0.004	0.006
E (WALL BOTTOM)	0.000 to 0.100	0.0025	0.004	0.007
	0.100 to 0.200	0.0025	0.004	0.007
	0.200 to 0.300	0.0025	0.004	0.007

SIDEWALL F DIMENSION ## Section thickness to be held relatively constant

F¹ Variation in wall thickness due to eccentricity, 0.005-0.007 in. Interlocking reduces this.

DRAFT ALLOWANCE	1/8°	1/4°	1°

DWG. CODE			
D, E	Compression Molded	Fine	Add 0.002 in. for each additional 10 sq. in.
	For projected area over 20 sq. in.	Standard	Add 0.004 in. for each additional 10 sq. in.
		Coarse	Add 0.006 in. for each additional 10 sq. in.

PLUS OR MINUS TOLERANCE IN THOUSANDTHS OF AN IN. (F= Fine; S= Standard; C= Coarse)

	1 2 3 4 5 6 7 8 9 10 11 12 13 14 15 16 17 18 19 20 21 22
Transfer, Jet, or Injection molded Any area	F S C
D — Single cavity	F S C
D — Multiple cavity	F S C
D — For each inch of depth over 1.000 add (in.)	0.002

These tolerances do not apply to screw threads, gear teeth, or fit of mating parts; dimensions in these classifications can generally be held to closer limits. These tolerances do not include allowance for aging characteristics of material.

See introduction to chapter.

‡ Tolerances shown are approximate and apply only where material is subjected to less than 50° C after molding.

TABLE 13-15

MATERIAL: COTTON-RAG-FILLED MELAMINE-FORMALDEHYDE MATERIALS‡

Plus or Minus in Thousands of An In.#

Diagonal tolerance bands labeled: COARSE, STANDARD, FINE (scale 1–30)

Cross-section drawing with dimension codes A, B, C, D, E, F.

Drawing Code	Dimensions (In.)	Fine ±	Standard ±	Coarse ±
A = Diameter or Length B = Diameter or Length C = Depth	0.000			
	0.500			
	1.000			
	2.000			
	3.000			
	4.000			
	5.000			
	6.000			
	6.000 to 12.000 For each inch over 6.000 add (in.)	0.002	0.0025	0.003
	Over 12.000 For each inch over 12.000 add (in.)	0.0025	0.004	0.006
D HEIGHT	Single Cavity 0.000–1.000	0.006	0.008	0.012
	Multiple Cavity 0.000–1.000	0.008	0.010	0.014
	For each inch over 1.000 add (in.)	0.002	0.004	0.005
WALL E BOTTOM	0.000 to C.100	0.004	0.006	0.009
	0.100 to C.200	0.004	0.006	0.009
	0.200 to C.300	0.004	0.006	0.009

SIDEWALL F DIMENSION*## Section thickness to be held relatively constant.

F' Variation in wall thickness due to eccentricity, 0.005–0.007 in. Interlocking reduces this.

DRAFT ALLOWANCE	1/8°	1/4°	1°

DWG. CODE		Fine	Standard	Coarse
D, E	Compression Molded For projected area over 20 sq. in.	Add 0.001 in. for each additional 10 sq. in.	Add 0.002 in. for each additional 10 sq. in.	Add 0.003 in. for each additional 10 sq. in.

Transfer, Jet, or Injection molded Any area

PLUS OR MINUS TOLERANCE IN THOUSANDTHS OF AN IN. (F = Fine; S = Standard; C = Coarse) (scale 1–22)

		Plus or minus tolerance
D	Single cavity	F S C
D	Multiple cavity	F S C
D	For each inch of depth over 1.000 add (in.)	0.0015

\# These tolerances do not apply to screw threads, gear teeth, or fit of mating parts; dimensions in these classifications can generally be held to closer limits. These tolerances do not include allowance for aging characteristics of material.

\#\# See introduction to chapter.

‡ Tolerances shown are approximate and apply only where material is subjected to less than 50°C after molding.

TABLE 13-16

MATERIAL: *MINERAL-FILLED ALKYDS*

Plus or Minus in Thousands of An In.#

Drawing Code	Dimensions (In.)	Graph (1–30)	Fine ±	Standard ±	Coarse ±
A = Diameter or Length	0.000				
B = Diameter or Length	0.500	COARSE / STANDARD / FINE			
C = Depth	1.000				
	2.000				
	3.000				
	4.000				
	5.000				
	6.000				
	6.000 to 12.000		0.001	0.002	0.004
	For each inch over 6.000 add (in.)				
	Over 12.000				
	For each inch over 12.000 add (in.)		0.001	0.002	0.004
D HEIGHT	Single Cavity 0.000-1.000		0.001	0.002	0.004
	Multiple Cavity 0.000-1.000		0.001	0.002	0.004
	For each inch over 1.000 add (in.)				
E WALL	0.000 to 0.100		0.002	0.004	0.007
BOTTOM	0.100 to 0.200		0.002	0.004	0.007
	0.200 to 0.300		0.002	0.004	0.007

SIDEWALL F DIMENSION** : Section thickness to be held relatively constant

F′ Variation in wall thickness due to eccentricity, 0.005–0.007 in. Interlocking reduces this.

DRAFT ALLOWANCE   1/8°   1/4°   1°

DWG. CODE				
D, E	Compression Molded For projected area over 20 sq. in.	Fine	Add	in. for each additional 10 sq. in.
		Standard	Add	in. for each additional 10 sq. in.
		Coarse	Add	in. for each additional 10 sq. in.

Transfer, Jet, or Injection molded Any area

PLUS OR MINUS TOLERANCE IN THOUSANDTHS OF AN IN. (F = Fine; S = Standard; C = Coarse)

1 2 3 4 5 6 7 8 9 10 11 12 13 14 15 16 17 18 19 20 21 22

D	Single cavity
D	Multiple cavity
D	For each inch of depth over 1.000 add (in.)

\# These tolerances do not apply to screw threads, gear teeth, or fit of mating parts; dimensions in these classifications can generally be held to closer limits. These tolerances do not include allowance for aging characteristics of material.

** See introduction to chapter.

TABLE 13-17

MATERIAL: CELLULOSE ACETATE, MEDIUM-FLOW

Plus or Minus in Thousands of An In.# — scale 1 to 30

Graph area with diagonal lines labeled COARSE, STANDARD, FINE (applies to Drawing Code dimensions A, B, C for 0.000 to 6.000 in.)

Drawing Code / Dimensions (In.)	Fine ±	Standard ±	Coarse ±
A = Diameter or Length			
B = Diameter or Length			
C = Depth			
0.000			
0.500			
1.000			
2.000			
3.000			
4.000			
5.000			
6.000			
D HEIGHT			
6.000 to 12.000	0.003	0.005	0.007
For each inch over 6.000 add (in.)	0.004	0.006	0.009
Over 12.000	0.003	0.005	0.008
For each inch over 12.000 add (in.)	0.003	0.005	0.008
E WALL			
Single Cavity 0.000-1.000	0.002	0.002	0.002
Multiple Cavity 0.000-1.000	0.003	0.004	0.005
For each inch over 1.000 add (in.)	0.004	0.005	0.006
BOTTOM WALL E			
0.000 to 0.100	0.005	0.006	0.007
0.100 to 0.200			
0.200 to 0.300			
SIDEWALL F DIMENSION ##	Section thickness to be held relatively constant		
DRAFT ALLOWANCE	1/8°	1/2°	1°

\# These tolerances do not apply to screw threads, gear teeth, or fit of mating parts; dimensions in these classifications can generally be held to closer limits. These tolerances do not include allowance for aging characteristics of material.

\## See introduction to chapter.

TABLE 13-18

MATERIAL: CELLULOSE ACETATE BUTYRATE, MEDIUM-FLOW

Drawing Code	Dimensions (In.)	Fine ±	Standard ±	Coarse ±
A = Diameter or Length	0.000			
B = Diameter or Length	0.500			
C = Depth	1.000			
	2.000			
	3.000			
	4.000			
	5.000			
	6.000			
	6.000 to 12,000 For each inch over 6,000 add (in.)	0.003	0.004	0.007
	Over 12,000 For each inch over 12,000 add (in.)	0.003	0.005	0.007
D HEIGHT	Single Cavity 0.000–1.000	0.003	0.005	0.007
	Multiple Cavity 0.000–1.000	0.003	0.005	0.007
	For each inch over 1.000 add (in.)	0.002	0.002	0.002
E WALL / BOTTOM	0.000 to 0.100	0.002	0.004	0.006
	0.100 to 0.200	0.004	0.006	0.008
	0.200 to 0.300	0.006	0.008	0.010
SIDEWALL F DIMENSION ##	Section thickness to be held relatively constant			
DRAFT ALLOWANCE		1/8°	1/4°	1°

\# These tolerances do not apply to screw threads, gear teeth, or fit of mating parts; dimensions in these classifications can generally be held to closer limits. These tolerances do not include allowance for aging characteristics of material.

\#\# See introduction to chapter.

TABLE 13-19

MATERIAL: ETHYL CELLULOSE, MEDIUM-FLOW

Drawing Code	Dimensions (In.)		Plus or Minus in Thousands of An In.#		
			Fine ±	Standard ±	Coarse ±
A = Diameter or Length B = Diameter or Length C = Depth	0.000 0.500 1.000 2.000 3.000 4.000 5.000 6.000				
	6.000 to 12.000 For each inch over 6.000 add (in.)		0.0025	0.0045	0.007
	Over 12.000 For each inch over 12.000 add (in.)		0.003	0.005	0.008
D HEIGHT	Single Cavity 0.000-1.000		0.003	0.005	0.007
	Multiple Cavity 0.000-1.000		0.003	0.006	0.008
	For each inch over 1.000 add (in.)		0.002	0.002	0.002
WALL E BOTTOM	0.000 to 0.100		0.003	0.005	0.008
	0.100 to 0.200		0.005	0.007	0.010
	0.200 to 0.300		0.007	0.009	0.012
SIDEWALL F DIMENSION##	Section thickness to be held relatively constant				
DRAFT ALLOWANCE			1/8°	1/2°	1°

\# These tolerances do not apply to screw threads, gear teeth, or fit of mating parts; dimensions in these classifications can generally be held to closer limits. These tolerances do not include allowance for aging characteristics of material.

\#\# See introduction to chapter.

TABLE 13-20

MATERIAL: METHYL METHACRYLATE, GENERAL-PURPOSE

Plus or Minus in Thousands of An In.# (scale 1–30, with diagonal lines labeled COARSE, STANDARD, FINE)

Drawing Code	Dimensions (In.)	Fine ±	Standard ±	Coarse ±
A = Diameter or Length B = Diameter or Length C = Depth	0.000 0.500 1.000 2.000 3.000 4.000 5.000 6.000			
	6.000 to 12.000	0.003	0.005	0.007
	For each inch over 6.000 add (in.)	0.004	0.006	0.009
	Over 12.000 For each inch over 12.000 add (in.)			
D HEIGHT	Single Cavity 0.000–1.000	0.0025	0.0045	0.0075
	Multiple Cavity 0.000–1.000	0.003	0.005	0.008
	For each inch over 1.000 add (in.)	0.002	0.004	0.006
E BOTTOM WALL	0.000 to 0.100	0.003	0.005	0.006
	0.100 to 0.200	0.003	0.005	0.007
	0.200 to 0.300	0.004	0.005	0.008
SIDEWALL F DIMENSION##	Section thickness to be held relatively constant			
DRAFT ALLOWANCE		1/4°	1/2°	1°
		1/2°	1°	

These tolerances do not apply to screw threads, gear teeth, or fit of mating parts; dimensions in these classifications can generally be held to closer limits. These tolerances do not include allowance for aging characteristics of material.

See introduction to chapter.

TABLE 13-21

MATERIAL: METHYL METHACRYLATE, HEAT-RESISTANT

Plus or Minus in Thousands of An In.#

Drawing Code	Dimensions (In.)	Fine ±	Standard ±	Coarse ±
A = Diameter or Length	0.000			
B = Diameter or Length	0.500			
C = Depth	1.000	COARSE		
	2.000	STANDARD		
	3.000	FINE		
	4.000			
	5.000			
	6.000			
	6.000 to 12.000	0.003	0.005	0.007
	For each inch over 6.000 add (in.)	0.004	0.006	0.009
	Over 12.000			
	For each inch over 12.000 add (in.)			
D HEIGHT	Single Cavity 0.000-1.000	0.0025	0.0045	0.0075
	Multiple Cavity 0.000-1.000	0.003	0.005	0.008
	For each inch over 1.000 add (in.)	0.002	0.004	0.006
E BOTTOM WALL	0.000 to 0.100	0.003	0.005	0.006
	0.100 to 0.200	0.003	0.005	0.007
	0.200 to 0.300	0.004	0.005	0.008
SIDEWALL F DIMENSION #*	Section thickness to be held relatively constant			
DRAFT ALLOWANCE		1/4°	3/4°	1 1/2°

\# These tolerances do not apply to screw threads, gear teeth, or fit of mating parts; dimensions in these classifications can generally be held to closer limits. These tolerances do not include allowance for aging characteristics of material.

\#* See introduction to chapter.

TABLE 13-22

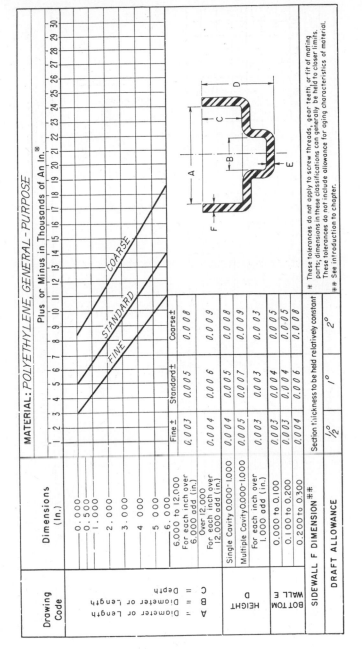

MATERIAL: POLYETHYLENE, GENERAL-PURPOSE

Plus or Minus in Thousands of An In.#

Drawing Code		Dimensions (In.)	Fine ±	Standard ±	Coarse ±
A = Diameter or Length		0.000			
B = Diameter or Length		0.500			
C = Depth		1.000			
		2.000			
		3.000			
		4.000			
		5.000			
		6.000			
		6.000 to 12.000	0.003	0.005	0.008
		For each inch over 6.000 add (in.)	0.004	0.006	0.009
		Over 12.000			
		For each inch over 12.000 add (in.)	0.004	0.005	0.008
D	HEIGHT	Single Cavity 0.000-1.000	0.004	0.005	0.009
		Multiple Cavity 0.000-1.000	0.005	0.007	0.009
		For each inch over 1.000 add (in.)	0.003	0.003	0.003
E	BOTTOM WALL	0.000 to 0.100	0.003	0.004	0.005
		0.100 to 0.200	0.003	0.004	0.005
		0.200 to 0.300	0.004	0.006	0.008
SIDEWALL F DIMENSION ##			Section thickness to be held relatively constant		
DRAFT ALLOWANCE			1/2°	1°	2°

\# These tolerances do not apply to screw threads, gear teeth, or fit of mating parts; dimensions in these classifications can generally be held to closer limits. These tolerances do not include allowance for aging characteristics of material.

\## See introduction to chapter.

TABLE 13-23

MATERIAL: POLYSTYRENE–ACRYLONITRILE COPOLYMER

Plus or Minus in Thousands of An In.#

Drawing Code		Dimensions (In.)	Fine ±	Standard ±	Coarse ±
A = Diameter or Length		0.000			
B = Diameter or Length		0.500			
C = Depth		1.000			
		2.000			
		3.000			
		4.000			
		5.000			
		6.000			
		6.000 to 12.000	0.002	0.004	0.006
		For each inch over 6.000 add (in.)	0.003	0.005	0.007
		Over 12.000			
		For each inch over 12.000 add (in.)			
HEIGHT	D	Single Cavity 0.000–1.000	0.002	0.004	0.006
		Multiple Cavity 0.000–1.000	0.002	0.004	0.006
		For each inch over 1.000 add (in.)	0.002	0.002	0.002
BOTTOM WALL	E	0.000 to 0.100	0.002	0.003	0.004
		0.100 to 0.200	0.002	0.003	0.004
		0.200 to 0.300	0.003	0.004	0.005
SIDEWALL F DIMENSION #.##		Section thickness to be held relatively constant			
DRAFT ALLOWANCE			1/4°	1/2°	1°

\# These tolerances do not apply to screw threads, gear teeth, or fit of mating parts; dimensions in these classifications can generally be held to closer limits. These tolerances do not include allowance for aging characteristics of material.

\#\# See introduction to chapter.

TABLE 13-24

MATERIAL: POLYSTYRENE-BUTADIENE COPOLYMER

Plus or Minus in Thousands of An In.#

Drawing Code	Dimensions (In.)	Fine ±	Standard ±	Coarse ±
A = Diameter or Length	0.000			
B = Diameter or Length	0.500			
C = Depth	1.000			
	2.000			
	3.000			
	4.000			
	5.000			
	6.000			
	6.000 to 12.000	0.002	0.004	0.006
	For each inch over 6.000 add (in.)	0.003	0.005	0.007
	Over 12.000 Single Cavity 0.000-1.000	0.002	0.004	0.006
	Multiple Cavity 0.000-1.000	0.002	0.004	0.006
	For each inch over 12.000 add (in.) / For each inch over 1.000 add (in.)	0.002	0.002	0.002
D HEIGHT	0.000 to 0.100	0.002	0.003	0.004
E WALL / BOTTOM	0.100 to 0.200	0.002	0.003	0.004
	0.200 to 0.300	0.003	0.004	0.005
	Section thickness to be held relatively constant			
SIDEWALL F DIMENSION ##				
DRAFT ALLOWANCE		1/4°	1/2°	1°

These tolerances do not apply to screw threads, gear teeth, or fit of mating parts; dimensions in these classifications can generally be held to closer limits. These tolerances do not include allowance for aging characteristics of material.

See introduction to chapter.

TABLE 13.25

MATERIAL: POLYSTYRENE, GENERAL-PURPOSE AND HEAT-RESISTANT

Drawing Code	Dimensions (In.)	Fine ±	Standard ±	Coarse ±
A = Diameter or Length / B = Diameter or Length / C = Depth	0.000			
	0.500			
	1.000			
	2.000			
	3.000			
	4.000			
	5.000			
	6.000			
	6.000 to 12.000 — For each inch over 6.000 add (in.)	0.002	0.004	0.0065
	Over 12.000 — For each inch over 12.000 add (in.)	0.006	0.008	0.012
D HEIGHT	Single Cavity 0.000-1.000	0.002	0.004	0.007
	Multiple Cavity 0.000-1.000	0.002	0.004	0.007
	For each inch over 1.000 add (in.)	0.0015	0.0015	0.0015
E BOTTOM WALL	0.000 to 0.100	0.002	0.003	0.004
	0.100 to 0.200	0.003	0.005	0.007
	0.200 to 0.300	0.006	0.009	0.011
F SIDEWALL	SIDEWALL F DIMENSION ##	Section thickness to be held relatively constant		
	DRAFT ALLOWANCE	¼°	½°	1°

Plus or Minus in Thousands of An In.#
(scale: 1 2 3 4 5 6 7 8 9 10 11 12 13 14 15 16 17 18 19 20 21 22 23 24 25 26 27 28 29 30)

COARSE
STANDARD
FINE

\# These tolerances do not apply to screw threads, gear teeth, or fit of mating parts; dimensions in these classifications can generally be held to closer limits. These tolerances do not include allowance for aging characteristics of material.

\#\# See introduction to chapter.

TABLE 13-26

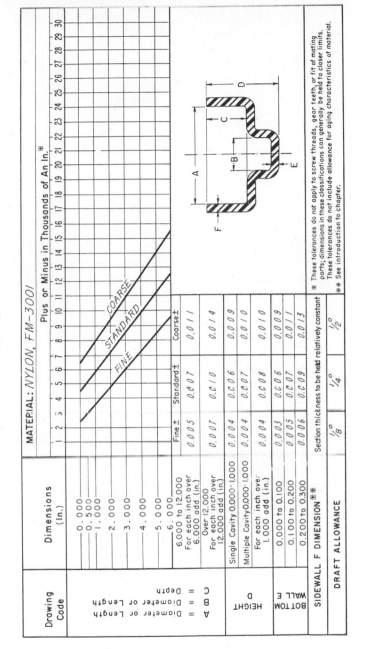

MATERIAL: NYLON, FM-3001

Drawing Code	Dimensions (In.)		Fine ±	Standard ±	Coarse ±
A = Diameter or Length	0.000				
B = Diameter or Length	0.500				
C = Depth	1.000				
	2.000				
	3.000				
	4.000				
	5.000				
	6.000		0.005	0.007	0.011
	6.000 to 12.000 For each inch over 6.000 add (in.)		0.007	0.010	0.014
D	Over 12.000 For each inch over 12.000 add (in.)				
	Single Cavity 0.000-1.000		0.004	0.006	0.009
	Multiple Cavity 0.000-1.000		0.004	0.007	0.010
HEIGHT	For each inch over 1.000 add (in.)		0.004	0.008	0.010
BOTTOM WALL E	0.000 to 0.100		0.003	0.006	0.009
	0.100 to 0.200		0.005	0.007	0.011
	0.200 to 0.300		0.006	0.009	0.013
SIDEWALL F DIMENSION **#	Section thickness to be held relatively constant				
DRAFT ALLOWANCE			1/8°	1/4°	1/2°

Plus or Minus in Thousands of An In.#

These tolerances do not apply to screw threads, gear teeth, or fit of mating parts; dimensions in these classifications can generally be held to closer limits. These tolerances do not include allowance for aging characteristics of material.

See introduction to chapter.

TABLE 13-27

MATERIAL: NYLON, FM-10001

Drawing Code	Dimensions (In.)	Fine ±	Standard ±	Coarse ±
A = Diameter or Length	0.000			
B = Diameter or Length	0.500			
C = Depth	1.000			
	2.000			
	3.000			
	4.000			
	5.000			
	6.000 to 12.000	0.005	0.007	0.011
	For each inch over 6.000 add (in.)	0.007	0.010	0.014
	Over 12.000			
	For each inch over 12.000 add (in.)			
D HEIGHT	Single Cavity 0.000-1.000	0.004	0.006	0.009
	Multiple Cavity 0.000-1.000	0.004	0.007	0.010
	For each inch over 1.000 add (in.)	0.004	0.008	0.010
E WALL BOTTOM	0.000 to 0.100	0.003	0.006	0.009
	0.100 to 0.200	0.005	0.007	0.011
	0.200 to 0.300	0.006	0.009	0.013
SIDEWALL F DIMENSION ##	Section thickness to be held relatively constant			
DRAFT ALLOWANCE		1/8°	1/4°	1/2°

Plus or Minus in Thousands of An In. #

COARSE / STANDARD / FINE

\# These tolerances do not apply to screw threads, gear teeth, or fit of mating parts; dimensions in these classifications can generally be held to closer limits. These tolerances do not include allowance for aging characteristics of material.

\#\# See introduction to chapter.

TABLE 13-28

MATERIAL: VINYLS, DUROMETER HARDNESS TYPE A 70±5

Plus or Minus in Thousands of An In.# (chart with COARSE, STANDARD, FINE lines, scale 1–30)

Drawing Code		Dimensions (In.)	Fine±	Standard±	Coarse±
A = Diameter or Length		0.000			
B = Diameter or Length		0.500			
C = Depth		1.000			
		2.000			
		3.000			
		4.000			
		5.000			
		6.000			
		6.000 to 12.000 For each inch over 6.000 add (in.)	0.002	0.004	0.006
		Over 12.000 For each inch over 12.000 add (in.)	0.004	0.006	0.009
D	HEIGHT	Single Cavity 0.000-1.000	0.003	0.005	0.008
		Multiple Cavity 0.000-1.000	0.003	0.005	0.009
		For each inch over 1.000 add (in.)	0.001	0.001	0.001
E	WALL BOTTOM	0.000 to 0.100	0.002	0.003	0.005
		0.100 to 0.200	0.003	0.004	0.007
		0.200 to 0.300	0.005	0.006	0.009
SIDEWALL F DIMENSION ##		Section thickness to be held relatively constant			
DRAFT ALLOWANCE			1/4°	1/2°	1°

\# These tolerances do not apply to screw threads, gear teeth, or fit of mating parts; dimensions in these classifications can generally be held to closer limits.

These tolerances do not include allowance for aging characteristics of material.

\## See introduction to chapter.

TABLE 13-29

MATERIAL: VINYLS, DUROMETER HARDNESS TYPE A 80±5

Drawing Code		Dimensions (In.)	Fine ±	Standard ±	Coarse ±
A = Diameter or Length		0.000			
		0.500			
		1.000			
B = Diameter or Length		2.000			
C = Depth		3.000			
		4.000			
		5.000			
		6.000			
		6.000 to 12.000 For each inch over 6.000 add (in.)	0.002	0.004	0.006
		Over 12.000 For each inch over 12.000 add (in.)	0.004	0.006	0.009
D HEIGHT		Single Cavity 0.000-1.000	0.003	0.005	0.008
		Multiple Cavity 0.000-1.000	0.003	0.005	0.009
		For each inch over 1.000 add (in.)	0.001	0.001	0.001
E WALL BOTTOM		0.000 to 0.100	0.002	0.003	0.005
		0.100 to 0.200	0.003	0.004	0.007
		0.200 to 0.300	0.005	0.006	0.009
SIDEWALL F DIMENSION##		Section thickness to be held relatively constant			
DRAFT ALLOWANCE			¼°	½°	1°

\# These tolerances do not apply to screw threads, gear teeth, or fit of mating parts; dimensions in these classifications can generally be held to closer limits. These tolerances do not include allowance for aging characteristics of material.

\## See introduction to chapter.

TABLE 13-30

MATERIAL: *VINYLS, DUROMETER HARDNESS TYPE A 90±5*

Drawing Code	Dimensions (In.)	Plus or Minus in Thousands of An In.*		
		Fine ±	Standard ±	Coarse ±
A = Diameter or Length	0.000			
B = Diameter or Length	0.500			
C = Depth	1.000			
	2.000			
	3.000			
	4.000			
	5.000			
	6.000			
	6.000 to 12.000 For each inch over 6.000 add (in.)	0.002	0.004	0.006
	Over 12.000 For each inch over 12.000 add (in.)	0.004	0.006	0.009
D HEIGHT	Single Cavity 0.000-1.000	0.003	0.005	0.008
	Multiple Cavity 0.000-1.000	0.003	0.005	0.009
	For each inch over 1.000 add (in.)	0.001	0.001	0.001
E BOTTOM WALL	0.000 to 0.100	0.002	0.003	0.005
	0.100 to 0.200	0.003	0.004	0.007
	0.200 to 0.300	0.005	0.006	0.009
SIDEWALL F DIMENSION ##	Section thickness to be held relatively constant			
DRAFT ALLOWANCE		1/4°	1/2°	1°

* These tolerances do not apply to screw threads, gear teeth, or fit of mating parts; dimensions in these classifications can generally be held to closer limits. These tolerances do not include allowance for aging characteristics of material.

\#\# See introduction to chapter.

TABLE 13-31

MATERIAL: VINYLS, DUROMETER HARDNESS TYPE A 100±5

Plus or Minus in Thousands of An In.#

Drawing Code		Dimensions (In.)	Fine ±	Standard ±	Coarse ±
A = Diameter or Length	B = Diameter or Length	C = Depth	0.000 0.500 1.000 2.000 3.000 4.000 5.000			
		6.000 to 12.000 For each inch over 6.000 add (in.)	0.002	0.004	0.006
		Over 12.000 For each inch over 12.000 add (in.)	0.004	0.006	0.009
D HEIGHT		Single Cavity 0.000-1.000	0.003	0.005	0.008
		Multiple Cavity 0.000-1.000	0.003	0.005	0.009
		For each inch over 1.000 add (in.)	0.001	0.001	0.001
WALL E BOTTOM		0.000 to 0.100	0.002	0.003	0.005
		0.100 to 0.200	0.003	0.004	0.007
		0.200 to 0.300	0.005	0.006	0.009
SIDEWALL F DIMENSION #‡		Section thickness to be held relatively constant			
DRAFT ALLOWANCE			¼°	½°	1°

Chart curves labeled: COARSE, STANDARD, FINE

These tolerances do not apply to screw threads, gear teeth, or fit of mating parts; dimensions in these classifications can generally be held to closer limits. These tolerances do not include allowance for aging characteristics of material.

‡ See introduction to chapter.

14. Design Standards for Inserts

The use of inserts in every type of molding operation presents certain difficulties, which should be recognized by the user. Where inserts are required for purposes of adding to the strength of the hold-down screws, for reasons of added life to the screw thread, such as is required where covers must be frequently removed, etc., for electrical conduction, or for numerous other reasons, it must be realized that the addition of inserts will slow down the molding cycle and will add to the cost of production. However, ingenious design frequently demonstrates that inserts may be eliminated or that the metal parts may be added subsequent to molding, and that such metal parts may be added by automatic means at a rate faster than is possible by incorporating such parts in the molding operation. Very often a tapped hole in the plastic, with a drive screw, a self-tapping screw, or bolt and nut can be used, with resultant saving in the cost of the molded article.

Inserts of many types are used: those made on screw machines and those made by cold forging, stamping and drawing. The discussion in this chapter is divided, rather loosely, according to these types, but general instructions and precautions given under one heading are largely applicable to the other also. Inserts of various designs are shown in Fig. 14-1.

Maintaining a proper accuracy in various dimensions of inserts has always been a problem with the plastics industry as well as the insert manufacturers, mainly because of the lack of information on design and standardization of dimensions. The technicians who were selected to prepare this engineering standard have endeavored to compile their own knowledge as well as that of the entire plastics industry. Engineers having a reasonable knowledge of plastics and an acquaintance with inserts and their use will find this standard of value in the proper design and selection of inserts.

Screw-Machine Inserts

Dimensions and Tolerances. Dimensions and tolerances for the usual types of male and female inserts in Fig. 14-2 and Table 14-1 are compiled with the cooperation of the National Screw Machine Products Association as being practicable for machining as a single operation on an automatic screw machine, and hence are most economical.

Note that the dimensions given for tapped inserts apply only to nonferrous metals where the depth of usable tapping is not more than $1\frac{1}{2}$ times the tap diameter. On A-2 (minor diameter) and C (length of tapped inserts)

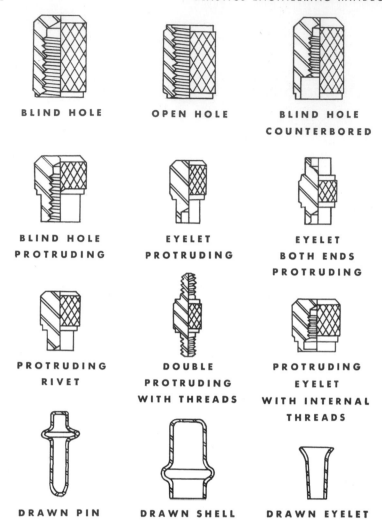

BLIND HOLE   OPEN HOLE   BLIND HOLE
                                       COUNTERBORED

BLIND HOLE   EYELET   EYELET
PROTRUDING   PROTRUDING   BOTH ENDS
                                       PROTRUDING

PROTRUDING   DOUBLE   PROTRUDING
RIVET   PROTRUDING   EYELET
                    WITH THREADS   WITH INTERNAL
                                       THREADS

DRAWN PIN   DRAWN SHELL   DRAWN EYELET

Fig. 14-1. Usual Types of Inserts.

the maximum "standard" tolerance should be specified whenever possible. However, for closer tolerances, "precision" can be specified when necessary. To maintain the "precision" tolerance, reaming and other additional operations will be necessary, at additional cost.

If steel inserts are required, Fig. 14-2 and Table 14-1 cannot be used in design without several modifications which will increase the cost over that of inserts made of brass or, in special cases, of aluminum.

Minimum wall thickness of metal in the inserts depends entirely upon

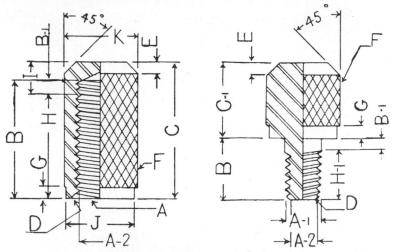

Fig. 14-2. Tolerance Index*

A	Tap Size "American National" Class 2	
A-1	Major Diameter	
A-2	Minor Diameter "Regular" Tolerance	+ .0025"
	"Precision" Tolerance	− .0005"
B	Depth of Minor and Length of Major Diameter	
B-1	Number of Unusable Threads from Bottom and Top	
C	Length "Regular" Tolerance	± .010"
	"Precision" Tolerance	± .001"
C-1	Length of Body Male Insert	± .010"
D*	Thread Chamfer	45° ± .005"
E*	Body Chamfer	45° ± .010"
F	Knurl	
G	Length of Sealing Diameter Minimum 1/32"	
H	Length of Usable Thread 1½ × Diameter	
H-1	Length of Usable Thread H-1 + B-1 = B	
I	Amount to Add to H to Obtain C. H + I = C.	
J	Sealing Diameter	± .002"
K	Minimum Bar Stock Diameter	

*See Table 14-1

the desired accuracy of the inside dimensions of the insert. If too thin a wall of metal is used, the combination of stress caused by shrinkage of the plastic and by molding pressure may collapse the wall of the insert, so that the inside diameter will be out of the range of specified tolerances. Table 14-1 shows the minimum recommended diameters of bar stock for various sizes of inserts.

Cold-Forged Inserts

In general, the volume or quantity needed to ensure economical production by cold-forging is about the same as that needed by other processes. As

TABLE 14-1. DIMENSIONS AND TOLERANCES*

Nonferrous inserts which have a usable thread length not more than 1½ times the tap diameter

COARSE	FINE	K	J	TAP DRILL	A-2	A-1 MAXIMUM	A-1 MINIMUM	B-1	I	D AND E	KNURL
2-56		3/16	9/64	#50	.0700	0.0860	0.0820	3	3/32	1/64	Fine
	2-64	3/16	9/64	#49	.0730	.0860	.0822	3	3/32	1/64	Fine
3-48		7/32	5/32	#45	.0820	.0990	.0946	3	7/64	1/64	Fine
	3-56	7/32	5/32	#45	.0820	.0990	.0950	3	3/32	1/64	Fine
4-40		7/32	11/64	#43	.0890	.1120	.1072	2½	7/64	1/64	Fine
	4-48	7/32	11/64	#42	.0935	.1120	.1076	2½	7/64	1/64	Fine
5-40		1/4	3/16	#37	.1040	.1250	.1202	2½	7/64	1/32	Med.
	5-44	1/4	3/16	#37	.1040	.1250	.1204	2½	7/64	1/32	Med.
6-32		1/4	13/64	#33	.1130	.1380	.1326	2½	5/32	1/32	Med.
	6-40	1/4	13/64	#32	.1160	.1380	.1332	2½	9/64	1/32	Med.
8-32		9/32	7/32	#29	.1360	.1640	.1586	2½	5/32	1/32	Med.
	8-36	9/32	7/32	#28	.1405	.1640	.1590	2½	9/64	1/32	Med.
10-24		5/16	1/4	#23	.1540	.1900	.1834	2½	3/16	1/32	Med.
	10-32	5/16	1/4	#20	.1610	.1900	.1846	2½	5/32	1/32	Med.
12-24		3/8	5/16	#16	.1770	.2160	.2094	2½	13/64	3/64	Med.
	12-28	3/8	5/16	#13	.1850	.2160	.2098	2½	11/64	3/64	Med.
1/4-20		13/32	11/32	#6	.2040	.2500	.2428	2	13/64	3/64	Coarse
	1/4-28	13/32	11/32	7/32	.2187	.2500	.2438	2	11/64	3/64	Coarse
5/16-18		15/32	13/32	G	.2610	.3125	.3043	2	7/32	3/64	Coarse
	5/16-24	15/32	13/32	I	.2720	.3125	.3059	2	13/64	3/64	Coarse
3/8-16		9/16	15/32	O	.3160	.3750	.3660	2	1/4	3/64	Coarse
	3/8-24	9/16	15/32	Q	.3320	.3750	.3684	2	7/32	3/64	Coarse
7/16-14		5/8	17/32	U	.3680	.4375	.4277	2	9/32	3/64	Coarse
	7/16-20	5/8	17/32	25/64	.3906	.4375	.4303	2	1/4	3/64	Coarse
1/2-13		11/16	19/32	27/64	.4218	.5000	.4896	2	5/16	1/16	Coarse
	1/2-20	11/16	19/32	29/64	.4531	.5000	.4928	2	17/64	1/16	Coarse
9/16-12		3/4	21/32	31/64	.4843	.5625	.5513	2	11/32	1/16	Coarse
	9/16-18	3/4	21/32	33/64	.5156	.5625	.5543	2	9/32	1/16	Coarse
5/8-11		13/16	23/32	35/64	.5469	.6250	.6132	2	3/8	1/16	Coarse
	5/8-18	13/16	23/32	37/64	.5781	.6250	.6168	2	5/16	1/16	Coarse

* See Fig. 14-2.

second operations are required, such as turning, drilling, tapping and others, larger quantities are needed.

In the discussion, below, of specific problems, the utility of cold-forged inserts will become apparent. None of the cold-forged inserts shown has been machined, but they could be, of course, by either automatic or single-purpose equipment. If machining, drilling, reaming or tapping is involved, the tolerances are the same as those for screw-machine inserts given in Table 14-1.

There are no specific formulas controlling the individual relationships of the diameters and widths of collars to the shank or controlling the kind and variety of shapes, like ribbed, finned, pinchneck, hexagon and so on, which may be combined with other symmetrical or unsymmetrical shapes in one piece. For each problem, therefore, the solution should be reached through cooperation between the designer of the molded piece and the manufacturer of the insert.

Materials. Almost any metal can be cold-worked, but cold-working grades of the following are preferred in the order named:

1. aluminum and aluminum alloys
2. brass
3. copper and copper alloys
4. carbon steels
5. alloy steels
6. stainless steel
7. silver and other precious metals.

Tolerances without Finishing Operations. The tolerances given for the parts in the layouts of Figs. 14-3 and 14-4 are those ordered, although closer ones could be met if necessary. Tolerances for any element such as length or diameter vary with the material and with the sizes and proportions of the piece, since they in turn determine the equipment or method of heading to be used.

In general, the following tolerances can be considered as commercial without finishing operation, although in some cases special care must be exercised to meet them:

length	$\pm$ 0.010 in. (maximum)
fillets	sharp or round, as specified
diameter	0.002 in. (minimum)
squareness, shoulders or collars with shank	$\pm$ 1° maximum

Tolerances with Finishing Operations. Whatever tolerance is needed can be met by adding finishing operations. For example, aircraft studs, bolts and specials are commonly made in production today to tolerances as close as 0.0005 in.

Special Inserts

It would be an endless task to cover the entire field of special inserts. Some of the more important phases of design will be covered in the succeeding paragraphs.

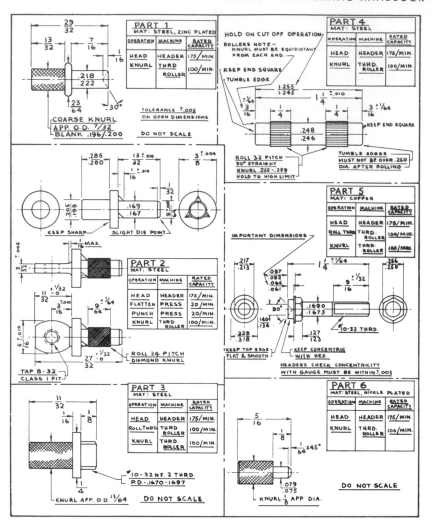

Fig. 14-3. Cold-Forged Inserts.

The design of special inserts for various applications requires as much engineering as other phases of preliminary work, if not more. In many cases too little significance is attached to planning special inserts. The design engineer, the manufacturer of the insert, and the molder must cooperate to obtain simplicity of design, which will result in the production of satisfactory articles and will promote economical production.

Typical applications of special inserts are commutators, wire-and-insert connections on telephone handsets, and radio resistors where carbon or other

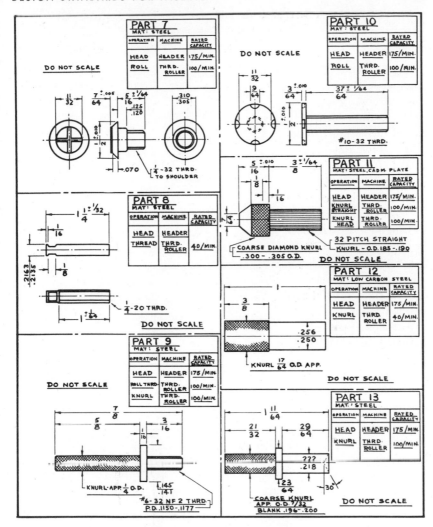

Fig. 14-4. Cold-Forged Inserts.

elements are molded inside of the plastic. A radio condenser is a good example of a built-up laminated insert.

Selection of Metal for Inserts

The correct selection of metal for inserts is essential because of the differences in coefficient of expansion between the various metals and plastics (see Table 14-2).

TABLE 14-2. COEFFICIENT OF THERMAL EXPANSION (30 TO 60°C)
PER DEGREE CENTIGRADE

Material		Coefficient $\times 10^6$
cellulose acetate		80–160
cellulose acetate butyrate		110–170
ethyl cellulose		100–140
melamine-formaldehyde		25–30
methyl methacrylate resin		70–90
nylon—Type FM-10001		103
phenolics:		
general-purpose		39
medium-impact		38
medium-impact—CFI-5		33
high-impact—CFI-10		29
high-impact—CFI-20		22
medium-heat-resistant		34
high-heat-resistant		26
electrical general-purpose		35
low-loss		19
arc-resistant		49
polyethylene		180
polystyrene		60–80
urea-formaldehyde		25–30
vinyl chloride-acetate resin		69
vinylidene chloride resin		190
aluminum 2S	99.2% Al	23.94
brass, ordinary	67 Cu, 33 Zn	18.5
bronze, commercial	90 Cu, 10 Zn	18.8
copper	99.9+	17.71
C.R. steel		14.
Monel	60 Ni, 12 Fe, 11 Cr, 2 Mn	14.
nickel		12.9
phosphor bronze		16.8
phosphor bronze 30	95.5 Cu, 4 Sn, 1 Zn	18.90
silver, German		18.
silver, standard	92.5 Ag, 7.5 Cu	18.
solder, half-and-half		24.
stainless steel	90–2 Fe + 8 Cr, 0.4 Mn, 0.12 C	11.
steel	99 Fe, 1 C	12.
zinc	95 Zn, 5 Al	28.

Minimum Wall Thickness of Material Around Inserts

The thickness of the wall of plastic required around inserts depends upon (1) whether the material is thermoplastic or thermosetting, (2) the type of material within each group, (3) the shrinkage of the material, (4) the modulus of elasticity and (5) the coefficient of expansion of the material, (6) the coefficient of expansion of the metal used in the inserts, (7) the temperature range over which the molded article will have to function, (8) the moisture-sensitivity of the plastic, (9) any loss of flexibility caused by aging, and especially (10) the design of the insert.

Very often the molded article is designed first and the necessary inserts then fitted into the remaining space. If inserts are required, they should be considered first and then the molded article designed around them. The shape and form of the insert governs the wall thickness of the plastic to a great degree, especially when the inserts are of irregular shape (rectangular, square, star, or of any other shape having sharp corners).

The two main factors in the properties, especially of phenolic, urea and melamine materials, are modulus of elasticity and the ability of the material to cold-flow after curing so that it can stretch slightly without cracking. No one property of the material will solve the problem. For instance, a material having a low shrinkage of 0.002 in. per in. but having a very rigid character will crack. Other materials which have a shrinkage of 0.010 in. per in. but are capable of being stretched will not crack despite a minimum thickness of wall. It is impossible to set up comprehensive standards of wall thickness of material in relationship to diameters of inserts, particularly for some of the special designs. An insert $\frac{1}{4}$ in. in diameter requires a $\frac{1}{8}$-in. wall, while an insert 6 in. in diameter might require $1\frac{1}{2}$-in. wall of material, depending upon the factors mentioned. Each individual article presents different problems and must be engineered according to the design of the insert and the material used. Table 14-3 shows recommended minimum wall thicknesses with plain round inserts for various plastics

Anchorage

Firm and permanent anchorage of inserts is essential, and since there is no chemical or natural adherence between plastics and metal inserts, anchorage must be obtained by mechanical means. The slight anchorage that is obtained by the shrinkage of plastic around the insert is never sufficient.

Inserts must be anchored sufficiently to prevent turning when torque is applied and to prevent pulling out of the plastic when subjected to tension. However, internal stresses in the molded plastic must be kept to a minimum.

In the early days of plastics, it was customary to use hexagon stock for inserts (Fig. 14-5). This is mechanically incorrect except in some special applications. Hexagonal stock provides torsional anchorage only. Grooves must be machined to obtain sufficient anchorage in tension. Combinations

TABLE 14-3. WALL THICKNESS OF MATERIAL (IN.)

DIAMETERS OF INSERTS (in.):	1/8	1/4	3/8	1/2	3/4	1	1-1/4	1-1/2	1-3/4	2
phenolics:										
general-purpose	3/32	5/32	3/16	7/32	5/16	11/32	3/8	13/32	7/16	15/32
medium-impact	5/64	9/64	5/32	13/64	9/32	5/16	11/32	3/8	13/32	7/16
high-impact	1/16	1/8	9/64	3/16'	1/4	9/32	5/16'	11/32	3/8	13/32
high-heat-resistant general-purpose type	1/8	3/16	7/32	1/4	11/32	3/8	13/32	3/16	15/32	1/2
high-heat-resistant impact type	5/64	9/64	5/32	13/64	9/32	5/16	11/32	3/8	13/32	7/16
low-loss	5/32	7/32	1/4	9/32	3/8	13/32	7/16	15/32	1/2	17/32
special for large inserts	3/64	7/64	1/8	5/32	7/32	1/4	9/32	5/16	11/32	3/8
cellulose acetate	1/8	1/4	3/8	1/2	3/4	1	1-1/4	1-1/2	1-3/4	2
cellulose acetate butyrate	1/8	1/4	3/8	1/2	3/4	1	1-1/4	1-1/2	1-3/4	2
ethyl cellulose	1/16	3/32	1/8	5/32	3/16	7/32	1/4	9/32	5/16	11/32
urea-formaldehyde	3/32	5/32	3/16	7/32	5/16	11/32	3/8	13/32	7/16	15/32
*melamine-formaldehyde (a)	3/32	5/32	3/16	7/32	5/16	11/32	3/8	13/32	7/16	15/32
(b)	1/8	3/16	7/32	5/16	11/32	3/8	13/32	7/16	15/32	1/2
vinylidene chloride resin	3/32	1/8	3/16	1/4	3/8	1/2	1/4	9/32	5/16	11/32
methyl methacrylate resin	3/32	1/8	3/16	3/16	7/32	1/4	5/8	3/4	7/8	1
polystyrene	3/16	3/8	9/16	3/4	1-1/8	1-1/2	1-7/8	2-1/4	2-5/8	3
polyethylene	1/16	3/32	1/8	5/32	3/16	7/32	1/4	9/32	5/16	11/32
nylon Type FM-10001	1/16	3/32	1/8	5/32	3/16	7/32	1/4	9/32	5/16	11/32
vinyl chloride-acetate resin	3/32	1/8	3/16	1/4	3/8	1/2	5/8	3/4	7/8	1

* melamine-formaldehyde
(a) mineral-filled melamine ignition material
(b) cellulose-filled melamine, electrical grade

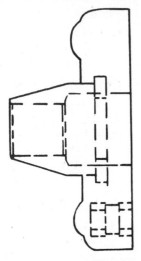

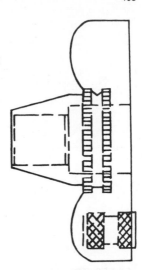

Fig. 14-5   Fig. 14-6

of sharp corners and grooves on hexagonal stock set up certain internal stresses in the plastic which often result in cracking. In practically all instances, round stock is recommended, so that a diamond knurling can be obtained. Diamond knurling provides the most satisfactory anchorage from the standpoint of torque and tension, and minimizes possible cracking around the insert. Knurling of inserts is best accomplished in screw machines with end knurling tools. The stock sizes given in Table 14-1 are ample to allow end knurling and to leave sufficient stock for a proper sealing diameter free of knurling at the open end of the insert.

Grooves can be used in conjunction with diamond knurl (Fig. 14-6). Sharp corners must be avoided when machining the grooves. When using grooves, provide one wide groove in the center of the insert rather than two grooves, one on each end. The center groove allows the material to shrink or creep toward the center and minimizes strain within the piece, and thus possible cracking. Right and wrong designs are illustrated in Figs. 14-7 and 14-8.

See p. 487 for a discussion on the anchorage of special inserts.

RADIUS

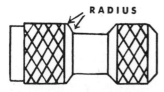

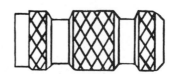

Fig. 14-7 *Right*   Fig. 14-8 *Wrong*

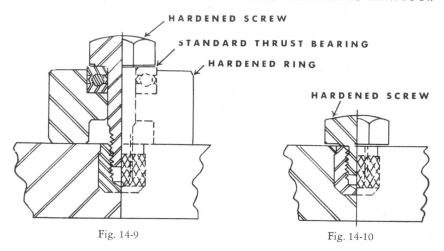

Fig. 14-9   Fig. 14-10

Torque and Tension Testing

A simple inexpensive method of test of anchorage is recommended. Figure 14-9 illustrates the method for tension and Fig. 14-10 for torsion. When conducting the torque test, a line can be scribed on the surface of the insert and the plastic in order to detect the slightest possible turn.

It is essential that special hardened and ground test screws be used to minimize friction. The screws should be well lubricated before conducting tests. A standard graduated torque wrench is recommended. Results of the tests are reported in inch-pounds of torque.

Problems in Molding Usual Types of Inserts

Floating of Inserts. Floating of inserts can be controlled or prevented by several methods:

(1) The retaining pins may be tapered slightly, starting the taper at the fillet and carrying it up to ⅓ of the length of the pin. If too much taper is allowed, making the insert too tight on the retaining pin, the insert may pull out of the material.

(2) It has been found that a straight knurl on the retaining pin provides sufficient holding surface.

(3) Square retaining pins can be used.

(4) Split pins are practical for blind-hole inserts.

(5) Spring tension pins can be used, in which the retaining pin is slotted and music wire is inserted into the slot. This method presents difficulties because the slightest flow of material into the slot prevents the spring from functioning properly.

(6)   An extended shoulder can be provided on the insert, shown in Fig. 14-2 as J (sealing), and this shoulder allowed to enter into the mold proper. This is an ideal method of preventing the insert from floating, although it is not permissible when inserts must be flush with the surface of the material.

(7)   On male inserts, a tapered hole can be provided for a drive fit if close accuracy of inserts is maintained. In such a case, 0.0005 to 0.001 in. for the depth of the hole is sufficient. If the insert is long enough, a small side hole can be drilled in the pin and music wire inserted to provide spring action. This spring action prevents the insert from floating in practically all methods of molding. The same method can be used for holding inserts in the top half of the mold.

(8)   When precise location of the insert is essential, removable threaded pins are provided in the mold. Inserts are screwed to these pins. However, this procedure increases the cost of production. Subsequent removal of the flash from the thread is in most cases avoided.

Crushing of Inserts. In transfer molding, there are very few difficulties with crushing of inserts if close tolerances on the length are maintained. In compression molding, however, when the insert must show on both sides and is molded vertically or in line with the press motion, crushing of inserts can be prevented by the use of preforms with holes to allow the preform to slip over the insert. Sliding pins are provided in the force plug, operated by spring, air, or hydraulic action. These pins are in a down position when the mold is being closed and they contact the surface of the inserts before the flow of material takes place. Since the pins are under constant pressure, no material can enter the insert. This method can be applied to blind- or open-hole inserts, and either top or bottom pins. Considerable pressure can be applied on the inserts. Actual tests on a brass insert $\frac{1}{2}$ in. long, 6 $\times$ 32 thread, with $\frac{1}{16}$-in. wall, show that the insert withstands 6 cycles of 500 lb total pressure with a reduction of 0.0005 in. in length. When the inserts are not of the through type, but are close to the rear surface of the molded part, preheating of the material and of the insert is recommended.

Flow of Material into an Open-Hole Through-Type Insert. In transfer molding, there is very little difficulty, if the length of the insert is maintained from 0.001 to 0.002 in. oversize. When the mold is closed, the insert is pinched in the mold, and it is impossible for the plastic to enter. In compression molding, however, it is impossible to prevent material from entering the hole unless pressure-type pins are used, as above, for prevention of crushing of inserts. If pressure pins cannot be used, it is advisable, especially on larger inserts, to tap the inserts undersize before molding and retap to proper size after molding. Extreme care should be taken in retapping to prevent stripping of threads, especially if considerable material has flowed into the thread. Small inserts are most economically molded with a drilled hole and tapped after molding.

Flow of Material into a Blind-Hole Insert. Difficulties with flow of material into blind-hole inserts are not as numerous as with the open-hole types. In most cases such flow is caused by loose retaining pins which allow the insert to float with the flow of material, uneven machining on the face of the insert, or knurling on the entire outside diameter of the insert, leaving extended burrs on the face which do not permit the insert to rest flat on the surface of the mold or the surface of the retaining pin. In all cases, it is good practice to provide a slight recess in the mold, accommodating the outside diameter of the insert. When the "J" diameter (Fig. 14-2) of the retaining pin is the same as that of the insert, and sharp corners can be retained in the hole, an 0.005-in. depth is sufficient to prevent the plastic from flowing in. This method allows the insert to protrude above the surface of the molded article, and this is desirable, especially when electrical contacts are made.

Protruding Inserts. Protruding inserts are frequently required and are molded in place for specific purposes. In most cases, the protruding section is used for assembly or for bearing points where mechanical action is required. In special cases, especially of large inserts where the molded article is subjected to considerable torque in order to obtain a tight connection, it is advisable to allow a hexagonal section of the insert to protrude above the molded surface for a wrench grip. Thus, strain is applied on the insert rather than on the plastic.

Perfect anchorage also is necessary. Where the wall of material is limited, the anchorage section of the insert is turned and coarsely diamond-knurled. A groove can be added to increase anchorage for tension. However, sharp corners must be avoided. In the event that the hexagonal shape is used for anchorage, sharp corners must be reduced by turning, and grooves provided for tension anchorage. Figure 14-11 shows a recommended design.

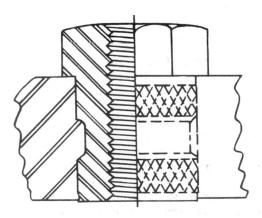

Fig. 14-11

Anchorage of Special Inserts

Thin Tubular Inserts. These inserts are extremely difficult to anchor properly. If a tubular insert is molded part way up a molded article, it is possible to invert a bead which will act as a satisfactory anchorage. The bead can be used on outside or inside inserts as shown in Figs. 14-12 and 14-13, respectively. A perforated surface around the circumference also can be used where permissible. When molding an outside tubular insert, it is often necessary to coat the inside of the insert with neoprene or vinyl to improve the bonding.

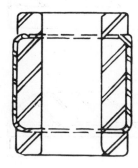

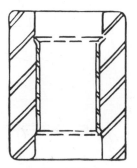

Fig. 14-12   Fig. 14-13

Flat Plate-Type Inserts. These can be anchored by means of countersunk holes wherever it is permissible. Bevel all edges of the insert or, if certain sections of the insert are not required for the functioning of the article, the section can be partially cut out and bent over to provide anchorage. This method is illustrated in Fig. 14-14. If metal inserts must be thick, bosses can be extruded and slightly flared to provide satisfactory anchorage. Anchorage may be obtained also by spot-welding lugs to the underside of the insert.

Drawn Shell-Type Inserts. Where a minimum wall thickness of plastic is specified and an insert of this type is used, extreme caution must be exercised to provide proper anchorage. Figure 14-15 shows unsatisfactory anchorage because it allows insufficient wall thickness of plastic to avoid cracking. Figure 14-16 shows an insert which is fairly well designed, and could be used to good advantage. In an insert of this type, the plastic has a chance to slide over the insert. However, to provide the best possible anchorage, the insert should be flared in slightly, as shown in Fig. 14-17. With this design, the plastic actually has a chance to anchor the insert and to creep while shrinking.

Drawn Pin-Type Inserts. Very often an insert of this type is molded into a plastic and then countersunk after molding, as illustrated in Fig. 14-18.

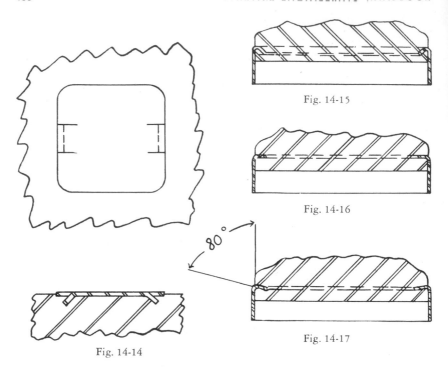

Fig. 14-15

Fig. 14-16

Fig. 14-17

Fig. 14-14

A slight bead provided as an undercut for anchorage on an insert of this type is entirely insufficient to hold the insert properly. Wherever possible, when an insert of this type is used, piercing pins should be provided in the mold, so that the insert can be pierced during the molding operation and the necessary countersink molded into the plastic. During this piercing operation, the insert is flared out to provide proper anchorage, as shown in Fig. 14-19.

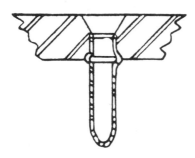

Fig. 14-18

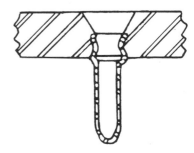

Fig. 14-19

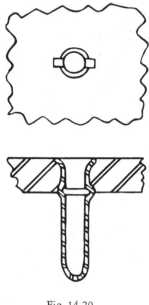

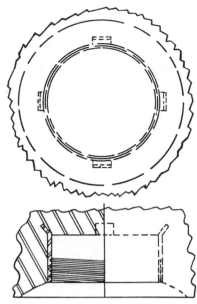

Fig. 14-20   Fig. 14-21

Figure 14-20 shows a drawn-type pin with an open end. Partial anchorage is obtained by shearing and folding two segments during the molding operation. Floating pressure-type piercing pins in the mold are recommended to minimize flow of plastic into the insert.

Drawn-Shell Threaded Inserts. As illustrated in Fig. 14-21, these are often used in large molded articles where it is not necessary to have 75 per cent of thread, or where insert space is limited. Because the shell is usually thin, approximately 50 per cent of the depth of thread is obtained. The four flared lugs provide a satisfactory anchorage in every respect. It is impossible to provide sealing points on an insert of this type, and hence flow of material into the thread must be expected. Tapping after molding is recommended for most satisfactory results.

Intricate Inserts. An intricate insert is shown in Fig. 14-22. Considerable difficulty with cracking of plastic was encountered until aluminum inserts were selected. Actually there were two factors in favor of aluminum, i.e., its coefficient of expansion and its ability to yield or spring slightly when the plastic was shrinking.

Large-Surface Inserts. It is often necessary to mold one or more large-surface inserts on one side of the plastic, as illustrated in Fig. 14-23. Inserts of this type cause nonuniform shrinkage of plastic and considerable warpage. Even when shrinkage or cooling fixtures are used, it is certain that surface *A*

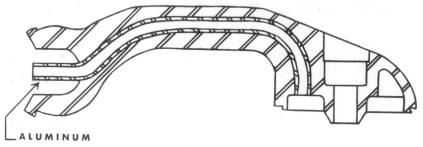

ALUMINUM

Fig. 14-22

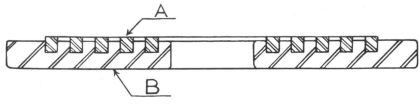

Fig. 14-23

will be convex and *B* concave after the piece is allowed to cool and age. If a flat surface is required, the surface must be machined. Best results will be obtained when the articles are allowed to age or, if possible, are baked in an oven for at least 72 hr, at suitable temperatures, before being machined.

Large Inserts with a Minimum of Wall Thickness of Material. Where a minimum thickness of a thermosetting plastic is allowed around a large insert, a special noncracking type will generally have to be used. Extreme care must be taken in the design of the insert to avoid sharp corners or other features which might create local stresses.

Irregular-Shaped Inserts. These inserts cause the greatest difficulty. Figure 14-24 shows a U-shaped insert approximately $1\frac{1}{2}$ in. long, on which two rib projections are required. From the standpoint of economy in forming this insert and loading it into the mold, it can be made in one piece, but it will cause difficulty with cracking of the plastic. It would be more economical in the long run to make two separate inserts, as shown in Fig. 14-25. If electrical contact is required, a wire can be fastened between the two inserts; or, if a more solid connection is desired, the insert can be made solid with cutout slots, as shown in Fig. 14-26. Provision must be made in one half of the mold to prevent these slots from being filled with plastic. When these slots are open, there will be a slight give in the insert when the plastic shrinks. This will consequently reduce or eliminate the possibility of cracking the plastic.

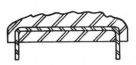

Fig. 14-24

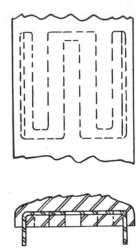

Fig. 14-25

Fig. 14-26

When a long bar-type insert is used, it is always advisable to provide an anchorage in the middle of the bar by means of grooves or slots, or coarse diamond knurl for round bars (see Anchorage, p. 481). The center anchorage will allow the plastic to creep along the surface of the insert while it is shrinking toward the center. If additional anchorage is desired on round bars, the ends can be knurled with straight knurl (Fig. 14-27) and still retain the creeping action. Where dimensional accuracy is required, full allowance for shrinkage should be made. If the article is of cylindrical shape, then, instead of using a knurl for anchorage, circular rings can be provided, which will give satisfactory anchorage and at the same time allow the plastic to creep uniformly around the periphery of the insert. When a knurl is used on a piece of this type and the plastic begins to shrink, it has a tendency to climb up on the knurl, producing stress on the plastic and causing it to crack.

Fig. 14-27

Leakproof Inserts

Because of the difference in the behavior between plastics and metals (e.g., difference in coefficient of thermal expansion), the characteristics of some plastics, and the problems of providing proper adequate anchorage, it is usually impossible to make an insert remain airtight within the plastic even under small pressures. If inserts are used in articles that must withstand high internal pressures, special methods must ordinarily be used to make them airtight.

To retain an airtight joint between the plastic and a metal insert it is necessary to provide a flexible wall of other material between the two. When the molded article and the insert expand and contract, this flexible material, although it consists of only a very thin coating, will compensate for the difference in coefficient of thermal expansion between metal and plastic.

A few successful methods are recommended. The insert is knurled the same as for normal anchorage and is provided with at least two grooves, about $\frac{1}{32}$ in. wide and 0.020 in. deep. The head or anchorage part is dipped in neoprene, polyvinyl chloride-acetate, or other rubbery synthetic material, and then oven-dried before using. This will supply sufficient coating on the insert to give it the necessary cushioning action.

It is possible also, especially on round inserts, to provide a groove in the anchorage head of the insert large enough so that a neoprene washer can be used. Under normal molding conditions, the washer will produce satisfactory results. On some applications, a retaining groove is molded or machined between the insert and the plastic. The groove is filled with alkyd resin and allowed to dry at room temperature, or is oven-baked.

Special Inserts for Reinforcement

It is often necessary to mold inserts into plastics as reinforcements to provide greater strength, greater rigidity, greater safety (as in automobile steering wheels) or greater dimensional accuracy.

In molding a thermoplastic housing, for example, instead of molding a thick wall to obtain rigidity, a sheet-metal reinforcement can be molded on the inside of the housing. This will not only produce greater rigidity with a minimum of wall thickness, but it will also assist in maintaining better dimensional accuracy. Various materials can be used as reinforcement—molding board, laminated phenolics, perforated metal, metal screens.

Nonmetallic Inserts

Inserts of various materials are used successfully. Wooden inserts, for example, are used as a core, especially for thermoplastic materials in compression molding. The use of wooden inserts in applications such as doorknobs or automobile gearshift knobs saves considerable material and shortens the molding cycle.

Glass inserts are being successfully molded into thermoplastics by injection and into thermosetting materials by transfer. Difficulties can be reduced during the initial engineering of mold design. The most difficult problems are caused by the nonuniformity of contours and dimensions. Glass, being of a brittle nature, does not lend iself to the application of full clamping pressures during molding. It is necessary to provide a cushion, by means of springs or rubber, to compensate for the normal irregularities in dimensions of glass inserts. In some cases, paper is glued to the surface of glass to provide additional cushion, and also to protect the surface from scratching during handling.

Locating the insert in the mold is difficult. Figure 14-28 illustrates a sleeve-type ejector method. The inside diameter of the sleeve is the same as the outside diameter of the glass insert. The insert is located by placing it inside of the ejector sleeve when it is protruding in ejected position. Figure 14-29 illustrates a step-molded article. The diameter of one of the steps must be the same as the outside diameter of the insert. A sleeve-type ejector is used on this step, to locate the insert, as in the preceding case.

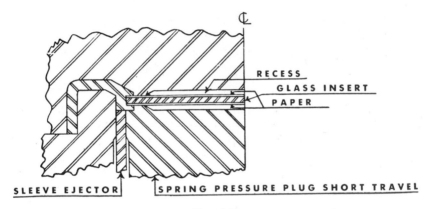

Fig. 14-28

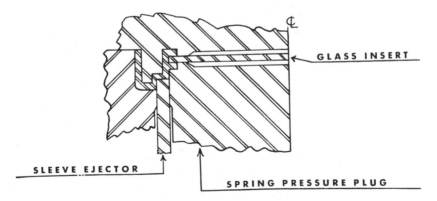

Fig. 14-29

Preparation of Inserts Before Molding

Cleaning of Inserts. Considerable significance should be attached to cleaning or washing of inserts prior to molding, especially screw-machine inserts. If inserts are improperly washed, even though they appear clean, there may be loose metal chips hanging on to the threads, or fine metal dust in the knurls. This latter is often rolled into the surface by the process of knurling, and it is not easily washed off, but it will be loosened by the flow of the plastic. These metal chips may flow up to the surface and impair the appearance of the molded article. The most serious difficulty, however, is in electrical applications, where a small particle or a slight amount of metal dust may cause a total breakdown electrically. Grease and oil also are detrimental to molded articles from the standpoint of appearance, and should be thoroughly washed off.

Cleaning processes are divided into three types:

(1) mechanical, including hand polishing, tumbling, shot- or sand-blasting, or washing with solvent or alkali;

(2) chemical, such as removal of iron rust and silver tarnish by an acid bath;

(3) use of electrolytic cleaners.

Oil and machining chips can best be removed by a well-stirred alkali bath followed by a rinse with hot water, except where the nature of the metal, such as aluminum, rules out the alkali in favor of degreasing with solvent.

In many cases a reasonable amount of tarnish can do no harm, but where the function or the appearance of the piece demands chemically clean inserts, an acid dip is necessary. For brass and bronze, a mixture of nitric and sulfuric acids or nitric alone is commonly used.

Silver tarnish can be removed with nitric acid or a diluted solution of one of the cyanides. Trisodium phosphate has been found to be an efficient remover of iron rust.

Preheating of Inserts. Large inserts should be preheated (above the mold temperature if possible) prior to molding. This will allow the maximum expansion and improve the flow and cure of the plastic. With thermoplastic materials, preheating of inserts will reduce the likelihood of weld marks, which often result in cracking of the plastic after molding.

Cleaning Flash from Inserts

Most of the difficulty with flash can be avoided in the design of the article and the insert by providing sealing points so that the flow of plastic is cut off or at least minimized. However, even with the best design there will be some material on the inserts, especially when the mold wears or close tolerance on inserts is not maintained. Several methods are recommended to minimize this, particularly lubricating the insert prior to molding with wax, soap, grease, or oil. Plating and polishing the inserts minimize the adherence of flash.

To remove the flash, cut it close to the molded article and peel it off. In most cases a mild solution of caustic soda will loosen the flash so that it can be easily removed. This method, however, requires extreme caution because too long contact or too strong a solution will harm the surface of the article, and may even loosen the insert in its anchorage.

Salvage of Inserts

When the inserts are of the through type, they can be knocked out by means of a foot press and fixture. When they are anchored part way in the material, a strong solution of caustic soda will loosen the inserts in thermosetting material so that they can be picked out. For thermoplastic material use suitable solvents for the plastic, or soften the articles in an oven and pull out the inserts.

Relieving Molding Stresses Around Inserts

Considerable stresses are set up in molded articles of irregular design, such as those having both thin and thick sections, and especially those with metal inserts. The best method to relieve stresses is to allow the article to cool slowly. The ideal condition would be to carry the articles on a conveyor through an oven which has various stages of temperatures, starting at 50°F below the molding temperature, then gradually decreasing until the article is cooled to room temperature. This method, however, requires special equipment.

The next best method requires two ovens, one at approximately 225°F and one at 150°F. The molded article remains in each oven successively until its temperature is reduced to oven temperature.

The final step is cooling to room temperature. In case of thermoplastic materials, molding stresses are relieved by baking at suitable recommended temperatures.

Methods of Pressing in Inserts after Molding

It is often more economical to press inserts into the article, after its removal from the mold, than to mold the inserts into place.

Pressing in of inserts should be done promptly after the molded piece is removed from the mold (within 3 minutes, and preferably immediately), in order to take advantage of the subsequent shrinkage of the plastic, which will promote anchorage.

Usually the inserts are placed and pressed in with the aid of a suitably designed fixture mounted in a small arbor press or punch press. If there is more than one insert to be pressed in, all can be handled simultaneously.

When an insert is to be pressed in after molding, the mold must be designed to provide a hole to receive it, and the size of this hole must be designed on the basis of the size of the insert, the normal shrinkage of the plastic, and any further allowance necessary to ensure anchorage. For small inserts, the diameter of the hole should be designed to be, after shrinkage, 0.001 to 0.002 in. smaller than the diameter of the insert. For large inserts, however, and particularly when there is only a thin wall of plastic surrounding the insert, an extra allowance for anchorage is not needed; on the contrary, the diameter of the hole may have to be designed on the basis of as little as 50 per cent of the normal shrinkage factor in order to prevent cracking of the plastic around the insert.

One of the advantages of pressing in inserts becomes evident in such cases: if, for example, an insert 4 in. in diameter were to be molded into an article which provided only a thin wall (say 0.200 in.) of plastic around the insert, the plastic would inevitably crack around the insert, since with a shrinkage factor of 0.008 in. per in. the plastic would shrink 0.032 in. in diameter; but if the hole is molded to shrink to only 0.016 in. less than 4 in., then the insert can be put in after the molding, and the subsequent shrinkage will not be enough to cause cracking.

Inserts with either diamond or straight knurls can be pressed in satisfactorily. For some special applications a coating of adhesive may be applied to the insert, to promote anchorage and to ensure an airtight joint.

An insert of new type has extended the practice of pressing in inserts. It can be pressed in with a single punch at the press, without the use of special fixtures. It reduces percentage of rejections and increases rate of production.

This insert, illustrated in Fig. 14-30, consists of (1) a knurled brass shield with four slots and internal threads, and, locked within it, (2) a four-eared brass spreader.

This insert can be fed by hand or by machine into the molded hole (or into a drilled hole). The spreader is then pushed downward, and the pressure of its ears on the surfaces of the slots expands the shield against the wall of the hole, without harming the threads. When the spreader has reached the

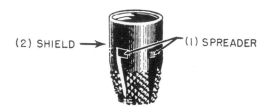

(2) SHIELD ⟶   ⟵(1) SPREADER

Fig. 14-30

end of its travel, it is locked into position by a shoulder on the inside of the shield.

The punch, drift pin, or other tool used for forcing down the spreader should have a diameter 0.002 to 0.004 in. less than that of the tap drill, and should have a shoulder which will rest upon the top of the insert when the spreader locks at the bottom of the insert.

Figure 14-31 shows three stages in the setting and full expansion of this insert.

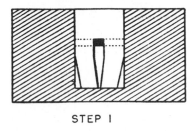

STEP 1

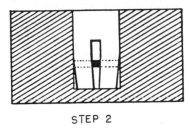

STEP 2

Fig. 14-31

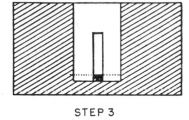

STEP 3

The diameter of the hole to receive the insert should be up to 0.002 in. greater than rod size. The bottom of the hole, upon which the insert rests, must be flat. As with all inserts, maximum torque strength is achieved when the screw is long enough to utilize all of the threads of the insert and at the same time short enough so that the under side of its head comes down tight on the surface to be held (see Fig. 14-32).

Comparison of Inserts

A comparison of various inserts, both molded-in and pressed-in, is given in Table 14-4, which shows the results of tests of blind-hole inserts in a general-purpose phenolic molding material. The testing was done in accordance with the torque and tension test already described in this chapter (Figs. 14-9 and 14-10.) The inserts molded in were (a) smooth-surfaced, (b) undercut, (c) fine-knurl and (d) coarse-knurl. Those pressed in were

(a) coarse-knurl and (b) the special type shown in Fig. 14-30. Table 14-4 shows the sizes used. The data are in inch-pounds.

It will be seen that the coarse-knurl and fine-knurl inserts, molded in, were so well anchored that either the test screw or the molded article failed before the insert could be pulled or twisted out.

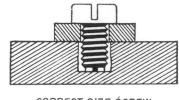

CORRECT SIZE SCREW

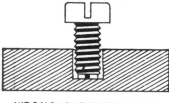

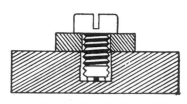

WRONG: SCREW TOO LONG   WRONG: SCREW TOO SHORT

Fig. 14-32

"Don'ts" in Insert Design

Don't use inserts if they can be avoided.

Don't mold a through-type insert unless the mold is designed for it.

Don't use an open-hole insert if it can be avoided.

Don't leave sharp corners on inserts. Chamfer wherever possible.

Don't try to mold inserts without proper anchorage.

Don't flatten inserts if the insert is loose on the retaining pin.

Don't put material into the insert to hold it on the retaining pin. This will require retapping.

Don't use inserts unless they are clean.

Don't use the drawn-type eyelets unless necessary.

Don't allow too thin a wall of plastic on the back of the insert. A thin wall will bulge up and appear like a blister caused by undercure.

Don't allow too thin a wall of plastic around the insert because the plastic will crack.

TABLE 14-4. TENSION AND TORSION TESTS OF VARIOUS INSERTS

(DATA ARE IN INCH-POUNDS)

thread size	tests	insert shown in Fig. 14-30. (pressed in)	plain insert (molded in)	undercut insert (molded in)	coarse-knurl (press fit)	fine-knurl insert (molded in)	coarse-knurl insert (molded in)
6-32	tension	10	10	20	35	30*	30*
	torsion	10	25	30*	35*	30*	30*
8-32	tension	25	10	25	40	30*	30*
	torsion	20	30	35	55*	60*	60*
10-32	tension	30	10	30	40	60*	60*
	torsion	20	30	35*	50*	90*	90*
10-24	tension	**	10	30	40	65*	65*
	torsion	**	30	35*	50*	65*	65*
1/4-20	tension	**	10	40	40	90*	90*
	torsion	**	65	80	120*	90*	90*

* The anchorage was sufficient to break either the test screw or the molded test piece
** No specimens

Don't design the part or insert until the correct plastic has been selected for the application.

Don't carry the knurl out to the edge of the insert.

Don't try to mold long inserts by supporting one end only.

Don't mold large inserts in either thermosetting or thermoplastic materials without heating the insert before molding.

Don't make the retaining pin too large or the hole for the male insert too tight. This will result in inserts' pulling out of the material.

Don't use standard nuts and screws.

Nomenclature

anchorage . . . . Part of the insert that is molded inside of the plastic and held fast by the shrinkage of the plastic.

blind hole . . . . Hole that is not drilled entirely through.

blind-hole
partial thread . . Thread counterbored from the front for terminal or other assembly fit.

crushing of insert . When a protruding insert is molded in a conventional mold without any protection, it will be crushed or collapsed by the material which flows into the hole provided for the protruded part in the upper part of the mold.

eyelet-type insert . Insert having a section which protrudes from the material and is used for spinning over in assembly.

floating of insert . When pressure is applied on the mold and the material softens, it flows upwards. If the insert is loose on the retaining pin, some of the material flows under the insert or into the anchorage points and carries or floats the insert off the retaining pin.

flow of material
into the insert . . If a threaded open-hole insert is being molded, the retaining pin does not prevent the material from flowing into the insert unless the retaining pin is threaded, which would increase the cost of molding.

open-hole insert . . One having a hole drilled completely through it.

protruding-type
insert . . . . One having a part which protrudes from the molded material.

retaining pin . . .   Pin on which insert is placed and located prior to molding.

rivet-type insert . .   One having a protruding part which is riveted in assembly.

sealing diameter . .   Portion of the insert which is free of knurl and is allowed to enter into the mold to prevent the flow of material.

through-type insert .   One which is exposed on both sides of the molded article.

15. Mold Design and Recommended Steels

MOLD DESIGN

Hand-Operated Compression Molds

The basis upon which the industry has been built is the hand mold. This means a mold which is assembled outside the press, and put into the press by hand. It is then taken out by hand and disassembled in order to extract the molded article.

Molds of the positive type were in use for many years previous to the use of synthetic resins. Such a mold consists of a chamber or cavity, in which material is put, and a force or plunger, which is put into the cavity and forced down by pressure for a predetermined distance in order to form a piece which will have the shape of the cavity. The force is then extracted and the molded article is pushed from the mold, usually in an arbor press.

Figure 15-1 will show the construction of this simple form of a truly positive mold.

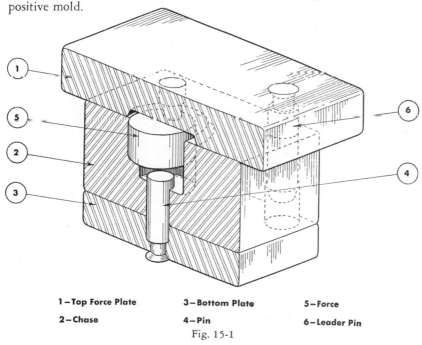

| 1—Top Force Plate | 3—Bottom Plate | 5—Force |
| 2—Chase | 4—Pin | 6—Leader Pin |

Fig. 15-1

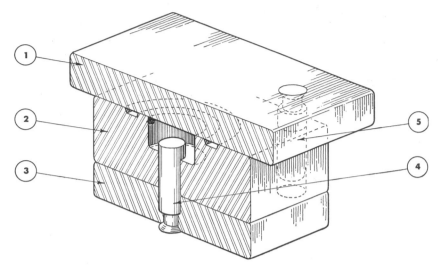

1 – Top Force Plate   **3 – Bottom Plate**   **5 – Leader Pin**

2 – Chase   **4 – Pin**

Fig. 15-2

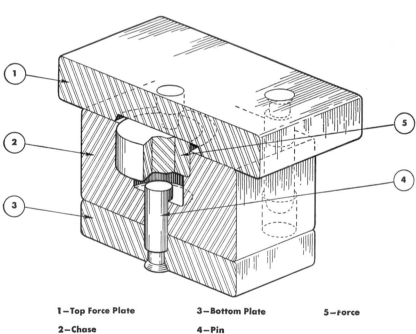

1 – Top Force Plate   **3 – Bottom Plate**   **5 – Force**

2 – Chase   **4 – Pin**

Fig. 15-3

A second type of mold is the flash mold. This design allows surplus material (flash) to be squeezed out when the mold is closed under pressure

Figure 15-2 illustrates the simplest form of the flash-type hand mold.

Variations of these two simple designs are the landed positive, Fig. 15-3, and the semipositive type, Fig. 15-4.

Where more than one cavity is to be filled from a single charge of molding material, the subcavity mold is used. Figure 15-5 shows a common design of a subcavity mold.

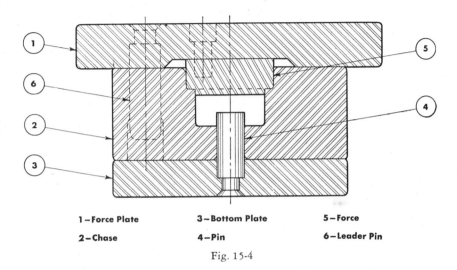

| 1 – Force Plate | 3 – Bottom Plate | 5 – Force |
| 2 – Chase | 4 – Pin | 6 – Leader Pin |

Fig. 15-4

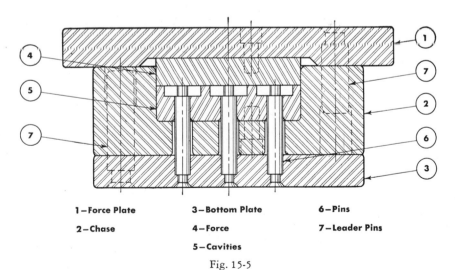

1 – Force Plate	3 – Bottom Plate	6 – Pins
2 – Chase	4 – Force	7 – Leader Pins
	5 – Cavities	

Fig. 15-5

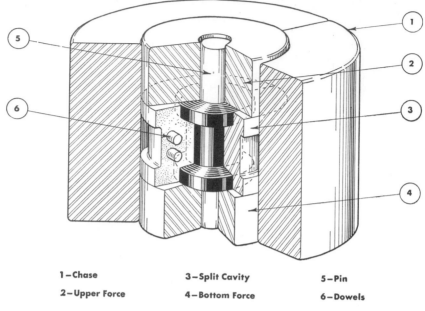

| 1 – Chase | 3 – Split Cavity | 5 – Pin |
| 2 – Upper Force | 4 – Bottom Force | 6 – Dowels |

Fig. 15-6

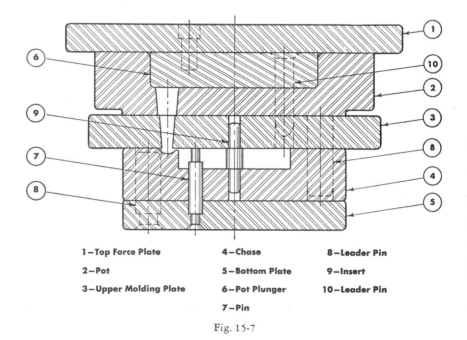

1 – Top Force Plate	4 – Chase	8 – Leader Pin
2 – Pot	5 – Bottom Plate	9 – Insert
3 – Upper Molding Plate	6 – Pot Plunger	10 – Leader Pin
	7 – Pin	

Fig. 15-7

There are times when it is necessary to make an article with wings or flanges, such as are found on a spool. Figure 15-6 illustrates how this is done with a split mold.

Hand molds are used also in transfer molding. Figure 15-7, a hand transfer mold, and Fig. 15-8, a hand transfer mold of stripper type, shows simple forms of molds used in this operation.

There are many variations of these general designs. Molded pieces may be made to stay in the cavity or on the forces by using undercuts, reverse tapers or a grit blast finish. In all cases, the molded article must be capable of being withdrawn from the mold.

After the pieces are molded, they will probably need to be finished. An article made in a positive mold may require the least finishing because the flash will be very thin. However, this design has a drawback in that it needs accurate charges of material and control of heat and pressure in order to eliminate variations in thickness.

The flash mold will give a very thin flash but the molded article may lack the proper density because the material is not truly confined.

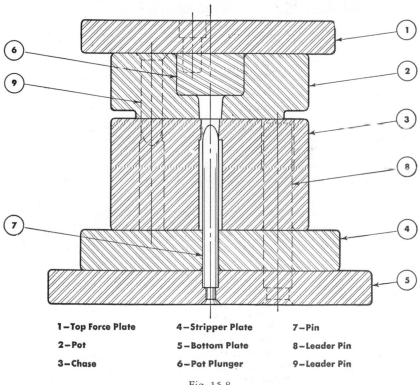

1—Top Force Plate	4—Stripper Plate	7—Pin
2—Pot	5—Bottom Plate	8—Leader Pin
3—Chase	6—Pot Plunger	9—Leader Pin

Fig. 15-8

These same considerations must be given to the other types of molds except for the transfer molds. With transfer molds the problem is to locate the gate where it can be removed most economically and with least damage to the appearance of the article.

Semiautomatic Compression Molds

The term "semiautomatic" is used to cover molds from which the molded articles are ejected by movement of mold parts actuated by the press.

In special cases parts of the mold will be shown as removable parts to be handled individually, even though they might conceivably be operated mechanically if production requirements were great enough to justify the expense of equipment for mechanical operation.

The almost limitless variety of shapes which can be produced by semi-automatic compression molds precludes the possibility of covering the subject completely in this chapter, but various shapes have been selected to illustrate a method of approach to the design of molds for such articles.

The several types of semiautomatic molds follow closely in nomenclature the hand molds previously described. They are positive, semipositive, landed positive, flash, floating stock-retainer and subcavity.

Semiautomatic Positive Mold (Fig. 15-9). This is ideal for the molded shape selected for this illustration, especially if the molded piece must have the greatest density.

It is well adapted for multiple-cavity production if small flash grooves are provided at location 9 to compensate for errors in size of cavity and weight of material charge.

Pressure pads, 7, away from molding material ensure reasonably accurate control of thickness if care is used to keep their surfaces free from stock and molded flash.

Proper clearance between 3 and 4, and very slight taper of filling space in 4, are required to prevent marring of the edge of the molded article by scoring of the sides of the filling space.

The article illustrated requires only bottom ejection, but top ejection could be provided in like manner if a somewhat similar article should tend to stick to the top force.

Semiautomatic Semipositive Mold (Fig. 15-10). This is something of a cross between a positive mold and a landed positive mold. It functions like a flash mold until the last fraction of an inch of closing. In this last fraction, A, the force enters the cavity in a truly positive manner. This last positive squeeze ensures a densely molded article, with consequent full strength and good finish. The depth of entry of the force into the cavity is small, and thus the chance of scoring the walls of the cavity is much less than in a positive mold. Great care must be exercised to keep the land surfaces of force and cavity clean, since otherwise the lands may be damaged or broken.

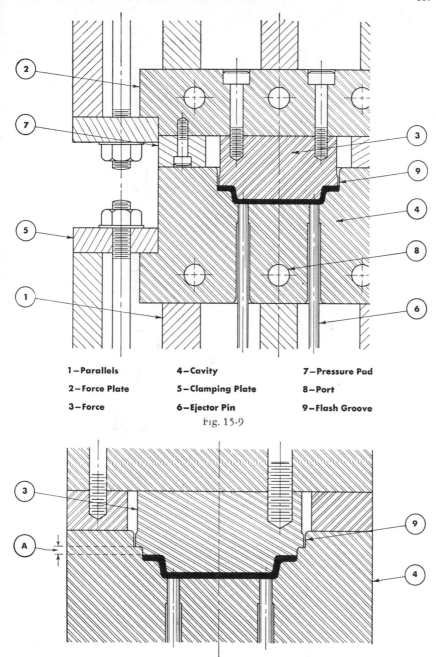

1 — Parallels   4 — Cavity   7 — Pressure Pad
2 — Force Plate   5 — Clamping Plate   8 — Port
3 — Force   6 — Ejector Pin   9 — Flash Groove

Fig. 15-9

3 — Force   4 — Cavity   9 — Flash Groove

Fig. 15-10

This construction is often used in multiple-cavity molds, but is less desirable on account of the extreme care which has to be used in cleaning the land surface of the cavity. Even in this type it is best to use pressure pads.

Semiautomatic Landed Positive Mold (Fig. 15-11). A bead around the top edge of the molded shape in this illustration necessitates the change in mold construction from positive to landed positive.

This mold also is adaptable to multiple-cavity construction if flash grooves, 9, are provided.

The landed positive feature is apt to cause some trouble if care is not exercised at all times to remove flash from the land surfaces. Continued

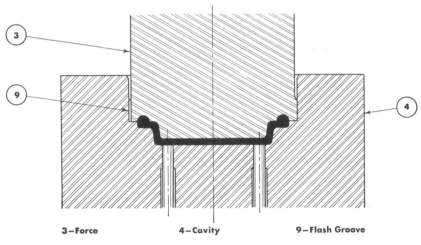

3—Force   4—Cavity   9—Flash Groove

Fig. 15-11

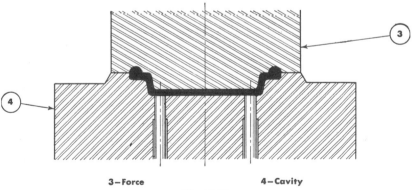

3—Force   4—Cavity

Fig. 15-12

operation with flash left on the land surfaces will probably result in damage or breakage of the lands.

The chance of marring of the edges of the molded piece by scoring of the sides of the filling space is eliminated. Again it is advisable to make provision for additional pressure pads outside of the cavity.

Semiautomatic Flash Mold (Fig. 15-12). For the article illustrated, this is probably the most foolproof type of mold, but in comparison with the types already described it will give a higher loss of material, and a molded article of lower density and poorer surface.

The life of the mold cavity should be longer, the initial cost less, and the maintenance cost less than for a semipositive or landed positive mold for the same article.

It is the best adapted to multiple-cavity construction.

Semiautomatic Floating Stock-Retainer Type (Fig. 15-13). In comparison with types previously described, this floating stock-retainer construction is more expensive, requires more complicated mechanism to actuate its upward and downward movement, and introduces a more difficult problem of alignment of force and cavity. But from the standpoint of the quality of the molded piece, it combines most of the desirable features of both the landed positive and flash molds.

It is easier for the operator to keep the land surfaces clean than in the case of the landed or semipositive molds, and relatively little damage to the lands will result if they are not kept clean, providing the pressure applied is little more than enough to prevent premature flashing.

Molds of this type are adapted to multiple-cavity construction, but a

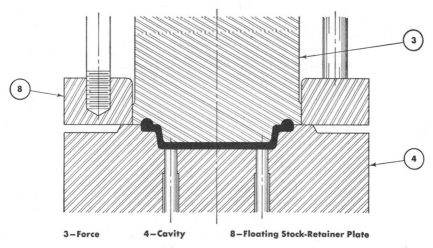

3 — Force   4 — Cavity   8 — Floating Stock-Retainer Plate

Fig. 15-13

given mold area will be restricted to fewer cavities than with the positive or flash type.

On account of the slight differences in design between the four molded articles shown thus far, a direct comparison cannot be made as a basis for selecting one of these four types of mold as the best.

If the top bead in the design can be eliminated, then the positive mold first described merits consideration.

The selection of the type of mold must be considered from all angles, and the various comments made on the different types may serve to assist the mold-designer in his selection.

To illustrate the general construction of a complete mold, a relatively simple molded shape is here selected (Fig. 15-14), and a semiautomatic compression mold designed around this piece. More complicated shapes will be illustrated later, but in these cases only special features of mold-design will be shown. It will be evident that practically all of the essential elements of construction required for the simple shape will have to be present in the mold for the more complicated shapes, and the special construction features illustrated are to be added to these essential elements.

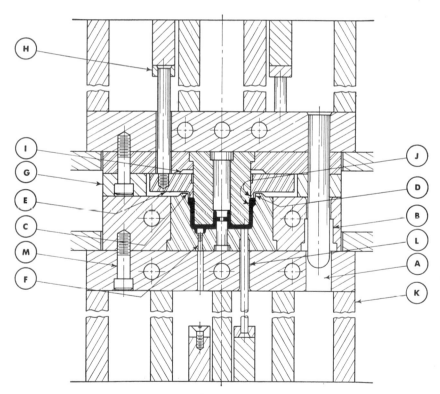

Fig. 15-14

In the shape illustrated in Fig. 15-14, we shall assume that no undercut or special taper can be allowed, to ensure that the molded article will stay either on the plunger or in the cavity when the mold is opened. Consequently both top and bottom ejection are provided.

In this case top ejection is of stripper-plate construction. This construction is selected primarily to illustrate how it may be handled in a mold design. However, ejection by a stripper plate should be avoided wherever possible in favor of ejection by a pin. The reason for this is that flash getting back of a stripper plate is likely to be troublesome.

It may be advisable to call attention to certain details of the mold design here illustrated which are axiomatic to one familiar with the subject, but which may not be immediately apparent to others.

A. Clearance under the dowels or leader pins.

B. The use of a hardened dowel or leader-pin bushing in a soft plate.

C. Slight positive action of force in the cavity to ensure alignment of the mold and full density of the molded articles.

D. Flash grooves in the force.

E. Clearance between under side of stripper plate and top of cavity to allow escape of material from flash grooves.

F. Clearance holes under inserts to allow any flash to fall completely through the mold.

G. Pressure pads or blocks to control the thickness.

H. Retainer plate for top ejection pins.

I. Clearance space above stripper plate so that flash working up between the top force and the stripper plate will not be confined and can easily be blown out.

J. Inside diameter of stripper plate made slightly greater than outside diameter of the force which shapes the inside of the molded article, in order to avoid scoring of the force, which would mar the inside surface of the molded article.

K. Placing of lower supporting parallels to avoid blocking off the clearance holes under the dowel bushings.

L. Counterbore in under side of ejection-pin holes to reduce friction.

M. Screws for holding mold parts together put in from under sides of plates, remote from the surfaces where molding material might get into the counterbored recesses for screw heads and cause trouble in cleaning.

Semiautomatic Mold for Spools or Articles with Undercuts in Side Walls (Fig. 15-15). Where molded shapes have undercut side surfaces in addition to irregularly shaped top and bottom surfaces—such as spools—the usual mold construction is that known as split-cavity design. To illustrate this design a spool has been selected (Fig. 15-15), and an assembly drawing of the mold for producing the spool is shown.

In this design the parts N and O, meeting at the center line of the spool, constitute the split cavity. These parts are removed from the chase after each operation of the mold and placed on an opening fixture so that the molded spool can be extracted. In such cases the split cavity is handled like a hand mold, and all other parts of the mold are fastened in the press.

If production requirements are great enough to warrant it, the split cavity can be mounted in an angle molding press and operated by side hydraulic cylinders of sufficient power to hold them together against the pressure of molding material tending to push them apart.

The mold design selected has the center core integral with the top force.

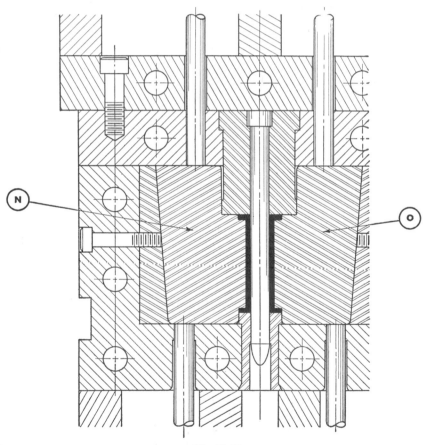

Fig. 15-15

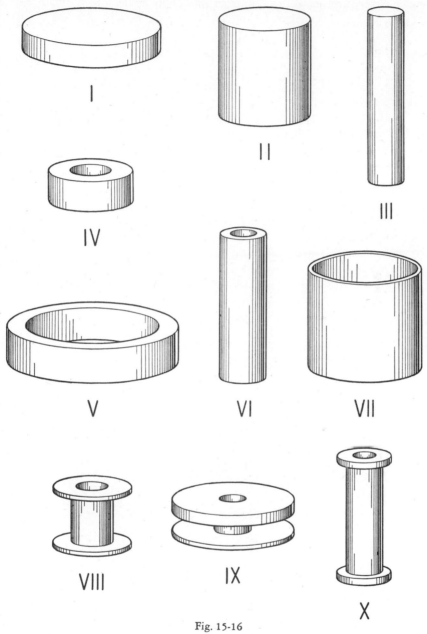

I

II

III

IV

V

VI

VII

VIII

IX

X

Fig. 15-16

This feature helps the downward flow of material, and its displacing action tends to force the material under it into the cavity space which forms the lower flange of the spool. This design requires a preform of ring shape. Instead, the center core may be integral with the bottom mold plate and remain stationary. In this case the top of the core pin will pass through a hole machined in the top force to receive it. In this construction either a ring preform or loose powder can be used.

Both designs will produce the article, but the subsequent finishing requirements will be somewhat different. Before deciding what mold design to employ, the problem should be considered from various angles, such as how the spool is to be mounted in assembly, which dimensions are most critical, and the cost of finishing.

How to Select the Type of Mold. Articles of the same general shape but of different proportions may require radically different mold designs. To illustrate this, the shapes shown in Fig. 15-16 have been selected.

For piece "I" a flash mold (Fig. 15-17) is selected, but positive, semi-positive, or landed positive could also be used.

For piece "II" a floating stock-retainer mold is selected (Fig. 15-18)

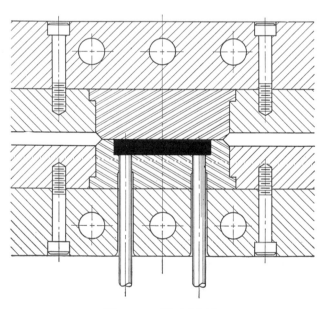

Fig. 15-17. Flash Mold.

because the depth of the filling chamber is reduced by having the diameter of the filling chamber appreciably greater than the diameter of the article. Without this floating feature the land surface would be difficult to observe and keep clean, because the filling chamber is so deep.

For piece "III", a multiple-cavity inverted subcavity mold is selected (Fig. 15-19). Top ejector pins should fit loosely to provide escape of air. Each cylindrical cavity should be tapered as much as permissible. The rods will be molded integral with a bottom disc. They can be cut off and the cut ends finished by a secondary operation.

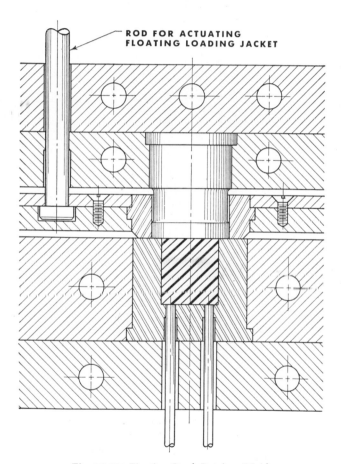

Fig. 15-18. Floating Stock-Retainer Mold.

For piece "IV", a flash mold is used (Fig. 15-20). The mold is loaded by placing a ring tablet over the center pin. Ejection is accomplished by raising the center shouldered pin and using a fork to strip the piece off the center pin when it is moved down again into molding position.

The mold selected for piece "V" is of the landed positive type (Fig.

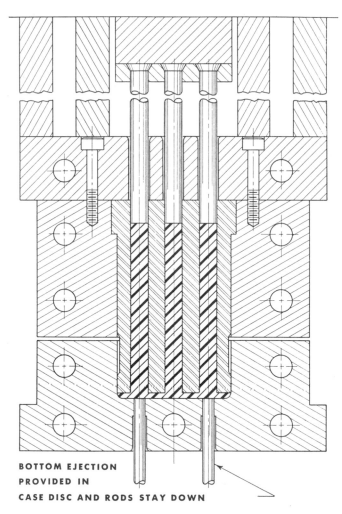

BOTTOM EJECTION PROVIDED IN CASE DISC AND RODS STAY DOWN

Fig. 15-19. Inverted Subcavity Mold.

15-21). The land surface is inside the annular cavity. The shape of the article makes it difficult to employ ejection pins, and hence ejection is accomplished by a top stripper ring and a bottom center pin. This rather complicated mold is necessary, since the ejection of thin and narrow annular shapes requires the use of top and bottom ejection, unless undercuts are permissible on either the outer or the inner wall of the ring surface, so that the molded article will definitely stay either on the force or in the cavity.

This mold illustrates the use of steam-cored ejection bars. The propor-

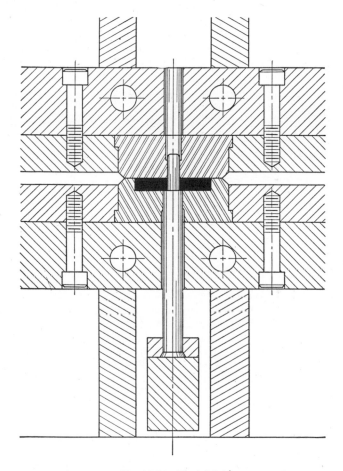

Fig. 15-20. Flash Mold.

tions of the mold parts are such that the ejection bar should be guided by dowels, which are not shown here.

For the long molded tube "VI", the mold (Fig. 15-22) is designed to have the parts P, Q, R, S and T slide in and out of the press like a hand mold. The reason for this is that most moving-up molding presses do not have enough stroke to provide the complete semiautomatic action which is required for stripping and ejecting.

Two gibs, U, are fastened to the lower steam plate so that the plunger, V, can be withdrawn from the loading chamber, P, during the opening of the press.

Means for taking apart the pieces P, Q, R, S and T, outside of the press, are so well known that no attempt is made to illustrate them here.

Three important points should be taken into consideration for the successful operation of this mold. The outside of the tubular article must be tapered slightly, allowing the inside tubular surfaces of the mold cavity to be tapered. Outside supplementary heat must be supplied to the mandrels, T, to ensure their being hot.

For large production, two sets of parts, P, Q, R, S, and T should be provided, one set to be in the press for molding, while the other is out for ejection, preheating and loading.

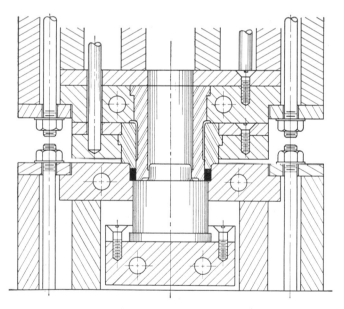

Fig. 15-21. Landed Positive Mold.

For the large thin-walled tube "VII", the mold (Fig. 15-23) is designed to mold a cup-shaped article with a center hole in the bottom. After the article is molded the bottom can be machined off and the tubular portion retained.

Assuming that the requirements are such that no taper is allowed either inside or outside, the mold design includes both top and bottom ejection. If a generous taper is permissible, either inside or outside, the mold can be simplified by having ejection from one end only. When stripper plates are used, great care should be taken to allow for escape of flash and proper clearance for cleaning.

Note that the center pin is stepped larger at point W, to facilitate the bottom ejection of the molded cup.

In a mold of this type, if the bottom of the cup is too thin, parts of the bottom may break off and stay in the mold. Failure to remove these broken-off pieces may result in crushing the steel cavity or force, or both.

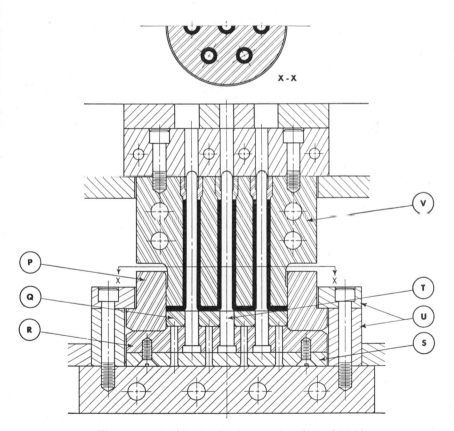

Fig. 15-22. Combination Semiautomatic and Hand Mold.

We come now to the three spool shapes shown as "VIII", "IX" and "X" in Fig. 15-16. Mold design suitable for "VIII" and "X" has previously been illustrated (Fig. 15-15). Although spool "IX" could be molded by compression, it would be advisable to consider a transfer mold for this shape, especially when the diameter of the flanges is considerably greater than the space between them. The objection to a compression mold for this shape is the risk of bending the split cavity which forms the outside of the spool.

Transfer Molds

This section will deal with the design of transfer molds which are operated in a conventional molding press.

The first item of importance is the pot plunger. The plunger is usually

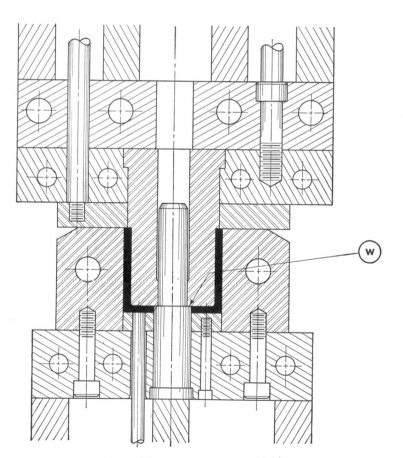

Fig. 15-23. Compression-Type Mold.

made with a seal groove around it to prevent flashing. An undercut on the face of the plunger is provided to pull out the cull. The usual practice is to allow clearance of 0.001 to 0.0015 in. around the plunger on sizes up to 4 in. in diameter and 0.0025 in. for plungers over 4 in. in diameter. Fig. 15-24 illustrates various types of cull-removing grooves and also shows the seal groove.

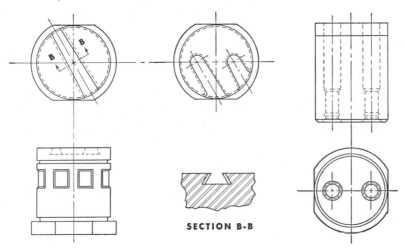

SECTION B-B

Fig. 15-24

The pot should be strong enough to withstand the high pressure used. The fit between the pot and retainer should be tight enough to prevent breakage. Some designers prefer a solid pot unit rather than an inserted pot in a retainer plate. A small radius at the bottom of the pot is recommended. It may be advantageous to chrome plate both the pot and the pot plunger.

The pot should be placed on the center line of the mold in order to equalize the stresses. Sprue holes also should be located on the center line; if more than one, they should be symmetrically located. Some designers insist that the base of the pot must cover at least 75 per cent of the projected area of the bottom molding cavity or cavities. The inside cross-section of the pot should at least equal the total projected area of all the articles to be molded, including the sprues and runners, with an added 25 per cent safety factor for clamping.

It may be necessary to increase this area in the pot to maintain the necessary heating area according to the total weight of the material charge. Somewhere between 5 and 10 sq in. of heating surface per ounce of material is necessary for transferring most materials. The use of dielectric preheating may eliminate the need for increasing the area to heat a heavy charge, and may even eliminate the need for all of the 25 per cent extra area for clamping.

Figure 15-25 shows sprue bushings for top or bottom gates. The area of the small end should equal the combined cross-sectional area of all the gates. In all cases the overall length of the bushing should be kept to a minimum in order to have the shortest possible distance from the pot to the cavity.

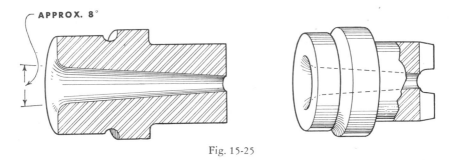

APPROX. 8°

Fig. 15-25

Directly below the bushing a sprue-well is provided. Figures 15-26 and 15-27 show types commonly used for general-purpose and impact materials. The back taper shown in Fig. 15-27 not only holds the runner in the lower

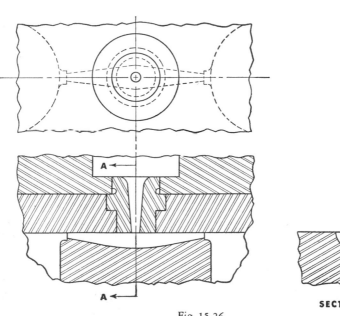

A

A

SECTION A-A

Fig. 15-26

member during molding of impact materials, but also helps hold down the molded article.

Runners should be short to avoid precuring of material. There should be no sudden change in the direction of flow, and generous radii should be used at all turns. The size and shape of runners are generally governed by the design of the article molded and the type of material used. Large runners and gates are necessary for impact materials in order to maintain as much of the mechanical strength as possible. Double gating of a single article should be avoided with impact materials. Small gates, about 0.010 in. deep, may be used in molding material containing finely divided filler. It may be possible to locate the gate where a hole is required, so that the gate may be removed by drilling.

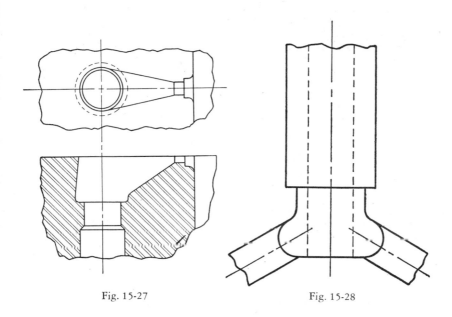

Fig. 15-27   Fig. 15-28

It is good practice to gate into a heavy section and on a surface which will be accessible for removal of the gate by a simple machining operation.

It is possible to design a sliding section of the mold to act as a shear, and so to remove the gate during the molding operation.

Figure 15-28 shows a ring gate sometimes used to avoid knit-lines where the material has to flow around a pin.

It is necessary that all runners be smoothly tapered, with no undercuts, and polished, and it generally helps to have the runners chrome-plated.

Molds for transfer and plunger molding should be designed (1) to require the smallest practicable pressure and (2) to minimize curing in sprue and runners. At the same time, the runners should be as small as practicable, to minimize waste of material, and the gates as small as practicable, to simplify finishing operations.

It has been proved that runners of circular cross-section are best, because for a given cross-section they offer (1) the least resistance to flow and (2) the most effective insulation of the center of the stream against the heat of the mold block, which would cause curing of the flowing stream.

Also it has been shown that for a gate of given cross-section a circular shape best promotes filling of the cavity under reasonable pressure, and thereby contributes to homogeneity of the molded article by minimizing premature curing before the cavity has become filled.

Vents may be needed to permit escape of gases. These are generally located at the point which fills out last. These vents are commonly cut from 0.002 to 0.005 in. deep and $\frac{1}{8}$ to $\frac{1}{4}$ in. wide. Deep recesses in the mold can be vented by pins with adequate clearance.

Slug wells are often used to eliminate knit-lines, especially when the design requires high mechanical strength and good dielectric characteristics. Such a slug well is shown in Fig. 15-29.

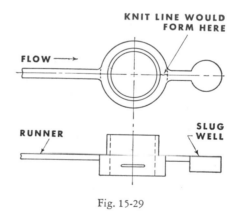

Fig. 15-29

Standard methods for heating the molds are used, with added provisions for varying the temperature of the different members of the mold.

Safety latches should be provided to prevent members of the mold from falling on the operator's hands.

The following sketches show various types of semiautomatic transfer molds.

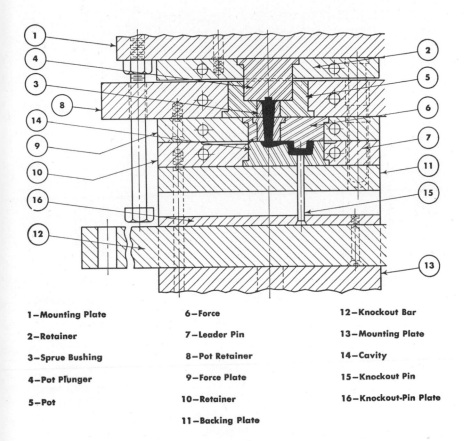

1 — Mounting Plate   6 — Force   12 — Knockout Bar

2 — Retainer   7 — Leader Pin   13 — Mounting Plate

3 — Sprue Bushing   8 — Pot Retainer   14 — Cavity

4 — Pot Plunger   9 — Force Plate   15 — Knockout Pin

5 — Pot   10 — Retainer   16 — Knockout-Pin Plate

           11 — Backing Plate

Fig. 15-30. Shows a design which requires only one ram for
clamping and transferring.

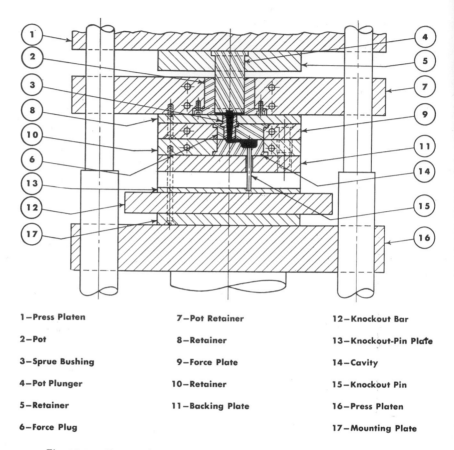

1–Press Platen	7–Pot Retainer	12–Knockout Bar
2–Pot	8–Retainer	13–Knockout-Pin Plate
3–Sprue Bushing	9–Force Plate	14–Cavity
4–Pot Plunger	10–Retainer	15–Knockout Pin
5–Retainer	11–Backing Plate	16–Press Platen
6–Force Plug		17–Mounting Plate

Fig. 15-31. Shows a design which requires only one ram for clamping and transferring, the transfer unit being part of the press equipment.

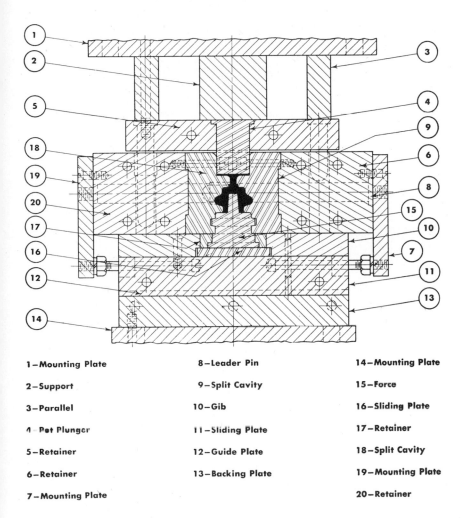

1—Mounting Plate   8—Leader Pin   14—Mounting Plate

2—Support   9—Split Cavity   15—Force

3—Parallel   10—Gib   16—Sliding Plate

4—Pot Plunger   11—Sliding Plate   17—Retainer

5—Retainer   12—Guide Plate   18—Split Cavity

6—Retainer   13—Backing Plate   19—Mounting Plate

7—Mounting Plate   20—Retainer

Fig. 15-32. Shows a design which requires the side ram for clamping and in which the top ram does the transferring. This design will fit a standard angle molding press.

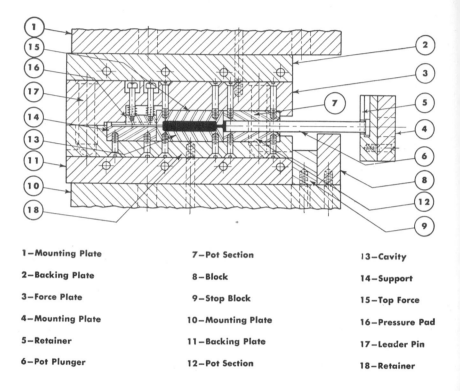

1—Mounting Plate	7—Pot Section	13—Cavity
2—Backing Plate	8—Block	14—Support
3—Force Plate	9—Stop Block	15—Top Force
4—Mounting Plate	10—Mounting Plate	16—Pressure Pad
5—Retainer	11—Backing Plate	17—Leader Pin
6—Pot Plunger	12—Pot Section	18—Retainer

Fig. 15-33. Similar to Fig. 15-32 except that the side ram does the transferring.

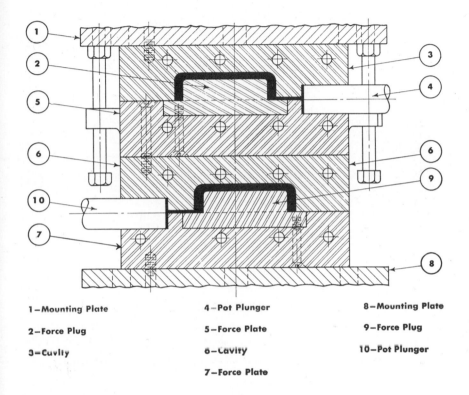

1—Mounting Plate   4—Pot Plunger   8—Mounting Plate

2—Force Plug   5—Force Plate   9—Force Plug

3—Cavity   6—Cavity   10—Pot Plunger

7—Force Plate

Fig. 15-34. Shows a design which requires a ram for clamping the mold and two side cylinders for transferring.

The following are specially designed for high-temperature molding, for materials such as "Mycalex."

Figure 15-35 shows another type and Fig. 15-37 shows the use of gas for heating.

Figure 15-36 is similar to 15-33 except for the inverted sprue, the insulation around the mold and electrical heating with cartridge-type units.

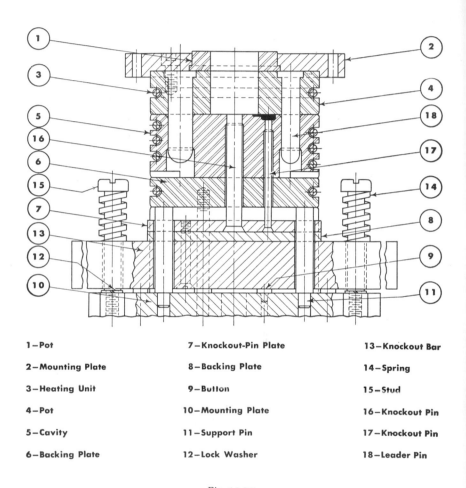

1—Pot	7—Knockout-Pin Plate	13—Knockout Bar
2—Mounting Plate	8—Backing Plate	14—Spring
3—Heating Unit	9—Button	15—Stud
4—Pot	10—Mounting Plate	16—Knockout Pin
5—Cavity	11—Support Pin	17—Knockout Pin
6—Backing Plate	12—Lock Washer	18—Leader Pin

Fig. 15-35

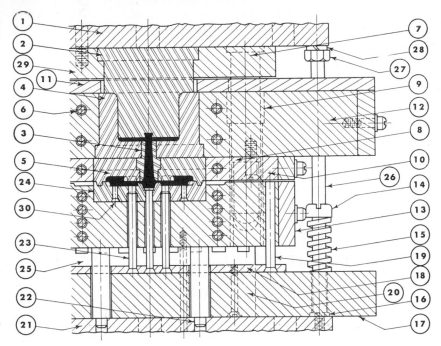

1—Mounting Plate	11—Insulation	21—Mounting Plate
2—Pot Plunger	12—Pot Retainer	22—Support Pin
3—Sprue Bushing	13—Retainer	23—Knockout Pin
4—Pot	14—Stud	24—Cavities
5—Force	15—Spring	25—Insulation
6—Heating Unit	16—Lock Washer	26—Bolt
7—Leader Pin	17—Knockout Bar	27—Hexagon Nut
8—Leader Pin	18—Knockout-Pin Plate	28—Lock Washer
9—Leader-Pin Bushing	19—Pushback Pin	29—Retainer
10—Force Plate	20—Parallel	30—Core Pin

Fig. 15-36

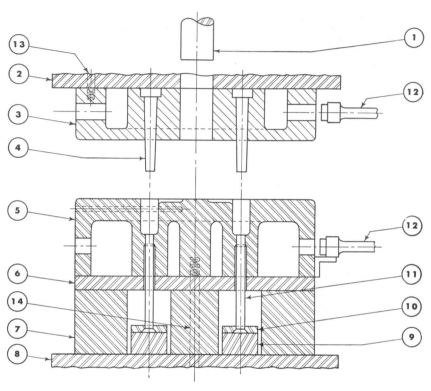

1—Pot Plunger

2—Mounting Plate

3—Retainer

4—Core Pin

5—Cavity

6—Backing Plate

7—Parallel

8—Mounting Plate

9—Knockout Bar

10—Knockout-Pin Plate

11—Knockout Pin

12—Nozzle

13—Screw

14—Screw

Fig. 15-37

Plunger Molds

There is a different type of molding which has recently come into wide use, known as high-speed plunger molding or duplex molding.

It uses an adaptation of a semi-automatic mold. The difference lies in the fact that the mold proper is held together by pressure supplied by a large ram and that a second ram or plunger with an independent and variable source of pressure supplies the push to inject the preheated material into the mold.

This type of molding has been largely advanced by the use of electronic heating. It depends upon careful control of temperatures and pressures, and upon having runners or gates of proper size.

The same general rules of mold design that apply to all the other types apply also to this type. One feature that is entirely different is the hardened plug known as the anvil, which is directly under the transfer ram.

Figures 15-38 and 15-39 will give an idea of the differences from the ordinary transfer mold.

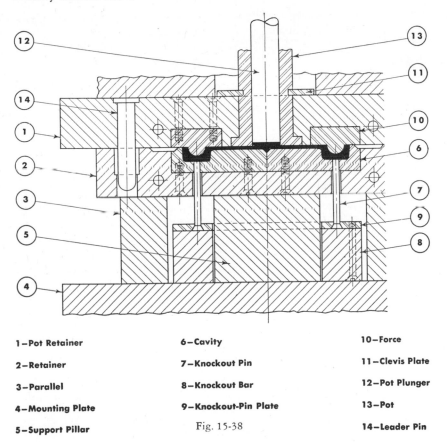

1 – Pot Retainer	6 – Cavity	10 – Force
2 – Retainer	7 – Knockout Pin	11 – Clevis Plate
3 – Parallel	8 – Knockout Bar	12 – Pot Plunger
4 – Mounting Plate	9 – Knockout-Pin Plate	13 – Pot
5 – Support Pillar	Fig. 15-38	14 – Leader Pin

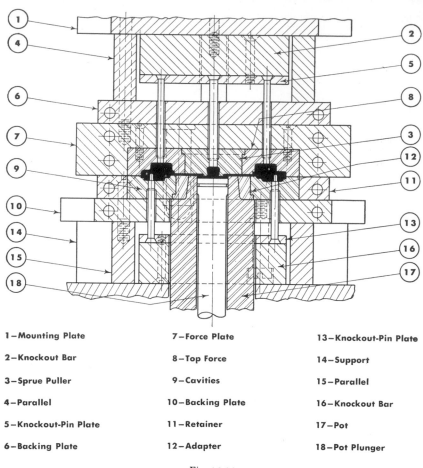

1 – Mounting Plate	7 – Force Plate	13 – Knockout-Pin Plate
2 – Knockout Bar	8 – Top Force	14 – Support
3 – Sprue Puller	9 – Cavities	15 – Parallel
4 – Parallel	10 – Backing Plate	16 – Knockout Bar
5 – Knockout-Pin Plate	11 – Retainer	17 – Pot
6 – Backing Plate	12 – Adapter	18 – Pot Plunger

Fig. 15-39

Extrusion Dies

Extrusion machines and dies are primarily used for the production from thermoplastics of continuous lengths of predetermined cross-sections, such as rods, filaments, tubing, wire-coating, and strips. To make a satisfactory product and to utilize the full capacity of the extruding machine usually involves making changes in the die or nozzle after an initial trial.

Such changes may involve not only the size of the orifice but also its shape.

If the equipment is properly designed and operated, a circular orifice will yield an extruded product of circular cross-section. But with orifices of other shapes the shape of the extruded material will differ, slightly or considerably, from that of the orifice as a result of asymmetry in frictional effects and in rate of flow at different parts of the cross-section. Hence the shape of the orifice has to be worked out by experiment.

The size of an extrusion die is only one of the factors which determine the cross-sectional dimensions of the extruded goods. They can be increased by increasing the pressure within the machine, and hence its rate of delivery, and they can be decreased by increasing the linear speed of the take-off mechanism to stretch the material issuing from the die, while it is still plastic. In order to gain the economy of operating the extruder at somewhere near its full capacity to deliver material to the die, it is customary to make the orifice of the die larger than the final cross-section of the extruded goods desired, and to reduce the oversized cross-section to the desired size by adjusting the speed of the take-off. Usually the orifice is made at first somewhat smaller than is likely to be needed, and is then enlarged on the basis of actual trial until it gives economical production of satisfactory extruded goods.

Figure 15-40 shows an extrusion die for a rectangular strip of thermoplastic. This die is made in two halves for economy in construction, and to facilitate any changes in size which may be found advisable.

The reduction in the width of the land at the mouth towards the outside

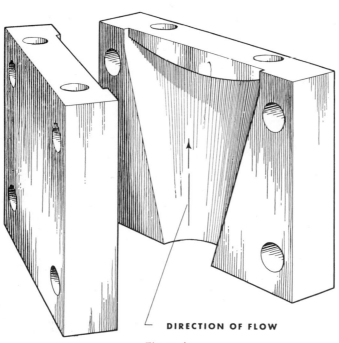

DIRECTION OF FLOW

Fig. 15-40

edges is to decrease the back pressure towards the outside, and increase the pressure in the center section, so as to maintain a uniform thickness across the full width of the extruded strip.

Figure 15-41 shows an extrusion die for tubing. This die is designed to extrude a range of tubing within certain limits, with a minimum outlay of material and labor. Thus, to increase the wall thickness, while maintaining the same outside diameter, requires merely replacing part *1* with another of smaller diameter. To increase outside diameter, while retaining the same inside diameter, requires making a new part *2,* of larger diameter. To decrease both outside and inside diameters, provided that this can not be done by stretching the extruded tube, requires replacing both parts *1* and *2* with others of suitable diameters. The adjusting screws are used to make the tubing concentric.

Air pressure is used to prevent the tubing from collapsing after leaving

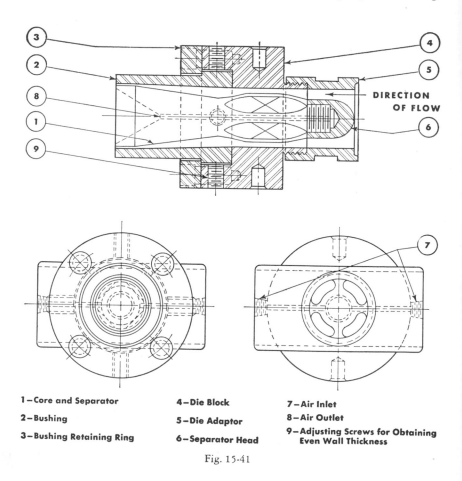

1—Core and Separator	4—Die Block	7—Air Inlet
2—Bushing	5—Die Adaptor	8—Air Outlet
3—Bushing Retaining Ring	6—Separator Head	9—Adjusting Screws for Obtaining Even Wall Thickness

Fig. 15-41

the die. Another method is to cool the tubing by passing it through a water-cooled jacket immediately after it leaves the die.

Figure 15-42 illustrates an extrusion die for tubing. This is the same as Fig. 15-41 except that a larger cross-section of material is provided between the end of the extruding member and the mouth of the die, as required for certain plastics.

Figure 15-43 shows an extrusion die for rods or filaments. Relief for back pressure has been incorporated in this die because of the small amount of material extruded. A pressure-relief valve is set while the machine is in operation, and when the back pressure builds up to this setting, the surplus material is either returned to the hopper or run off into a container.

The heater-adapter is designed to permit the use of a hinged band heater to prevent the material from cooling while being extruded through a small orifice.

Injection Molds for Thermoplastics

An injection mold is a mold, clamped under pressure, with an orifice through which a heat-softened thermoplastic is forced, or injected, to fill a cavity or cavities, in which it is allowed to cool before being ejected.

For controlling the temperature of the mold, channels or drilled passage-

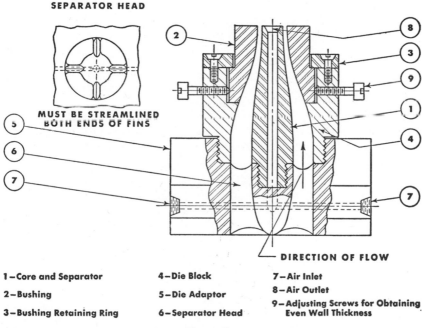

SEPARATOR HEAD

MUST BE STREAMLINED BOTH ENDS OF FINS

DIRECTION OF FLOW

1 – Core and Separator   4 – Die Block   7 – Air Inlet

2 – Bushing   5 – Die Adaptor   8 – Air Outlet

3 – Bushing Retaining Ring 6 – Separator Head   9 – Adjusting Screws for Obtaining
                                                        Even Wall Thickness

Fig. 15-42

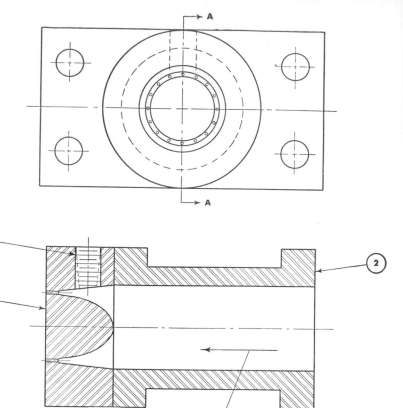

SECTION AA

1 — Back Pressure Relief Port   **2 — Heater Adaptor**   **3 — Die Body**

Fig. 15-43

ways, for circulating cold water, or water under controlled temperature, or steam, should be incorporated in the mold. To obtain maximum efficiency these channels or drilled passageways should be included in the original design and not added as an afterthought, when they cannot be properly located. Molds should be designed for rigidity to prevent deflection and consequent flashing of the material. Wide spans between supports should be reduced by the use of parallels or pillars.

The size of sprue, runners and gates is predicated on the characteristics of the molding material and the size, cross-section, and weight of the molded article. Materials having a low viscosity require a smaller sprue, runners and gates than do those of high viscosity. Both materials require larger sprue, runners and gates for articles of heavy cross-section than for articles of thin cross-section. Sprue, runners and gates should be smooth and polished.

Sprues. Figure 15-44 illustrates a sprue bushing. Sprues are generally tapered, the entry end being of the small diameter and the taper flaring outward toward the mold. The amount of taper is optional, but the larger tapers permit of easier removal from the sprue bushing.

Size of sprues at the small end may range from $\frac{5}{32}$ to $\frac{9}{16}$ in. in diameter, depending on the size, weight and cross-section of the molded article.

Cold-Slug Well and Sprue-Puller. The cold-slug well is a depression or well at the large end of the sprue, located in the movable half of the mold and provided with an ejector pin which forms the bottom. It acts as a receptacle to receive the relatively cool charge of material which emerges first from the nozzle, and also serves as an anchor to pull the sprue away from the nozzle when the mold is opened. It should be larger in diameter than the large

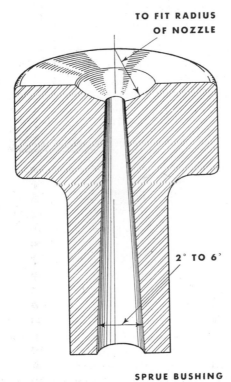

TO FIT RADIUS
OF NOZZLE

2° TO 6°

SPRUE BUSHING

Fig. 15-44

end of the sprue bushing; otherwise it may fail to serve its purpose, since the material will follow the path of least resistance and flow into the runners instead of being trapped in the slug well.

There are three methods in general use of providing an anchor to pull the sprue (see Fig. 15-45). The type to use is optional since all are equally effective.

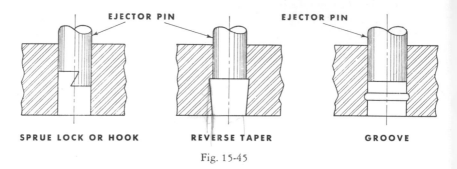

Fig. 15-45

Runners. Runners (Fig. 15-46) are of three types, full round (*A*), half round (*B*), and trapezoidal (*C*) in cross-section. The full round runner has the advantage of having the smallest periphery for a given diameter or cross-sectional area, and hence the least chilling effect on the thermoplastic material as it passes through the runner. It has the disadvantage that it must be cut in

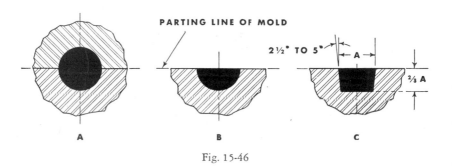

Fig. 15-46

both halves of the mold and be properly registered or mitered. The half round requires cutting in only one half of the mold, but, for the same diameter as the full round, the perimeter effective in chilling of the material as it passes through the runners is proportionately greater by approximately 60 per cent. A half round of the same cross-sectional area as the full round would have approximately 15 per cent greater perimeter. The trapezoidal shape requires cutting in only one half of the mold and is the preferred cross-section for runners, especially for materials of high viscosity. The depth of the runner should be approximately ⅔ of the width, and the sides should be tapered for easy removal from the mold.

Gates. The gate is the terminal portion of a runner which leads into the cavity. If possible, gates should be located for economical removal and finishing of the molded article. As a general rule they should be located on the heavy section of the article, since it is relatively easier to fill thin sections from the heavier sections than vice versa. A better flow pattern can be obtained and

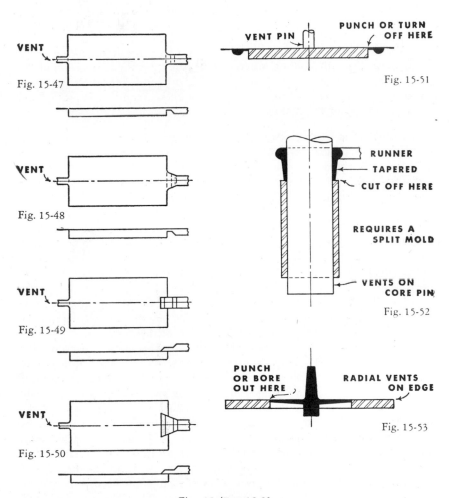

Figs. 15-47 to 15-53

weld lines reduced to a minimum. The various types of gates are as follows:

Straight gate on the side or edge of the molded article .... (Fig. 15-47)

Fan gate on the side or edge of the molded article .... (Fig. 15-48)

Straight top gate on the top or face of the molded article ... (Fig. 15-49)

Fan top gate on the top or face of the molded article .... (Fig. 15-50)

Ring gate around the outer periphery of the molded article
    (material flows from the outside to the center) .... (Fig. 15-51)

Collar gate on the end of tubular molded article (requires a
    split mold) .... (Fig. 15-52)

Center, disc or diaphragm gate (material flows from the
    center outward) .... (Fig. 15-53)

Vents. Vents are provided to allow the air to escape during filling of the cavity or cavities with molding material. They are generally in the form of flat grooves 0.002 to 0.008 in. deep and from $\frac{1}{8}$ to $\frac{1}{4}$ in. wide, located opposite the gate or at any point where air can form a pocket, and be compressed and cause "burning" of the molded article.

Ejector Pins. Proper location of ejector pins is essential to successful molding. Several factors should be considered. An ejector pin usually causes a mark on the molded article which, in many cases, has to be polished off. Deformation of parts by ejecting must be prevented. Sticking to the pins should be prevented, since that usually slows down production.

Molds having stripper plates usually function without causing these difficulties. Unfortunately, however, stripper plates can be used only under certain conditions, depending on the shape of the article that is to be molded. Ejector sleeves should always be recommended for articles that have cored holes, provided it is possible to make the sleeve thick enough to avoid breakage.

Holes to accommodate ejector pins should be relieved, i.e., given a clearance of 0.002 to 0.005 in., up to within a fraction of an inch of the face of the cavity, to facilitate the alignment and operation of the pins.

Figure 15-54 illustrates the use of overflow lugs as a means of preventing the ejector pins from marking the article. Care should be taken in determining the shape of this overflow. If it is properly designed, a minimum amount of flash will be left on the molded article. The gate, C, Fig. 15-55, should be made as short as possible—hardly more than $\frac{1}{32}$ in. The angle of the lug, D, Fig. 15-55, should be about 45 degrees. The distance E should be at least three times the diameter of the ejector pin. If the lug is made too short at this point, failure can be expected, since the lug will tend to tip rather than go out straight. A slight chamfer at F, Fig. 15-55, will prevent the edge of the molded article from breaking off when the lug is removed. The ejector pin should be placed as close to the cavity as possible. There is danger in

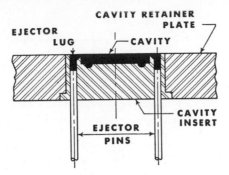

Courtesy Detroit Mold Engineering Co.

Fig. 15-54

placing the ejector pin too close, however, since that may cause section *G* to break.

Figure 15-56 shows another convenient way of placing ejector pins. This method of ejecting has, of course, its limitations and can be used only where little pressure is required to eject the article from the cavity.

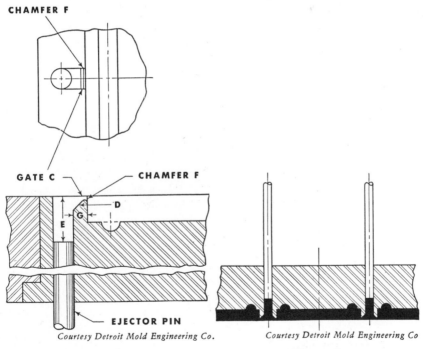

Courtesy Detroit Mold Engineering Co.   *Courtesy Detroit Mold Engineering Co*

Fig. 15-55   Fig. 15-56

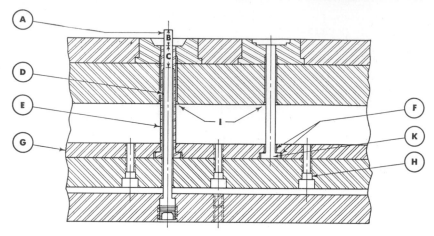

Fig. 15-57

There are various methods of fastening ejector pins into the ejector plate. Some of the most common designs are illustrated in Figs. 15-57 through 15-60. The advantages and disadvantages of each type are discussed below.

The most common design is illustrated in Fig. 15-57. An ejector-retainer plate, *G,* is fastened to the ejector plate proper. All ejector pins, ejector

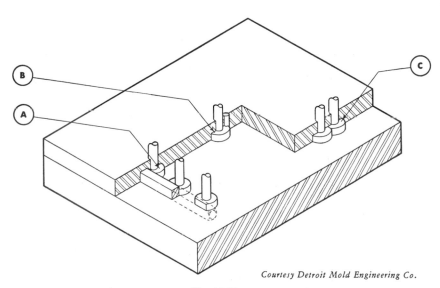

Fig. 15-58

sleeves and return pins are located in this plate. This construction makes
assembling of the mold easy, since the pins can be entered one by one into the
cavity plate. It is often very difficult to assemble large molds with a great
number of small ejector pins if the construction does not allow the pins to be
inserted individually. There is nearly always a slight misalignment between
the holes in the cavity plate and the ejector plate. Therefore, it is well to
make a clearance of from 1/64 to 1/32 in. around the heads of the pins, and
at least 0.001 in. clearance at K. This will permit the pins to find their
proper locations when the mold is assembled. The return pins, however,
should be installed rigidly, if no other guide for the ejector plate is provided.
The two-plate construction is also the most practical when ejector pins have to
be placed close together, as shown at C (Fig. 15-58). Figure 15-58 shows at B
an ejector pin which is locked in a certain position with a stop pin. This is
easily accomplished in a two-plate construction. Several pins can be locked
in position by inserting the bar as shown at A.

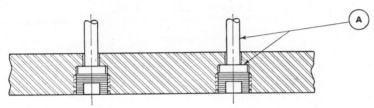

Courtesy Detroit Mold Engineering Co.

Fig. 15-59

Single plates, as shown in Fig. 15-59, can be used economically only when
a few ejector pins of small diameter are required. This construction also
makes it possible to adjust the pins for length, since the shoulder A can be
machined down to suit.

Figure 15-60 shows another single-plate design. This construction is far
more expensive than the two-plate arrangement illustrated in Fig. 15-57. It may
be argued that this is stronger than the two plates, but if the ejector-pin-
retainer plate (Fig. 15-57) is made heavy enough and has a sufficient number
of screws to hold the two plates together, equal strength can be obtained.

Ejector sleeves, E (Fig. 15-57), are preferred when the molded articles
have to be stripped off of one or more cores.

For ejector sleeves, it is important to select a suitable steel. Ejector
sleeves are subjected to severe stress and wear. The inside surfaces, as well
as the outside surfaces, should be made as hard as possible. If these surfaces
are not sufficiently hard, scoring of both cavity and core may take place. The
lower portion of the sleeve should be drawn to obtain maximum toughness,
while the upper part should be left hard to the full length of the ejector
movement.

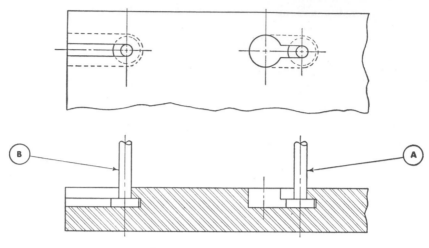

A AND B — EJECTOR PINS

Courtesy Detroit Mold Engineering Co.

Fig. 15-60

The outside diameter of the sleeve should be held about 0.001 to 0.002 in. smaller than the hole in the cavity. An equal clearance between the core and the sleeve should be maintained for a distance C (Fig. 15-57). The inside diameter of the sleeve should be held about 1/64 to 1/32 in. larger than the core, leaving a clearance as shown at D. The core, A, should be dimensioned so that the portion which extends into the molded article (distance B) is at least 1/64 in. smaller in diameter than the lower part. If this is not done, the reciprocating movement of the sleeve will injure the fine finish of the core. Distance C should be at least $\frac{3}{8}$ in. longer than the entire movement of the ejector plate. If the clearance extends too far, the shoulder and the end of the core may be damaged when the sleeve is retracted. It is also important that a clearance of $\frac{1}{64}$ in. be made around the outside of the sleeve. This clearance, however, should not extend too far, since it is necessary to have a bearing at least $\frac{1}{2}$ in. long at the cavity. In order to facilitate assembling of the mold, a large chamfer should be made in all holes where ejector pins and sleeves are entered, as shown at I.

Usually cavity plates can be drilled in such fashion as to obtain uniform control of temperature. However, deep cavities of complicated cross-section are apt to necessitate cooling of the cores. Two variations of a common method of water-cooling cores are shown in Figs. 15-61 and 15-62. Air instead of water can be used also.

Figure 15-61 shows a core with an enlarged shank. A water line is drilled from the bottom of the core and sealed with a large pipe plug. The plug, in turn, is drilled and tapped to admit a tube which extends to the top of the hole

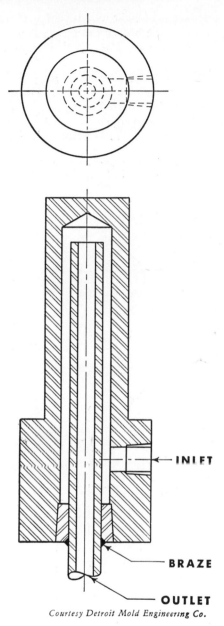

Courtesy Detroit Mold Engineering Co.

Fig. 15-61

in the core. A second hole is brought into the enlarged part of the core from the side. The pipe through the bottom can serve as inlet or outlet. The side hole must be connected to the outside source of water by a pipe threaded into the core.

When it is not convenient to bring one of the lines out through the bottom of the core, an arrangement as in Fig. 15-62 is used. The water channel is drilled as before, and a baffle is brazed to the plug, to seal the bottom of the hole. The baffle is flat and wide enough to fit snugly in the drilled hole. Water inlet and outlet are drilled on opposite sides of the baffle.

Unscrewing Devices. For unscrewing threaded articles simultaneously from a multiple-cavity mold, a rack and pinions can be used if the articles have

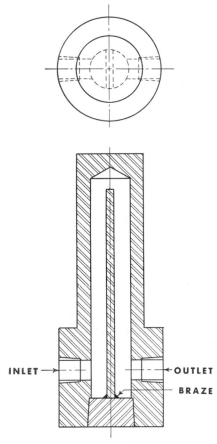

Courtesy Detroit Mold Engineering Co.

Fig. 15-62

short threads. For long threads a reduced-speed motor-driven device is used. This is operated by limit switches which start and stop the motor at certain positions of the moving platen when the mold is opening.

The means for rotating the members of the unscrewing device may consist of a train of spur gears, worm and worm wheels, or sprockets and chain (Fig. 15-63).

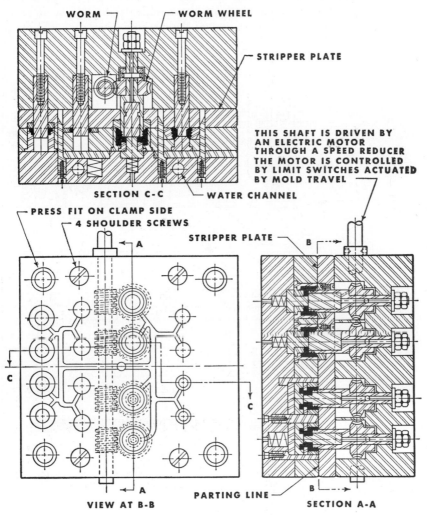

WORM ⌐   ⌐ WORM WHEEL

⌐ STRIPPER PLATE

THIS SHAFT IS DRIVEN BY
AN ELECTRIC MOTOR
THROUGH A SPEED REDUCER
THE MOTOR IS CONTROLLED
BY LIMIT SWITCHES ACTUATED
BY MOLD TRAVEL

SECTION C-C   ⌐ WATER CHANNEL

⌐ PRESS FIT ON CLAMP SIDE
⌐ 4 SHOULDER SCREWS

A

STRIPPER PLATE ⌐   B

C

C

A

VIEW AT B-B   PARTING LINE ⌐   B   SECTION A-A

Courtesy Santay Corp., From "Plastics Mold Engineering,"
The American Technical Society, Publishers

Fig. 15-63

Mold Designs. The number and variety of pieces which can be molded is infinite. In the following pages will be shown those in common use, and no attempt will be made to illustrate any of the exceptional or complicated designs.

Molded pieces having holes or apertures through their sides, or undercuts, require side cores, which must be retracted as the mold is opened and before ejection takes place.

For relatively short draws this is accomplished by using round guide-pins set at an angle, or offset cams which are either square or rectangular in cross-section and operated by the movement of the machine when the mold opens

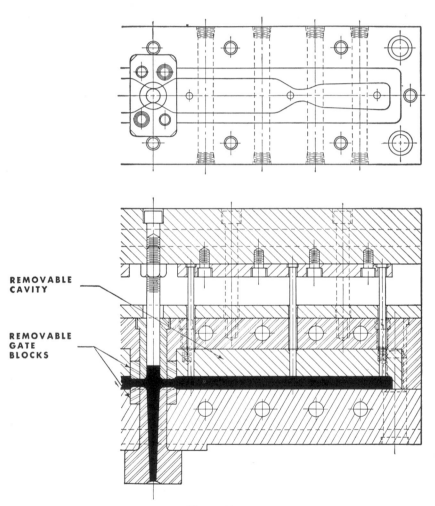

REMOVABLE
CAVITY

REMOVABLE
GATE
BLOCKS

Fig. 15-64

and closes. This type of cam motion is used also to open and close split dies. Rack and pinion also may be used.

For exceptionally long draws, and especially for pulling long core pins, where the movement of the platen is insufficient to provide the necessary length of draw, it is customary to use auxiliary hydraulic or air cylinders.

Figure 15-64 illustrates a simple design of two-cavity injection mold for brush backs. This mold has "set-in," or removable, cavities and gate blocks, with ample water ports for control of temperature.

Molded articles of thick cross-section require large gates and runners to produce good flow-pattern.

Figure 15-65 illustrates a multiple-cavity injection mold of the conventional ejector type for molding golf tees. The ejector pins serve to form the points on the ends of the tees, to vent the cavity and to eject the molded articles.

Figures 15-66 and 15-66A illustrate a multiple-cavity mold for molding internal threads in caps and external threads on tubular containers. The split-cavity, cam-actuated design is used for the external threads, and rack-and-pinion design for unscrewing the core pins which form the internal threads. The ejector pin which forms the bottom of the container serves also as a vent for trapped air.

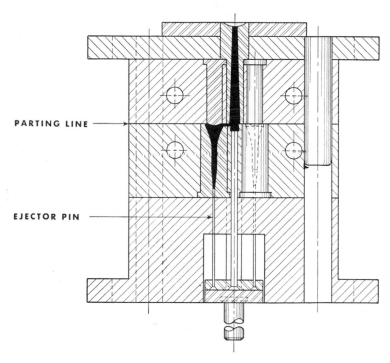

PARTING LINE

EJECTOR PIN

Fig. 15-65

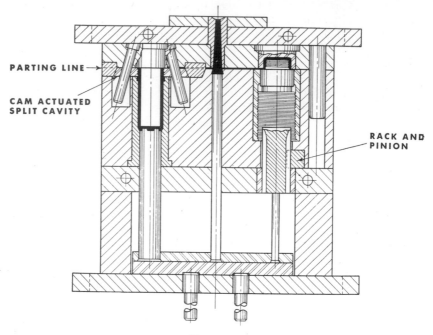

PARTING LINE →

CAM ACTUATED
SPLIT CAVITY

RACK AND
PINION

Fig. 15-66

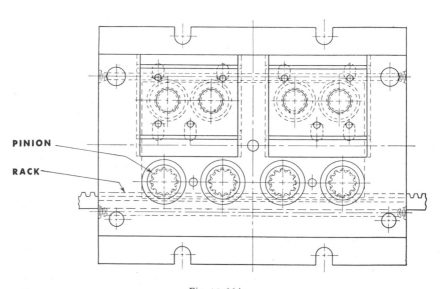

PINION

RACK

Fig. 15-66A

Figure 15-67 illustrates the type of design used for coring horizontal openings or undercuts in a molded article, and a method for holding inserts during the molding operation. This design contains cammed movements. The article requires cores to be drawn in three directions, and production necessitates four cavities in the mold.

The core for the rectangular opening is pulled by the conventional cam and locked by a small heel-block wholly contained in the front cavity-retainer plate as shown in section D-D. The opposed cores are needed to hold the two brass inserts in place during molding. Had these cores been pulled in the same manner as the rectangular window, it would have been quite difficult to load the inserts. However, a novel mechanism, the feature of this mold, shown in section C-C made this easy.

Round pins, $1\frac{1}{2}$ in. in diameter, are mounted on gibs at an angle in the ejector plate so that the forward movement of the ejector plate forces the ends of the pins away from the cavities both horizontally and vertically. The cores which hold the inserts are attached to the ends of the pins. This motion serves both to strip the articles from the mold and to remove the cores from the inserts. In the "out" position the cores are readily accessible for loading the inserts on them.

The best time for removing the gates from an injection-molded piece is when it is still warm and the material slightly plastic. This permits shearing a heavy gate with minimum effort and without danger of tearing into the article. This can be done by hand in the case of a single cavity, but when several articles are molded at once on a rapid cycle the operator can seldom trim as fast as the machine produces. Special trimming fixtures for trimming a complete shot are usually made when production warrants.

If this operation can be performed inside the mold itself, conditions are perfect for trimming. Round articles that can have at least a 1/16 in. shoulder, such as the knob shown, are adapted for trimming inside the mold. The essential conditions for successful gate-shearing are a round cross-section and a slight straight section on the bottom of the article where the gate is cut. The design of a mold for such an article is shown in Fig. 15-68.

This is a six-unit mold to produce a knob. It is a three-plate mold. What is normally the "X" or stripper plate is a floating plate containing the lower part of the cavities. A conical opening is bored in the center of this plate and blued to match a truncated cone turned on the top of the "B" plate. The sprue bushing extends through the "A" plate to the "B" plate. Runners are cut in the "X" plate from the sprue bushing to the bottom of the cavities in the "X" plate.

When the mold opens, the sleeves push the moldings out and in so doing shear the gates against the bottom of the cavity. The pressure of the sleeves against the gates is sufficient to move the "X" plate as far as the

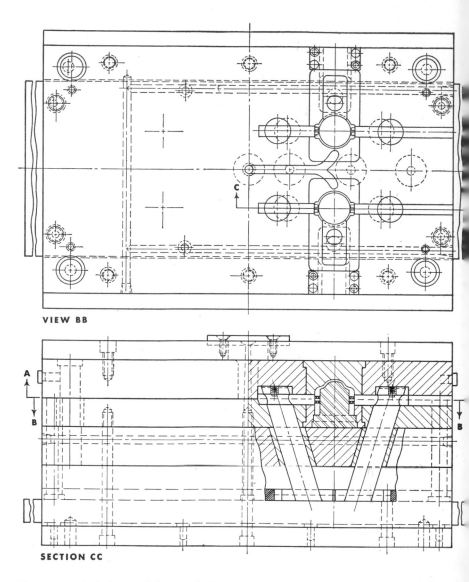

VIEW BB

SECTION CC

Fig. 15-67. A design used for coring horizontal openings or undercuts in a molded article, and a method for holding inserts during molding operation.

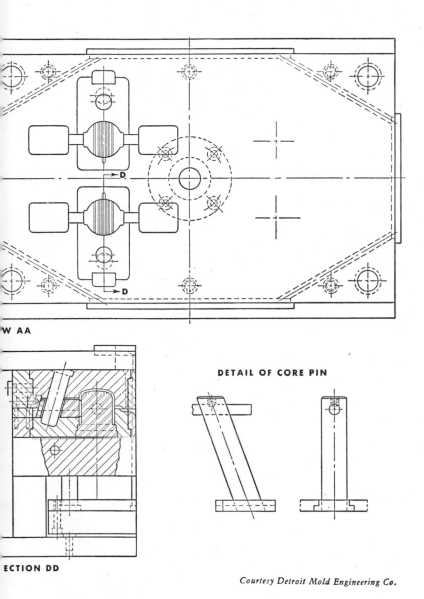

W AA

DETAIL OF CORE PIN

ECTION DD

Courtesy Detroit Mold Engineering Co.

Fig. 15-67 (*cont'd*)

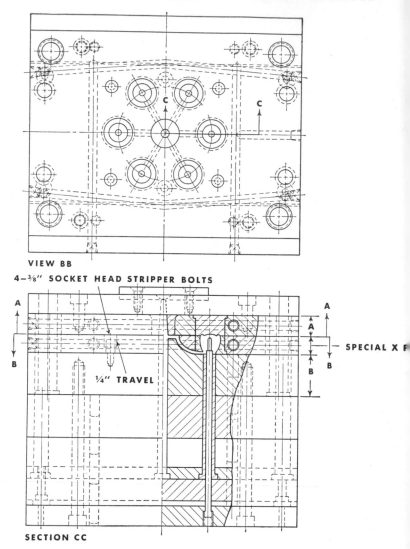

VIEW BB

4-⅜" SOCKET HEAD STRIPPER BOLTS

¼" TRAVEL

SPECIAL X P

SECTION CC

Fig. 15-68. A six-cavity gate-shearing mold.

stripper bolts will allow. At this point the shearing takes place. The sprue-puller continues to move forward, pushing out the runners, which have been freed when the "X" plate was moved, through the hole in the "X" plate.

Figure 15-69 illustrates one type of design used for center-gating multiple-cavity molds.

The first molds for molding escutcheons or rings had the cavities gated

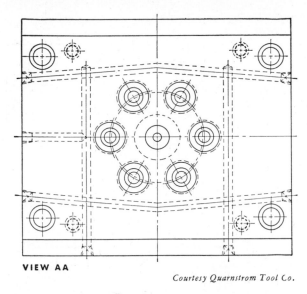

VIEW AA

Courtesy Quarnstrom Tool Co.

Fig. 15-68 (*cont'd*)

on the parting line at one side, but this method of gating resulted in many cases in a weld line opposite the gate. Subsequent shrinkage of the escutcheon due to variations of temperature or loss of plasticizer caused the rings to tighten on the handles, and breakage at the weld line took place.

The solution for this problem is gating in the center. The plastic flows radially from the center of the cavity to the outside, thus eliminating any chance for weakness due to a weld line.

Figure 15-69 shows the layout of a six-cavity mold for making the article illustrated in Fig. 15-69A. A floating plate, attached to the front die, is added to the mold. The cavities are inserted in this plate and runners are cut partially in it and partially in the "A" plate. The runners are made heavy so that the plastic can enter the cavity as quickly as possible and with a minimum of cooling.

It is essential, when the mold opens, for the small sprue to break at the point where it joins the heavy runner. If it should not break here, and should pull off of the sprue-puller, it would be difficult to get the articles out of the mold. Thus the small end of the small sprue should be made as small as is consistent with good molding.

The latch mechanism makes it impossible for the mold to open incorrectly. The floating plate is anchored by the latch to the back die until the back die has moved $2\frac{1}{4}$ in. At this point the main sprue will be free of the sprue bushing, and the latch will release. Thus there will be a clearance

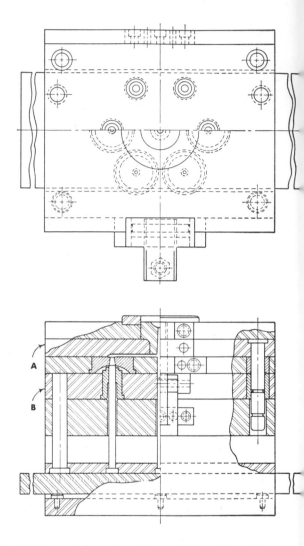

Fig. 15-69. A design used for center-gating multiple-cavity molds.

**NING TO
T TRAVEL
IRED**

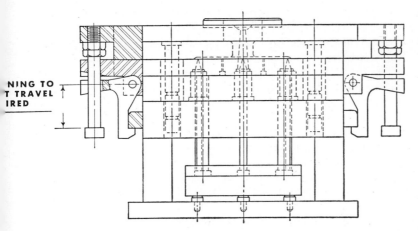

Courtesy Detroit Mold Engineering Co.

Fig. 15-69 (*cont'd*)

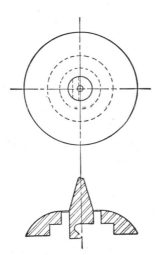

Courtesy Detroit Mold Engineering Co.

Fig. 15-69A

of 2¼ in. between the floating plate and the "A" plate, providing adequate space for knocking out the runners and sprue. Further travel pulls the moldings from the cavities.

It is not advisable to cut multiple runners instead of a solid disc gate, as runners will cause weld lines and defeat the purpose of the center gate.

The balance of the mold is of conventional design. The cores are held by shoulders counterbored in the "B" plate. They need not be dowelled or screwed in place for they are circular in section and rotation will not change the molded article. No ejector pins are needed, as the sprue-pullers serve also to remove the moldings. The latches are screwed and dowelled to the long sides of the floating plate and are simple and sturdy.

Removal of the center gate from the article can be accomplished in several ways—by turning in a lathe or by using a rotating tool in a drill press, or a punch and die in a small punch press.

Figure 15-70 illustrates a direct center-gated single-cavity tumbler mold with excellent coring of the male and female halves of the mold for accurate control of temperature.

Figure 15-71 illustrates a four-cavity center-gated tumbler mold. When the mold starts to open, the spring-loaded plate, 2, moves away from plate 1 a sufficient distance to allow the sprue and runners to drop through the space formed by the separation. The movement of plate 3 continues after plate 2 has reached the limit of its movement, and the individual sprues are broken off at the runners.

Restricted Gates

Definition. The term "restricted gates" as used in this section has a special meaning, being applied to gates having thickness so small that the material in them solidifies rapidly as soon as the cavity has been filled. This rapid solidification can be made to serve further purposes in the production of sound uniform moldings, as will be discussed later.

The gate, which constitutes the entrance from the runner (or from the sprue) into the mold cavity, is normally made smaller than the runner, for two reasons: (1) to facilitate the cutting off of the molded article from the runner (degating) and to minimize the resulting scar on the article, which may have to be smoothed off afterward; (2) to promote uniformity of filling of the several cavities.

Balancing of Cavities. In designing a multicavity mold, it is desirable to place all cavities at the same distance from the sprue, but more often than not this is impossible by reason of the number and size of the cavities (and particularly so in "family molds" containing cavities of various sizes for the simultaneous molding of a variety of articles).

In any mold in which access to some cavities is more direct and easy than to some others, one or more cavities may receive material which has had time

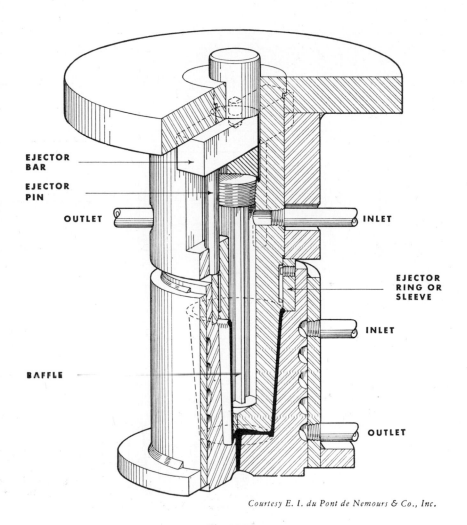

EJECTOR
BAR

EJECTOR
PIN

OUTLET

INLET

EJECTOR
RING OR
SLEEVE

INLET

BAFFLE

OUTLET

Courtesy E. I. du Pont de Nemours & Co., Inc.

Fig. 15-70

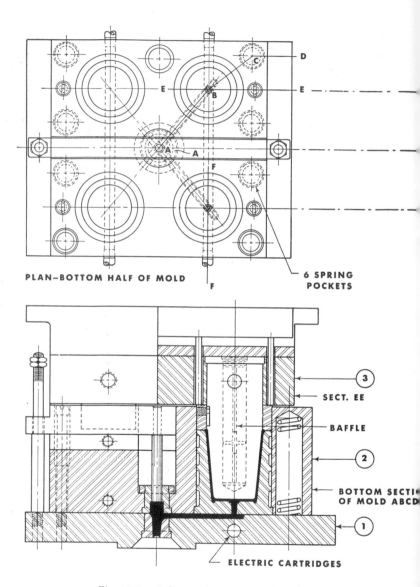

PLAN—BOTTOM HALF OF MOLD

6 SPRING POCKETS

③ SECT. EE

BAFFLE

②

BOTTOM SECTION OF MOLD ABCD

①

ELECTRIC CARTRIDGES

Fig. 15-71. A four-cavity center-gated tumbler mold.

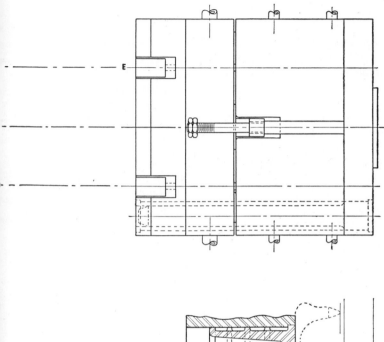

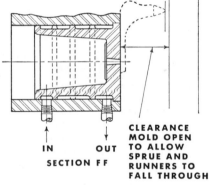

IN   **OUT**   **CLEARANCE
MOLD OPEN
TO ALLOW
SPRUE AND
RUNNERS TO
FALL THROUGH**

SECTION F F

Courtesy E. I. du Pont de Nemours & Co., Inc.

Fig. 15-71 (*cont'd*)

to cool, and may become only incompletely filled, or filled under smaller pressure than that applied to other cavities. This and any other dissimilarity in the manner of filling is likely also to result in differences in dimensions of articles produced in cavities which themselves have exactly the same dimensions, and thus to make it difficult or impossible to mold within specified tolerances.

Such inequalities are commonly corrected by adjusting the sizes of the gates.

An example of a layout in which balancing of cavities is essential is a series of cavities lying in the same plane and fed laterally from a single runner. If the gates are large, the cavity nearest the sprue will become partially filled before the runner itself has been filled throughout its length. Then, before the first cavity has been completely filled, the successive cavities beyond it begin to receive material, the material in the first cavity starts to solidify, and by the time the runner is full and beginning to apply full pressure on the several gates the first gate may be so obstructed by solidification that this cavity will remain only incompletely filled. If, on the other hand, the gates be made sufficiently small, the runner will be filled to its entire length before any of the cavities begins to receive material, and if the resistances offered by the successive gates are properly graduated (with access easiest at the most distant gate), then the several cavities will become filled simultaneously and uniformly.

Thus, merely for the two reasons already stated (ease of degating and equalization of fill), gates are generally speaking restricted, in the sense that they are small in comparison with the runners.

Typical Forms. Typical restricted gates are shown in Figs. 15-72 - 15-74. Figure 15-72 shows an edge gate of rectangular cross-section, entering the cavity at the parting line and at the edge or end of the cavity. Figure 15-73 shows a circular cross-section, entering the mold cavity at any advantageous position, usually not at the parting line; such a gate, of very small diameter, is normally called a pinpoint gate. The annular gate typified by Fig. 15-74 is a restricted gate of which the circumference corresponds to the width of a rectangular gate.

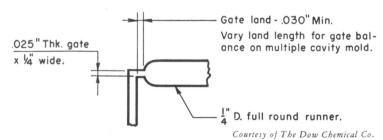

Courtesy of The Dow Chemical Co.

Fig. 15-72. Typical restricted edge gate (single or multiple cavity).

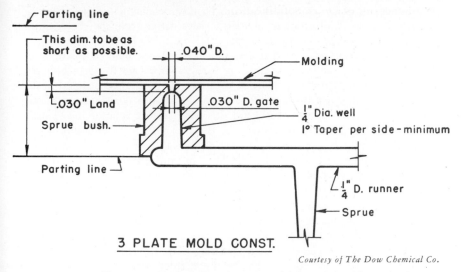

3 PLATE MOLD CONST.

Courtesy of The Dow Chemical Co.

Fig. 15-73. Typical pin-point gate multiple cavity mold.

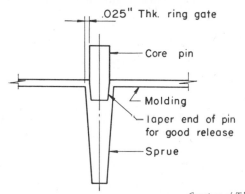

Courtesy of The Dow Chemical Co.

Fig. 15-74. Typical restricted gate at cored hole.
Direct sprue one cavity.

Functions of Small Size. The utility of restricted gates in balancing cavities, and in degating, results solely from their small size, as such. Two other minor benefits result also from the restrictions, as such: (1) passage through the restricted gate promotes homogenization of the plastic, and this may be of especial value in the molding of materials colored by dry blending (on the other hand, it defeats any attempt to produce articles having a distinct mottle) ; (2) a rise in temperature of the plastic caused by internal friction as it traverses the restricted gate increases its fluidity and thus promotes the perfect molding of articles having very thin sections.

Functions of Quick Solidification. Further benefits of restricted gating to the quality and uniformity of molded articles derive from the rapid solidification of material in the restricted gate after the cavity has been filled.

When a gate is so large that material in it remains fluid or plastic after the cavity is filled, and ram pressure is withdrawn before the gate becomes sealed by solidification, the pressure of compressed unsolidified material in the cavity, and of the compressed metal of the mold itself, may force some plastic out of the mold through the gate, and this may create a zone of low density in the article, adjacent to the gate. On the other hand, if ram pressure is maintained until the gate is closed by solidification, thermal shrinkage within the cavity may permit additional material to be forced through the gate into the cavity, and a zone of high density is thereby created. In either case, the lack of uniformity of the molded article may manifest itself in residual stresses, which may cause warpage or crazing, or localized mechanical weakness near the gate, or may impair the resistance of the article to being distorted by elevated service temperature.

Also, there is evidence that the packing of too much material into the cavity may make it difficult to remove the molded article from the cavity, and tempt the operator to combat the sticking by reducing the temperature of the mold to a point which will be damaging to the surface quality and the form-stability of the article.

These difficulties can be largely eliminated by using a restricted gate, since the rapid solidification which takes place in it, when initial flow has stopped, seals the cavity so that secondary flow, either out or in, cannot take place.

Design and Dimensions. Since the gate must be not so much restricted as to obstruct the proper filling of the mold, and since also the various gates in a multicavity mold may have to be made different, for purposes of equalizing the flow into the respective cavities, the design must be based on compromise, and usually worked out by trial and error.

The dimensions of a restricted gate are its thickness (height), its width, and its length (land), and these dimensions must be selected to achieve (1) the desired degree of restriction of flow for purposes of balancing a multicavity mold and (2) the desired rapidity of solidification of material in the gate.

The restrictive effect of a small gate upon the flow of plastified material from runner to cavity depends upon its cross-section (thickness and width) and its length, and also to some degree upon the way in which the cross-section of the runner is decreased as it enters the gate. The rate of solidification of plastic within the gate depends primarily, however, upon one dimension, namely the minimum cross-sectional dimension; usually the thickness is less than the width, and is thus the determining factor, but this distinction does not hold, of course, for a gate which is square or circular.

Thickness is usually the most important dimension. It affects principally the rate of solidification in the gate, but also it influences the amount of loss of pressure sustained in passing through the gate, and the velocity of the stream of plastic entering the cavity. Too great velocity must be avoided, since jetting of the stream from the gate to the opposite end of a long cavity is likely to cause foldovers, and hence flow marks, irregularities of shrinkage, and even entrapment of air within the molded article.

Practical experience has shown that the thickness (or the diameter) of the gate should be from 0.4 to 0.6 of the thickness of the section of the cavity at which the gate is located. But a gate having a thickness (or a diameter) greater than 0.080 in. is usually ineffective as a restricted gate within the meaning of this section, because material in it will not solidify fast enough to seal it promptly.

The width of a ribbon-type rectangular gate (Fig. 15-72), or the circumference of an annular gate (Fig. 15-74), does not influence the rate of solidification, but does directly affect the rate at which material enters the cavity.

The length (or land) of a restricted gate of given thickness has a direct effect upon the resistance to flow presented by the gate. Advantage of this is taken in equalizing the flow into several cavities by giving them gates of different lengths.

The length of land influences also the rate of solidification of material in the gate after the cavity has been filled.

It is a general practical rule that the length of the land be not less than the thickness of the gate.

When it is necessary to vary the degree of restriction of various gates in a single mold, in order to equalize the filling of cavities at different distances from the sprue, this minimum land is used in gates for the most distant cavities, and progressively longer lands for cavities nearer to the sprue; those nearest to the sprue may have lands twice as long as the minimum.

(If for some special reason all of the gates in a mold must be identical, then some degree of balancing can be achieved by differences in the sizes of runners, provided the runners are narrow enough to exert appreciable resistance to flow.)

The size of a restricted gate must be designed with consideration of the fluidity of the material which it is to handle. For nylon, which at molding temperature is the most fluid of current plastics, the gates may be smaller than, e.g., for acrylics. And the same applies to the size of runners.

In a mold designed for nylon the diameter of the runner should be not less than half the thickness of the thickest section of the article being molded, and should in no case be less than $\frac{1}{16}$ in. And at every right-angle turn the diameter of the runner, passing toward the sprue, should be increased by $\frac{1}{16}$ in. For other plastics, these minima should be greater, to accommodate their greater viscosities.

Since the temperature of the mold has a considerable effect upon the flow of the plastic through the gates and within the cavities, it is obvious that during trial runs, made as basis for adjusting the cavities into balance, the temperature must be that at which the mold is to be operated in commercial production.

The junction of a restricted gate with the cavity should always be rounded off slightly (e.g., on a radius of 0.010 in.), to reduce jetting of the plastic into the cavity and to prevent the molded article from being marred by breakage of the gate material from its point of attachment to the article.

Location. For molding articles of thin section, it is usually desirable to locate the gate midway in the section and midway in the length. For articles of thick section, the gate should be located to feed at right angles to the principal face of the article and at or near one end. But with very small gates, and particularly with pinpoint gates, these general rules can be relaxed, and also less attention needs be given to locating the gate at a point where any scar from its separation will be inconspicuous.

Pressure Losses. The benefits of restricted gates are gained only at the expense of the loss of pressure which they occasion (variously estimated at half or more of the available applied pressure). Thus, when restricted gates are used, it becomes important to minimize losses of pressure elsewhere in the system, from ram to gate.

In the cold end of the heating cylinder, dissipation of pressure can, with some plastics, be reduced by an external lubricant on the granules. A long tapered nozzle can advantageously be replaced by one in which the channel diameter is decreased to the orifice diameter by an abrupt curvature. Runners are preferably of circular cross-section; if the runner must be located entirely in one section of the mold, then a slightly tapered square (i.e., trapezoidal) cross-section is best. The change of cross-section from runner to gate should be abrupt, by way of a spherical radius, rather than gradual, by taper. Secondary sprues used for surface gates should have the smallest practicable taper.

Operation. When restricted gates are used, the cycle can in many cases be shortened, since the time of dwell of the plunger can be very brief—usually not more than 1 or 2 seconds after completion of the forward stroke. For if the gates have been sealed by solidification in accordance with design, there is nothing to be gained by continuing the pressure. If the moldings exhibit sink marks, the remedy is not to continue the dwell, in order to force more plastic through a gate which is sealed, or in process of being sealed, but rather to increase slightly the thickness of the gate, so as to fill the mold more quickly and to retard slightly the rate of solidification in the gate.

Benefits. The use of restricted gates (in the sense defined earlier) may yield several benefits:

(a) accurate equalization of the conditions of filling of all of the cavities in a mold, with resulting uniformity in dimensions and quality of the molded articles;

(b) control of the degree of filling of the cavities, through prevention of secondary flow, into or out of the cavities, after the initial filling, and thereby

(1) a reduction in the development of internal stresses which tend to cause warpage, crazing, local weakness near the gate, and distortion under heat in service;

(2) a reduction in tendency of the article to stick in the mold, which reduction permits the use of higher temperature in the mold, with benefit to finish and form-stability of the article;

(c) a shortening of molding cycle by reducing the time of dwell;

(d) improvement in homogenity of material entering the cavity;

(e) greater ease of filling cavities of small cross-section;

(f) greater ease of degating and finishing, and hence more latitude of choice in location of the gate on the article.

A special case, in which the use of very small gates is mandatory, is the technique of "hot runner" molding. The material in the sprue and runners, instead of being hardened by chilling, and removed from the mold along with the molded articles, is kept hot and remains in the mold between shots. The chilled molded article, with hardened gate material attached, must be detached from the fluid or plastic material in the runner. If the gate is not very small, the hardening of the article next to the gate is unduly retarded, and there is risk of distorting this soft portion while detaching it. Also, with a large gate, the detachment is not clean—even if the material in the gate has been properly solidified, it will drag behind it some soft material from the runner. For these reasons, a quickly-freezing gate is essential in this technique.

Design of Molds for Nylon

The design of a mold for nylon should be based on the same general considerations that are followed in designing for other commercial thermoplastics.

Some mold-makers, having in mind the fluidity of nylon in the molten state, tend to reduce clearances on a mold for nylon to such an extent that scoring of moving metal parts occurs. This is not necessary, for nylon sets so fast that it will not flow as far in a thin groove as will some other, slower-setting, molding compounds. Also the tendency of nylon to flash may be effectively minimized by adjustment of ram speed in combination with use of low injection pressure, which latter may, however, require careful attention to the design of the gate, in order to ensure filling of the cavity.

When objectionable flashing occurs, a measurement of the thickness of the flash will indicate the method to be used in overcoming it. If the thickness of the flash is less than 0.002 in., alteration of the molding conditions or of the design of the gate should eliminate it. If the flash measures 0.002 in. or more, the mold should be altered to reduce the clearance.

A vent for a cavity to be used for molding nylon should be no deeper than 0.0015 in. unless a fin on the molding can be tolerated.

Mold Shrinkage. Shrinkage, number of cavities, and sizes of gates and runners are factors which may require special consideration with any thermoplastic. This is equally true of nylon.

The mold shrinkage of FM-10001 nylon, the most common formulation for injection molding, is usually between 0.010 in. per in. and 0.025 in. per in., depending on the thickness of the molded article and the conditions of molding. Thin sections show less unit shrinkage than do thick sections. Shrinkages as low as 0.007 in. per in. and as high as 0.040 in. per in. have been observed. Estimating shrinkage is a disconcerting task, but the following is offered as a guide:

Thickness of Molded Article (In.)	Estimated Shrinkage (In. per In.)
$\frac{1}{32}$	0.010
$\frac{1}{16}$	0.012
$\frac{1}{8}$	0.015
$\frac{1}{4}$	0.022

The factors affecting the shrinkage of nylon are the same as for other thermoplastics. Temperature of mold, length of cycle, and dwell time of the plunger are the important factors.

High mold temperatures increase shrinkage. Incidentally, many molders think that a hot mold is required for nylon. Actually, a cold mold, at about 70°F, should be used for thin sections when maximum toughness is desired.

Short cycles and short dwell times increase shrinkage. Cycles are generally estimated on the basis of one minute for each $\frac{1}{4}$ in. of thickness of the molded piece, but, if good dimensional accuracy is to be maintained, the estimated cycle is usually increased by 50 per cent. (This rule of thumb for estimating the cycle assumes that the cycle is determined by set-up time in the mold rather than by the plastifying capacity of the cylinder.)

Although the shrinkage of nylon is relatively high, it is being molded commercially with the accuracy required in such industrial items as bearings, gears, and cams. On a close-tolerance job it is generally necessary to operate a sample cavity in the production mold base, with a complete runner system and under anticipated production conditions, in order to establish the exact shrinkage, and thus to determine the proper dimensions for the production cavities. For gear cavities, it is suggested that the sample cavity be made to mold a simple gear blank, to save the expense of cutting teeth in a sample cavity; it can be assumed that the teeth in the production cavities will not have a significant effect on shrinkage.

Where good dimensional stability is required of articles of nylon in high-temperature service, it is recommended that they be heat-treated to relieve residual molding stresses. This treatment will immediately develop the additional shrinkage which might otherwise occur in service. When heat-treatment is to be used, this additional shrinkage must be allowed for in establishing the dimensions of the cavity. Pieces molded in the sample cavity are annealed and measured. The production cavities can then be made to give articles of correct dimensions after heat-treatment.

It has been found that heat-treatment tends to reduce variation in the dimensions of molded articles, and that factors that ordinarily have considerable effect on shrinkage, such as mold temperature, are not so important if the article is to be heat-treated.

The heat-treating of nylon should be done in the absence of air, and hence preferably by immersion in a suitable liquid.

Heat-treatment at a given temperature ensures against dimensional change caused by relief of stresses in service below the temperature of the heat-treatment. Hence, the temperature of the heat-treating liquid should be well above the temperature to which the molded article will be exposed in service, and thus will be preferably about 350°F; but it should not be above 400°F.

Upon removal from the bath, the molded articles must be cooled slowly, and in the absence of drafts, to prevent development of stresses. This can be done conveniently in cardboard boxes.

The liquid used for the heat-treating bath must be stable at the temperature used; must not give off unpleasant or toxic fumes or vapors; must not present a fire hazard; must not attack nylon; should not require special or expensive equipment; and should be cheap.

High-boiling hydrocarbons (oils or waxes) may be used, if the residual film which they leave on the articles is not objectionable.

Usually preferable is a heat-transfer salt, which melts completely at about 290°F. It attacks aluminum, but can be melted in a vessel of iron or steel, Its water-solubility simplifies the cleaning of the articles afterward.

The bath should be heated electrically, with thermostatic control of the temperature. Heat should be supplied from the side walls as well as the bottom of the vessel.

Small items may be heat-treated in quantity by loading them into a wire basket and immersing the basket. The basket has a lid to prevent the articles from floating.

For articles of wall thickness less than 0.125 in., the minimum time of immersion is 10 min. Articles of greater wall thickness may require up to 30 min. No harm is done by adopting 30 min as standard for articles of all sizes.

Rinsing with water to remove residues of heat-transfer salt must be deferred until the articles have been cooled.

Number of Cavities. A common mistake in the design of molds for nylon is to put too many cavities into the mold. This is particularly true for articles of thin section. In determining the optimum number of cavities, the following factors should be considered, and a calculation made of limit imposed by each upon the number of cavities which can be used:

1. shot capacity of the machine;
2. clamping capacity of the machine;
3. plastifying capacity of the machine;
4. total cost of mold and operation.

Calculations are made as follows:

N_1 = number of cavities based on shot capacity of the machine;

N_2 = number of cavities based on clamping capacity of the machine;

N_3 = number of cavities based on plastifying capacity of the cylinder;

N_4 = number of cavities based on costs;

S = shot capacity of the machine, in ounces;

W_p = weight of the molded piece, in ounces;

W_r = weight of the sprue and runner, in ounces;

C = clamping capacity of the machine, in tons;

A_r = projected area of the sprue and runners, in square inches;

A_p = projected area of the molded piece, in square inches;

P = plastifying capacity of the heating cylinder, in pounds per hour;

T = over-all cycle, in seconds.

The calculation on the basis of shot capacity is usually based on the assumption that the size of the shot should not exceed two-thirds of the shot capacity of the machine. Hence

$$N_1 = \frac{\frac{2}{3}S - W_r}{W_p}$$

But for some machines this is not the case, and the fraction preceding S in the formula may be altered to suit the particular machine.

The clamping capacity of the machine is usually the limiting factor in the molding of thin flat articles. It is desirable to have five tons of clamping force for each square inch of projected cavity area. Hence the formula for calculating the number of cavities on the basis of clamping capacity is

$$N_2 = \frac{C/5 - A_r}{A_p}$$

On the basis of the plastifying capacity of the cylinder, the number of cavities is calculated by the formula

$$N_3 = \frac{PT/225 - W_r}{W_p}$$

Judgment must be used in assigning a value for P, the plastifying capacity of the cylinder. The records of past performance of the machine constitute a starting point, but it must not be expected that maximum past performance can be duplicated in a given case. For one thing, the temperature to which the compound must be heated by the cylinder will directly affect P—the higher the temperature, the higher the plastifying capacity in pounds per hour. It is desirable to estimate P from the past performance of the cylinder in the molding of articles of about the same thickness as those which are to be molded.

N_4 may be determined as shown in the following example. Assume that the mold cost for a particular article would be as follows:

Number of Cavities	Cost of Mold
64	$4500
32	3000
16	2000
8	1500

Also, assume a charge of $10 per hr for operating the machine, and a total production which will require a 64-cavity mold to operate 60 hr. The following table may then be prepared:

No. of Cavities	Operating (Hr)	Operating Cost	Mold Cost	Total Cost
64	60	$ 600	$4500	$5100
32	120	1200	3000	4200
(24)	(160)	(1600)	(2500)	(4100)
16	240	2400	2000	4400
8	480	4800	1500	6300

Interpolation shows that total cost will be minimum with a mold having about 24 cavities, and hence from the standpoint of cost this will be the optimum number of cavities.

The status of current production schedules for the machine in question, or for the shop as a whole, may dictate the choice of a number of cavities different from the most economical number, but the number selected must not be greater than the smallest of N_1, N_2, and N_3, which are governed by the limits of performance of the machine.

Design of Runner. A full-round runner is the best for any material because it has the least cooling surface and least volume for a given thickness. If it is desirable to keep the runner in one half of the mold, a compact trapezoidal runner is recommended. For molding thin sections, the runners should be quite small, so that most of the shot will go into useful articles rather than into sprues and runners. When the cycle is governed by the plastifying capacity of the cylinder, smaller runners will permit shorter cycles. One-eighth-inch full-round runners have been found to be large enough for small thin articles. Thin articles of moderate size, such as automotive domelight lenses, require runners $\frac{3}{16}$ to $\frac{1}{4}$ in. in diameter or thickness. Molded pieces with a thickness of $\frac{1}{8}$ to $\frac{5}{16}$ in. frequently require a runner slightly thicker than the piece, so that pressure may be maintained on the molding to avoid voids and sink marks. Seldom is a runner larger than $\frac{3}{8}$ in. required, even for very thick moldings.

Design of Gate. Nylon, being so fluid when melted, behaves well in cavities having restricted gating. However, gates smaller than 0.025 in. in diameter have not been satisfactory except on very small articles. Experience indicates that a good basic rule is to make the gate at least $\frac{2}{3}$, and preferably $\frac{3}{4}$, of the thickness of the molded piece. This rule may be ignored for small articles in which the cavity fills quickly, on center-gated articles, and on articles for which deflected gating is used. But if the rule is ignored on an edge-gated piece, a gate that is too small will extrude into the cavity a rod or ribbon which doubles over and causes fold-back lines near the gate. The gate should be short, and streamlined at both ends. A length or land of 0.040 in. is usually recommended for restricted gates for molding nylon.

Very little draft allowance is needed on cavities for nylon. The relatively high shrinkage, toughness, and heat-resistance of nylon, and its low coefficient of friction against steel, make nylon a comparatively easy material to eject from molds. Most nylon bearings and bushings are molded without taper on the cavity walls or cores. Tumblers, or other cup-shaped items that are closed at one end, usually need a taper, but a draft of $\frac{1}{8}$ degree is often adequate in such cases.

Molds for Cold-Molding Materials

The molds are generally single-cavity, semiautomatic, and positive. They are constructed of hardened steel, mounted permanently on the press, and are operated at room temperature. The cavities contain no land. With this design, the molding material receives the full pressure of the press.

The molds may be classified into two general types, regular and volumetric, according to the method used in loading them. In the regular mold, the amount of material is carefully weighed and put into the mold. In the volumetric mold, the depth of the cavity is adjusted so that it will hold the proper amount.

The Design of a Regular Mold. The mold as shown in Fig. 15-75 has an upper plate-holder, *1*, screwed into the top plate, *2*. The top force, *3*, is dowelled and screwed to the top plate. The hardened steel stops, *4*, are

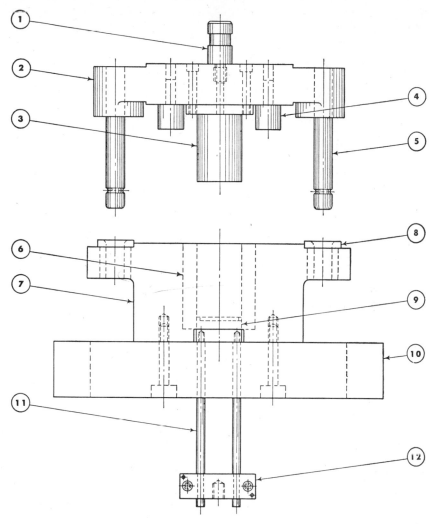

Fig. 15-75. Design of regular mold (cold molding).

pressed into the top plate and regulate the travel of the force into the cavity of the mold. The guide pins, 5, made of steel, are hardened, ground and pressed into the top plate. During the molding, the mold is aligned by the guide pins entering the guide-pin bushings, 8. The guide-pin bushings are made of steel, hardened and ground. They are pressed into a chase, 7. The molding material is placed in the box, 6, which is machined from steel, hardened, polished and pressed into the chase. The inside, or molding surface, is highly polished so that the molded article can be ejected freely. The bottom plunger, *9*, made of steel, hardened and polished, serves as the knockout as well as a molding surface. The bottom plunger rests on the backing plate, *10*, which is screwed and dowelled to the chase. The backing plate is fastened to the base of the press with cap screws. The two knockout rods, *11*, are screwed into the bottom plunger. These knockout rods are aligned by the knockout-pin plate, *12*, attached to them by screws. The knockout-pin plate also acts as a stop to adjust the distance of travel of the bottom piston to that necessary to eject the molded article from the box. The knockout-pin plate is made from steel and is fastened to the knockout mechanism of the press.

The Design of a Volumetric Mold. The mold as shown in Fig. 15-76 consists of a top force, *2*, made of steel and hardened. This is screwed and dowelled to the top plate, *1*, into which are pressed the guide-pin bushings, *3*, of hardened steel. The top plate is fastened to the movable head of the press,

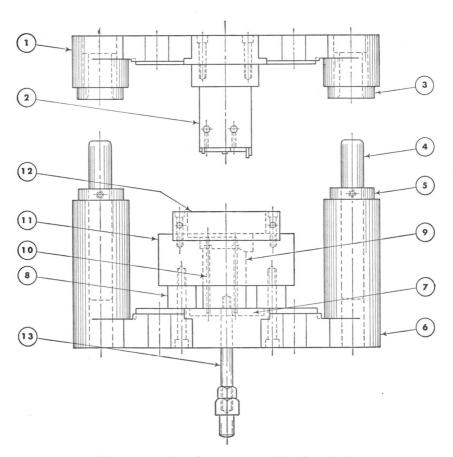

Fig. 15-76. Design of volumetric mold (cold molding).

and during the molding the guide-pin bushings align the mold on the guide pins, 4. The travel of the moving part of the mold is governed by stops, 5, of hardened steel which are fastened to the guide pins with setscrews. The steel guide pins are hardened and ground, and are pressed into the backing plate, 6, which is fastened to the base of the press. The molding material is placed in a hopper and by gravity falls into the loading space, 12, from which it is hoed into the cavity, 11. The cavity may be cut from good steel or may be hobbed, depending on the design of the article to be molded. In either case, the cavity is hardened and highly polished to facilitate ejection of the molded article. The cavity is mounted on parallels, 8, and is held in position by screws through the parallels and backing plate. The molded article is ejected from the mold by the bottom plunger, 9, which telescopes the molding pins, 10. The bottom plunger is made from steel and hardened. The molding pins are peened into a pin plate, 7, made of steel, which is held in position by the parallels. The knockout rod, 13, made of steel, is screwed into the bottom plunger and is fastened to the knockout mechanism of the press.

STEELS RECOMMENDED FOR MOLDS FOR PLASTICS

Introduction

The production of satisfactory molded articles is primarily dependent on the quality of the mold in which they are made. Similarly, the quality of the mold is no better than the quality and mechanical characteristics of the mold steel used. This section is designed to provide a brief description of those steels which have proved in service to be satisfactory for construction of molds for plastics.

The design of the molded article is usually a compromise between engineering standards, sales appeal to the customer, sales potential, and requirements of profit. Therefore, the mold must be built within specific restrictions, of which the most important is usually cost. But since the cost of the steel required for the mold is normally only a fraction of the cost of the labor involved, the moldmaker should select the best steel for the purpose, regardless of its cost.

Selection of Steels for Molds

The basic prerequisites for the construction of top-quality molds for plastics are as follows:

1. proper design of the mold;

2. proper selection of the steel to meet fully the requirements of service;

3. proper response of the steel to heat treatment;

4. provision of proper operating conditions, such as alignment of mold, pressures, and temperatures.

The success of any mold is assured only by meeting all of these requirements. Since the first and fourth requirements are discussed elsewhere in this handbook, this section will be restricted to detailed discussion of requirements (2) and (3).

All individual grades of heat-treatable steels have specific combinations of mechanical properties after heat treatment under certain specified conditions. By mechanical properties is meant the combination of hardness, tensile and yield strengths, elastic limit, ductility and toughness, and such allied properties as ability to be hobbed and machined. These properties can be changed within certain fundamental limits by changing the conditions of heat treatment.

A discussion of hardness as a mechanical property involves some distinction between the attainable hardness and the hardenability of a given steel. Attainable hardness is the maximum hardness obtained in very small sections by quenching from the optimum hardening temperature. Steel is basically an alloy of iron and carbon, and the higher its carbon content (up to 0.70 per cent), the higher is its attainable hardness. For example, a straight carbon steel containing 0.40 per cent of carbon has a higher attainable hardness than a 0.10 per cent-carbon high-alloy steel. Hardenability, on the other hand, is the depth to which uniform hardening is achieved by quenching, regardless of the attainable hardness. In other words, a steel which can be hardened uniformly through a 12-in. section has greater hardenability than one which can be hardened throughout in sections only up to 4 in. thick. Generally, the proper combination of alloying elements will increase the hardenability.

In addition, any heat-treatable steel has a certain combination of properties which is inherent and cannot be changed by heat treatment. These properties are basically controlled by the chemical composition of the steel and the melting practice followed.

The most important property required in a satisfactory mold steel is maximum cleanness. From a steel of a given composition, melting by electric furnace will, in general, produce a cleaner product than will melting by open hearth. Also, in the electric furnace, tool-steel practice will produce, in general, steels more uniformly clean than will commercial melting practice, and also more uniformly responsive to heat treatment for the development of mechanical properties.

The manufacturer making mold steel should have a complete knowledge of the properties required. In the processing, therefore, every care is taken from selecting scrap for melting to final inspection. Methods of inspection include both the deep-etch test (immersion of a disc in hot hydrochloric acid) and the ultrasonic test (the use of ultra-high frequency sound-wave reflections). In connection with ultrasonic testing, it should be noted that this method does not produce results of a "go" or "no go" variety as does a snap gage, but rather gives the metallurgist additional information to consider in deciding whether a particular lot of steel is of mold-steel quality.

Types of Steel for Molds

In the construction of molds for plastics, the cavities are produced by cold hobbing or by machining. The cores are generally produced by machining.

Steels for Molds made by Hobbing. Steels to be cold-hobbed must be in the fully annealed dead-soft condition. Into the mold blank in this condition, the master hob, in the shape of the article to be molded, is pressed at room temperature. The cavity may sometimes be formed in one operation, but in other cases the limitations of the ability of the steel to be hobbed may necessitate one or more intermediate annealings between applications of the hob.

The steels listed in Table 15-1 are the types now most used.

TABLE 15-1

Steel No.	Type	C	Mn	Si	Ni	Cr	Mo	V
1-H	low-carbon iron	0.07 max	0.20					option to 0.10
2-Ha	low-Cr-Ni-Mo alloy	0.07 max			0.55	1.35	0.20	
2-Hb	medium-Cr alloy	0.10 max	0.30	0.20		2.30		
3-H	air-hardening	0.10 max	0.30	0.20		5.00	0.50/ 1.00	option to 0.25

The choice of any steel for hobbing must be based on the relationship between its ability to be hobbed and the safety of the hob. In this respect, hob and cavity should be designed to avoid thin sections where possible. In some instances, it is preferable to hob the greater part of cavity and then to machine-cut the thin sections.

Since all of the steels in Table 15-1 have very low carbon content, they must be carburized before hardening, in order to develop a high attainable hardness on the surface. Therefore, the hardenability of each steel is the measure of its resistance to molding pressures, and also of its hobability.

Steel 1-H has the maximum hobability and the lowest hardenability of the steels in this group. It is normally supplied annealed to Brinell 101 (maximum), and can be used satisfactorily only for cavities in which molding pressures are extremely low.

Steel 2-Ha and Steel 2-Hb are alloy hobbing steels. Both are normally supplied annealed to Brinell 114 (maximum). Steel 2-Ha has slightly the greater hobability, and Steel 2-Hb slightly the greater hardenability.

Steel 3-H is a medium-high-alloy hobbing steel, normally supplied annealed to Brinell 125 (maximum). As a hobbing steel, its comparatively high hardenability is balanced by its relatively low hobability. This grade requires gas carburizing under extremely close control.

The heat treatment and processing recommendations for these steels are shown below:

Steel 1-H

Critical temperature. Ac1 1350°F.

Forging. Heat slowly, uniformly and thoroughly to 1450 to 1550°F. Do not forge below 1250°F.

Annealing. Heat uniformly to 1650°F, hold at temperature until heated through, and cool slowly in the furnace.

If an intermediate annealing between hobbing operations is required, heat to 1200 to 1250°F, hold at temperature until heated through, and cool in air.

Heat treatment. Carburize at 1650°F long enough to obtain the desired depth of case, and cool in the pot. Reheat to 1450°F and hold until heated through. Before tempering, quench in oil or water to a temperature at which the dies may be held comfortably in the bare hands.

Tempering. Temper immediately to the desired hardness. The usual temperature is 300 to 400°F, and the usual time is 2 to 4 hr.

Remarks. When tempered at 350°F for 3 hr, the mold should show a surface hardness of Rockwell C 62 to 64.

Mechanical properties of core. Quenched in water from 1450°F and tempered 3 hr at 350°F.

tensile strength	60,000 psi
yield point	40,000 psi
elongation in 2 in.	30%
reduction of area	65%
Brinell hardness	120

The mechanical properties given above are representative. Variations in size, in conditions of heat treatment, and in method of cooling may cause slight deviations from these figures.

Steel 2-Ha

Critical temperature. Ac1 1400°F.

Forging. Steel 2-Ha should be forged at 1900 to 2000°F and finished above 1500°F. Reheat if necessary.

Annealing. Steel 2-Ha should be annealed by heating to 1450°F, soaking through, and cooling in the furnace. If an intermediate annealing is required by the hobbing operations, Steel 2-Ha should be soaked at 1300 to 1350°F and cooled in the furnace.

Heat treatment. Steel 2-Ha should be carburized at 1650°F long enough to obtain the desired depth of case, and be cooled in the pot. Reheat to 1525 to 1550°F and quench in oil down to about 100 to 125°F. Then temper immediately to the desired hardness; the usual time is 2 to 4 hr at 350 to 400°F.

Properties after heat treatment.
Case: depth:
      time held,   8 hr: 0.040 to 0.045 in.
      time held, 16 hr: 0.060 to 0.070 in.
       hardness:
      as quenched ....65-68 Rockwell C
      tempered at 350°F ....63.5 Rockwell C
      tempered at 400°F ....62 Rockwell C

Core: properties:
      Rockwell C 16-23, depending upon section
      tensile strength ....98,000 to 119,000 psi
      yield strength ....67,000 to 84,000 psi

Steel 2-Hb

Critical Temperature. Ac1 1420°F.

Forging. Steel 2-Hb should be forged at 1900 to 2000°F and finished above 1500°F. Reheat if necessary.

Annealing. Steel 2-Hb should be annealed by heating to 1600°F, soaking through and cooling in the furnace. If an intermediate annealing is required by the hobbing operations, it should be soaked at 1300 to 1350°F, and cooled in the furnace.

Heat treatment. Carburize in clean compound or gas at 1600°F, to secure required depth of case. Six to 8 hr at 1600°F usually produces a case of about $\frac{3}{64}$ in. After carburizing, remove from the furnace and cool in air. Steel 2-Hb also can be carburized satisfactorily in conventional salt baths.

When cold, reheat the cavities to 1550 to 1600°F and quench in either oil or water. Excellent case hardness, with some sacrifice in core strength, may be obtained by quenching in water from temperatures as low as 1450 to 1475°F. This low temperature is not recommended when cavities are to be oil-quenched. To keep surfaces clean, a salt bath (with brine quench) or the pack method is recommended for heating. If mold cavities are large and recesses are deep, flushing with brine is recommended.

Tempering. Temper at about 200 to 300°F.

After heat-treating from 1550°F, the core will show a hardness of about Rockwell C 20 to 25 and a yield strength of 69,000 to 91,000 psi (depending on heat treatment). Case hardness will be Rockwell C 64 to 65.

Steel 3-H

Critical Temperature. Ac1 1480°F.

Forging. Steel 3-H should be forged at 1900 to 2000°F and finished at about 1600°F. Reheat if necessary.

Annealing. Steel 3-H should be annealed by heating to 1600°F, holding 1 hr, cooling to 1400°F, holding 16 hr and cooling in air. If an intermediate annealing is required by the hobbing operations, Steel 3-H should be heated at 1400°F and cooled in air. Holding 1 hr will produce a hardness of about 131 Brinell, while holding for 8 to 12 hr will produce a hardness of about 116 to 121 Brinell.

Heat treatment. Steel 3-H should be carburized at 1700°F long enough to obtain the desired depth of case and cooled in air or quenched in oil. It should then be tempered immediately to the desired hardness, the usual time being 2 to 4 hr at 350 to 400°F.

Properties after heat treatment.

Case: depth:
    time held,   8 hr: 0.040 to 0.050 in.
    time held, 16 hr: 0.070 to 0.080 in.
    hardness:
    as quenched ....65-68 Rockwell C
    tempered at 350°F ....63.5 Rockwell C
    tempered at 400°F ....62 Rockwell C

Core: full section air-cooled from 1700°F; tempered at 400°F for 1 hr*:

	1 x 1 x 6 in.	3½-in. round x 6 in.**
tensile strength, psi	157,000	152,000
0.2% yield strength, psi	113,000	103,000
elongation in 2 inches, %	16.9	16.0
reduction of area, %	60.6	59.4
Rockwell C	34	33

* Comparable properties may be obtained by oil-quenching.
** Test piece machined half way from center to outside of 3½-in. round bar.

Steels for Master Hob. The selection of a steel for the master hob is important second only to the selection of the steel to be hobbed. Steels for master hobs must have certain prime characteristics, as follows:

1. high strength in compression and in tension;

2. high wear-resistance after heat treatment;

3. minimum movement in heat treatment;

4. minimum susceptibility to scaling in heat treatment;

5. good machinability after annealing.

The steels listed in Table 15-2 are those normally used in current practice.

TABLE 15-2

Steel No.	Type	C	Mn	Si	Cr	Mo	V	W
H-1	2.75W, 1.25Cr shock-resisting	0.50		0.75	1.25		0.20	2.75
H-2a	nondeforming	0.90	1.25		0.50			0.50
H-2b	nondeforming	0.90	1.60	0.25				
H-3a	air-hardening (low temperature)	0.70	2.00	0.30	1.00	1.35		
H-3b	air-hardening	1.00	0.40		5.25	1.15	0.40	
H-4	high-carbon high-chrome, air-hardening	1.50			11.50	0.80	0.20	

Steel H-1 is most generally selected for initial runs and general applications. It is primarily a shock-resisting tool steel and its success as a master hob is dependent upon a carburizing treatment to increase its wear-resistance after heat treatment.

Steel H-2a and Steel H-2b are nondeforming oil-hardening tool steels having slightly better machinability and hardening stability (minimum movement) and slightly lower wear-resistance than Steel H-1.

Steel H-3a and Steel H-3b are air-hardening tool steels. Steel H-3a can be hardened from a relatively low temperature as compared to most air-hardening steels. Steel H-3b has better wear-resistance and dimensional stability.

Steel H-4 is an air-hardening high-carbon high-chromium tool steel having extremely good wear-resistance and hardening stability (minimum movement).

The recommended heat treatments for these steels are shown below:

Steel H-1

Critical temperature. Ac1 1425°F.

Forging. Heat slowly, uniformly and thoroughly to 1800 to 1900°F for forging. Do not forge below 1650°F. After forging, cool slowly in ashes, in lime, or in the furnace. Steel H-1 should always be annealed after forging.

Annealing. Heat uniformly to 1440°F, hold at temperature until heated through, and cool slowly in the furnace. For cycle annealing heat to 1440°F, hold 2 hr, cool to 1300°F, hold 3 hr. It is very important to note that these are actual temperatures of the steel, not furnace temperatures; otherwise, unsatisfactory results may be obtained. Steel H-1 should always be annealed before rehardening.

Hardening. Preheat to 1400 to 1450°F, then heat to 1700 to 1800°F and hold until heated through (1750°F is usual). Before tempering, quench in oil to below 150°F, or to a temperature at which the tool may be held comfortably in the bare hands.

Tempering. Temper immediately to the desired hardness.

Carburizing. When it is desired to carburize Steel H-1, the following heat treatment may be followed:

Pack in 50/50 old and new carburizing compound. Heat to 1650 to 1700°F, no higher. Hold at 1650 to 1700°F for 3 to 6 hr, depending on the depth of case desired. Case depths will vary from 0.015 to 0.045 in., depending on the time at temperature and the concentration of the carburizing compound. Quench in oil and temper for not less than 2 hr. For sections greater than 2 in., temper a minimum of 1 hr per in.

Hardness.

tempering temperature (°F)	Rockwell C hardness of specimen 2x2x0.5 in. quenched in oil from 1700°F	Rockwell C hardness of rod 4.5 in. diameter, 3 in. long, quenched in oil from 1750°F	Rockwell C hardness (case hardness) of rod 4.5 in. diameter, 3 in. long, carburized 4 hr at 1700°F and quenched in oil
as hardened	57 to 59	58 to 60	62 to 64
300	57 to 59	58 to 60	62 to 64
400	56 to 58	57 to 59	61 to 63
600	55 to 57	56 to 58	61 to 63
800	54 to 56	55 to 57	58 to 60
1000	51 to 53	52 to 54	54 to 56
1100	45 to 47	47 to 49	50 to 52

The values given in this table are representative. Variations in size, conditions of heat treatment and method of cooling may cause slight deviations from these figures.

Steel H-2a

Critical temperature. Ac1 1370°F.

Forging. Heat slowly, uniformly and thoroughly to 1800 to 1900°F. Do not forge below 1500°F. After forging, cool slowly in ashes, in lime, or in the furnace.

Normalizing. For large forgings: after forging, heat uniformly to 1600°F and cool in still air.

Annealing. Heat uniformly to 1440°F, hold at temperature at least 2 to 3 hr after the charge is heated through, and cool slowly in the furnace to below 1000°F.

For cycle annealing, hold 4 hr at 1350°F, heat to 1440°F, hold 2 hr, cool to 1275°F, hold 6 hr. It is very important to note that these are actual temperatures of the steel, not furnace temperatures; otherwise unsatisfactory results may be obtained. The steel may then be cooled in air if desired.

Steel H-2a should always be annealed after forging and before rehardening.

Hardening. Preheat at 1200 to 1250°F, then heat to 1450 to 1500°F, and hold until heated through. A soft skin on hardened tools can be avoided if heating is done in a slightly oxidizing atmosphere. Before tempering, quench in warm thin oil to below 150°F, or to a temperature at which the tools may be held comfortably in the bare hands. Where minimum change of size is desired, the parts may be taken out of the oil at just below the flash point of the oil (about 400°F), and allowed to cool in air to below 150°F.

Tempering. Temper immediately to the desired hardness. The usual tempering temperature is 350 to 450°F, and the usual tempering time is 2 hr, but sections thicker than 2 in. should be tempered a minimum of 1 hr per in.

Hardness. Quenched in oil from 1475°F and tempered 2 hr:

tempering temperature (°F)	Rockwell C hardness
as hardened	63 to 65
250	63 to 65
300	63 to 65
350	62 to 64
400	61 to 63
450	60 to 62
500	58 to 60
600	55 to 57
700	51 to 53
800	48 to 50
900	43 to 45
1000	39 to 41

The hardness values given in this table are representative. Variations in size, conditions of heat treatment, and method of cooling may cause slight deviations from these figures.

Steel H-2b

Critical temperature. Ac1 1460°F.

Forging. Heat slowly, uniformly and thoroughly to 1800 to 1900°F. Do not forge below 1500°F. After forging, cool slowly in ashes, in lime or in the furnace.

Normalizing. For large forgings: after forging, heat uniformly to 1600°F and cool in still air.

Annealing. Heat uniformly to 1440°F, hold at temperature at least 2 to 3 hr after the charge is heated through, and cool slowly in the furnace to below 1000°F.

Hardening. Preheat at 1200 to 1250°F, then heat to 1450 to 1500°F, and hold until heated through. A soft skin on hardened tools can be avoided if the heating is done in a slightly oxidizing atmosphere. Before tempering, quench in warm thin oil to below 150°F, or to a temperature at which the tools may be held comfortably in the bare hands. Where minimum change of size is desired, the parts may be taken out of the oil just below the flash point of the oil (about 400°F), and allowed to cool in air to below 150°F.

Tempering. Temper immediately to the desired hardness. The usual tempering temperature is 350 to 450°F, and the usual tempering time is 2 hr, but sections thicker than 2 in. should be tempered a minimum of 1 hr per in.

Hardness. Quenched in oil from 1475°F and tempered 2 hr:

tempering temperature (°F)	Rockwell C hardness
as hardened	63 to 65
250	63 to 65
300	63 to 65
350	62 to 64
400	61 to 63
450	60 to 62
500	58 to 60
600	55 to 57
700	51 to 53
800	48 to 50
900	43 to 45
1000	39 to 41

The values given in this table are representative. Variations in size, conditions of heat treatment, and method of cooling may cause slight deviations from these figures.

Steel H-3a

Critical temperature. Ac1 1380°F.

Forging. Steel H-3a should be forged from a temperature of about 2025°F. The finished forgings should be cooled slowly in ashes, in lime, or in the furnace.

Annealing. Pack in a suitable container with clean cast-iron borings, heat uniformly to 1350 to 1375°F, and cool very slowly in the furnace (not faster than 20°F per hr).

Hardening. Pack the tool in clean cast-iron chips. Place pack in furnace at 1525 to 1600°F, depending on size of tool. Soak the pack at temperature, for 20 minutes plus 15 minutes for each inch of thickness. Remove pack and cool the tool to room temperature in free circulating air. Steel H-3a can also be hardened in conventional salt baths.

Tempering. Temper to desired hardness after the tool has cooled to room temperature.

Hardness. Hardened in air from 1575°F and tempered 2 hr:

tempering temperature (°F)	Rockwell C hardness
as hardened	61 to 62
200	61 to 62
300	60 to 61
350	59 to 60
400	58 to 59
500	56 to 57
600	55 to 56
700	54 to 55
800	52 to 53
900	50 to 51
1000	48 to 49

Steel H-3b

Critical temperature. Ac1 1460°F.

Forging. Heat slowly and uniformly to 1900 to 2000°F. Do not forge below 1650°F. Reheat if necessary. After forging, cool slowly in ashes, in lime, or in the furnace.

Annealing. Steel H-3b should always be annealed after forging and before rehardening.

Heat slowly and uniformly to 1650°F, hold at temperature for 2 hr, and cool slowly in the furnace.

For cycle annealing, heat to 1650°F, hold at temperature for 2 hr, cool to 1400°F, and hold at this temperature for 4 to 6 hr. The steel may then be cooled in air if desired.

Hardening. Equalize at preheating temperature of 1450 to 1500°F, then raise the temperature to 1775 to 1825°F, and cool in air.

To prevent decarburization or carburization, it is desirable to use a furnace having a controlled atmosphere. When this is not available, pack-hardening is recommended. Wrap tools in paper and pack in a container with a suitable material such as 6- to 8-mesh spent pitch coke.

An interrupted oil quench may be used on larger sections or on certain parts which may require a very fine surface finish after hardening and on which a slight scaling, caused by the cooling from the hardening temperature, may be objectionable. To do this, quench from 1750 to 1800°F in oil, but remove from the oil when the parts have reached about 1000 to 1100°F (dull red), and allow to cool from this temperature in air until below 150°F, or to a temperature at which the tools may comfortably be held in the bare hands. With this method slightly greater distortion in hardening may be expected.

Steel H-3b may also be hardened by quenching from 1750 to 1800°F in a salt bath at 1000°F. Hold until the parts have reached 1000°F, remove from the hot salt, and allow to cool in air until below 150°F.

Tempering. Steel H-3b should be tempered as soon as the parts are cool enough to be held in bare hands. The usual temperature employed is 450°F, but this may be varied to suit the needs. For any section below 2 in., a minimum of 2 hr should be used. For sections 2 in. and over allow a minimum of 1 hr per in.

Hardness. Specimen $4 \times 4 \times 3$ in. hardened in air from 1800°F and tempered 3 hr:

tempering temperature (°F)	Rockwell C hardness
as hardened	63 to 65
400	60 to 62
500	59 to 61
600	58 to 60
700	57 to 59
800	57 to 59
900	57 to 59
1000	56 to 58

Hardness values given in this table are representative. Variations in size, conditions of heat treatment and method of cooling may cause slight deviations from these figures.

Steel H-4

Critical temperature. Ac1 1490°F.

Forging. Heat slowly and uniformly to 1900 to 2000°F. Do not forge below 1650°F. Reheat if necessary. Cool slowly from the forging temperature in furnace, in ashes or in lime.

Annealing. Steel H-4 should always be annealed after forging and before rehardening.

Heat uniformly to 1650°F, hold at temperature for 2 hr, and cool slowly in the furnace.

For cycle annealing, heat to 1650°F, hold at temperature for 2 hr, cool to 1425°F, and hold at this temperature for 4 to 6 hr. The steel may be cooled in air if desired.

Hardening. Equalize at preheating temperature of 1450 to 1500°F, then raise temperature to 1800 to 1850°F, and cool in air.

In order to prevent decarburization it is desirable to use a furnace having a controlled atmosphere. When this is not available, pack hardening is recommended. Wrap parts in paper and pack in a container with an inert material such as 6- to 8-mesh spent pitch coke.

The interrupted oil quench may be used on larger sections, or on certain parts which require a very fine surface after hardening, and on which the slight scaling caused during the air cooling from the hardening temperature may be objectionable. To do this, quench from 1800°F in oil, but remove from the oil when the parts have reached about 1000 to 1100°F (dull red), and allow to cool from this temperature in air until below 150°F, or to a temperature at which the tool may be comfortably held in bare hands. With this method slightly greater distortion in hardening may be expected.

Tempering. Steel H-4 should be tempered as soon as the parts are cool enough to handle in bare hands. The usual temperature is 400 to 600°F, but this may be varied to suit the needs. Tempering time should be 3 to 5 hr. Sections over 3 in. should be tempered a minimum of 1 hr per in.

Hardness. Air-cooled from 1800°F and tempered 3 hr:

tempering temperature (°F)	Rockwell C hardness
as hardened	62 to 64
400	60 to 62
500	59 to 61
600	58 to 60
700	57 to 59
800	57 to 59
900	57 to 59
1000	54 to 56

The hardness values given in this table are representative. Variations in size, conditions of heat treatment and method of cooling may cause slight deviations from these figures.

Steels for Machined Cavities and Cores. Steels for machined mold cavities and cores are the most important of all steels used by the plastic-molding industry. The requirements of top-quality steel vary with the type of molding to be done. However, maximum cleanness is required in every case. In addition, it is of utmost importance that the steel, in its final heat-treated condition, take a mirror finish.

The steels most widely used for machine-cut mold cavities and forces are listed in Table 15-3.

TABLE 15-3

Steel No.	Type	C	Mn	Si	Ni	Cr	Mo	V	W
1-Ma	1Cr-Mo low-alloy	0.33	0.75	0.50		0.80	0.25		
1-Mb	1Cr-3½Ni low-alloy	0.10	0.40		3.50	1.60			
1-Mc	1Cr-½V low-alloy	0.45	0.70			1.00		0.20	
2-Ma	non-deforming	0.90	1.25			0.50			0.50
2-Mb	non-deforming	0.90	1.60	0.25					
3-M	Cr-Mo-V hot-work	0.40		1.05		5.00	1.35	1.00	
4-Ma	air-hardening low-temperature	0.70	2.00	0.30		1.00	1.35		
4-Mb	air-hardening	1.00	0.40			5.25	1.15	0.40	
5-M	stainless	0.30				12.00			

Sizes of molds spread over a tremendous range. Compression molds range from the very small to molds for large television cabinets requiring cavity-block forgings weighing 14,000 lb in the planed square condition and having dimensions as large as $40 \times 28 \times 43$ in. Planed square core plugs and face plates weighing 6000 and 5000 lb, respectively are used with these cavity blocks. Similarly, injection molds range from the small to molds requiring planed square cavity and core blocks weighing 7000 lb each, and as large as $46 \times 7 \times 64$ in.

Another important consideration is required hardness of the mold. Most compression molds require cavities of great surface hardness, to resist the abrasive and erosive action of thermosetting resins. On the other hand, most injection molds need be hard enough only to resist abuse in operation and to provide resistance to abrasion at cutoffs. However, injection molds do require a certain amount of compressive strength at the lands, to resist the high clamping pressures and to resist flash sinking. In cases where a mold of either type is relatively small, it is sometimes possible and desirable to insert the mold-cavity block into a holder block, so as to combine the advantages of extremely hard cavity surfaces and the toughness of the holder block.

Steels 1-Ma, 1-Mb, and 1-Mc are the relatively low-alloy mold steels. In analysis, these grades are essentially AISI alloy steels. However, they are produced, for mold-steel applications, under tool-steel practice, and are offered under tool-steel trade names. Of the three grades, Steel 1-Mc has the highest attainable hardness and Steel 1-Ma the next highest. Steel 1-Mb has the greatest hardenability, and Steel 1-Ma the next greatest. Steels 1-Ma and 1-Mb may be carburized before heat treatment to produce cavity surfaces of relatively great hardness. All three grades may be heat-treated conventionally to relatively low hardness. When annealed, or normalized and tempered, to about Brinell 200 the machinability of the three grades is as follows: Steel 1-Ma, the highest; Steel 1-Mc, the next; and Steel 1-Mb, the lowest. This same relative rating also holds true when the steels are heat-treated to about Brinell 300, in which condition many large injection molds are machined and polished without subsequent heat treatment.

Steel 2-Ma and Steel 2-Mb are oil-hardening non-deforming tool steels having a high hardenability and an attainable hardness of Rockwell C 60. However, their machinability and toughness are considerably lower than those of the 1-M group. These grades are normally used for small cavity blocks inserted into alloy holder blocks.

Steel 3-M is basically a hot-work tool steel which has high hardenability and heat-treating stability in relatively large sections at an attainable hardness of about Brinell 475.

Steels 4-Ma and 4-Mb are air-hardening tool steels used for relatively small molds when great hardness and wear-resistance are required. Steel 4-Ma can be hardened from a relatively low temperature for an air-hardening steel, whereas Steel 4-Mb has higher wear-resistance and dimensional stability in heat treatment.

Steel 5-M is a hardenable stainless steel having high hardenability and an attainable hardness of about Brinell 525. It is normally used for relatively small molds having fairly shallow cavities. It is important to specify mirror-finish quality when ordering this grade of steel.

The recommended heat treatments for these steels are shown below.

Steel 1-Ma

Critical temperature. AC1 1350°F.

Forging. Heat slowly and uniformly to 1900 to 2000°F. Do not forge below 1650°F. After forging, cool slowly in ashes, in lime, or in the furnace.

Annealing. Steel 1-Ma should always be annealed after forging and before rehardening.

Heat uniformly to 1425°F, hold at temperature until heated through, and cool slowly in the furnace.

Carburizing. The carburizing treatment for plastic-molding dies made from Steel 1-Ma may be either of the following:

(a) Carburize at 1600°F for 8 to 12 hr, depending on size of die. Quench in oil direct from the pot.

(b) Carburize at 1650°F for 8 to 10 hr, depending on the size of the die. Cool in pot to 1500 to 1550°F. Quench in oil direct from the pot.

Heat treatment (b) results in considerably less change of size than heat treatment (a).

Tempering. Temper immediately to the desired case hardness. The usual temperature is 400 to 500°F, and the usual time is at least 2 hr.

Remarks. The case depth from treatments suggested should be from 0.030 to 0.040 in. When tempered at 400°F for 2 hr, the die should show a surface hardness of Rockwell C 60 to 61.

Mechanical properties of core. Quenched in oil from 1550°F and tempered 2 hr at 400°F:

tensile strength	190,000 psi
yield point	170,000 psi
elongation in 2 in.	13%
reduction of area	51%
Rockwell hardness	C 36 to 38

These mechanical properties are representative. Variations in size, conditions of heat treatment and method of cooling may cause slight deviations from these figures.

Heat treatment without carburizing.

Hardening. Heat to 1550 to 1575°F, and hold until heated through. Before tempering, quench in oil to a temperature at which the molds may be held comfortably in the bare hands.

Tempering. Temper immediately to the desired hardness.

Hardness. Quenched in oil from 1550°F and tempered 2 hr:

tempering temperature (°F)	Rockwell C hardness	Brinell hardness
as hardened	41	388
800	34	320
900	32	305
1000	30	290
1100	28	270
1200	22.5	240

These values are representative. Variations in size, conditions of heat treatment and method of cooling may cause slight deviations from them.

Steel 1-Mb

Critical temperature. Ac1 1305°F.

Forging. Heat slowly and uniformly to 1900 to 2000°F. Do not forge below 1500°F. After forging, cool slowly in ashes, in lime, or in the furnace.

Normalizing. Heat slowly and uniformly to 1550°F, allow to heat through, and cool in air, followed by tempering at 1180°F for 10 to 12 hr.

Carburizing. Carburize at 1650°F long enough to obtain the desired depth of case, and cool in the pot. Reheat to 1450 to 1500°F. Before tempering, quench in oil to a temperature at which the mold may be held comfortably in the bare hands.

Tempering. Temper immediately to the desired hardness. The usual temperature is 250 to 400°F, and the usual time is 2 to 4 hr.

Remarks. When tempered at 300°F for 3 hr, the die should show a surface hardness of Rockwell C 61 to 63.

Mechanical properties of core. Quenched in oil from 1500°F and tempered 3 hr at 350°F:

tensile strength	165,000 psi
yield point	135,000 psi
elongation in 2 in.	16%
reduction of area	50%
Brinell hardness	369

These values are representative. Variations in size, condition of heat treatment and method of cooling may cause slight deviation from them.

Hardening. Heat to 1500 to 1550°F, and hold until heated through. Before tempering, quench in oil or air to a temperature at which the molds may be held comfortably in the bare hands.

Tempering. Temper immediately to the desired hardness.

Hardness. Quenched in oil from 1550°F and tempered 2 hr:

tempering temperature (°F)	Rockwell C hardness	Brinell hardness
as hardened	40	379
800	34	320
900	31	295
1000	27	265
1100	23.5	245
1200	19	220

Steel 1-Mc

Critical temperature. Ac1 1360°F.

Forging. Heat slowly, uniformly and thoroughly to 1850 to 1950°F. Do not forge below 1550°F. After forging, cool slowly in ashes, in lime, or in the furnace.

Annealing. Heat uniformly to 1425°F, hold at temperature until heated through, and cool slowly in the furnace. Steel 1-Mc should always be annealed after forging and before rehardening.

For cycle annealing, heat to 1425°F, hold 2 hr, cool to 1310°F, hold for 4 hr. These are actual temperatures of the steel, not furnace temperatures, and should be followed to ensure satisfactory results. The steel may then be cooled in air if desired.

Hardening. Heat to 1625 to 1675°F and hold until heated through. Before tempering, quench in oil to a temperature at which the tools may be held comfortably in the bare hands. If the shape is simple, water may be used for quenching. In this case, heat thoroughly to 1500 to 1525°F, and hold until heated through. Quench in water to a temperature at which the tools may be held comfortably in the bare hands.

Tempering. Temper immediately to the desired hardness.

Hardness. Quenched as indicated below and tempered 2 hr:

tempering temperature (°F)	quenched in oil from 1650°F Rockwell C	quenched in water from 1525°F Rockwell C
as hardened	55 to 57	59 to 61
400	53 to 55	55 to 57
500	52 to 54	53 to 55
600	50 to 52	51 to 53
700	47 to 49	48 to 50
800	42 to 44	45 to 47
900	40 to 42	41 to 43

The values given are representative. Variations in size, conditions of heat treatment and method of cooling may cause slight deviations from them.

Steel 2-Ma

Critical temperature. Ac1 1370°F.

Forging. Heat slowly, uniformly and thoroughly to 1800 to 1900°F. Do not forge below 1500°F. After forging, cool slowly in ashes, in lime, or in the furnace.

Normalizing. For large forgings: after forging, heat uniformly to 1600°F and cool in still air.

Annealing. Heat uniformly to 1440°F, hold at temperature at least 2 to 3 hr after the charge is heated through, and cool slowly in the furnace to below 1000°F.

For cycle annealing, hold 4 hr at 1350°F, heat to 1440°F, hold 2 hr, cool to 1275°F, hold 6 hr. It is very important that these temperatures be maintained in the steel itself; otherwise unsatisfactory results may be obtained. The steel may then be cooled in air if desired.

Steel 2-Ma should always be annealed after forging and before rehardening.

Hardening. Preheat at 1200 to 1250°F, then heat to 1450 to 1500°F, and hold until heated through. A soft skin on hardened molds can be avoided if the heating is done in a slightly oxidizing atmosphere. Before tempering, quench in warm thin oil to below 150°F, or to a temperature at which the molds may be held comfortably in the bare hands. Where minimum change in size is desired, the parts may be taken out of the oil at just below the flash point of the oil (about 400°F), and allowed to cool in air to below 150°F.

Tempering. Temper immediately to the desired hardness. The usual temperature is 350 to 450°F and the usual time is 2 hr, but sections thicker than 2 in. should be tempered a minimum of 1 hr per in.

Hardness. Quenched in oil from 1475°F and tempered 2 hr:

tempering temperature (°F)	Rockwell C hardness
as hardened	63 to 65
250	63 to 65
300	63 to 65
350	62 to 64
400	61 to 63
450	60 to 62
500	58 to 60
600	55 to 57
700	51 to 53
800	48 to 50
900	43 to 45
1000	39 to 41

The values given are representative. Variations in size, conditions of heat treatment and method of cooling may cause slight deviations from them.

Steel 2-Mb

Critical temperature. Ac1 1460°F.

Forging. Heat slowly, uniformly and thoroughly to 1800 to 1900°F. Do not forge below 1500°F. After forging, cool slowly in ashes, in lime, or in the furnace.

Normalizing. For large forgings: after forging, heat uniformly to 1600°F and cool in still air.

Annealing. Heat uniformly to 1440°F, hold at temperature at least 2 to 3 hr after the charge is heated through, and cool slowly in the furnace to below 1000°F.

Hardening. Preheat at 1200 to 1250°F, then heat to 1450 to 1500°F, and hold until heated through. A soft skin on hardened tools can be avoided if heating is done in a slightly oxidizing atmosphere. Before tempering, quench in warm thin oil to below 150°F, or to a temperature at which the tools may be held comfortably in the bare hands. Where minimum change of size is desired, the parts may be taken out of the oil at just below the flash point of the oil (about 400°F), and allowed to cool in air to below 150°F.

Tempering. Temper immediately to the desired hardness. The usual temperature is 350 to 450°F and the usual time is 2 hr, but sections thicker than 2 in. should be tempered a minimum of 1 hr per in.

Hardness. Quenched in oil from 1475°F and tempered 2 hr:

tempering temperature (°F)	Rockwell C hardness
as hardened	63 to 65
250	63 to 65
300	63 to 65
350	62 to 64
400	61 to 63
450	60 to 62
500	58 to 60
600	55 to 57
700	51 to 53
800	48 to 50
900	43 to 45
1000	39 to 41

These values are representative. Variations in size, conditions of heat treatment and method of cooling may cause slight deviations from them.

Steel 3-M

Critical temperature. Ac1 1560°F.

Forging. Heat slowly, uniformly and thoroughly to 1900 to 2000°F. Do not forge below 1650°F. After forging, cool slowly in ashes, in lime or in the furnace.

Annealing. Heat to 1625°F, hold at temperature until heated through, and cool slowly in the furnace.

For cycle annealing, heat to 1625°F, hold 2 hr, cool to 1400°F, hold 4 to 6 hr. It is very important to maintain these temperatures in the steel itself, not just in the furnace, to ensure satisfactory results. The steel may then be cooled in air if desired. Steel 3-M should always be annealed after forging and before rehardening.

Stress-relief. When necessary to relieve stresses set up during the rough machining operation and before finish machining, a temperature of 1200 to 1300°F is recommended.

Hardening. In order to prevent decarburization, it is desirable to use a furnace with a controlled atmosphere. When this is not available, pack-hardening is recommended. Wrap dies or parts in paper and pack in container with an inert material, such as 6- to 8-mesh spent pitch coke.

Before tempering, preheat thoroughly at 1400 to 1500°F, then heat to 1800 to 1850°F and hold until heated through, cool in air to below 150°F or to a temperature at which the dies or parts may be handled with bare hands.

Better response to hardening and resistance to softening may be obtained by cooling in air from 1950°F rather than from 1800 to 1850°F.

Tempering. For this steel, after hardening from 1800 to 1850°F, it is possible to use a single prolonged tempering (at 1050 to 1100°F for a minimum of 4 hr for a 2-in. section, increasing 2 hr for each additional in.). However, a double temper is recommended: heat to 1050 to 1100°F, hold 2 to 4 hr, cool to room temperature, reheat to the same temperature for 4 hr for a 2-in. section, increasing 2 hr for each additional in.; cool to room temperature. For large sections, a somewhat lower tempering temperature should be used.

Hardness. Hardened in air from 1800°F, and from 1950°F, and tempered at indicated temperatures for the times shown:

tempering time (hr)	tempering temperature (°F)	1800°F		1950°F	
		Rockwell C	Brinell	Rockwell C	Brinell
	as hardened	47 - 49	443 - 469	52 - 54	512 - 543
4	1000	50 - 52	481 - 512	54 - 56	543 - 577
4 + 4	1000	48 - 50	455 - 481	52 - 54	512 - 543
4	1050	48 - 50	455 - 481	52 - 54	512 - 543
4 + 4	1050	47 - 49	443 - 469	51 - 53	496 - 525
4	1100	46 - 48	432 - 455	49 - 51	469 - 496
4 + 4	1100	41 - 43	381 - 400	45 - 47	421 - 443

The values given for hardness are representative. Variations in chemical analysis, size, conditions of heat treatment and method of cooling may cause slight deviations from these figures.

Steel 4-Ma

Critical temperatures. Ac1 1380°F.

Forging. Steel 4-Ma should be forged from a temperature of about 2025°F. The finished forgings should be cooled slowly in ashes, in lime, or in the furnace.

Annealing. Pack in a suitable container with clean cast-iron borings, heat uniformly to 1350 to 1375°F, and cool very slowly in the furnace (not faster than 20°F per hr).

Hardening. Pack the tool in clean cast-iron chips. Place pack in furnace at 1525 to 1600°F, depending on size of tool. Soak the pack at temperature for 20 minutes plus 15 minutes for each in. of thickness. Remove pack and cool the tool to room temperature in free circulating air. Steel 4-Ma can also be hardened in conventional salt baths.

Tempering. Temper to desired hardness after the tool has cooled to room temperature.

Hardness. Hardened in air from 1575°F and tempered 2 hr:

tempering temperature (°F)	Rockwell C hardness
as hardened	61 to 62
200	61 to 62
300	60 to 61
350	59 to 60
400	58 to 59
500	56 to 57
600	55 to 56
700	54 to 55
800	52 to 53
900	50 to 51
1000	48 to 49

Steel 4-Mb

Critical temperature. Ac1 1460°F.

Forging. Heat slowly and uniformly to 1900 to 2000°F. Do not forge below 1650°F. Reheat if necessary. After forging, cool slowly in ashes, in lime, or in the furnace.

Annealing. Steel 4-Mb should always be annealed after forging and before rehardening.

Heat slowly and uniformly to 1650°F, hold at temperature for 2 hr, and cool slowly in the furnace.

For cycle annealing, heat to 1650°F, hold at temperature for 2 hr, cool to 1400°F, and hold at this temperature for 4 to 6 hr. The steel may then be cooled in air if desired.

Hardening. Equalize at preheating temperature of 1450 to 1500°F, then raise the temperature to 1775 to 1825°F, and cool in air.

In order to prevent decarburization or carburization, it is desirable to use a furnace having a controlled atmosphere. When this is not available, pack-hardening is recommended. Wrap tools in paper and pack in a container with a suitable material, such as 6- to 8-mesh spent pitch coke.

The interrupted oil quench may be used on larger sections or on certain parts which may require a very fine surface finish after hardening, and on which a slight scaling, caused by the cooling from the hardening temperature, may be objectionable. To do this, quench from 1750 to 1800°F into oil, but remove from the oil when the parts have reached about 1000 to 1100°F (dull red), and allow to cool from this temperature in air until below 150°F or to a temperature at which the tools may comfortably be held in bare hands. With this method slightly greater distortion in hardening may be expected.

Steel 4-Mb may also be hardened by quenching from 1750 to 1800°F into a salt bath maintained at 1000°F. Hold until the parts have reached 1000°F, remove from the hot salt, and allow to cool in air until below 150°F.

Tempering. Steel 4-Mb should be tempered as soon as the parts are cool enough to be held in bare hands. The usual temperature employed is 450°F, but this may be varied to suit the needs. A minimum of 2 hr for any section below 2 in. should be used. For sections 2 in. and over allow a minimum of 1 hr per in.

Hardness. Hardened in air from 1800°F and tempered 3 hr (specimen $4 \times 4 \times 3$ in.) :

tempering temperature (°F)	Rockwell C hardness
as hardened	63 to 65
400	60 to 62
500	59 to 61
600	58 to 60
700	57 to 59
800	57 to 59
900	57 to 59
1000	56 to 58

The values given are representative. Variations in size, conditions of heat treatment and method of cooling may cause slight deviations from them.

Steel 5-M

Critical temperature. Ac1 1490°F.

Forging. Steel 5-M should be forged at 1950 to 2050°F, and finished not lower than 1750°F. Reheat if necessary.

Annealing. Steel 5-M should be annealed for maximum softness by a thorough soaking at 1600°F for 6 hr, followed by cooling in the furnace. This grade can be cycle-annealed by heating to 1600°F, holding 2 hr, cooling to 1300°F, and holding 4 hr. The steel may then be cooled in air if desired.

Hardening and Tempering. Steel 5-M can be hardened for maximum hardness by quenching in oil from 1800 to 1900°F. Large sections should be preheated to about 1250°F before bringing up to the hardening temperature. It is desirable to avoid tempering between 800 and 1100°F, as there is a drop in impact strength within this range, and a drop in resistance to corrosion. This does not occur when Steel 5-M is tempered at 1100°F or above.

Machining. The machining of the chromium grades such as Steel 5-M is characterized by the tendency of the chip to gall or build up on the cutting edges and radii of the tool. This results in high pressures and temperatures on the cutting point of the tool and the tearing of the machined finish of the work. The chips formed in machining are brittle and stringy. For the majority of applications, material in the fully annealed condition is preferred. In general, machining speeds are about 40 per cent of that for mild steel.

Mirror-finish applications. When this grade is ordered specifically for mirror-finish applications, material will be supplied which has been suitably processed to that end. Care should be taken, in grinding and polishing this grade, to avoid excessive heating, which may lower its resistance to staining. In general, Steel 5-M resembles tool steels in that it requires great care in fabrication and hardening.

Hardness. Hardened from 1850°F, oil-quenched and tempered as shown:

tempering temperature (°F)	Rockwell C hardness
as hardened	55
500	50
600	50
700	51
800	52
900	52
1000	43
1100	28

In recent years, a number of metals other than steel have been successfully used to make cavities and cores for molds.

CHROME-PLATING OF MOLDS FOR PLASTICS

Molds are sometimes chrome-plated for purposes of preventing corrosion and of increasing surface hardness and hence prolonging useful life. Whether a mold is chrome-plated or not depends upon the requirements of the job. Chrome-plating is a difficult operation and should be entrusted to an experienced custom plater.

STANDARD MOLD BASES

History

Commercial standardization of tools for molders of plastics is a very recent development. Prior to 1940 no work had been attempted on an industry-wide scale. Standardization was limited at the start to the problem of the individual molder or moldmaker.

In 1940 I. T. Quarnstrom, a custom moldmaker in Detroit, recognizing the lack of commercial standardization, started to determine to what extent molds could be standardized. The results of this research first appeared on the market in 1942 in the form of standard mold bases, or die sets, for injection molds. The same parts used for an injection mold could be rearranged for use as a compression or transfer mold. Accessories such as locating rings, sprue bushings and ejector bars were made standard so that molds could be interchangeable between the various kinds of injection presses. Items such as ejector pins, baffles for steam lines, sprue-reamers and a host of small articles never before carried as standard stock items were made available to the moldmaker.

Today a moldmaker, instead of having to design and make every part of a mold except the screws, can in most cases buy every part.

Standard Designs

Up to the present time the mold bases offered for injection molds have followed the conventional styles. Figure 15-77 shows an exploded view of a typical mold base.

The stationary half of the mold is of two-plate construction and is supplied with a sprue bushing and locating ring to fit a designated press. Leader pins also are contained in this half. The top and bottom plates are made wider than the mold itself, to provide a means of clamping the mold to the platen of the press.

The ejector half of the mold is composed of three plates, two spacer blocks, and the ejector mechanism. The top plate carries hardened bushings to match the leader pins; the second plate supports the cavities, and the bottom plate, slightly wider than the support plate, is used to clamp the

Fig. 15-77

mold to the rear platen of the press. Ejector bars of optional length are supplied to fit the various presses. Return pins and a sprue-puller pin are standard equipment, and are held between the ejector bar and the ejector-retainer plate. Cavities can be mounted in any one of three ways, (1) screwed directly to the cavity-retainer plates, (2) inserted in pockets milled part way through the cavity-retainer plates, or (3) inserted in holes cut completely through the cavity-retainer plates. Occasionally the cavities are cut directly in the plate, and in this case the plate is made of a tool steel.

The same setup with only minor changes makes a mold base into a plunger-type transfer mold. A hardened bushing of suitable size is substituted for the sprue bushing, a hardened runner plate is added, together with a heavy center support, and the change is made (Fig. 15-78). The addition of another plate to carry a transfer pot and the mold base will make the equipment serve as a conventional transfer mold. Compression molds involve a much less complicated buildup, and hence standardization is limited to cavity-retainer plates, steam plates and accessories such as ejector pins, leader pins and bushings, baffles for steam lines, etc.

Standardization has refined and improved fundamental designs. The ability to buy a stock base enables the moldmaker to concentrate on cavity work, with increased total output for the shop.

After all is said and done, there is this one thing to remember in mold designing. We can mold an article only as good as the mold. It does not pay to make cheap molds. It does pay to use care in designing a mold so that the article will come from the mold in such a condition that it may be easily finished. It does pay to design a mold so that the average workman can run it without too much brainwork, and to make it as foolproof as possible. Again, we say, "We can mold an article only as good as the mold."

SPI MOLD-DESIGN NOMENCLATURE

air vent . . . . Small outlet, usually a groove, to prevent entrapment of gases.

anneal . . . . To heat steel to a predetermined temperature above the critical range and slowly cool it to relieve stresses and reduce hardness.

backing plate . . . . . . A plate which backs up the cavity blocks, guide pins, bushings, etc. (sometimes called support plate).

back-pressure-relief port . An opening from an extrusion die for escape of excess material.

back taper . . . . Reverse draft used in mold to prevent molded article from drawing freely. (See *undercut*).

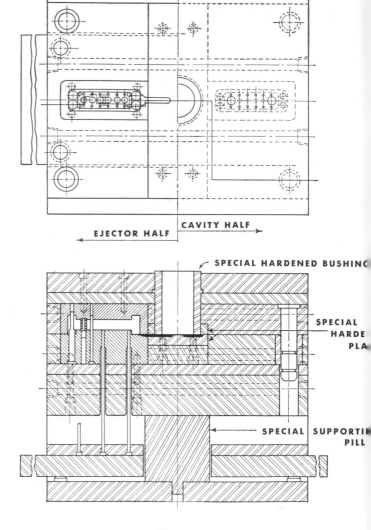

Fig. 15-78

PIPE TAPS

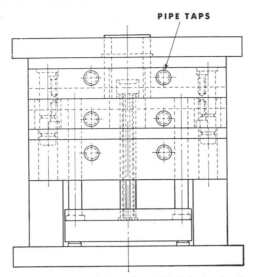

Courtesy Detroit Mold Engineering Co.

Fig. 15-78 (*cont'd*)

bolster . . . . Spacer or filler.

cam . . . . Device used to actuate movable mold members.

carburize . . . . To increase carbon content of surface of any steel.

case harden . . . . To harden surface of a piece of steel to a relatively shallow depth.

cavity . . . . That portion of the mold which forms the outer surface of the molded article.

cavity-retainer plate . . . See *chase.*

channel . . . . See *port.*

chase . . . . The main body of the mold which contains the molding cavity or cavities, or cores, the mold pins, the guide pins (or the bushings), etc.

chase ring . . . . A ring used in hobbing to restrain the blank against spreading during the sinking of the hob.

clamping plate . . . . . A mold plate fitted to the mold and used to fasten the mold to the machine.

cold slug . . . . The first material to enter an injection mold; so called because in passing through the sprue orifice it is cooled below effective molding temperature.

cold-slug well . . . . . . Space provided directly opposite the sprue opening of the injection mold to trap the cold slug.

cooling fixture . . . . . Equipment used to hold molded article while cooling after removal from the mold; it may be channeled to be cooled with water.

core . . . . That portion of the mold that forms the required inner surfaces of the molded article.

core and separator . . . . The center section of an extrusion die.

core pin . . . . Pin used to mold a hole.

core-pin plate . . . . . . Plate holding core pins.

core-retainer plate . . . . See *chase*.

cull . . . . Material remaining in the transfer pot after the mold has been filled.

diaphragm gate . . . . . Gate used in molding annular or tubular articles.

die-adaptor . . . . That part of an extrusion die which holds the die block.

die block . . . . That part of an extrusion die which holds the forming bushing and core.

die body . . . . That part of an extrusion die used to separate and form material.

disc gate . . . . See *diaphragm gate*.

dowel . . . . Pin used to maintain alignment between two or more parts.

draft . . . . The degree of the taper of a side wall or the angle of clearance, designed to facilitate removal of molded article from the mold.

draw . . . . See *temper*.

duplicate cavity-plate . . . Removable plate that retains cavities used where two-plate operation is necessary for loading inserts, etc.

ejector pin . . . . Pins used to eject the finished article from the mold.

ejector-pin-retainer plate . Retainer into which ejector pins are assembled.

ejector plate . . . . A plate which backs up the ejector pins and holds the ejector assembly together.

ejector rod . . . . A rod which actuates the ejector assembly when the mold is opened.

fin . . . . That part of the flash which remains attached to the molded article.

flash . . . . That portion of the charge which flows from or is extruded from the mold cavity during the molding.

flash groove . . . . A groove ground in a force to allow the escape of excess material.

flash ridge . . . . That part of a flash mold along which the excess material escapes until the mold is closed.

floating chase . . . . Mold member, free to move vertically, which fits over a lower plug or cavity, and into which an upper plug telescopes.

force and force plug . . . The force is the member which transmits the pressure from the press unit to the top of the molding charge. In positive molds, there is an extension to or protuberance beneath the force which telescopes within the molding cavity (or loading chamber) and which is termed a *force plug* (Compression molding). When used in reference to injection molding, see *core*).

force plate . . . . Plate for holding force plug or plugs in compression molding.

gate . . . . The short, usually restricted section of the runner at the entrance to the cavity of an injection or transfer mold.

grid . . . . Channel-shaped mold-supporting members.

guide pin . . . . Pin which assures alignment of the mold halves.

guide-pin bushing . . . . A guiding bushing through which the leader pin moves.

heater-adapter . . . . . That part of an extrusion die around which heating medium is held.

heat-treat . . . . Term used to cover annealing, hardening, tempering, etc., of metals.

hob . . . . A master model used to sink the shape of a mold into a soft steel block.

hobbing . . . . A process of forming a mold by forcing a hob of the shape desired into a soft steel blank.

hold-down groove . . . . A small groove cut into the side wall of the molding surface to assist in holding the molded article in that member while the mold opens.

holder block . . . . . . See *chase.*

hub . . . . See *hob.*

hubbing . . . . See *hobbing.*

knockout . . . . Any part or mechanism of a mold used to eject the molded article.

knockout bar . . . . . . A bar or plate in a knockout frame used to back up a row or rows or knockout pins.

knockout-pin plate . . . See *ejector-pin plate.*

knockout pins . . . . . See *ejector pins.*

land . . . . The portion of a mold which provides the separation or cutoff of the flash from the molded article.

landed force . . . . . . Force with shoulder which seats on land in landed positive mold.

landed plunger . . . . . See *landed force.*

latch . . . . Device used to hold two members together.

leader pin . . . . See *guide pin.*

leader-pin bushing . . . . See *guide-pin bushing.*

loading space . . . . . . Space provided in a compression mold or in the pot used with a transfer mold to accommodate the molding material before it is compressed.

locating ring . . . . . . A ring which serves to align the nozzle of an injection cylinder with the entrance of the sprue bushing and the mold to the machine platen.

mold base . . . . The assembly of all parts making up an injection mold, other than the cavity, cores, and pins.

mold insert (removable) . Part of a mold cavity or force which forms undercut or raised portions of a molded article.

mounting plate . . . . . See *clamping plate.*

normalize . . . . To heat ferrous alloys above the critical temperature range and then air-cool.

nozzle . . . . Restricted orifice at the end of the heating cylinder of an injection or transfer machine.

out of miter . . . . . . A mold is said to be out of miter or out of register when the halves of the cavity are not matched all around.

overflow groove . . . . . Small groove used in molds to allow material to flow freely to prevent knit-lines and low density, and to dispose of excess material.

pack hardening . . . . . Heating of steel for hardening in a closed container packed with either an inert or an active material.

parallels . . . . Spacers or supports used under the top and/or bottom halves of the mold to prevent deflection, or to provide space for an ejector mechanism.

pickup groove . . . . . See *hold-down groove.*

plunger . . . . See *force* and *pot plunger.*

port . . . . Inlet or outlet of oil, water or steam channel.

pot . . . . Chamber to hold and heat molding material for a transfer mold.

pot plunger . . . . . . A plunger used to force softened molding material into the closed cavity of a transfer mold.

pot-retainer . . . . . . Plate channeled for heat and used to hold pot of transfer mold.

pressure pad . . . . . . Hardened steel reinforcements distributed around a mold to help the land to absorb the final closing pressure.

pushback pins . . . . . See *return pins.*

return pins . . . . Pins which return the ejector mechanism to molding position.

ring gate . . . . Annular opening for entrance of material into cavity of injection or transfer mold.

runner . . . . A channel connecting the sprue with the gate, through which the material flows.

shoe . . . . See *chase.*

sleeve ejector . . . . . . Bushing-type knockout.

sliding plate . . . . . . See *duplicate cavity-plate.*

spacers . . . . See *parallels.*

split cavity . . . . Cavity made in sections.

split-cavity blocks . . . . Blocks which when assembled contain a cavity for molding articles having undercuts.

sprue . . . . The slug formed in the sprue bushing.

sprue bushing . . . . . . In an injection mold, a hardened steel insert which contains the tapered sprue hole and has a suitable seat for making close contact with the nozzle of the injection cylinder.

sprue-ejector pin . . . . See *sprue-puller*.

sprue-puller . . . . . . A pin having a Z-shaped slot undercut in its end, by means of which it serves to pull the sprue out of the sprue bushing.

stop buttons . . . . . . Multiple islands limiting travel of ejector mechanism when returned to molding position.

stripper plate . . . . . . A plate which strips the molded article from mold pin, force or cores.

stripping fork . . . . . Tool, usually of brass or laminated sheet, used to remove articles from the mold (also called comb).

support plate . . . . . . See *backing plate*.

support post or pillar . . Post used to resist deflection under pressure.

temper. . . . . To reheat after hardening to some temperature below the critical temperature, followed by air cooling to obtain desired mechanical properties and to relieve hardening strains.

undercut . . . . Any depression on the mold which prevents or hinders withdrawal of the molded article.

vent . . . . See *air vent*.

Section III—Finishing and Assembly

16. Machining, Finishing, and Decorating

Scope

In this chapter, the basic principles of machining, finishing, and decorating of plastics of various types will be set forth in general and supplemented by data for specific materials and forms. The information given is intended to serve as a starting point and guide, to assist operators in determining their own optimum operating conditions.

The operations of machining and finishing include filing, drilling, tapping, turning, sawing, piercing, trimming, routing, tumbling, grinding, sanding, ashing, polishing, buffing, transparent coating, polishing by solvent and also annealing and postbaking.

Under the heading of decorating is included also the marking of articles for reasons of utility.

General description is given of jigs, fixtures, and automatic feeding devices used to facilitate many of these operations.

Many finishing operations on molded articles can be avoided by careful design of the article and the mold, placing flash lines and gates so as to simplify the finishing. If it is impossible to design the article to be molded in one operation, then consideration must be given to proper location of bosses and holes to facilitate assembly.

Almost all molded articles require finishing, if only for removal of flash and gates. Some require machining and finishing to meet very narrow tolerances; in such a case the critical dimension may be molded oversize, and the gating so planned that the gate will be machined off in the same operation with the machining to size.

No single method is satisfactory in all cases for removal of flash and gates. Each article presents its own problem and requires development of a procedure that will give desired results at least cost. These techniques for removal of flash, fins, and gates are tumbling, filing, sanding, machining, and buffing.

Filing

Files are used for finishing molded articles, and for bevelling, smoothing, burring and fitting the edges and corners of sheets of plastic. For removal of flash, tumbling is to be preferred if feasible, but the shape, size, or contours of the article may require filing to remove both heavy and thin flash as well as gates of heavy section, or burrs left by machining operations such as drilling and tapping. Filing by hand is more costly than using special machine setups, but may be more economical on short runs.

The selection of the proper file is of great importance, as the shape, cut, size and pattern of the file will determine the ease and speed of removal of stock, and also the appearance of the filed surface.

The type of the file must be adapted to the plastic — its hardness, brittleness, flexibility, and heat-resistance. The size and shape of the file are determined by the size, shape, and contour of the article to be filed. For removal of flash, files should have very sharp, thin-topped teeth which will hold their edge, well-rounded gullets to minimize the tendency to clog, and the proper rake for clearing of the chips.

Filing Thermoplastics. With thermoplastics, files are rapidly falling into disuse, since flash is more effectively removed by three-square scrapers. Thermoplastics on which files are used include those that are relatively soft, such as cellulose acetate, acetate butyrate and polyethylene, and those that are harder, such as the vinyls, acrylics, polystyrene and copolymers of styrene. Nylon, because of its toughness and abrasion-resistance, is not easily filed.

For the soft thermoplastics, fine files should be avoided, because they become clogged. Coarse single-cut shear-tooth files should be used, with teeth cut on a 45° angle, and in flat or half-round shape. The combination of coarse teeth and long angle promotes self-cleaning. Shear-tooth files are used with long sweeping light strokes, to avoid running off of the work.

Clogging is not encountered with the harder thermoplastics, but still the shear type should be used.

For filing edges of sheet stock, milled-tooth files are recommended. The file should be held at approximately a 20° angle with the edge.

Filing Thermosetting Plastics. Articles molded from thermosetting plastics always require some finishing operation for removal of flash from parting lines (plus, in the case of articles molded by transfer, plunger, or jet, the removal of gates).

Flash should be filed off in such a way as to break it toward a solid portion rather than away from the main body, in order to prevent chipping. The file is pushed with a firm stroke to break off the flash close to the body, and then filing is continued to smooth the surface.

Since selection is made by trial and error, it is well to have a variety of files on hand.

Mill files in bastard and western cuts are used extensively to remove the flash from flat or convex surfaces of molded articles and on the corners and edges of sheets, to remove the burrs from sawing, or to bevel the corners. The western cut is slightly the coarser.

Milled-tooth files are recommended for large areas or for bevelling the corners and edges of large sheets. They are relatively coarse files with curved teeth, and are available in both flexible and rigid types.

Various shapes of Swiss-pattern files are used, coarse enough to effect rapid removal of material, and fine enough to leave a good finish. These small files of various shapes, in cuts from No. 00 to No. 4, are used for small, intricate moldings, in which the surfaces to be filed are hard to reach. Round and half-round files are used for cleaning out holes or slots with rounded surfaces; knife and warding files are used to reach down between flutes and into other narrow slots and grooves. Figure 16-1 shows shapes commonly used for plastics.

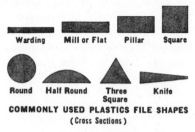

COMMONLY USED PLASTICS FILE SHAPES
(Cross Sections)

Courtesy of Nicholson File Co.

Fig. 16-1

Files are designed to cut in one direction only; pressure should be applied in that direction, and relieved on the return stroke. Experience has shown that on some fine, intricate articles a steady pressure on both strokes may result in a better finish, but it is damaging to the file. As much as possible of the filing surface, in both length and width, should be used, so that the file will wear uniformly.

The life of a file is greatly shortened by improper selection, improper use and improper care. Since many resins and fillers cause rapid wear of cutting tools, it is imperative that the files be given proper care to retain their sharpness. Proper care must be given in storage. Files should never be thrown into a drawer with other tools, or stacked on top of each other, since such treatment ruins the cutting edge of the teeth. They should be stored standing with the tangs in a row of holes, or hanging on racks by their handles, and in a dry place so that they will not rust. Files should be kept clean of filings or chips, which collect between the teeth during use, by tapping the end after every few strokes. A file card or brush should be used to remove the chips before storage. Oil or grease is removed by applying chalk and then brushing. When a file becomes dull, but is otherwise in good condition, it should be sharpened. Files can be resharpened as often as four times, even though they do not then do as good a job as when new.

Machine Filing. Removal of flash from circular or cylindrical articles in large production runs is sometimes accomplished by semiautomatic machines. A circular revolving table carries from 6 to 10 work-holding stations past a series of fixed stations equipped to remove flash, to polish, and to buff.

The work-holding stations revolve on their individual axes as they pass the work stations. If the articles are perfectly round, the work stations may be equipped with tool-holders to accommodate files, etc. If the articles are slightly out of round, or vary in size, as may be the case with pieces produced in multicavity molds, then motor-driven sanding belts, spring-loaded files, or buffing wheels are used. The efficiency of these machines is limited by the quality of the molding. Excessively heavy flash or even a slight mismatch will seriously reduce production or make hand finishing necessary.

The edges of round articles can be finished in a simple button machine, comprising a drive chuck which rotates at high speed and can be moved axially by means of a pedal. The work is put against a stationary center, the drive chuck is brought forward to engage and rotate the work, and then the operator applies a file, usually about 70° from the flash plane, to remove the fin. Frequently as many as three different flash edges may be smoothed in one handling. When the pedal is released, the work falls into a tray and the operator inserts another piece. Recommended peripheral speed for machine filing is 450 to 600 fpm.

Drilling and Reaming

Drilling of Thermoplastics. In view of the variety of materials and operations involved, the following discussion is of a general nature. It is followed by some special instructions for specific thermoplastics.

Standard horizontal or vertical drill presses, single, gang, or multiple, can be used for drilling thermoplastics.

Drills are commercially available, especially designed for plastics.

Drills having one or two wide and highly polished or chrome-plated flutes, narrow lands, and large helix angles are the most desirable, since they expel chips with minimum friction, and hence with minimum overheating and gumming.

Points should have an included angle of 60 to 90°, and a lip clearance of 12 to 18°. A substantial clearance on the cutting edges makes for a smoother finish. Drill points must be sharpened frequently and carefully, with care to avoid loss of the desired point angles. Carbide-tipped points will hold cutting edges longest, may be used at high speeds, and in some applications do not require to be cooled by liquid.

The use of liquids as lubricants or cooling agents should be avoided if practicable, since it necessitates a subsequent cleaning of the articles. In the drilling of most holes, an air blast will suffice to assist in clearing chips, and to prevent overheating which would cause clogging.

The speeds used in drilling holes in thermoplastics will depend upon the type of material and size and depth of the holes. In general, speeds will be decreased with increase in the size of the hole, and increased with the hardness of the material.

Recommended speeds for thermoplastics are given below. Use slower speeds, if necessary, to avoid overheating.

Drill Size	rpm	Drill Size	rpm
No. 1 through No. 16	2500	5/16 in.	1700
No. 17 through No. 32	3000	3/8 in.	1300
No. 33 and up	5000	7/16 in.	1000
1/16 in.	5000	1/2 in.	1000
1/8 in.	3000	A through D	2500
3/16 in.	2500	E through M	1700
1/4 in.	1700	N through Z	1300

Drilling equipment must be in good condition if accurate holes are to be obtained. Loose spindle bearings or bent or poorly sharpened drills will give inaccurate results with any material. The speed should be the greatest that will not cause burning or gumming, and the feed should be slow and uniform, to produce a smooth hole of uniform diameter. Chips should be removed by frequently withdrawing the drill from the work to clear the hole. In deep holes, the application of cutting oil or other cooling agent will prevent sticking of the chips. Pressure should be relaxed near the termination of through holes, to prevent break-through. In deep holes, an intermittent relaxing of the drill pressure will reduce clogging and run-off.

Drilling can be expedited by specially designed drill jigs. (See p. 639)

(1) *Cellulose acetate and acetate butyrate.* Standard twist drills developed for wood or metal are frequently used on acetate or butyrate, but the drills especially designed for plastics, mentioned above, are preferred.

Drilling with the conventional twist drills of the type used for metal require much slower speeds and feeds to give a clean hole and to keep the material from gumming, and more frequent backing out of the drill to clear chips. Quality of work can best be controlled by air-operated feeds and mechanical feeding devices.

Reaming of holes drilled in acetate or butyrate is not recommended. Where accurate dimensions are required in thin sections, good results are obtained by drilling to within about 0.001 in. of size and then running a hardened polished rod through the hole to smooth it.

(2) *Polystyrene.* Polystyrene is best drilled by tools of "Carboloy." Carbide-tipped straight-flute drills can be used, but slow-twist drills of high-speed steel, with polished flutes, carbide-tipped, are usually satisfactory, provided the feed is not so rapid as to plug the flutes. The tools should be extremely sharp, and fed uniformly.

A negative rake of about 8° in the carbide-tipped tools has been found most efficient. If the top surface of the tungsten carbide has been polished with a diamond wheel, the chips will slide away easily from the cutting contact. Drills should be ground with a 25° angle, and stoned on both the cutting angle and in the flute, to remove all trace of burrs.

Spindle speeds with carbide-tipped tools of negative rake should be kept above 3000 rpm. Liquid cooling agents, such as soapy water and water-soluble oils, may be used to prevent overheating which would impair the quality of the work, but this is often unnecessary with "Carboloy"-tipped drills. The best and cleanest method of cooling drills is to direct an air blast upon the work area. Cooling by one means or the other will contribute toward high quality of work.

If carbide-tipped drills are not available, drills of high-speed steel can be used at lower speeds. Such drills for polystyrene should have a lip angle of 70° and a clearance of 10 to 15°. A slow helix is best for most such work. Polished flutes, though not essential, will promote clean drilling. For drilling cleanly in holes that are deep or of small diameter, the web of the drill should be sharpened practically to a point. Care must be taken not to alter the clearance, rake and other angles. Spindle speeds of 600 rpm can be used for such work, by accommodating the rate of feed to the depth and diameter of the hole.

(3) *Acrylics.* Because of the transparency of acrylics, it is usually desirable that the inside of a drilled hole have a high finish. Hence the drilling of acrylics requires extra care, and may call for special drills.

Though standard metal-type twist drills are satisfactory for the average drilling job in acrylics, they have a tendency to grab in large or deep holes. Better results are obtained with a sharp drill having a flute angle of 17 to 18°, an included lip angle of 70°, and a lip clearance angle of 4 to 8°. The lands of the drill should be highly polished and about one-fourth the width of the heel. Special drills for acrylics, now commercially available, usually have a slow spiral with highly polished flutes. Outstanding results can be achieved with a jet drill, the point of which is cooled with a lubricant fed through a hole in the drill. Holes of large diameter can be cut with either hollow-end mills or fly cutters. It is important that tools for drilling acrylics be kept free of nicks and burrs. All types of tools can be used on standard vertical or horizontal presses.

Rates of feed can be determined only by experience. The proper feed will result in smooth, continuous spiral chips or ribbons. Feed should be slowed as the depth of the cut increases.

In drilling deep holes in acrylics a lubricant is needed to prevent clogging and possible burning or scarring of the wall of the hole. An air blast to cool the drill will be found beneficial in all cases.

(4) *Nylon.* Nylon can be drilled satisfactorily with conventional twist drills, but more rapidly with special drills, designed for plastics, and having deep flutes, highly polished to facilitate removal of chips. In some, the flute leads are much longer than in conventional drills.

Drilling of Thermosetting Plastics. The following table gives a general basis for selecting speeds of drills for conventionally molded thermosetting plastics.

Drill Size	rpm	Drill Size	rpm
No. 1 through No. 10	1700	$\frac{5}{16}$ in.	1300
No. 11 through No. 27	2500	$\frac{3}{8}$ in.	1000
No. 28 through No. 41	3000	$\frac{7}{16}$ in.	600
No. 42 and up	5000	$\frac{1}{2}$ in.	600
$\frac{1}{16}$ in.	5000	A and B	1700
$\frac{1}{8}$ in.	3000	C through O	1300
$\frac{3}{16}$ in.	2500	P through Z	1000
$\frac{1}{4}$ in.	1700		

Hot-Molded. To drill holes in molded articles or to remove flash or fins in molded holes, it is best to use standard high-speed steel drills with deep flutes. Nitrided high-speed drills do not require frequent sharpening, and will last a long time. Drill points should be ground to an included angle of 70 to 90°, and have a lip clearance or relief made by grinding the back away to 1/16 in. wide, which reduces friction between the drill and the work and gives clearance for the chips. Backing off the cutting lip (rake angle) prevents the grabbing which occurs with a drill with a normal point, and will sometimes prevent chipping of the hole when the drill breaks through the under side of the work.

Most drilling is done without lubricant, but a blast of air at the drill point will keep the drill and work cool, prolong the life of the point, and help clear away chips. Drill speeds should be from 100 to 150 fpm, or faster if proven by trial. Drills should be about 0.002 to 0.003 in. oversize. For drilling thin sections, the point of the drill can be ground with a sharper included angle to stop chipping around the hole.

Some manufacturers will make to order special drills for use in long-run or automatic drilling operations. These are made on slow-twist blanks, and tipped with tungsten carbide. This is about the most economical drill for phenolics if the production will warrant the cost, and the best for very deep holes.

In drilling deep holes, good results are obtained, however, with steel drills having specially polished flutes and 0.0001 to 0.0002 in. of chromium plate.

For drilling through holes in canvas-filled materials, the drill may be specially ground. The end is ground like that of a wood drill. The outer edges of the drill are cut like circle-cutting tools, while the center acts as a pilot. Thus at the breakthrough the cutting is done through a thin section supported on both sides by heavier areas, and the final chip is a disk with a hole.

Reducing the friction between the drill and the material by grinding the drill off-center (which results in a slightly larger hole) will often prolong the life of the drill.

Cold-Molded. Because the high percentage of asbestos sometimes used in these materials dulls drills very rapidly, holes are usually molded when such fillers are present, rather than drilled or tapped. Where they must be drilled, drills tipped with tungsten carbide are recommended. These are usually operated at a surface speed of 250 to 350 fpm. For special twist drills of high-speed steel, the speed is 50 to 150 fpm. The speed of the drill depends upon its size, the depth of the hole and the capacity of the machine. As a rule, no lubricant is used, but a good supply of air under pressure is required.

Cast Phenolics. For small holes, drill speeds of about 2800 to 12,000 rpm are commonly used. Drills of diameter $\frac{1}{4}$ in. or more should have large flutes, for efficient removal of material, and the cutting edges should be ground with a negative rake. For the drilling of small holes for self-tapping screws, the hole is usually one drill size smaller than the screw.

Rapid production is obtained by a multiple drill assembly. Multiple drill heads are likewise effective. Where neither is available, drilling with a jig can be made both fast and accurate.

Tapping and Threading

The following data on sizes of tap drills for plastics* are based on experience, and are specifically for thermosetting plastics. Thermoplastics may require one size larger for a given tap.

The sizes given are the nearest available drill sizes, identified by number, letter or dimension. If one does not have the specified type, the nearest larger size should be used. Specification of percentage thread is based upon diameters in small sizes and upon pitch in larger sizes.

The formula used is:

$$D = T - n \times 2d, \text{ in which}$$

$D =$ drill diameter

$T =$ outside diameter of thread or tap

$d =$ depth of thread

$n =$ percentage of thread depth desired. (expressed as a decimal)

"C" indicates Standard N.C.S. size; "F" indicates Standard N.F.S. size. Percentage depths used in preparing the table were:

     50% below No. 6

     60% No. 6 through 14

     70% 15 through 30

     70% $\frac{1}{4}$ through $\frac{1}{2}$ in. N.C.S.

     70% $\frac{1}{4}$ through 1 in. N.F.S.

     75% $\frac{9}{16}$ through 1 in. N.C.S.

---

* Courtesy Boonton Molding Co.

Tap	Drill	Tap	Drill	Tap	Drill	Tap	Drill
F0 x 80	55	8 x 30	28	16 x 16	3	N.C.S.	
1 x 56	1/16	C8 x 32	28	16 x 18	7/32		
C1 x 64	52	F8 x 36	27	16 x 20	2	1/4 x 20	5
F1 x 72	51	9 x 24	27	17 x 16	1	5/16 x 18	G
2 x 48	49	9 x 28	25	17 x 18	A	3/8 x 16	O
C2 x 56	48	9 x 30	24	17 x 20	B	7/16 x 14	3/8
F2 x 64	48	9 x 32	24	18 x 16	B	1/2 x 13	7/16
3 x 40	45	C10 x 24	22	18 x 18	D	9/16 x 12	31/64
C3 x 48	44	10 x 30	19	18 x 20	E	5/8 x 11	17/32
F3 x 56	43	F10 x 32	19	19 x 16	E	3/4 x 10	21/32
4 x 32	42	11 x 24	17	19 x 18	F	7/8 x 9	49/64
4 x 36	42	11 x 28	16	24 x 18	G	1 x 8	7/8
C4 x 40	41	11 x 30	16	26 x 14	H		
F4 x 48	40	12 x 20	16	26 x 16	I	N.F.S.	
5 x 30	37	12 x 22	15	28 x 14	J		
5 x 32	36	C12 x 24	13	28 x 16	L	1/4 x 28	2
5 x 36	36	F12 x 28	12	30 x 14	M	5/16 x 24	I
C5 x 40	35	13 x 20	12	30 x 16	5/16	3/8 x 24	R
F5 x 44	34	13 x 22	10	24 x 16	O	7/16 x 20	25/64
6 x 30	32	13 x 24	9	19 x 20	P	1/2 x 20	29/64
C6 x 32	31	14 x 20	6	20 x 16	Q	9/16 x 18	33/64
6 x 36	31	14 x 22	5	20 x 18	11/32	5/8 x 18	37/64
F6 x 40	1/8	14 x 24	4	20 x 20	23/64	3/4 x 16	11/16
7 x 28	1/8	15 x 18	5	22 x 16	U	7/8 x 14	13/16
7 x 30	1/8	15 x 20	4	22 x 16	W	1 x 14	15/16
7 x 32	30	15 x 22	3	24 x 14	X		
8 x 24	29	15 x 24	7/32				

Thermoplastics. Unless special accurate tapping machines with lead screws are available, it is unwise to attempt Class 2 or 3 fits. In any case, a higher percentage of rejects and higher costs may be expected, especially with nylon.

United States Standard (American Coarse Thread Series), Whitworth Standard (British Standard Series) and Acme are generally satisfactory. Sharp V-threads are to be avoided because the apex is easily broken. Coarse-pitch threads are preferred because they are stronger.

Bottom taps should be avoided wherever possible. If a bottom tap must be used, it should be used in a second operation done by hand, and only when a Class 2 or 3 fit is required. For maximum strength and dimensional stability, all tapped parts should be annealed to relieve the stresses set up by the tapping.

Before tapping, it is recommended that the hole be drilled to such size as to permit not more than 75 per cent of a full thread, to minimize difficulty in clearing the tap.

To obtain effective clearance of chips, with a minimum of friction, large, highly polished flutes are recommended. Taps should be nitrided or chrome-plated. All new taps should be stoned to remove burrs.

Taps for all thermoplastics should have maximum back clearance. In most cases, the pitch diameter should be 0.002 in. oversize. For tapping nylon, 0.005 in. oversize is recommended, unless a tight fit is desired.

Designs and speeds for several of the thermoplastics are as follows:

	Number of Flutes	Cutting Speed (fpm)
cellulose acetate	2 or 3	50 to 100
methyl methacrylate	4 (a)	35 to 75
nylon	3 or 4 (b)	75 to 125
polystyrene	3 or 4 (c)	25 to 35

(a) Grind back rake angle to about 2° positive.

(b) Or use No. 2 flute spiral.

(c) Grind to zero rake.

The use of air or a lubricant is not essential in tapping, but it facilitates clearing the chips and permits faster tapping. The tap should be backed out before enough chips are formed to block the cooling agent.

In threading or tapping thermoplastics to fit a metal bolt or nut, allowance should be made for the difference in thermal expansion between the two materials. A slight increase over normal metal clearances is usually ample. But if variations in service temperature are to be extreme, dimensional changes will be too great to be accommodated in this way, and threading should be avoided.

Instead of being tapped, thermoplastics may be threaded on conventional lathes or screw machines. On automatic and semiautomatic machines, with self-opening dies, chasers should be ground to zero rake, highly polished and chromium-plated. For nylon, a conventional rake, as for mild steel, is recommended. In most cases, two passes should be made, and the work flooded with water containing a high percentage of mild soap, or other cooling agent that will not attack the plastic. If a single-point tool is used in a lathe, the point should have a 2° side rake and a zero back rake (for nylon, a zero side rake and a 2° back rake). The best possible results will be given by diamond-pointed tools.

Thermosetting Plastics. *Hot-Molded.* Phenolics may be tapped with standard taps. The most durable are commercial ground taps with rather short chamfer and with 0.0001 to 0.0002 in. of chromium plate. If it is required to hold Class 2 or Class 3 threads, the taps should be oversize by 0.002 to 0.003 in.

Holes should be chamfered to the maximum diameter of the thread. Here again is an instance where a planned mold design may help. Frequently a hole may be spotted or molded to a shallow depth, to be drilled and tapped to final depth later. In such cases, if the hole is to be tapped, the chamfer may be molded in at the same time as the hole, to eliminate one operation.

For long production runs a high-speed nitrided and chromium-plated tap, having three flutes rather than four, is recommended. Solid carbide taps will pay for themselves if used in a machine equipped with torque-control. A negative rake of about 5° on the front face of the land, and ample clearance, are necessary to ensure accurate cutting and to prevent binding and chipping during backing out. For tapping mineral-filled material, which tends to dull the tap very rapidly, sometimes a carbide tap can be used, provided that the work is clamped tightly under a torque-controlled tapping spindle so as to prevent breakage of the tap.

Flutes of taps can be opened by grinding, to make room for clearance of chips. Most tapping is done dry, but oils can be applied as lubricants. Paraffin wax is sometimes applied to the point of the tap to help to prevent heating, but air blasts on the tap, operated by the stroke of the tapping head, will help to clear the chips and cool the tap and the work. This minimizes overheating, prolongs the life of the tap and promotes greater production per tap.

Peripheral speeds for tapping molded phenolics are from 50 to 80 fpm for taps up to $\frac{1}{4}$ in. diameter. Taps larger than this are impractical in phenolics.

A blind hole should not be machined-tapped unless there is plenty of clearance at the bottom for the tap.

Cold-Molded. Cold-molded articles are very seldom tapped. Instead, threaded metal inserts are usually molded into the article.

Cast Phenolics. Cast phenolics may be easily tapped on vertical or horizontal tapping machines with standard taps. To provide strength, fairly coarse threads should be used. Tapped holes should be checked with plug gauges, as the abrasive action of the material causes wear. Standard machine screws can be used for assembly.

Cutting of threads of large diameter or coarse pitch, such as on bottle caps or jar covers machined from solid material, is done on a thread-milling machine, with a small milling cutter of the proper shape.

Turning and Milling

Thermoplastics. For turning and milling of thermoplastics, four cutting materials fill most needs: high-speed steel, high-speed steel chrome-plated, tungsten carbide, and diamond. They may be rated as follows (the range is arbitrary from 1 (best) to 10 (worst)):

	Interrupted Cutting	Surface Finish	Wear-resistance	Uniformity of Finish	Tool Cost per Cut	Accuracy
high-speed steel	1	5	10	10	10	10
chrome-plated high-speed steel	1	4	8	8	8	8
tungsten carbide	5	6	5	5	5	5
diamond	10	1	1	1	1	1

Tools of standard carbon steel or high-speed steel may be used for short runs, if their cutting edges are kept very sharp, and their faces highly polished. But carbide-tipped or diamond tools are almost essential for long runs, because they hold a keener edge for a longer time. Such tools make possible a highly polished surface finish. To minimize surface friction at maximum cutting speed, the side and front clearances of the tools should be somewhat greater than those of standard turning tools. Both steel and diamond end-mills should have the same cutting angles and rakes as standard carbide tools.

The cutting edges of all tools should be kept honed very keen. Standard carbide-tipped tools are very satisfactory except that clearance angles should be ground to from 7 to 12°. The top surface should be lapped to a bright finish. A soft iron wheel impregnated with a fine grit of powdered diamond is often used. Diamond tools are usually designed like the standard carbide tools described above, except that for turning nylon a sharp-pointed tool with a 20° positive rake is used.

A circular tool is economical in quantity production wherever it can be used.

With most thermoplastics, surface speeds may run as high as 600 fpm with feeds of from 0.002 to 0.005 in. The speed and feed must be determined largely by the finish desired and the kind of tool used. It is difficult to make fine finish cuts on nylon except with a carbide or diamond-tipped tool.

Good results are obtained without lubricating the cutting and turning tools if feed pressure is relaxed often enough to avoid overheating. On turret lathes, good lubrication is obtained, if necessary, by flowing a mixture of equal parts of soluble oil and water, or a soap solution, over the tools.

Milling operations must be held to very light cuts, not over 0.010 in. at normal feeds. End milling with a centercutting tool may be performed on an ordinary drill press, as long as the work is rigidly supported and the feed is steady and slow. Feeds may be increased with the aid of a suitable cooling agent. It is entirely practicable to use hand feed, but for best finishes power feed is advisable.

Vibration of the machine will cause a poor finish.

Thermosetting Plastics. *Hot-Molded.* Molded phenolics and ureas should not be machined unless it is impossible to form the desired shape by molding. Since machining of molded articles destroys their lustrous surface, machining is restricted to articles made for utility rather than appearance. Only with a few special materials can the machined surface be satisfactorily polished.

Fillers cause difficulties in machining in the order (1) wood flour (least), (2) fabric, (3) cotton, (4) mineral, and (5) glass (most).

One of the greatest problems in machining phenolics is their inability to dissipate heat. Another is their tendency to chip.

The procedures for machining phenolics are similar to those for machining brass. The cutting action is more a scraping than a peeling. The speed in feet per minute is high and compares with those for brass. The principal difference is in the abrasive action. Phenolics dull the regular steel tool very quickly.

Most turning and boring of the phenolics on a lathe is done dry. A jet of air at the point of the cutting tool reduces the rate at which the tool is dulled, and clears away the chips.

Cold-Molded. Cold-molded articles are machined usually in a double-end lathe, with carbide-tipped tools, at a surface speed of 500 to 700 fpm. Articles molded from earlier cold-molding materials by older techniques frequently required machining to meet dimensional tolerances. But with newer materials (having low shrinkage) and newer techniques (high pressures while setting), machining is seldom required.

Cast Phenolics. Regular machine-shop equipment is used in producing articles from cast phenolics. In quantity production on screw machines, operations similar to those applied to metal, such as drilling, turning, threading, tapping and milling, require only differently-ground tools, and ranges of feed and speeds adjusted to the requirements of the materials.

There are a few hard-and-fast rules governing the machining of cast phenolics, but in general high speeds and light cuts are preferable. Nearly all the work is done dry. Nonalkaline cooling agents may be employed, but are rarely required. In producing articles on an automatic screw machine, where the taper of cast phenolic rod may hamper the feeding of it, the rod may first be centerless-ground accurately to uniform diameter.

Turning tools are sharpened very much as for brass. There should be plenty of clearance, 10 to 20°, and a slightly negative or zero rake is desirable. The tool should be set 1 to 2° above the center of the material. Cutting edges should be in condition to produce long ribbon shavings or chips. Honed tools produce the smoothest cuts. Diamond, carbide, or high-speed steel may be used to get the longest runs without resharpening or resetting.

For maximum efficiency and best working conditions, dust and shavings should be removed by a blower.

Spindle speeds in turning operations range from 450 to 6000 rpm, depending on the specific work being done and the diameter of the material, and should be regulated to give a surface speed of about 600 fpm.

Sawing

The greatest single problem in the sawing of most plastics is the dissipation of heat. Since many plastics, especially thermoplastics, have very low softening temperatures, and all plastics are poor thermal conductors, a cooling agent (liquid or compressed air) is needed, unless the cut is very short, such as in the removal of a gate.

Round saws should be hollow-ground, with burrs from sharpening removed by stoning, and band and jig saws should have enough set to give adequate clearance to the back of the blade. This set should be greater than is usual for cutting steel. It is always best to relieve the feed pressure near the end of a cut to avoid chipping.

The proper rate of feed is important and, since most sawing operations are hand-fed, it can be learned only through experience. Attempts to force the feed will result in the heating of the blade, gumming of the material, loading of the saw teeth, and an excessively rough cut. Before the next cut is made, the saw must be cleaned. Chromium plating of the blade reduces friction and tends to give better cuts.

Above all, the saw, whether band or circular, must be kept sharp. Frequent sharpening of circular saws pays for itself. Dull bandsaws should be replaced.

Circular saws are usually from $1/32$ to $1/8$ in. thick. The width of band-saws is usually $3/16$ to $1/2$ in.

Both thermoplastic and thermosetting resins can be sawed also by use of cutoff machines having abrasive wheels. This equipment is used for cutting rods, tubes, etc., into lengths, for slicing profiled bars of cast phenolics, and for removing large gates. Narrow-faced wheels are used (0.02 to 0.125 in.), containing usually a silicon-carbide abrasive in the range of No. 36 to No. 50. With an appropriate wheel properly used, clean cuts can be made. If necessary, water is used to prevent overheating.

Thermoplastics. The following table may be useful as a guide in sawing thermoplastics:

Material	Thickness, in.	Circular Saw Diameter, in.	Bandsaw: Type of Tooth	Speed fpm	Pitch	Feed	Lubricant
cellulose acetate	1/16-1/4	6-9	precision	4,500	10	light	soluble oils or water-soap solution
	1/4-3/4	8-10	precision	3,000	10-6	light	water-soap solution
	3/4-3	10-12	claw	3,000	6-3	light to medium	water-soap solution
acrylic	1/16-1/4	6-9	precision	4,000	14	light	water-soap solution
	1/4-3/4	8-10	precision	3,000	10-6	light	water-soap solution
	3/4-3	10-12	claw	3,000	6-3	light to medium	water-soap solution
nylon	1/16-1/4	6-9	precision	6,000	14	light	water-soap solution
	1/4-3/4	8-10	claw	5,000	10-4	light	water-soap solution
	3/4-3	10-12	claw	4,000	4-3	medium	water-soap solution
polystyrene	1/16-1/4	6-9	precision	2,500	10	light	water-soap solution
	1/4-3/4	8-10	precision	2,000	6-4	light	water-soap solution
	3/4-3	10-12	claw	1,500	4-3	light	water-soap solution

Courtesy The DoAll Company

Thermosetting Plastics. The sawing of these plastics is confined to bandsaws (solid or inserted-segment), carbide circular saws, and abrasive cutoff disks.

Nearly all of these plastics are extremely abrasive. Some of them, notably the glass-filled alkyds, will dull a circular saw of high-speed steel in a cut of a few inches in ¼ in. material. In production runs of this material, it is probably best to use an abrasive cutoff disk, 0.040 to ¹⁄₁₆ in. thick, 6 to 20 in. in diameter, run at from 3500 to 6000 rpm.

Phenolics, ureas and melamines are usually cut by bandsaws, which have the advantage of dissipating the heat.

The following table shows the recommendations of one of the manufacturers of bandsaws:

Material	Thickness, in.	Type of Tooth	Speed fpm	Teeth per In.	Feed
melamine-formaldehyde	1/16-1/4	precision	6,000	14	light
	1/4-1/2	precision	5,000	10	light
	1/2-1	precision	4,000	6	medium
	1-3	claw	3,500	3	medium
phenolic (cast, molded or laminated, asbestos or fabric filler)	1/16-1/4	precision	4,000	18	light
	1/4-1/2	precision	3,000	14	medium
	1/2-1	precision	2,500	10	medium
	1-3	claw	2,000	4	heavy
phenolic (cast or molded, no filler)	1/16-1/4	precision	6,000	14	light
	1/4-1/2	precision	5,000	10	light
	1/2-1	precision	4,000	6	medium
	1-3	claw	3,500	3	medium
phenolic (cast, molded or laminated, glass or mineral filler)	1/16-1/4	precision	150	18-14	medium
	1/4-1/2	precision	75	10	medium
	1/2-1	precision	50	8	heavy
	1-3	precision	50	6	heavy
urea-formaldehyde	1/16-1/4	precision	6,000	14	light
	1/4-1/2	precision	5,000	10	light
	1/2-1	precision	4,000	6	light
	1-3	claw	3,500	3	medium

Courtesy The DoAll Company

An air jet should be used at the point of contact, and a suction hose to remove the dust.

Piercing, Trimming and Routing

Thermoplastics. Small holes may be punched through thin sheets of thermoplastics on standard hand-operated arbor presses, but an ordinary punch press or shearing machine is generally used. Thin sheets may be processed cold, but thicker sheets should be heated. For acrylics, about 185°F will be required for the heavier sections, while the other materials should be heated not above about 120°F, in order to prevent damaging the surface and finish.

It is common practice to remove ring gates from injection-molded articles by shearing, even to the extent of making multiple-cavity punching dies for multiple-cavity moldings. It is important that the punch and die fit closely, in order to avoid producing ragged edges.

Blanking or shaving dies are frequently used for removing parting lines and flash lines. The punch and die are sometimes heated, so as to leave the best possible finish.

Routing and shaping are done on standard woodworking equipment. For fine cuts at high speed, single- or multiple-bladed fly cutters should be used.

Routing is a grooving or milling operation, used, e.g., in finishing the cavities for supporting the glass in mirror frames. It is done by means of cutters of small diameter having three or more teeth of the desired profile, and mounted on vertical spindles which project above a metal table top. These cutters revolve at high speeds, e.g., 12,600 rpm, so as to produce smooth cuts.

The work is held in a special fixture equipped with a metal master guideplate which is kept in contact with a metal collar on the table, directly below the cutter. The fixture is moved by hand.

For bringing rough-sawed articles of flat stock to size and shape, edge-molders are used, of the type used for finishing articles of wood. A cutter of desired profile is mounted on a vertical spindle, which revolves at 7000 to 10,000 rpm, depending on the size of the cutter and the amount of stock to be removed. The work is held in a fixture equipped with a metal master guideplate, which is kept in contact with a collar on the spindle below the cutter. The fixture is moved by hand. Fixtures of semiautomatic type have been developed to accomplish this same result; the operator loads and unloads the fixtures as they advance to and from the cutters. The cut is made rapidly to prevent burning the material.

Thermosetting Plastics. If the quantities are sufficiently large to warrant the cost of piercing tools, they provide the best method for removing flash from holes. A simple pad die with stripper plate may be made to pierce all holes and trim the outside shape of an article, at the rate of about 700 per hr. Small articles with several holes may be pierced in a dial press at the rate of about 1200 per hr. The piercing punches for removal of flash should be round-nosed and should have two or three helical grooves around the working end. These grooves should pass by the flash line in the hole, to rake the flash out of the hole. If the flash is on the surface of the article, it should be punched into the hole rather than out of it in order to prevent chipping.

Although thin sheets ($\frac{1}{8}$ to $\frac{3}{16}$ in.) of cast phenolic may be blanked with a steel-rule die, this is not recommended, because of the difficulty in obtaining accurate cuts. Blanks are better and more economically obtained by casting a bar of the desired profile and slicing or cutting it with standard slicing equipment or abrasive cutoff equipment.

Tumbling

Thermoplastics. Tumbling is used to round corners, to remove stumps of gates, and to apply finish to surfaces. It is the cheapest way of doing these things, for the equipment is not expensive and the only labor involved is in the loading and unloading of barrels. It is applicable chiefly to small objects which do not have projections that are easily broken off. Tumbling does not produce as high a finish as that obtainable by ashing and polishing, but for many articles a very high polish is not necessary and is not worth the higher labor cost involved.

The articles to be tumbled are placed in octagonal wooden barrels, 20 to 30 in. in diameter, which may be divided into two or more pockets to permit the handling of two or more colors or shapes simultaneously. The barrels are mounted on a horizontal axis and driven through pulleys and gears, and are usually run at a speed of 15 to 30 rpm.

Abrasives and hardwood pegs are put in the pockets of the barrels with the articles to be tumbled. The pegs serve to rub the abrasive against the articles during the tumbling. Sawdust and pumice are used in the first stage because of their rapid abrasive action; finer abrasives and polish are used later to give better finishes.

Thermosetting Plastics. *Hot-Molded.* Tumbling is used on all kinds of thermosetting materials, for removing flash. It is done in barrels of various types, with several different materials as filling agents.

A cylindrical ("cement-mixer") barrel, running at speeds of 15 to 25 rpm, is used for light articles which have little or very thin flash. The articles are allowed to roll by themselves, from two to five minutes as necessary.

An octagonal barrel with alternate closed and open sides running horizontally is used for heavier articles and where more positive action is needed. The open sections are covered by screens of suitable coarseness to let the fragments of flash fall out. Lignum vitae balls from $\frac{1}{2}$ to 1 in. in diameter are used to give a rolling action to the articles and to prevent chipping. It has been found that a mixture of two parts of balls to one part of moldings, by volume, generally gives good results. Hardwood blocks or scrap molded parts also are used on some jobs. The speed of this barrel should be variable from 5 to about 30 rpm. The time required varies with the work, some jobs running as long as 2 to 3 hr.

Tumbling may be used also to reduce size of molded articles. This is done in a closed barrel running at a fairly high speed, and employs a cutting agent. Rubber impregnated with an abrasive is cut into various shapes and sizes and tumbled with the articles to give a satiny finish without a harsh cutting action. For fast removal of stock, strips of abrasive cloth or abrasive paper, mixed with the articles, are used. The barrel may be lined with abrasive cloth. For very light cuts, especially before polishing, pumice and small pegs are used. Octagonal barrels running at 20 to 35 rpm have proven best for this work.

With articles having grooves or projections, it is more difficult to achieve a uniform complete polishing, and the polishing agent tends to accumulate in grooves or other pockets on the surface. Such articles are best polished by being tumbled in barrels with string mops which have been impregnated and coated with specially compounded wax by being tumbled in clean barrels with balls of the wax. The tumbling together of articles and mop is done in a closed octagonal barrel having no screens, and no metal on the inside, which would scratch the surface of the articles. The barrel, on a horizontal axis, is rotated at speeds from 15 rpm (for large articles) up to 30 rpm (for small articles).

Another procedure for removing flash utilizes the impact of small pellets of relatively soft and nonabrasive nature, e.g., crushed apricot pits.

A conveyor carries the articles, in tumbling motion, through a stream of pellets projected at high velocity by a rotating bladed wheel. Figure 16-2 is a schematic drawing of this equipment.

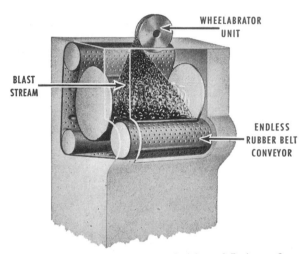

Courtesy of American Wheelabrator & Equipment Corp.

Fig. 16-2. Schematic view of Wheelabrator Tumblast Deflasher.

Figure 16-3 shows another method of removing flash from delicate or large articles.

Cold-Molded. The tumbling barrels are of wood, metal, or wire screen, revolving at 25 to 30 rpm. For removal of burrs or flash, the articles are usually tumbled by themselves, but sawdust and wooden pegs may be added.

For polishing, they are tumbled with sawdust, wooden pegs or leather findings treated with a hard wax and light oils. The time required may be from 10 min to several hours.

Cast Phenolics. Articles of cast phenolic are finished more commonly by tumbling than by expensive hand operations. The diversity of tumbling practice is very great. Because of the number of variables involved it is much better to run tests or have them run by specialists in the field, than to follow any set rules.

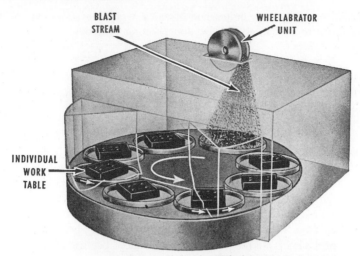

Courtesy of American Wheelabrator & Equipment Corp.

Fig. 16-3. Schematic view of a Wheelabrator Table Deflasher.

Grinding and Sanding

These operations, if conducted dry, require an exhaust system to dispose of dust.

Thermoplastics. Standard sanding machines of belt and disk types, run wet or dry, are used for form sanding, or for long production runs. A variable speed-control provides the proper speed in accordance with the amount of material to be removed.

For belt sanding, the information given below for thermosetting plastics is generally applicable. Belts carrying coarse abrasive, and run dry, may be used for fast, rough cutting, if the speed is kept down to avoid excessive heating. In most cases, however, particularly in fine sanding, belts are run wet, as a precaution against overheating.

On polystyrene, wet belt sanders are used, with light pressure. Any sharp grain cuts well when wet. Dry sanding is used on very light fins.

On methyl methacrylate resin, the finest sandpaper that will remove the scratch or other defects (no coarser than grade 320) is used first. The paper should be of waterproof type. The paper is wrapped around a soft block of felt or rubber, and the area is rubbed lightly with a circular motion, using water, or soap and water, as a lubricant. An area having a diameter two or three times the length of the defect should be sanded, in order to minimize local optical distortion. Initial sanding should be followed by similar treatment with progressively finer grades of sandpaper (grade 360A, 400A and 500 or 600A), each of which removes the deeper scratches left by the preceding. The plastic must be washed after each sanding operation. Where a large amount of polishing is to be done, ashing compounds may be used in place of sandpaper.

Thermosetting Plastics. Belt sanding is commonly used for the removal of heavy flash and sprue projections, and for flat surfacing and beveling. The belts should carry silicon-carbide abrasive bonded by waterproof synthetic resin. Popular grit sizes are 50, 120, 180, 220 and 400 —the coarse for heavy flash and sprues, the fine for lighter operations. Speeds recommended are from 2000 to 5000 linear fpm, but 4000 is most commonly used.

With a good exhaust system to remove dust and do some cooling by pulling air past the edge being sanded, thermosetting plastics can be successfully sanded at medium speeds on dry belts, thus avoiding the washing and drying required after wet sanding. But wet sanding offers the advantages of freedom from dust and overheating, longer life of belts, freedom from clogging of the belt, and the finer surface produced because of the lubrication.

On cold-molded articles, both disk and belt grinders are used. Disk grinders are run at 1750 to 2000 rpm; the grit ranges from 40 to 60 to 120. Belt grinders are operated at a surface speed of 3000 to 4000 fpm. All work is done dry.

Until the development of water-lubricated grinding wheels, the heavy flash on the face of a radio cabinet, or similar large castings, was removed either by a tedious manual sanding operation (which was likely to be inaccurate) or by a very large water-lubricated abrasive cutoff wheel. There is now available a semiautomatic grinding machine having an 18-in. wheel 3 in. thick, recessed in the center beginning about 3 in. from the circumference. This wheel operates in water, and a carriage moves the article against the wheel. Since the unrecessed area is the only grinding surface, its wear is relatively uniform, and it does accurate work. At normal capacity, these machines can remove the flash from 75 cabinets per hour.

It is seldom necessary to resort to sanding the surfaces of well-machined pieces, but sanding can be done with any good abrasive cloth or abrasive paper which can be used in belt form or in rotating disks. The finer the paper and the slower the cutting, the less pronounced are the marks left by the abrasive. Facets and other surfaces can be cut in this way, with care to avoid overheating and discoloring the work. Surface speed for sanding cast phenolics is about the same as, or slightly less than, that for sanding wood.

In the finishing of rough-cast phenolic castings it is frequently necessary to produce radii, bevels, etc., which cannot be formed in the usual straight-draw lead molds. The necessary shaping is done with tools, usually of bronze, honed in much the same manner as are tools for shaping wood, but having a larger number of teeth, operated at a lower speed. These can be used to put a radius on the square end of a radio cabinet and to obtain bevels, beads and other decorative lines.

Ashing, Buffing and Polishing

The finishing department requires polishing lathes, buffing wheels and suitable compositions for the ashing, polishing, cutdown buffing and luster buffing which may be required.

Lathes for ashing, buffing and polishing are available in types ranging from low-powered bench models, which are essentially converted bench grinders, to 50-hp floor models.

For finishing plastics a popular machine is a 2- or 3-hp floor-type lathe, with motor in base, and V-belt drive. This is preferred over the motor-on-spindle lathe because its speed can be changed by merely changing the diameters of the pulleys. Where speeds must be changed frequently, variable-speed lathes are available, in 3-, 5-, and 7½-hp sizes, which permit changes of speed between 1500 and 3000 rpm generally without stopping the machine. With these machines, it is possible to operate at the most efficient peripheral speed, regardless of the diameter of the buff.

For production buffing of articles of simple contours, automatic buffing machines are available, which must, however, be engineered for the particular job.

All dry buffing and polishing operations require an efficient exhaust system. Suitable sheet-metal hoods should enclose as much of the wheel as is practicable, and be connected to the exhaust piping. The exhaust should pass through a dust-collector rather than to open air. Since many of the dusts are combustible, care should be taken so that, if steel inserts are ground, incandescent metal particles are not drawn into the exhaust system.

Buffing wheels for finishing plastics are generally made up of sections of muslin disks, either with or without sewing, depending on the flexibility required. The cloth should be a high-count sheeting, such as 84 × 92, for the faster cutting, and a lower count, such as 64 × 68, for buffing and polishing. For waxing, canton flannel and 48-48 muslin are both very popular.

Where the contours of the article are regular, and fast cutting is desired, the buffing wheel is composed of sewed buffing sections with stitching spaced ¼ or ⅜ in. Wider spacings, and narrower, down to ⅛ in., are available. The wider spacings give the softer wheels. The next softer medium is the pocketed or folded buff, which presents pockets of cloth to the work and which makes for greater cooling of the surface, a faster cut than that given by a loose full-disk buff, and greater flexibility than that of conventional sewed buffs. Loose buffs made of full disks of muslin, while not cutting as fast as these, have a greater flexibility and give a smoother, more even, intermediate finish than do the harder wheels, and are generally to be preferred, especially for articles with curved or irregular contours.

For special cases, extremely soft wheels are needed, such as the packed buff or the string brush. The packed buff is made up of large disks of cloth alternated with smaller disks in the proportions of 1:1, 2:1, or 1:2, depending on the degree of hardness needed. The string brush, comparatively new in the finishing field, is like a bristle brush, with cotton string substituted for the bristles. The wheel offers the maximum in flexibility, and in conjunction with greaseless compound is recommended for smoothing the edges of intricate articles.

Thermoplastics. In the ashing and polishing of thermoplastics, overheating must be carefully avoided, since it may soften and distort the surface into ripples. Hence, it is necessary to avoid excessively hard buffing wheels, excessive speed of wheels, and excessive pressure of the work against the wheel.

Ashing is frequently required for the removal of "cold spots," teardrops, etc., from irregular surfaces which cannot be smoothed by wet sanding.

For ashing, wet pumice, grade No. 00 to No. 1, is used, on a loose muslin buff running at about 4000 linear fpm. The buff is often packed to increase its flexibility. The buff must be well hooded, since the wet pumice does not adhere to it, and tends to be thrown off. After wet ashing, the articles must be washed and dried before being polished.

As wet ashing is essentially a messy operation, attempts are continually being made to get more cut in a buffing operation than is usual in cutdown buffing, so as to obviate the need for wet ashing. Certain commercial compounds are available which perform a fast cutting job, that can be called semiashing, on cellulose acetate and cellulose acetate butyrate.

For the buffing of thermoplastics, fine silica powders in special grease binders, differing considerably from mixtures that have been developed for finishing metals, are generally most successful. Compositions must be formulated to give sufficient lubrication to prevent excessive heating.

Pocketed and ventilated buffs are an aid in prevention of overheating, although soft packed buffs are preferred for final luster buffing. Speeds generally run from 3000 to 4000 surface fpm.

Thermoplastics can sometimes be polished with greaseless compounds such as are used with thermosetting resins, but only with very soft wheels, and with especial caution against overheating.

Thermosetting Plastics. For thermosetting plastics, a polishing operation with greaseless compositions on muslin buffing wheels is recommended for the removal of surface defects, light or residual flash, and marks from machining operations, and for the smoothing of irregularities left by the belt sander. The cutting face is formed and maintained by periodic transfer of greaseless compound in bar form to the face of the revolving wheel. A wheel coated in such a manner presents a fast-cutting face similar to the surface of emery cloth, and because of its resilience has the ability to smooth irregularly shaped parts without distorting or gouging. Although conditions and materials differ somewhat with the individual job, it is common procedure to use a No. 220 grade greaseless compound on a full-disk loose muslin buff at 5000 linear fpm.

Cutdown buffing is a procedure that converts a dull sanded surface into a smooth semigloss, preliminary to final luster buffing. In cases where a very high luster is not needed, this becomes the final operation. For cutdown buffing of thermosetting plastics, compositions or "waxes," are used, composed essentially of a fast-cutting buffing powder in a grease binder. A dry, fast-cutting bar with no free grease is well adapted to this operation, and produces a minimum of buffing dirt. Sewed, pocketed or full-disk loose buffs are used, depending on the imperfections to be removed. Speeds range from 4000 to 6000 linear fpm.

Luster-buffing compositions or "waxes" are composed essentially of the finest abrasive buffing powders, such as levigated alumina, in a grease binder. The powders are finer and contain less grease than those used for cutdown buffing. Loose muslin buffs at 4000 to 5000 linear fpm are generally used.

Pigments can be added to white luster-buffing bars to match the shade of the plastic being buffed. This has the distinct advantages of coloring spots of the filler, such as wood flour, that may be exposed, and of not being noticeable if not thoroughly removed from the molded article. In cutdown bars, black pigments are often incorporated for the same reason, but light or bright-colored pigments are not effective, because of the dark color of the buffing powders used in fast-cutting bars.

If compositions with excess grease have been used, the soft residual film of grease can be removed by wiping with a clean, dry, soft buff to expose the lustrous surface.

Transparent Coatings, and Polishing with Solvent

Solvent-dip treatments for dissolving surface irregularities left by machining are applied mostly to cellulosic plastics. Vinyls hold the solvent too tenaciously to make this method generally desirable. With craze-sensitive plastics such as polystyrenes it is necessary to minimize the time in contact with the solvent, and hence spraying is preferred to dipping. For solvent dip-polishing an immersion of 1 min is usual. The method lends itself to mechanization.

The use of solvent dips has declined greatly with improvements in spray coating.

As larger and larger objects are made from plastics, the cost of the material becomes increasingly important compared to the cost of the fabrication. This gives incentive to developing surface treatments which give to a cheaper plastic the surface properties of a more expensive one. Also, it is desirable to be able to apply to a plastic which is tough and dimensionally stable, but, e.g., sensitive to solvents and easily crazed, a transparent coating which will give it the better surface properties of a more resistant plastic, e.g., resistance to oils, gasoline, cleaning fluid, fungi, etc. In a sense the coating of plastics for such purposes is analogous to the electroplating of metals.

Today effective surface coatings are available for all important plastics with the exception of polytetrafluoroethylene and, perhaps, polyethylene. The glass-filled polyester, epoxy and melamine laminates are effectively surface-treated to close pinholes, cover blemishes and improve appearance.

Coatings are applied usually by spraying, preferably with automatic equipment. Skill is required, since the transparency makes every blemish apparent. However, spraying of transparent coatings has been used for some years on a full production scale, particularly on articles having large flat or mildly curved surfaces free from undercuts, deep narrow grooves, or sharp corners.

When the coating is to be dried in an oven, it is usually best to use circulating warm air. Infrared heating lamps, so successful in drying lacquered metal objects, are not recommended for drying coated plastics, because the poor thermal conductivity of the plastics permits the development of hot spots, which result in distortion, wrinkling, or crazing. Freedom from dust is mandatory.

In all transparent coating or dip-polishing operations there is danger that strained pieces will craze. If the strains are sufficiently great, even the mildest solvent will occasion crazing. It is, therefore, always a wise precaution to try out the procedure on some test pieces.

To a large extent strains, and hence crazing by solvents, can be reduced by proper mold design, and by not shortening too much the cycle in injection molding. If crazing occurs in a certain operation in spite of these precautions, it may be necessary to anneal the article (for example, in hot water at a temperature safely below the distortion point) before coating or dip-polishing. A check with crossed "Polaroids" will quickly show whether the annealing has gone far enough to relieve all strains, or whether the original part requires the annealing operation.

To use a weak solvent, in order to reduce the risk of crazing, introduces the risk that the coating will not adhere properly and will fail in the grease test, which consists of exposure for 100 hr at room temperature to a 50-50 mixture of lard and oleic acid. This grease test is very important, not only because of the surprising frequency of contact, in service, with oily and greasy substances, even of articles not normally exposed to these, but also because a coating which fails the grease test is likely to show poor results in other tests as well. The grease test, therefore, is important as a quick screening test, not only of performance of a given coating under given conditions, but also of the relative values of different coating materials.

Solvent systems for dip-polishing and transparent coating have been formulated very carefully, and no change in solvent or thinner should be made without a careful study of the over-all effect of such a substitution, including possibilities of pinholing, orange peel, crazing, etching, humidity blush, resin blush, and impairment of adhesion to the plastic or to any subsequent coating. For best results it is desirable to work out a ratio of thinner and stay with it. Humidity blush can be particularly insidious, inasmuch as it can affect adhesion to the plastic, and go unobserved if inspection is lax. It may be discovered weeks later and lead to large losses.

Whenever atmospheric humidity is high during the coating operation, adhesion should be checked as a regular part of inspection. A quick test consists of scratching a cross on the test piece, pressing upon it a piece of pressure-sensitive tape, and pulling the tape off rapidly. If the coating does not come off under these conditions, adhesion is usually good.

Excellent resistance to humidity is a mark of quality in the coating, and most appliance companies specify materials on this basis, to avoid failure in the field. A good transparent surface coating, properly applied, will not soften or cloud when immersed in water, and will stand 1000 hr at 110°F at 100 per cent relative humidity. Light-stability and abrasion-resistance should be checked when required for a specific application.

Etching is the result of attack of solvent on the plastic. In contrast to blushing, it is particularly apt to occur when humidity is low. It can usually be overcome by increasing the percentage of aliphatic hydrocarbon solvent.

Failure in adhesion of a good product correctly applied to the plastic for which it was developed is usually due to some outside influence, e.g., an incompatible mold lubricant; too much mold lubricant; water or oil in the air line in spraying; oil spray from ventilating systems or metal operations nearby; or humidity blush.

Sprayed coatings and dips may be used to reduce the tendency of plastics to develop static charges. Some depend on the application of surface-active agents such as sulfonates. Others depend on humectants such as glycol and glycerine; these are highly effective, but not permanent because they are more or less easily removed, even by wiping or handling. Some, however, withstand a remarkable amount of handling indoors. Coatings of plastics having a relatively low tendency to accumulate static charges are permanent, but only partially effective; for some purposes, however, their effect is sufficient to be well worthwhile.

Certain coating materials assume a positive electric charge, others a negative charge, but it is fallacious to believe that the two can be mixed with each other to give an electrically neutral surface.

Jigs, Fixtures, and Automatic Feeding Devices

The primary purpose of jigs and fixtures is to facilitate machining, so as to reduce manufacturing costs and to make practicable various operations which cannot be performed by hand. With their aid it is possible to produce more pieces per hour, to use less skilled labor, to improve accuracy of dimensions, and to reduce the fitting necessary in assembling.

It is generally agreed that a fixture is a device which holds the article while the cutting tool is performing the work, whereas a jig is a device which not only holds the object but also incorporates special arrangements for guiding the tool to the proper position. It would follow, therefore, that jigs are used principally for drilling, boring, etc., while fixtures are used in milling and grinding. Regardless of the nomenclature, the most important feature of any jig or fixture is its ability to perform the work for which it was made.

Simplicity of design makes for low cost, long life and inexpensive maintenance. Keeping this in mind, the following rules may be used as a guide to proper design of jigs and fixtures.

(1) First, it should be shown, on the basis of cost studies, that the cost of designing and making a proposed tool will be less than the gross savings which its use will yield.

(2) All clamping devices should be quick-acting, easily accessible, and so placed as to give maximum resistance to the direction of the force of the cutting tool.

(3) The clamping pressure must not crack or distort the article of plastic.

(4) Locating points should be visible to the operator when positioning the article, in order to minimize loading time.

(5) All bearings should be of sealed type, for protection against the highly abrasive plastic chips and dust.

(6) Proper consideration should be given to cooling the cutting tool.

(7) The fixture must be foolproof, so that the operator cannot position the article in any way but the correct one.

(8) Lubrication must be provided for moving parts.

(9) The tool should be made as light as possible by using light materials or coring out unnecessary metal.

(10) Holes should be provided for the escape of chips or dirt.

When designing jigs or fixtures, it is well to keep in mind the possibilities of converting to automatic operation if production runs will be large enough to make this worth the cost. By coupling electrical or air-powered devices and automatic feeders to the fixture, it is possible to eliminate the need of an operator except to load the hopper and remove the finished pieces. Since one operator can service a number of automatic fixtures, this may reduce the manufacturing cost per piece to a very small fraction of the original cost.

The design of automatic feeding devices requires extensive experience. As a rule, it is wiser, and probably less expensive in the long run, to buy a properly designed feeder from a reputable concern whose business is the manufacture of such equipment. Those who either cannot buy the equipment or wish to try their own design must remember that any automatic feeder must deliver articles in the correct position at the correct time without any deviation. Poorly designed feeders may jam the articles, or deliver them at the wrong time. Possible nonuniformity of dimensions of articles from multiple-cavity molds, or dimensional instability of articles, must be allowed for, to minimize trouble in the operation of the equipment.

Also to be considered are the number of pieces per minute required, the capacity of the hopper, the method of operation (whether vibrating, oscillating, gravitational, etc.), and more particularly the method of transferring the articles from the feeder to the fixture.

Decorating of Plastics

Decoration or marking is frequently required in the manufacture of articles from any plastic, whether thermoplastic or thermosetting. Each presents its own characteristics and hence its own problems. The discussion in this section is necessarily of a general nature.

Included is a discussion of processes of metallizing, which may have purposes other than decorative.

Among the methods most widely used in the industry today are hot stamping, silk-screening, offset printing, fill-in, spray coating, and metallizing. Other methods utilize paper labels, decalcomanias, engraving, and rubber stamping. The method to be used is selected in accordance with the appearance desired.

The most versatile and least expensive method is hot stamping. It is simple and economical, and yields decorations of good durability. It is used on all types of thermoplastics, and on some thermosetting plastics. On the latter it does a less satisfactory job, because these plastics require the use of so much heat and pressure that the process becomes more of a branding operation. Hot stamping is never used with melamines, and relatively seldom with urea plastics.

Various stamping presses used in this process range from manually operated to fully automatic. The piece to be decorated is placed in the machine (usually in a fixture) under a hot stamping die. A pigmented leaf or foil, made in various colors, is placed between the hot die and the piece by means of rollers which automatically move the foil so that an unused portion is located under the die during each cycle. The die is lowered under controlled pressure and held for a predetermined time. The pigment is thereby transferred from the foil to the plastic and firmly attached. The proper type of foil must be used, and the temperature, pressure and time of dwell must be worked out to give best results. Production on these machines ranges from 60 to as high as 4500 pieces per hour, depending on the plastic and the type of foil. Hot stamping can be done in multicolor design in a single operation, by appropriate mechanical arrangements in the press, but is economical only in large runs in which tooling can be amortized.

Silk screening is a proven and inexpensive method, and gives decorations of good appearance and resistance to wear. The process consists of transferring paint or ink through a silk screen to the product by means of a rubber squeegee, by manual or mechanical means. The paint or ink adheres as result of solvent action on the plastic. Maximum wear-resistance, flexibility, gloss and chemical resistance are obtained by the use of thermoactive inks and paints which polymerize, when heated, to unsoluble films. On thermosetting materials the adherence of even the best inks or paints is not always reliable, and it is recommended that the decoration be coated with a clear lacquer or varnish. Hourly production is about 250 to 500 pieces by hand, and about 400 to 1500 pieces by machine. The choice of inks and paints, mesh of screen, and consistency of rubber squeegee will determine the quality of the product. Multicolor decorations can be applied, one color at a time.

For smoothness, fine detail, and delicacy of design, offset printing cannot be matched. But it does not produce a strong opaque impression, and is not a rapid process. Solvents in the ink ensure good adherence and wear-resistance on thermoplastics. On thermosetting plastics the decoration should be covered with a clear lacquer or varnish. The outstanding advantage of offset printing is its ability to apply a decoration in several colors in a single operation. Essential to success with this process are the proper choice of ink and the correct type of rubber or glycerine rollers. The process is not sensitive to small variations in dimensions between articles.

Fill-in painting involves molding the design into the product and then filling it in with a paint of proper consistency, containing an appropriate solvent. The excess paint must be wiped off before it is thoroughly dry. This method is somewhat more expensive than the three previously described, but its independence of dimensional tolerances makes it sometimes the more economical. Spray-painting, through cutout masks, may be used, as described below. For volume production of small articles of thermosetting plastics requiring permanent marking, such as handles of tumbler switches, this method is superior in economy and in results to hot stamping, which is the only other possible method.

Spray painting has become an important process for decorating plastics. The areas not to be painted are covered by a durable form-fitting metal mask. Masks made by electroforming are preferred because they conform to the contour of the article, and are superior to shaped sheet metal, stampings, or metal castings. Castings of conventional metals, made from the plastic article as a pattern, do not fit well because of shrinkage; castings of low-melting alloys fit satisfactorily, but are weak and not durable.

The comments on testing for crazing and blushing, discussed under transparent coatings (p. 637), are applicable here, particularly to decorations which are translucent, or light in color.

There are four basic types of electroformed masks.

The lip-type mask (Fig. 16-4) is used for painting a depressed name or design. In this mask a lip of metal extends down the vertical side wall of the depressed design, all the way or only part way down the side wall, depending on the result desired. This lip must be thin, yet strong. The centers of letters and numbers such as O, A, 6, 8 must be securely held in place by bridges. The fit and the lip of the mask ensure a clean sharp paint line. The draft angle of the depressed design should be at least 5°.

The cap type (Fig. 16-5) is the reverse of the lip. It is used where the

PAINT

Fig. 16-4. The lip mask for sunken design.

Where a depressed design is to be painted, besides form-fitting the contours of the part, the mask must have a "lip" of metal which extends down the sidewalls of the depression in order to trap the sprayed paint in the depressed well and thus eliminate fogging. The extent of filling can be controlled within reasonable limits by the depth of the lip.

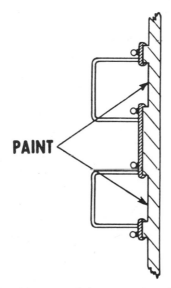

PAINT

Fig. 16-5. The cap mask for capping raised design.

This same lipping principle is also employed where an embossed design is to be protected from the paint. In this case the lip keeps clean the top and all, or as much as may be desired, of the sidewalls of the embossing. In the first type of lip mask, free sections, such as the centers of the numeral "8," are held in place by wire bridging. The same type of bridging is employed to hold the cappings of embossed mask sections.

embossed name or design is to be kept clean while painting the background. The lip of metal must cover the vertical side walls all the way to the bottom, so as to protect the embossing completely.

The plug mask (Fig. 16-6) is used for protecting a depressed design while painting the background. Its principal use is with transparent articles such as automobile horn buttons and doors of refrigerator evaporators, and where vacuum plating is required. Here again the positive fitting essential to prevent fogging on vertical side walls and bottoms of such designs is accomplished by electroforming directly into the design. The plugs are cut out, and finished with the proper radii and draft angles to facilitate painting. They are then suspended by fine wires, usually attached to a frame so as to provide a unit which can be handled in production.

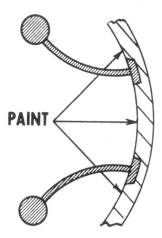

Fig. 16-6. The plug mask.

Where a depressed design is to be kept clean instead of painted, plugs suspended from wire bridging must fully fill such depressed sections to prevent paint leakage when spraying the background area. When vacuum plating is a specified part of the design, plug masks are a must in order to protect the areas to be plated while color is sprayed on other surfaces of the part.

In designing molds, the engineer must remember that the draft angles of the depressed design should be kept to a minimum, preferably not more than 5 or 7°.

Spray painting through a block cut-out mask (Fig. 16-7) is a variant of fill-in painting. The method is used primarily in filling depressed letters and calibration marks on such articles as knobs for stoves and radios. (For articles which have fine calibrations, spray painting is not satisfactory.) As

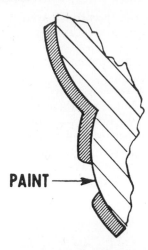

Fig. 16-7. Block cut-out plane surface mask.

Where calibration lines or lettering, such as appear on many dials, are too small for practical individual masking, a cut-out area outlining a character or group of characters is more feasible from a rapid production standpoint. By confining the paint to a relatively small area, economies are achieved, since fewer wiping or buffing passes are necessary to clean the pieces of excess paint. Because a positive fit is not paramount, such mask can be relieved sufficiently to be interchangeable on parts from multiple cavity molds, making for greater economy in total mask cost.

a rule, it is not practicable to mask perfectly; for masking small letters and pips, the openings in the mask would be so small that they would immediately become filled with paint. Instead, a cutout is made to enclose each character or group of characters, to confine the paint to the immediate area. Then the excess on the surface is removed by wiping or buffing, leaving the depressed characters filled with paint. Articles made in multiple-cavity molds are not fully uniform in dimensions, but the block cutout mask can usually be designed to accommodate all of them.

The mold engineer should design the mold with thought to the problems of masking. Slight changes in the demarcation of colors which will not essentially change the design of the article may definitely facilitate the masking.

Other factors in mold design and molding have more fundamental influence on the ease of decorating the molded article. The position of knockout pins, radii, flat spots, and contours can make the decorating job very difficult and costly or easy and inexpensive. If dimensional differences between cavities cause trouble, articles with different cavity numbers can be handled separately. Mold lubricants should be used very sparingly unless provision is made for removing them from the molded articles.

Paper labels and decalcomanias for decorating are very inexpensive, but their application is slow and costly. The adhesive must be appropriate to the plastic.

Rubber stamping is a fast operation, but gives results of poor appearance, and is used only for identification purposes.

Plastics can be coated with metal by vacuum deposition (aluminum), by electroplating, and by chemical spray (silver).

In vacuum deposition, the first step is to jig up the article so that when in the vacuum chamber no part of it will be shielded, and thus fail to be coated (see Fig. 16-8). Jigging is different for every shape and size to be metallized. Experience, or trial and error, sets the final pattern for jigging. Jigs should be made of metal.

Courtesy of Metaplast Process, Inc.

Fig. 16-8

Next, it is usually necessary to lacquer the plastic to provide a base sufficiently shiny to give the deposited aluminum a reflective surface. Only rarely do the shape of the article and the high polish of the mold make this lacquering unnecessary. The lacquering is done by a dip with slow removal, by spraying, or by dipping and spinning, whichever will best provide a coating free from runs.

The lacquered articles are dried in an oven. All solvents should be removed, since residual solvent will interfere with attaining a vacuum in the chamber.

The jigged-up pieces of plastic are placed on rotating stations inside the vacuum machine. In the chamber, on tungsten wire filaments carried by fixtures, are hanging ¾-in. pieces of aluminum wire. The door of the chamber is closed and the vacuum pump started. When the gauge indicates the necessary vacuum, a transformer is turned on to heat the tungsten filaments so that the aluminum evaporates and coats the rotating pieces of plastic.

The thin coat of aluminum thus deposited is protected by a coat of lacquer, either water-white or colored, as required.

Adhesion of the lacquer to the plastics is very important to the quality of the product. Probably the most difficult plastic in this respect is polystyrene; the problem has not been fully solved. For every undercoat there must be a top coat that will not attack the undercoat, and both coats must be developed simultaneously.

It is essential that the plastic be free from mold lubricants, especially external ones. With polystyrene, no solvent will remove mold lubricants without attacking the plastic itself, and scrubbing each piece is not practicable. Hence, external mold lubricants should be avoided for articles which are to be metallized.

Scratches or flaws on the surface of the plastic will be exaggerated by metallizing. The undercoat of lacquer follows the contour of the plastic itself, and its mirror-like surface magnifies the defects underneath. Similarly, an orange-peel surface is likely to be exaggerated by metallizing.

Good results in metallizing can be promoted by the designer and maker of the mold. A highly polished mold that does not require an external lubricant will provide a favorable surface on the molded article, and simplify the process of metallizing. The problem of jigging the article for metallizing, without leaving a mark in a prominent place, can sometimes be solved by the designer of the mold, by providing a hole or a plug, or the like, by which the piece can be attached to a screw, spring, or taper pin, to facilitate jigging. Some very small articles are most economically metallized while still attached to the sprue. In such a case the gates are enlarged to ensure that the pieces will remain on the sprue until the metallizing has been done.

Aluminum does not tarnish, but the coating of aluminum is protected against abrasion by a coating of air-drying lacquer; a baked lacquer cannot be used, because the plastics themselves cannot tolerate baking temperatures. Hence, the metallized finish is appropriate only on expendable items, or other items that do not require abrasion-resistance.

The chemical-spray method of metallizing plastics was derived from the old art of mirroring glass. The plastic is first lacquered, to obtain a shiny coat. Then the proper application of the chemical spray produces on it the desired mirror coating of silver. This is then protected by a water-white lacquer to keep the silver from tarnishing or being rubbed off.

Because of the unstable nature of the chemical solutions, it is very difficult to obtain a consistent mirror on large pieces. Humidity and temperature also influence the success of the process.

If the article is flat, and only the front needs metallizing, it can be laid on a tray. If the entire surface of an article is to be metallized, it must be jigged up on a fixture throughout the whole process. Because these jigs do not have to go into a vacuum chamber, they can be made of wood.

Over-all costs of vacuum deposition and chemical spray are probably about the same. The former involves expensive equipment; the latter uses the more expensive materials. The coating produced by the vacuum process is usually preferred, both because it is less subject to imperfection and because aluminum does not tarnish, as silver does.

Plastics are electroplated to produce decorative finishes, to give dimensional stability to articles subjected to changes of humidity and temperature, to increase strength, and to provide reflecting surfaces. Small objects are most economically handled by barrel plating. Still-tank plating is feasible, but costlier because of the greater complication of the plating technique and of methods for preparing the surface prior to plating, and because of the final manual polishing required for a high finish.

To prepare the articles for electroplating, a conductive coat of silver is precipitated on them from silver nitrate solution, in order to make them conductive. They are then plated in rotating plating barrels that contain acid copper-plating solutions, and copper anodes. In from 12 to 24 hr a thickness of copper from 0.002 to 0.005 in. is deposited. The articles are then polished with steel shot in a burnishing barrel, and then a plating of gold, silver or nickel is deposited on them by another barrel plating operation.

Cellulose acetate is the most easily plated. Polystyrene and urea-formaldehyde are being plated commercially, but with some difficulty. Polystyrene floats in the ordinary copper-plating solutions. Therefore, a first coating of copper is deposited from solutions made up light enough to enable the polystyrene to sink; then the articles are transferred to a regular barrel to deposit the additional thickness required. Articles of urea-formaldehyde, because of their weight, tend to rub against each other vigorously enough to dislodge the bond coat of silver before it can become plated with copper, and the copper plate will therefore be imperfect, with pin holes or scratches where the bare plastic is exposed. A special technique is required to deal with this problem.

The electroplating of plastics has been mainly limited to buttons, bottle caps, charms and novelty items, which are small enough to be plated economically in barrels.

Annealing of Molded Thermoplastics

Strains exist in practically all molded pieces, and can be minimized only by careful design of molds and by skillful attention to conditions of molding. Strains in thermoplastics manifest themselves in dimensional instability, and in susceptibility to being crazed by solvent and crazed by thermal shock.

The procedures of annealing, described below specifically for polystyrene, may be followed in general with other thermoplastics, but with, of course, the use of appropriately different temperatures, methods of test, etc.

Polystyrene, having, in comparison with other plastics, a relatively high coefficient of expansion and a relatively low coefficient of thermal conductivity, is particularly sensitive to the effects of thermal shock, which may·develop, for example, in housewares subjected alternately to hot water and room temperature (or refrigerator temperature).

Methods of annealing or tempering have been developed, to reduce the strains in articles molded of polystyrene.

Massive items (bars and slabs) may require a cycle of annealing running as long as 18 hr:

(1) immersion in a bath of 40 per cent of ethylene glycol in water, at 184°F;

(2) slow cooling, in the bath, to 170°F;

(3) more rapid cooling, to 160°F;

(4) still more rapid cooling, to 150°F.

For the ordinary injection-molded article of polystyrene, in which the section is fairly thin, it suffices to take the article from the mold at a temperature not below 130°F, and preferably 160°F, and to immerse it for 5 to 15 min in water at 176 to 190°F.

The effectiveness of the annealing can be tested in several ways:

(1) Immerse for 1 min in kerosene at room temperature. Examine for cracks after 30 min.

(2) Do the same with "Varsol" No. 2 (a proprietary kerosene which does not vary in composition as does ordinary kerosene).

(3) Apply three drops of "Varsol" No. 2 to the sprue region and examine for cracks after 4 min.

(4) Apply thermal shock by dipping alternately into water baths at 203 and 40°F.

(5) Transparent materials may be examined under crossed "Polaroids."

Postbaking Molded Phenolics

Molded phenolics may be baked to accomplish several purposes:

(1) to anneal them, i.e., to remove molding stresses, which may be particularly troublesome in articles involving a combination of thin and thick sections;

(2) to improve dimensional stability by releasing strains and by accelerating the aftershrinkage of the piece;

(3) to improve electrical properties by reduction of moisture content, if this has not been done by conditioning and preheating of the molding powder.

For best results in dimensional stability, it is best to use low temperature, even though it takes a longer time. For uniform thin sections, 4 hr at 250°F is sufficient; thick sections may require as long as 24 hr at 220°F.

17. Cementing, Welding, and Assembly

Scope

This chapter is concerned with the three basic methods of joining plastics to themselves and to other materials.

The subject of cementing is subdivided into three categories:

(a) cementing of thermoplastics

(b) cementing of thermosetting plastics

(c) cementing of dissimilar materials.

An "Adhesives Reference Chart" is included. Its primary purpose is to indicate to a fabricator a satisfactory type of adhesive for his use and to list manufacturers who have indicated to SPI that they are in a position to supply the required adhesive.

Thermoplastics can be joined by methods analogous to those used in the welding of metals, and referred to in this chapter as "Welding."

The subject of mechanical assembly of plastics deals with the use of rivets, bolts, screws and inserts for joining components.

Cementing of Thermoplastics

Acrylic Resins. *Cast Acrylic Sheeting* Articles of considerable size and complexity can be fabricated from methyl methacrylate plastics by cementing sections together.

The technique described in this sub-section refers to cast sheeting. Cementing of articles made from methyl methacrylate molding powders or extruded rod, tubing or other shapes is more specialized, and reference should be made to the instructions applicable to these materials, in the sub-section which follows.

With the exercise of care and practice, the clarity of acrylic resin can be retained in cemented joints; the joint will be clear and sound as the result of complete fusion of the two surfaces brought into contact. In order to accomplish this, the surfaces to be cemented are thoroughly softened by means of a solvent, to the extent that a soft layer or cushion is produced on each, and then the uniting and hardening will effect a homogeneous bond. This principle underlies all cementing of acrylic resins.

Usually one of the two surfaces to be joined is soaked in the cement until a soft layer has been formed upon it. This soft surface is then pressed against the surface to be attached and, in contact with it, softens it by means of the excess cement contained in the soaked area.

For some purposes it may be desirable to dissolve clean shavings of methyl methacrylate resin in the cement in order to raise the viscosity, so that it may be handled like glue. However, even with a thickened cement it is still necessary to provide a period of soaking to effect the formation of the soft cushion of resin necessary to establish a sound bond.

Most of the conventional types of joint-construction can be employed, such as overlap, butt, rabbet, miter, scarf, etc., depending on the service required of the article. The area of the joint must be large enough to develop sufficient strength, and the joint must be so designed as to give even distribution of stresses.

An accurate fit of mating pieces is essential in cementing acrylic resins. This need is primarily due to their rigidity, and the inability of a solvent cement to compensate for discrepancies in fit. In butt joints, it is necessary that both edges be true and square before cementing. Flat surfaces are more easily cemented than curved ones, and hence, wherever possible, it is desirable to rout or sand curved surfaces to form flat ones. When two curved surfaces are to be cemented, both must have the same radius of curvature. It is not good practice to force either piece in order to bring the surfaces into complete contact. The only exception to this is the case of very thin sheeting, such as 0.060 or 0.080 in., and even here the deviation must not be great.

The surfaces to be cemented should be smooth and clean, but need not be polished. A smooth machined surface is most satisfactory for cementing.

When ribs are to be cemented to curved pieces, such as airplane enclosure panels, each rib should be machined from flat sheet stock, heated in an oven to shaping temperature, and then, without cement, and with the aid of a jig, shaped against the surface to which it is later to be cemented, and allowed to remain in contact until cool. Then the curved rib is soaked in cement, and cemented to the curved panel with the aid of the same jig.

In soaking the plastic in the cement, the softening action should be confined to the immediate region of the joint. This is done by masking the rest of the surface with a tough paper or cellophane tape coated with a pressure-sensitive adhesive. The tape should be applied firmly, and with special care at the edges. The tape used should be impervious to the cement, and should not be applied long in advance of cementing, since its adhesive may come loose if it is allowed to stand too long.

The role of the cushion formed by soaking the surface in the cement is solely to enable the two surfaces to be brought into complete conformity, with exclusion of air bubbles or of spatial irregularities in the joint. The thickness of the cushion must be great enough to provide complete contact, but preferably no greater than this, since an excess prolongs unnecessarily the setting of the bond. With solvent cements, a soaking time of 15 min is usually enough to form an adequate cushion. Inadequacy of cushion is one cause of bubbles or uncemented areas in the finished joint. The soaking time will be considerably longer when monomer cement is employed, and when the sheeting to be cemented is of heat-resistant grade.

The soaked surface, after removal from the cement, should be brought rapidly, while still wet, into contact with the surface to which it is to be joined, since soaked surfaces that have become dry do not wet the mating surface adequately. The softened surface, however, should not be dripping, since superfluous cement will run out and cause smears. The tray of cement and the work should be so situated that the transfer from cement to jig can be made conveniently and rapidly. A soaked surface that has become dry can be re-wet by brushing additional solvent cement on it.

Too early application of pressure on the joint results in squeezing out some of the solvent needed to soften the dry surface. After the two surfaces have been brought into contact, only very slight pressure should be applied at first. Then, after about $1/4$ to $1/2$ min, the cementing jig can be tightened and pressure applied.

The assembly is best accomplished in well-designed cementing jigs (Fig. 17-1) capable of holding the pieces firmly together until the joint is hard, without forcing either of them out of shape. Excessive pressure should be avoided, since it is likely to cause stress-crazing. The pressure should be adequate to squeeze out air bubbles or pockets from the joint, should be evenly applied over the entire joint, and should be maintained throughout the period of setting. These requirements are met through the use of spring clips or clamps, either alone in the case of simple assemblies or in conjunction with cementing jigs of wood or metal in more complicated cases. For most joints, a pressure in the neighborhood of 10 psi is suitable, provided that it does not force either of the parts appreciably out of shape.

After assembly of the work in the jig, any excess cement that has been extruded from the joint should be removed by scraping onto the masking paper, which is subsequently to be removed. Cleaning up soft cement promptly will save time in finishing after the bond has set.

The assembly should be allowed to remain in the jig for from 1 to 2 hr, and there should elapse an additional 4 hr before the work is subjected to heat-treatment or to finishing operations. These times are approximate only, depending on the complexity of the job.

Heat-treatment or annealing of joints made with solvent cements is highly desirable, but frequently not necessary because the joints are adequately strong without it. Solvent joints never become completely dry; that is, are never entirely freed of solvent through evaporation and diffusion. If the cemented piece is placed in an oven, the penetration of the diffusing solvent progresses further away from the bond, with the result that there is some increase in strength of the cemented joint. Heat-treatment of joints made with solvent cement should be done carefully, so as not to warp the assembly or to approach the boiling point of the cement and thus produce bubbles. Generally,

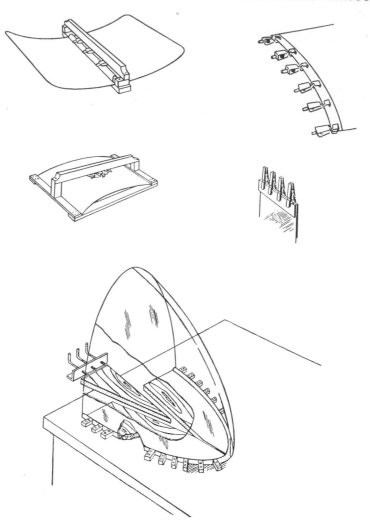

Fig. 17-1. Typical cementing assembly jigs.

the temperature should not exceed 120°F, and at least 48 hr is required for best results.

Heat-treatment is desirable where cements contain methyl methacrylate monomer, since its polymerization increases the strength of the joint. The strongest joints are obtained by the use of monomer itself as the cement, followed by heat-treatment that results in complete polymerization; but monomer cements are not so convenient to use as solvent cements, since their slower solvent action requires much longer soaking times.

Hardening of the joint, with or without heat-treatment, should be complete before finishing operations such as sanding, machining, or polishing are carried out. Otherwise the softened material in the joint will subsequently recede into the joint.

A valuable technique, particularly in small cementing jobs, consists of using a hypodermic needle for applying the cement between two pieces brought into intimate contact. The procedure is useful also in removing air bubbles and in filling voids in cemented joints made in other ways.

The most rapid cements are of the mixed-solvent type, whose ingredients have been specially selected. These adhesives are mobile liquids, volatile, rapid in action and capable of yielding strong, sound bonds. They should be used with adequate ventilation.

An example of one of these is a 50-50 mixture of methyl methacrylate monomer and methylene chloride. To ensure formation of the correct depth of cushion, the ratio of these two solvents should be maintained, within reasonable limits; this can be readily checked by measuring the specific gravity of the cement. Permissible ranges of specific gravities at various temperatures are as follows:

| Temperature | | Permissible Range of |
(°C)	(°F)	Specific Gravity
20	68	1.13-1.18
25	77	1.12-1.17
30	86	1.11-1.16
35	95	1.10-1.15
40	104	1.09-1.14

If the specific gravity is found to be low, it should be adjusted by adding methylene chloride.

Acetic acid cement consists of glacial (100 per cent) acetic acid (this should not be confused with the 28 per cent acid used in photographic work). This cement requires a soaking time of about 1 hr at room temperature or 2 to 5 min at 140°F (60°C). The cemented joints can be handled in 3 to 5 hr and machined in 16 to 24 hr. The fumes of glacial acetic acid, especially when used hot, are irritating; adequate ventilation is required.

Monomer cement consists essentially of methyl methacrylate monomer stabilized with a small amount of hydroquinone to prevent thickening in storage and transportation. This monomer is closely related to the materials from which the acrylic resins themselves are cast. In the curing of a joint cemented with it, the hardening takes place by polymerization. In order to hasten polymerization, it is necessary to dissolve in the monomer a small amount (about 0.1 per cent) of benzoyl peroxide as catalyst to overcome the effect of the hydroquinone stabilizer. After addition of the catalyst to the monomer, the liquid should be kept in a refrigerator, since otherwise it will begin to harden.

Monomer cements are, like acetic acid cement, essentially slower than the solvent cements. The time required to soften the stock will be from 20 min to 1 hr, and the cushion obtained will be shallower than with the solvent cements. Also, the setting time required in the cementing jigs will be longer. With monomer cements, the work must be cured in an oven at about 120°F in order to effect polymerization. Unless this is done, the monomer remains unpolymerized in the joint, which does not harden until the monomer has evaporated or diffused from the joint. Monomer cements are difficult to use, particularly for applications requiring optical perfection.

Molded Acrylic Pieces. With molded acrylics, cemented joints are not as satisfactory as with cast sheeting. Considerable difficulty is frequently encountered, and many precautions must be taken in order to obtain best results. It is preferable to design molded articles so as to employ mechanical fasteners or closures, rather than cemented joints, but this is not always feasible and recourse must sometimes be had to solvent cements.

Cemented joints in molded methyl methacrylate are frequently unsightly as a result of stress-crazing. Hence the recommended procedure is intended to avoid strain as much as possible. When articles are to be cemented, this should be considered in the design of the dies, since the molding conditions determine to a large extent the degree of strain that will be present in the molded articles. The gate should be located away from the area to be cemented, since frozen strains are usually encountered near the gate. In designing the pieces to be cemented, the exact dimensions should be very carefully considered, so that the pieces will fit together easily and accurately without forcing, since stresses developed in assembly will promote solvent-crazing.

When a cover is to be cemented into a recess or groove, right-angled corners should if possible be replaced by bevels. This promotes the escape of air, and reduces the wiping away of cement, when the surfaces are brought together.

A cover which will have to be cemented should be made circular, if possible, so as to permit the cemented parts to be given a slight twist to remove air bubbles immediately after cementing.

The finishing operations that will be required should be anticipated when the original design is made. The design of the gate should be such as to minimize chipping, since surface fractures occasion solvent crazing. For the same reason, the removal of the sprue from the molded article should be very carefully done.

The molding conditions also are important. To minimize strain, injection-molded articles should be run with the die as hot as possible and with as long a cycle as is feasible. This will vary with the composition used and the ease of knockout from the die. After removal, the pieces should be annealed for a time and at a temperature depending upon the composition and the nature of the molded piece. In general as high a temperature should be used as is possible without warping or distorting the articles. The time required (several hours) will depend upon the thickness of the piece. Actual trials will be required to determine this. For example, the following conditions have been found suitable in some applications:

ANNEALING TEMPERATURE

acrylic (easy-flow)	140°F	2 hr*
acrylic (hard-flow)	170°F	2 hr*

*Approximate time for thin sections; longer times required for heavy sections.

Easy-flow molding compositions tend to require less annealing than hard-flow materials. Although easy-flow materials may sometimes be cemented satisfactorily without annealing, this will depend upon the amount of strain in the article, resulting from its shape and from the manner of molding it, particularly the size and location of the gate. In general, it is good practice to anneal all molded articles which are to be cemented.

The selection of a cement is of less importance than the foregoing precautions to minimize strain. A minimum amount of cement should be used. Cement is generally applied to well-fitting molded parts by a brush, but in some cases the use of a hypodermic needle is advantageous. The solvent-type cements may be employed.

Cellulose Acetate Plastic. Sheeting and molded articles of cellulose acetate can be cemented readily to pieces of the same plastic with a bond practically as strong as the material itself. The usual precautions necessary for best results in cementing of plastics must be observed.

The cements used with cellulose acetate plastics are of two types: (1) solvent-type, consisting only of a solvent or a mixture of solvents; (2) dope-type, consisting of cellulose acetate plastic dissolved in a solvent or mixture of solvents.

The solvent-type cement is generally employed when the surfaces to be cemented are in a single plane and simple in nature, and when the surfaces can be readily held to a perfect fit. The dope-type cement is used when the surfaces are irregular and not easily accessible.

Acetone and mixtures of acetone and methyl "Cellosolve" are commonly used as solvent cements for cellulose acetate. Acetone is a strong solvent for the plastic, but evaporates rapidly. The addition of methyl "Cellosolve" retards the evaporation, prevents blushing, and permits more time in handling parts after application of the cement. Solvents and diluents for cements for cellulose acetate plastics are given in the following table:

Solvents for Cellulose Acetate	Boiling Points (°C)
acetone	56.1
methyl acetate	57.1
ethylene dichloride	60.3
ethyl acetate	77.1
methyl "Cellosolve"	124.0
methyl "Cellosolve" acetate	144.5
ethyl lactate	154.0
"Cellosolve" acetate	156.3

Diluents for Cellulose Acetate Cements	Boiling Points (°C)
methanol	64.5
ethanol	78.5
toluene	110.5

Cement of the dope type for cellulose acetate plastic, by virtue of its containing plastic in solution, leaves upon drying a film of plastic that forms the bond between the surfaces to be joined. These cements are generally used when an imperfect fit of the parts requires filling. Dope cements, satisfactory for many purposes, can be made by dissolving cellulose acetate plastic in solvents, as, for example:

cellulose acetate plastic	130 grams
acetone	400 grams
methyl "Cellosolve"	150 grams
methyl "Cellosolve" acetate	50 grams

A general formula, suitable for use with a wide variety of ingredients, would be the following:

	per cent
cellulose acetate (low viscosity)	8-12
low- and medium-boiling solvents and diluents	45-75
high-boiling solvents	20-50

After being cemented, the pieces being united should be held under light pressure for 1 to 10 min, depending on the nature of the bond and the type of cement used. The assembly should be allowed to stand at least 24 hr before subsequent operations are performed, such as sanding, polishing, testing, and packing.

The following general rules should be observed in cementing cellulose acetate plastics:

1. the surfaces to be cemented must be clean; a slight film of oil, water or polishing compound may cause poor bonding;

2. the surfaces must be smooth, and aligned as nearly perfectly as practicable;

3. where solvent or dope is used, it must be sufficiently active to soften the surfaces to a depth such that when pressure is applied a slight flow occurs at every point in the softened area;

4. the solvent or cement must be of such composition that it will dry completely without blushing;

5. light pressure must be applied to the cemented joint until it has hardened to the extent that there is no movement when released;

6. subsequent finishing operations must be postponed until the cement has hardened;

7. care must be taken to assure that the vapor from solvent cements is not confined, in order to prevent the surface of the molded piece from becoming etched.

In using solvent-type cements the preferred technique is to immerse the surfaces to be cemented in the solvent until the plastic has been softened substantially, and then to clamp the object in position with light pressure only, and hold it until the bond has set.

A convenient method of applying the cement is to hold the object to be cemented in such a position that the surfaces to be cemented just touch the solvent. This may be done by maintaining a constant level of solvent in a shallow pan and supporting the object on a felt pad covered with a fine wire screen. The pad will act as a wick to bring solvent into contact with the plastic, while the screen will prevent contamination of the surface.

Because of differential loss by evaporation of mixtures, it is desirable to use a single-component cement having as low a rate of evaporation as is practicable. Blends of solvents including diluents (nonsolvents), however, are frequently advantageous in preventing blushing. In such blends the unequal rates of evaporation of the components will gradually increase the percentage of the higher-boiling constituents. This may be corrected by replenishing with a mixture proportionately richer in the low-boiling ingredients.

In cementing with dope-type adhesives, the preferred technique is to prepare the surfaces carefully and then to apply the cement with a brush or other mechanical applicator. The subsequent handling is similar to that employed with solvent-type cements. The formulations employed are made up of solvents (as shown in the previous table) and dissolved plastic. In addition, however, low-boiling solvents such as acetone, or diluents such as methanol, ethanol, and toluene, are frequently used to increase penetrating power and drying rate, and to reduce cost. In their use, however, it is essential that the proportions be selected so that the residual constituents maintain their solvent power throughout the drying. The last constituent to leave should be a fairly high-boiling solvent having considerable tolerance for moisture. Failure to provide this will result in blushing and, consequently, poor bonding and poor appearance. Excessively damp atmospheres should be avoided, since they are likely to cause blushing, even with otherwise satisfactory cements.

Occasionally articles of cellulose acetate plastics are cemented by means of solvent- or dope-type cements to materials other then cellulose esters, but the bond is usually weak. Mechanical means of assembly are preferable.

Before assembling articles of cellulose acetate with other materials, consideration should be given to the effect of migration of plasticizer, since these ingredients frequently have solvent action on other thermoplastics. In the softer-flow grades the plasticizer will, in some cases, migrate to the other material and soften it. This can usually be avoided by selecting a formula with less of the same plasticizer, or one containing a different plasticizer. Most cellulose acetate plastics will cause crazing of polystyrene when in close contact.

Cellulose Acetate Butyrate Plastic. This plastic is cemented in accordance with the technique described for cellulose acetate. Solvent cements may be formulated from the same solvents and diluents as for cellulose acetate. In the case of dope cements, the plastic to be dissolved in solvents is, however, the acetate butyrate.

Cellulose Nitrate Plastic. This thermoplastic may be readily joined to itself with acetone or other solvents for cellulose nitrate. The joint hardens rapidly, the low-boiling solvents evaporate readily, and the bond is strong (see also Section on cellulose acetate p. 657, which is applicable as well to cellulose nitrate).

Ethyl Cellulose Plastic. Pieces of ethyl cellulose plastic may be readily cemented strongly and permanently to one another with solvent-type cements. A wide variety of adhesives may be used, but usually mixtures of toluene and alcohol, containing dissolved ethyl cellulose plastic, are employed. For example, for cementing parts of injection-molded ethyl cellulose, a suitable cement may contain 10 per cent of the molding powder in an 80/20 mixture of toluene and 2B alcohol (special denatured alcohol). Other solvent combinations that may be used include mixtures of ethyl acetate with alcohol and of butyl acetate with toluene and alcohol.

The procedure necessary for joining well-fitted injection-molded pieces is relatively simple. The surfaces to be welded are immersed to a depth of about $\frac{1}{16}$ in. in a solvent cement for 2 to 3 min. The mating surfaces are brought into contact for about 1 min and then held under light pressure of about 5 psi in a jig for 10 min. Then the article may be removed from the jig and dried in the open air or in an oven. If an oven is used, the temperature should not exceed 150°F, and generally 120 to 130° F is satisfactory. The drying time depends upon the adhesive used and may be from 1 to 10 hr.

The cement used in joining ethyl cellulose plastic should be selected with reference to the nature of the joint and the type of plastic involved. The viscosity of the adhesive should be adjusted to the needs of the method used in applying the adhesive. Adhesives which will be applied by brushing should be more viscous than those applied by dipping. The solvent cements are produced as viscous solutions which can be thinned to the desired consistency.

Nylon. Nylon molding resins are normally not cemented by solvent-type cements, because of their lack of solubility in ordinary solvents. Several types may be cemented by formic acid or molten phenol, but these substances are difficult to handle and are rarely used.

Nylon moldings or extruded sections are generally cemented by means of chemical cements of the thermosetting (resorcinol) type.

Polyethylene. Polyethylene resins are extremely inert, and solvent-type cements are not applicable. Heat-sealing is the most satisfactory method of joining polyethylene resins. Careful control of temperature is necessary and overheating must be avoided.

Polyvinyl Alcohol. Polyvinyl alcohol (sheeting and tubing) can be cemented to itself with water or with solutions of 10 to 20 per cent of glycerine or ethylene glycol in water. These adhesives work best with the aid of heat. Polyvinyl alcohol sheeting and tubing cannot be satisfactorily heat-sealed without the use of water. Strong bonds are obtained also with room-temperature-setting resorcinol adhesives.

Polystyrene. Complex assemblies of polystyrene, usually molded in sections, may be joined by means of adhesives. Solvent action on the surface is the usual mechanism by which cemented pieces are held together. The plastic is soluble in a wide variety of organic solvents.

One of the after-effects of cementing polystyrene with an adhesive containing an active solvent is crazing. This may appear as superficial or internal cracks, or as surface clouding. The condition may be due to excessive local mechanical stresses or to loss of volatile constituents at localized points or areas. The adjacent uncrazed section must withstand tensile loads and elongations beyond its ability, and it finally fails. Therefore, with adhesives which depend on solvent action for their effectiveness, the solvent or combination of solvents must be carefully chosen. In general, low-boiling solvents mean fast drying, good strength, and severe surface crazing; with the high-boiling solvents, the result is often slow drying, poor strength, and much less crazing.

The most commonly used adhesives for polystyrene are of the solvent or bodied-solvent type. The solvent-type are divided into three groups based largely upon their relative volatilities, namely fast-, medium-, and slow-drying. Those with low boiling point and thus high volatility are the fast-drying types. They combine the advantages of low cost, ready availability, and speed of drying and are generally satisfactory when used with opaque materials or when the joint is not conspicuous. These solvents are unsatisfactory with transparent articles having a prominent joint, because of the crazing which becomes apparent within a few weeks.

The second type of solvent adhesive is classified as medium-drying. This has a higher boiling temperature than the fast-drying type and is slower to cause crazing. It is commonly used except in those applications requiring optical clarity over long periods.

High-boiling solvents are, of course, much slower in drying. The time required to obtain a bond of sufficient strength to permit handling is often excessive. Good high-boiling solvents should give craze-free joints for a period of at least two years, and in many cases much longer, under normal usage. In most cases, it is desirable to mix the slow-drying solvents with up to 65 per cent of methylene chloride or trichloroethylene to speed up the drying without seriously adding to the tendency to craze.

Bodied adhesives may be required by certain joint designs and may be used to produce airtight or watertight seals because they may cause less crazing. A satisfactory bodied adhesive may be easily made by mixing a colorless or colored polystyrene with a solvent. The choice of solvent depends upon the properties desired, such as setting time, flammability, toxicity, etc. The amount of polystyrene required depends on the intended use, but usually 10 to 15 per cent by weight is adequate.

SOLVENT CEMENTS FOR POLYSTYRENE

Solvent	Boiling Point (°C)	Tensile Strength of Joint (psi)	Time Before Appearance of Crazing, Months (Approximate)
fast-drying			
methylene chloride	40	1800	½
carbon tetrachloride	77	1350	½
ethyl acetate	77	1500	¾
benzene	80	——	¾
methyl ethyl ketone	80	1600	¾
ethylene dichloride	84	1800	¾
trichloroethylene	87	1800	¾
medium-drying			
toluene	111	1700	1
perchlorethylene	121	1700	1
ethyl benzene	136	1650	4
xylenes	138-144	1450	4
diethyl benzene	185	1400	12
slow-drying			
mono-amyl benzene	202	1300	>20
ethyl naphthalene	257	1300	>48

It has been reported that pure turpentine gives very satisfactory results from the standpoint of craze-resistance. Its drying rate, however, is low.

There are numerous commercial adhesives of the solvent type available for polystyrene. In an adhesive joint, high tensile strength is considered to be 2000 psi, low strength, 500 psi; a high impact strength, 0.2 ft-lb, low, 0.1 ft-lb; a short setting time, 5 min, a long setting time, several hours.

The design of the joint plays a large part in the effectiveness of the adhesive, the appearance, and the ease and cost of assembly. Butt, lap, and tongue-and-groove joints are in most frequent use, but angled or scarf joints and V-joints are used in some assemblies. If the strength of the joint is to be equivalent to that of the adjacent wall, the area of the joint should be increased by at least 50 per cent. A joint which combines both shear and tensile strength is most effective.

The lap joint has some advantages over the others, in regard to both appearance and, to some extent, strength. For best appearance, the adhesive can be applied by felt pad to the half of the joint which fits on the inside of the article. Then no exudation of adhesive will appear at the outer parting line.

When two pieces of annular cross-section are to be cemented with a lap joint, it is advantageous to make the outer lip thin in proportion to the inner (e.g., in a ratio of 1:4), since the greater periphery thus gained adds to the area, and hence the strength, of the joint.

A butt joint gives less contact area than a lap joint. Solvent adhesives may be applied from a felt pad. The butt joint often has the disadvantage of unsightly bond lines, but it is probably the easiest type to provide for in molding. The butt joint is not a self-locating joint, and locating pins or fixtures are often required to prevent slipping during clamping.

A tongue-and-groove joint is self-positioning, but unless it is very shallow it will require application of adhesive by other than felt-pad methods. If the adhesive is applied by a flow gun into the groove, the amount must be controlled so that after assembly the fluid will come to the edge of the joint, but not flow out to mar the outer appearance of the finished article.

The V-joint and the scarfed joint are variations of the preceding joints. They have the disadvantage of requiring a somewhat more complex method of application. The V-joint is self-positioning, and the scarfed bond is self-positioning on certain types of articles. It is difficult to mold the component parts to the close tolerance required by these joints.

In the application of adhesives, it is very important that the surfaces of the joint be clean and well matched. Poor contact of mating surfaces can cause many troubles. The problem of getting proper contact is aggravated by warpage, shrinkage, flash, marks from ejector pins, and non-flat surfaces.

Care must be taken to prevent application of adhesive to surfaces other than those to be joined, in order to avoid disfigurement of the surface. The adhesive should be applied evenly over the entire joint surface in sufficient quantity to ensure against voids. The assembly should be made as soon as the surfaces have become tacky, which usually means within a few seconds after application. Enough pressure should be applied to ensure good contact until initial bond strength has been achieved. Stronger bonds result when the adhesive is applied to both pieces of an assembly. Adhesives may be applied by a variety of methods, such as felt pad, brush, flowing equipment, and knife.

In joining pieces of polystyrene, a clamping device is commonly used to make certain that the bonding surfaces are in good contact until the initial set is obtained. For small assemblies, rubber bands, clothespins, light springs, or weights may often be used. With more complicated moldings, which may tend to warp after molding, specially designed jigs may be required. For large assemblies or irregularly shaped pieces, wood can be cut to fit the contours and lined with a soft cloth, felt, or sponge rubber. Experience will show how long the joint must remain clamped, in order to reach handling strength or initial set. Considerable additional time (perhaps 24 hr) will be required before the bond can be expected to withstand service loads.

Polyvinyl Chloride and Vinyl Chloride-Acetate Copolymers. Greater diversity of composition, and, correspondingly, of ability to be cemented by solvents, exists among the vinyl chloride-acetate copolymer resins than in most of the other plastics that are cemented. This is due to the relative insolubility of polyvinyl chloride.

As the percentage of vinyl acetate is increased in the copolymer resins, the effect of solvents is markedly increased. For this reason, the cements which depend upon solvent action for strength will be the more effective with copolymers containing the greater percentages of vinyl acetate. In general, cementing by use of solvent is less satisfactory with these copolymers than with the more soluble plastics, such as those of the cellulose esters.

Copolymer resins are available also in plasticized forms, and these, particularly in the more highly plasticized formulations, are more rapidly cemented than are the unplasticized resins.

In the case of cements depending on their tackiness alone for adhesion, little difference between the resins will be encountered. In heat-sealing operations also there will be little difference in weldability, providing the optimum temperature for the particular composition is used.

Cements for copolymer resins are usually of two types: (1) solvent cements (also called "laminating thinners") ; (2) dope-type cements.

Cementing with Solvent. Where smooth, rigid surfaces are to be joined, the solvent adhesives may be readily used. The adhesive is applied to the edges of the two pieces, which are held closely together, and flows between them by capillary action. Initial bonding takes place rapidly, usually within a few seconds, but the full strength of the joint is not reached until the solvent has completely evaporated. The ultimate strength of properly prepared bonds is practically as high as that of the original plastic.

The vinyl chloride-acetate copolymer resins are most rapidly dissolved by the ketone solvents such as acetone, methyl ethyl ketone, and methyl isobutyl ketone. The cyclic ketones such as cyclohexanone form solutions of the highest solids content, but they evaporate slowly and are ordinarily used only for copolymers of high molecular weight and straight polyvinyl-chloride polymers. Propylene oxide also is a very useful solvent in hastening solution of copolymer resins, especially those of high molecular weight and straight polyvinyl chloride. Mixtures of ketones and aromatic hydrocarbons have a more rapid softening action than do the ketones alone. Mixtures of solvents and non-solvents are preferable to solvents alone, and additions of aliphatic hydrocarbons and alcohols are sometimes advantageous. Two per cent of glacial acetic acid, added to the solvent cement, improves wetting and speeds the capillary flow of the cement between the two surfaces being joined. It should not be used, however, in formulations containing propylene oxide.

Embrittlement by solvent is one of the most troublesome factors in the bonding of rigid sheets through the use of laminating thinners. This is probably due to molecular orientation and strain-release when solvent is applied. Two procedures which minimize this embrittlement have been used in solvent bonding, with considerable success. In the first, mixtures based on the less powerful solvents are used. These apparently do not penetrate the sheet at a rate rapid enough to bring about embrittlement. In the second method, resin solutions are used for the bonding. The viscosity apparently minimizes penetration of the solvent.

The formulations of a number of typical laminating thinners are shown in the following table. The solvents are arranged in order of increasing solvent power and decreasing rate of setting of the joint.

	A	B	C	D
		parts by weight		
dioctyl phthalate	5	2.5	2.5	
methyl acetate (82%)	58			
ethyl acetate (85%)	10			
butyl acetate	10			
methyl ethyl ketone		63		40
dioxane		20		
isophorone		2.5	2.5	
methylene chloride			50	
ethylene dichloride			43	
cyclohexanone				40
propylene oxide				20
petroleum solvent (bp 94.4-121.7°C)	15			
acetic acid	2	2	2	
methanol		10		
	100	100	100	100

Propylene oxide penetrates vinyl chloride-acetate copolymer resins very rapidly and, in amounts up to about 20 to 25 per cent, improves the "bite" into the resin. Under conditions where propylene oxide evaporates too rapidly, acetone may be substituted. Solutions containing propylene oxide should be stored with care and well stoppered to prevent evaporation, since its boiling point is only 93°F.

The chlorinated hydrocarbons also are excellent solvents for the vinyl chloride-acetate copolymer resins, and are suitable for use in cements.

Cyclohexanone and isophorone are extremely high-boiling solvents which impart slow drying and prolonged tackiness. By themselves they are very slow penetrants, and are most useful in combination with low-boiling solvents.

Since many of the solvents discussed above present possible toxic hazards, they should always be used with adequate ventilation.

Dope-Type Cements. These are prepared by the addition of small amounts of resin to solvent cements to thicken them. Dope-type cements are used where the surfaces to be cemented are in contact only over a very small area or are mated so inaccurately that a thin solvent cement will not fill the gap.

Small percentages of vinyl chloride-acetate resin, in the form of shavings, turnings, or chips, may be dissolved in the previously mentioned solvent cements to impart viscosity. In conjunction with the vinyl resin there should be included 0.2 to 0.5 per cent of propylene oxide to help stabilize the solution against discoloration by light and heat when stored. Adhesion may be increased by the addition of about 5 per cent of a plasticizer, such as tricresyl phosphate.

In general, the dope-type adhesives set slowly with vinyl chloride-acetate copolymer resins and have little strength immediately after application. The strength of the bond develops as the solvent evaporates.

The vinyl chloride-acetate resin cements do not possess a high degree of tackiness when wet. However, this can be greatly increased by incorporation of certain other compatible resins, to yield cements of improved adhesion. Data covering resins suitable for this purpose may be obtained from the suppliers.

Vinylidine Chloride Copolymers. Vinylidine chloride resin is more inert chemically than most other thermoplastic synthetic resins. For this reason it is not possible to cement it with the same ease and strength of bond with solvent- or dope-type cements that perform so well with other plastics. No cement or adhesive is available which will produce a bond strength equal to that of the plastic itself. The best success in cementing this resin to itself has been obtained by bonding or welding by heat, without the use of solvents or adhesives.

Cements used, of the solvent type, consist of a resinous adhesive base dissolved in a volatile solvent. The adhesive dries by evaporation of the volatile solvent, leaving a thin, uniform deposit on the surfaces to be joined. The solvent does, however, in many cases, penetrate the surface slightly and anchor the adhesive. The solvent- and dope-type adhesives are applied to one or both surfaces, and the surfaces are allowed to become tacky before the pieces are joined. In some cases, the procedure may be accelerated by coating both surfaces, drying thoroughly (preferably at elevated temperatures, such as 140°F), and then activating with a small amount of the solvent used as the volatile portion of the adhesive.

The pieces should be kept under light pressure until the volatile solvent has escaped. If one of the surfaces is absorbent, volatilization of the solvent is facilitated.

With bonds of the resin to itself, best results are obtained by aging for one month before using.

Thermoplastic cements sometimes used are represented by synthetic resins of the thermoplastic type and hot-melt adhesives. They are applied in the molten state and set up as they cool after the bond is made. Pressure is maintained until the joint has reached normal temperature. These cements are limited to those applications which do not involve exposure to heat. They are not satisfactory with film or other oriented form, because of shrinkage that occurs when the cement is applied in the molten state.

Chemical cements have limited utility. This type comprises synthetic resins of the thermosetting (resorcinol) and polymerizable varieties which set up by a change in chemical composition. These changes are usually brought about by the addition of a catalyst or by rise in temperature.

Cementing of Thermosetting Plastics

The cementing of thermosetting materials to themselves poses problems which are not inherent in the cementing of thermoplastics. The insolubility of thermosetting materials makes it impossible to use the various solvent techniques used in bonding of thermoplastics, and the smoothness of surface of molded thermosetting plastics adds to the difficulty of cementing them.

The surfaces to be joined must mate perfectly, unless a gap-filling cement can be used. The smooth surface must be roughened; if machining is not required for mating, then the surfaces should be sanded.

Cements of many types are capable of giving bonds which will be satisfactory in service at room temperature and in the absence of conditions which would attack the cement. For more difficult service conditions fewer cements are available, and these usually require the use of heat and pressure in making the joint.

Obviously, the cement must be chosen to meet the conditions of service of the cemented article.

Information is not generally available as to the strength characteristics of joints made with the various cements, nor as to the effects of temperature and other service conditions. Hence, for any cementing problem it is best to seek advice and instructions either from the manufacturer of the plastic in question or from manufacturers of adhesives, and then to make appropriate tests of their recommendations.

Cements used for bonding thermosetting plastics include those based on:

> rubber
> di-isocyanates
> polyester resins
> urea and melamine resins
> phenolic and resorcinol resins
> resin and rubber
> furfuryl alcohol resins
> vinyl-modified phenolics
> epoxy resins

Some of these are single-package cements; others require mixing with catalysts or accelerators.

For molded phenolics, cements of the last five types above are used, and likewise for laminated phenolics and for phenolic-impregnated laminated wood. The fibrous nature of the filler in many of these laminates promotes a good bond.

For molded alkyds, a polyester cement is usually best, but success has been reported with rubber-resin cements.

For molded urea-formaldehyde and melamine-formaldehyde, cements based on these resins are generally used, but in applications not subjected to heat a good enough bond may be obtainable with a thermoplastic cement or rubber cement.

For molded and laminated polyesters, polyester cements are probably best; these may be accelerated for cure at room temperature or higher temperature, according to the facilities available. Other possibilities, depending on the conditions of use of the product, are cements based on di-isocyanates, rubber-resin, epoxy resin, and phenolic and resorcinol resins.

Information on the cementing of thermosetting materials to other materials is given in the following pages.

Cementing of Dissimilar Materials

From the beginning of the plastics industry, particularly in fabrication involving hard rubber and molded and laminated phenolics, adhesives have played an important role. The cements used were, in general, thermoplastics based on cyclized rubber or nitrocellulose; occasionally, in cases where heating could be tolerated, liquid phenolic resins were used.

In the commercial use of adhesives, need arose for improvement in mechanical properties such as impact strength and fatigue-resistance, and for better performance at high temperatures than was obtainable with the thermoplastics. This led to the development of a class of adhesives in which thermosetting resins were combined with thermoplastics or elastomeric high polymers to give better heat-resistance, high structural strength, good durability, and freedom from creep.

The cementing of dissimilar materials by means of such adhesives became competitive with well-known mechanical techniques such as riveting, screwing, soldering, etc., both in ease of operation and in cost.

With the development of an increasingly wide variety of resins and plastics, not only were there more materials adaptable to being combined with other structural materials, but also a larger variety of raw materials with which the adhesives themselves could be formulated.

There was developed also the technique of putting adhesives into the form of film or dry tape which could be applied without solvent, by automatic or mechanical means.

It is now possible to formulate adhesives to suit various techniques of application and to meet various requirements in performance, in which such factors as shear strength, peel strength, impact strength, flexural strength, and fatigue resistance are of paramount importance.

For joining dissimilar materials, adhesives specifically formulated for the purpose are to be preferred.

For solving the problems of industrial cementing, the facilities of many companies are available to the fabricator. Some suppliers are exclusively in the adhesives business, while other large companies have departments or divisions devoted to this field. These suppliers have laboratory and engineering facilities which can be devoted to any adhesives problem of real importance to the plastics industry.

The "Adhesives Reference Chart" follows.

The preceding "Adhesives Reference Chart" refers to the following reference numbers and chemical types:

Reference No. 1

CHEMICAL TYPE: Synthetic Rubber or Thermoplastic Resin Combined with Thermosetting Resin

SUPPLIER	*SUPPLIER'S ADDRESS*
American Resinous Chemicals Corp.	103 Foster St., Peabody, Mass.
Armstrong Cork Co.	Lancaster, Pa.
Atlas Mineral Products Co., The	Mertztown, Pa.
Bakelite Co., Division Union Carbide & Carbon Corp.	30 E. 42nd St., New York 17, N. Y.
B B Chemical Co.	784 Memorial Dr., Cambridge, Mass.
Calresin Corp.	4545 Brazil St., Los Angeles 39, Calif.
Carboline Co.	331 Thornton Ave., St. Louis 19, Mo.
Chrysler Corp., Cycleweld Cement Products Div.	5437 W. Jefferson, Trenton, Mich.
Ciba Company, Inc.	627 Greenwich St., New York 14, N. Y.
Coast Manufacturing & Supply Co.	Livermore, Calif.
Federal Adhesives Corp.	210-220 Wythe Ave., Brooklyn 11, N. Y.
Flintkote Company, Inc., The	30 Rockefeller Plaza, New York 20, N. Y.
Furane Plastics Corp.	4516 Brazil St., Los Angeles 39, Calif.
Goodrich, B. F., Co., The	Akron, Ohio
Goodyear Tire & Rubber Co., Inc., The Chemical Div.	Akron 16, Ohio
Heresite & Chemical Co.	Manitowoc, Wis.
Maas & Waldstein Co.	2121 McCarter Highway, Newark 4, N. J.
Marbon Corp.	Gary, Ind.
Minnesota Mining & Manufacturing Co., Adhesives & Coatings Div.	411 Piquette Ave., Detroit, Mich.
Miracle Adhesives Corp.	214 E. 53rd St., New York 22, N. Y.
Narmco Resins & Coatings Co.	600 Victoria St., Costa Mesa, Calif.
National Adhesives, Div. of National Starch Products, Inc.	270 Madison Ave., New York 16, N. Y.
Polymer Industries, Inc.	11-08 30th Ave., Astoria, N. Y.
Reichhold Chemicals, Inc.	601-707 Woodward Heights Blvd., Detroit 20, Mich.
Snyder Chemical Corp.	Bethel, Conn.

Union Bay State Laboratories, Inc.	491 Main St., Cambridge 42, Mass.
Union Paste Co.	1605 Hyde Park Ave., Hyde Park 36, Mass.
United States Plywood Corp.	55 W. 44th St., New York 36, N. Y.
United States Rubber Co.	4300 New Haven Ave., Fort Wayne 4, Ind.
Watson-Standard Co.	225 Galveston Ave., Pittsburgh 12, Pa.
Wilross Products Co.	Hawthorne, N. J.
Xylos Rubber Co., Div. of The Firestone Tire & Rubber Co.	Akron 1, Ohio

Reference No. 2
CHEMICAL TYPE: Natural Rubber

SUPPLIER	*SUPPLIER'S ADDRESS*
American Resinous Chemicals Corp.	103 Foster St., Peabody, Mass.
B B Chemical Co.	784 Memorial Dr., Cambridge, Mass.
Federal Adhesives Corp.	210-220 Wythe Ave., Brooklyn 11, N. Y.
Flintkote Company, Inc., The	30 Rockefeller Plaza, New York 20, N. Y.
Goodrich, B. F., Co., The	Akron, Ohio
Polymer Industries, Inc.	11-08 30th Ave., Astoria, N. Y.
Union Bay State Laboratories, Inc.	491 Main St., Cambridge 42, Mass.
United States Rubber Co.	4300 New Haven Ave., Fort Wayne 4, Ind.
Xylos Rubber Co., Div. of The Firestone Tire & Rubber Co.	Akron 1, Ohio

Reference No. 3
CHEMICAL TYPE: Synthetic Rubber

SUPPLIER	*SUPPLIER'S ADDRESS*
American Products Manufacturing Co., Inc.	8127-33 Oleander St., New Orleans 18, La.
American Resinous Chemicals Corp.	103 Foster St., Peabody, Mass.
Armstrong Cork Co.	Lancaster, Pa.
B B Chemical Co.	784 Memorial Dr., Cambridge, Mass.
Borden Co., The, Chemical Div.	350 Madison Ave., New York 17, N. Y.
Chemical Development Corp.	Danvers, Mass.
Chrysler Corp., Cycleweld Cement Products Div.	5437 W. Jefferson, Trenton, Mich.

Federal Adhesives Corp.	210-220 Wythe Ave., Brooklyn 11, N. Y.
Flintkote Company, Inc., The	30 Rockefeller Plaza, New York 20, N. Y.
Goodrich, B. F., Co., The	Akron, Ohio
Goodyear Tire & Rubber Co., Inc., The Chemical Div.	Akron 16, Ohio
Maas & Waldstein Co.	2121 McCarter Highway, Newark 4, N. J.
Minnesota Mining & Manufacturing Co., Adhesives & Coatings Div.	411 Piquette Ave., Detroit, Mich.
Miracle Adhesives Corp.	214 E. 53rd St., New York 22, N. Y.
National Adhesives, Div. of National Starch Products, Inc.	270 Madison Ave., New York 16, N. Y.
Naugatuck Chemical, Div. of U. S. Rubber Co.	Naugatuck, Conn.
Polymer Industries, Inc.	11-08 30th Ave., Astoria, N. Y.
Swift & Co.	U. S. Yards, Chicago 9, Ill.
Union Bay State Laboratories, Inc.	491 Main St., Cambridge 42, Mass.
Union Paste Co.	1605 Hyde Park Ave., Hyde Park 36, Mass.
United States Rubber Co.	4300 New Haven Ave., Fort Wayne 4, Ind.
Williamson Adhesives, Inc.	8222 Kimball Ave., Skokie, Ill.
Wilross Products Co.	Hawthorne, N. J.

Reference No. 4

CHEMICAL TYPE: Reclaimed Rubber

SUPPLIER	SUPPLIER'S ADDRESS
Armstrong Cork Co.	Lancaster, Pa.
B B Chemical Co.	784 Memorial Dr., Cambridge, Mass.
Chrysler Corp., Cycleweld Cement Products Div.	5437 W Jefferson, Trenton, Mich.
Flintkote Company, Inc., The	30 Rockefeller Plaza, New York 20, N. Y.
Goodrich, B. F., Co., The	Akron, Ohio
Minnesota Mining & Manufacturing Co., Adhesives & Coatings Div.	411 Piquette Ave., Detroit, Mich.
Miracle Adhesives Corp.	214 E. 53rd St., New York 22, N. Y.
National Adhesives, Div. of National Starch Products, Inc.	270 Madison Ave., New York 16, N. Y.
Swift & Co.	U. S. Yards, Chicago 9, Ill.
United States Rubber Co.	4300 New Haven Ave., Fort Wayne 4, Ind.
Wilross Products Co.	Hawthorne, N. J.
Xylos Rubber Co., Div. of The Firestone Tire & Rubber Co.	Akron 1, Ohio

Reference No. 5
CHEMICAL TYPE: Epoxy

SUPPLIER	*SUPPLIER'S ADDRESS*
Armstrong Cork Co.	Lancaster, Pa.
Armstrong Products Co.	P. O. Box 1, Warsaw, Ind.
Atlas Mineral Products Co., The	Mertztown, Pa.
Bakelite Co., Div. Union Carbide & Carbon Corp.	30 E. 42nd St., New York 17, N. Y.
Borden Co., The, Chemical Div.	350 Madison Ave., New York 17, N. Y.
Carboline Co.	331 Thornton Ave., St. Louis 19, Mo.
Chrysler Corp., Cycleweld Cement Products Div.	5437 W. Jefferson, Trenton, Mich.
Ciba Company, Inc.	627 Greenwich St., New York 14, N. Y.
Furane Plastics Corp.	4516 Brazil St., Los Angeles 39, Calif.
Goodrich, B. F., Co., The	Akron, Ohio
Merchants Chemical Co.	55 Day St., South Norwalk, Conn.
Minnesota Mining & Manufacturing Co., Adhesives & Coatings Div.	411 Piquette Ave., Detroit, Mich.
Miracle Adhesives Corp.	214 E. 53rd St., New York 22, N. Y.
Narmco Resins & Coatings Co.	600 Victoria St., Costa Mesa, Calif.
Polymer Industries, Inc.	11-08 30th Ave., Astoria, N. Y.
Shell Chemical Corp.	50 W. 50th St., New York 20, N. Y.
Wilross Products Co.	Hawthorne, N. J.

Reference No. 6
CHEMICAL TYPE: Phenol-Formaldehyde

SUPPLIER	*SUPPLIER'S ADDRESS*
Armstrong Cork Co.	Lancaster, Pa.
Bakelite Co., Div. Union Carbide & Carbon Corp.	30 E. 42nd St., New York 17, N. Y.
Barrett Div., The, Allied Chemical & Dye Corp.	40 Rector St., New York 6, N. Y.
B B Chemical Co.	784 Memorial Dr., Cambridge, Mass.
Borden Co., The, Chemical Div.	350 Madison Ave., New York 17, N. Y.
Carboline Co.	331 Thornton Ave., St. Louis 19, Mo.
Catalin Corporation of America	1 Park Ave., New York, N. Y.
Chemical Development Corp.	Danvers, Mass.
Ciba Company, Inc.	627 Greenwich St., New York 14, N. Y.

Durez Plastics & Chemicals, Inc.	Walck Rd., North Tonawanda, N. Y.
Federal Adhesives Corp.	210-220 Wythe Ave., Brooklyn 11, N. Y.
Heresite & Chemical Co.	Manitowoc, Wis.
Marblette Corp., The	37-21 30th St., Long Island City, N. Y.
Marbon Corp.	Gary, Ind.
Minnesota Mining & Manufacturing Co., Adhesives & Coatings Div.	411 Piquette Ave., Detroit, Mich.
Monsanto Chemical Co., Plastics Div.	Springfield, Mass.
National Casein Co.	601-619 W. 80th St., Chicago 20, Ill.
Reichhold Chemicals, Inc.	601-707 Woodward Heights Blvd. Detroit 20, Mich.
Rohm & Haas Co.	Washington Square, Philadelphia, Pa.
Snyder Chemical Corp.	Bethel, Conn.

Reference No. 7

CHEMICAL TYPE: Urea-Formaldehyde

SUPPLIER	SUPPLIER'S ADDRESS
American Cyanamid Co.	30 Rockefeller Plaza, New York, N. Y.
Bakelite Co., Div. Union Carbide & Carbon Corp.	30 E. 42nd St., New York 17, N. Y.
Barrett Div., The, Allied Chemical & Dye Corp.	40 Rector St., New York 6, N. Y.
Borden Co., The, Chemical Div.	350 Madison Ave., New York 17, N. Y.
Catalin Corporation of America	1 Park Ave., New York, N. Y.
Federal Adhesives Corp.	210-220 Wythe Ave., Brooklyn 11, N. Y.
Miracle Adhesives Corp.	214 E. 53rd St., New York 22, N. Y.
Monsanto Chemical Co., Plastics Div.	Springfield, Mass.
National Casein Co.	601-619 W. 80th St., Chicago 20, Ill.
Reichhold Chemicals, Inc.	601-707 Woodward Heights Blvd., Detroit 20, Mich.
Rohm & Haas Co.	Washington Square, Philadelphia, Pa.
United States Plywood Corp.	55 W. 44th St., New York 36, N. Y.
Wilross Products Co.	Hawthorne, N. J.

Reference No. 8

CHEMICAL TYPE: Melamine-Formaldehyde

SUPPLIER	SUPPLIER'S ADDRESS
American Cyanamid Co.	30 Rockefeller Plaza, New York, N. Y.

Federal Adhesives Corp.	210-220 Wythe Ave., Brooklyn 11, N. Y.
Monsanto Chemical Co., Plastics Div.	Springfield, Mass.
National Casein Co.	601-619 W. 80th St., Chicago 20, Ill.

Reference No. 9
CHEMICAL TYPE: Synthetic Thermoplastic Resins

SUPPLIER	SUPPLIER'S ADDRESS
American Phenolic Corp.	1830 So. 54th Ave., Chicago 50, Ill.
American Products Manufacturing Co., Inc.	8127-33 Oleander St., New Orleans 18, La.
American Resinous Chemicals Corp.	103 Foster St., Peabody, Mass.
Armstrong Cork Co.	Lancaster, Pa.
Atlas Mineral Products Co., The	Mertztown, Pa.
Bakelite Co., Div. Union Carbide & Carbon Corp.	30 E. 42nd St., New York 17, N. Y.
Borden Co., The, Chemical Div.	350 Madison Ave., New York 17, N. Y.
Calresin Corp.	4545 Brazil St., Los Angeles 39, Calif.
Chemical Development Corp.	Danvers, Mass.
Colton Chemical Co., The	1545 E. 18th St., Cleveland 14, Ohio
Dow Chemical Co., The	Midland, Mich.
Eastman Chemical Products, Inc.	Kingsport, Tenn.
Federal Adhesives Corp.	210-220 Wythe Ave., Brooklyn 11, N. Y.
Goodrich, B. F., Co., The	Akron, Ohio
Jones-Dabney Co.	Delancey & Rutherford Sts., Newark, N. J.
Koppers Co., Inc., Chemical Div.	Koppers Bldg., Pittsburgh 19, Pa.
Maas & Waldstein Co.	2121 McCarter Highway, Newark 4, N. J.
Marbon Corp.	Gary, Ind.
Merchants Chemical Co.	55 Day St., South Norwalk, Conn.
Minnesota Mining & Manufacturing Co., Adhesives & Coatings Div.	411 Piquette Ave., Detroit, Mich.
Miracle Adhesives Corp.	214 E. 53rd St., New York 22, N. Y.
Narmco Resins & Coatings Co.	600 Victoria St., Costa Mesa, Calif.
National Adhesives, Div. of National Starch Products, Inc.	270 Madison Ave., New York 16, N. Y.
Naugatuck Chemical, Div. of U. S. Rubber Co.	Naugatuck, Conn.
Pennsylvania Industrial Chemical Corp.	Clairton, Pa.
Polymer Industries, Inc.	11-08 30th Ave., Astoria, N. Y.
Rohm & Haas Co.	Washington Square, Philadelphia, Pa.
Schwartz Chemical Co., Inc.	326 W. 70th St., New York 23, N. Y.

Shawinigan Products Corp.   350 Fifth Ave., New York, N. Y.

Swift & Co.   U. S. Yards, Chicago 9, Ill.

Union Paste Co.   1605 Hyde Park Ave., Hyde Park 36, Mass.

Williamson Adhesives, Inc.   8222 Kimball Ave., Skokie, Ill.

Wilross Products Co.   Hawthorne, N. J.

Xylos Rubber Co., Div. of The Firestone   Akron 1, Ohio
Tire & Rubber Co.

Reference No. 10 (with subdivisions a, b, c, d, e, f, g, h)
CHEMICAL TYPE: Miscellaneous

SUPPLIER	*SUPPLIER'S ADDRESS*

10a. *Resorcinol Formaldehyde*

Borden Co., The, Chemical Div.	350 Madison Ave., New York, N. Y.
Catalin Corporation of America	1 Park Ave., New York, N. Y.
Durez Plastics & Chemicals, Inc.	Walck Rd., North Tonawanda, N. Y.
Koppers Co., Inc., Chemical Div.	Koppers Bldg., Pittsburgh 19, Pa.
Monsanto Chemical Co., Plastics Div.	Springfield, Mass.
National Casein Co.	601-619 W. 80th St., Chicago 20, Ill.
Reichhold Chemicals, Inc.	601-707 Woodward Heights Blvd., Detroit, Mich.
United States Plywood Corp.	55 W. 44th St., New York 36, N. Y.

10b. *Casein*

Borden Co., The, Chemical Div.	350 Madison Ave., New York 17, N. Y.
Monsanto Chemical Co., Plastics Div.	Springfield, Mass.
National Casein Co.	601-619 W. 80th St., Chicago 20, Ill.

10c. *Oleoresinous*

Armstrong Cork Co.	Lancaster, Pa.

10d. *Animal Glue*

Swift & Co.	U. S. Yards, Chicago 9, Ill.

10e. *Soy Bean*

Monsanto Chemical Co., Plastics Div.	Springfield, Mass.

10f. *Furane*

Carboline Co.	331 Thornton Ave., St. Louis 19, Mo.

Furane Plastics Corp.   4516 Brazil St., Los Angeles 39, Calif.

Minnesota Mining & Manufacturing Co.,   411 Piquette Ave., Detroit, Mich.
  Adhesives & Coatings Div.

10g. *Sodium Silicate*

Philadelphia Quartz Co.   Public Ledger Building, Philadelphia 6, Pa.

10h. *Polyesters*

Barrett Div., The, Allied Chemical   40 Rector St., New York 6, N. Y.
  & Dye Corp.

Celanese Corporation of America   290 Ferry St., Newark 5, N. J.

Welding of Thermoplastics

Welding by heat provides an advantageous means of joining many thermoplastics. The method is applicable to most thermoplastics, although the details differ depending upon the properties of individual materials. An exception is nitrocellulose plastic, which should not be heat-welded because of its instability toward high temperature. This material should be joined by means of solvent cements.

The following thermoplastic materials can be heat-welded:

    acrylic resins
    cellulose acetate
    cellulose acetate butyrate
    ethyl cellulose
    nylon
    polyethylene
    polystyrene
    polytetrafluorothylene (partially)
    polytrifluorochloroethylene (partially)
    polyvinyl chloride
    polyvinyl chloride-acetate copolymers
    polyvinylidine chloride

Heat-sealing of thin thermoplastic sheeting has been practiced for many years with cellulose acetate and with vinyl copolymers, but the temperatures employed have generally been lower than those for heat-welding, and the source of heat usually steam.

Rapid progress is being made in the welding of thermoplastics, particularly the newer ones, and the manufacturers of these materials should be consulted for detailed information pertaining to particular assembly problems. Polytetrafluoroethylene and polytrifluorochloroethylene can be heat-welded, but only under very specialized conditions, and welding of these materials should be undertaken only after discussion of the details with the suppliers of the materials.

Heated-Tool Welding. In this process the edges to be united are heated to fusion and then brought into contact and allowed to cool under slight pressure. Electrical strip heaters, hot plates, soldering irons, and the like are convenient means of providing high temperatures locally. The method has been used principally with vinylidine chloride polymers and with methyl methacrylate sheeting, but is applicable to other thermoplastics as well.

The butt-welding of methyl methacrylate sheets in order to obtain areas larger than standard size has been accomplished by heat welding. The process is rapid, but requires suitable equipment, including jigs and fixtures. The bond obtained is transparent, and the strength of the joint is substantially that of the plastic itself.

The edges of the sheets to be joined are softened by contact with an electrically-heated resistance strip, and while the plastic is soft the heater strip is removed, and the two pieces of sheeting are brought into contact and allowed to cool under pressure (Fig. 17-2). During the heating there is some depolymerization of resin to liquid monomer, which softens the surfaces sufficiently to provide good contact in the joint. The heating is usually accompanied by some smoking and evolution of fumes of monomer, for which ventilation should be provided.

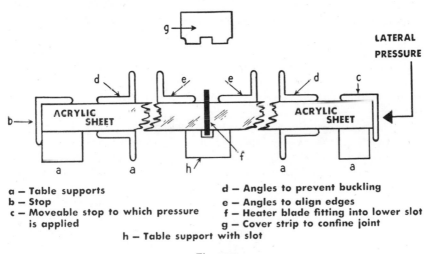

a — Table supports
b — Stop
c — Moveable stop to which pressure
    is applied
d — Angles to prevent buckling
e — Angles to align edges
f — Heater blade fitting into lower slot
g — Cover strip to confine joint
h — Table support with slot

Fig. 17-2

A suitable welding jig is required. The sheets should be firmly held on adjustable tracks so that they can be made to approach one another. Because of the flexibility of the plastic, the sheets should be well clamped, particularly near the edges to be joined. The electrically-heated resistance blade is held taut (e.g., by springs) in position over the edges of the two sheets to be joined, and is provided with an adjusting mechanism for lowering it into the plane of the sheets, and for subsequently raising it away from the edges of the sheets after they have been softened.

The blade used should be slightly wider than the thickness of the sheets being joined. It should be heated to a temperature of 650 to 750°F, depending on the conditions of the job. If the blade is not hot enough, there is insufficient depolymerization and softening of the surfaces to provide a satisfactorily soft layer, while if the blade is too hot the monomer produced by the depolymerization is volatilized, so that there is insufficient liquid in the joint. Frequent checking of the temperature with a pyrometer is recommended.

In operation, the blade is brought into position and the two pieces of sheet to be joined are set in contact with it. Sufficient pressure is applied, preferably by a hand-screw, to bring the plastic firmly against the blade along its entire length. The electric current is then applied for a predetermined, accurately measured period of time, dependent upon the dimensions of the blade, the thickness of the sheets and the temperature. One minute is frequently suitable. The timing should be done with a stop watch.

After the expiration of the measured heating time, the sheets are drawn slightly apart and the blade raised from the joint. The sheets are then brought rapidly together, clamped by means of the hand-screw and thus held together until cool.

To avoid contamination of the joint, it is necessary to clean the heating blade after each use with fine abrasive garnet paper.

Pressure on the softened edges of the sheets results in the formation of a rounded bead. When the stock has cooled, and if the joined stock is to be used without further shaping, the bead is removed by sanding and the area is polished. If, however, the welded sheet is to be heated for shaping, the bead should be left on, since otherwise a depression will develop during the shaping.

The contour of the bead may be controlled by pressing rigid surfaces against each side of the joint after the lateral pressure has been applied.

Since the temperatures required are high, the voltage source for the heater unit is normally the secondary of a transformer. The voltage and amperage needed to obtain the required temperature will vary with the size and shape of the heater blade, which, of course, depend upon the dimensions and shape of the joint. In one application, a blade 30×2 in. and 0.060 in. thick was heated to 660°F by means of a heavy-duty transformer operating on a 220-volt primary with a secondary output of 450 amp at 3 volts.

The temperature required will vary with the thickness of the plastic, and may be different for materials from different manufacturers. Accurate control of temperature is necessary, and there should be included a variable autotransformer to adjust the voltage to the heavy-duty transformer, and an indicating pyrometer permanently connected to the heater strip.

Welding by means of a hot plate has been extensively used with polyvinylidine chloride plastics.

In this method, heat is applied to the surfaces to be joined by holding them in contact with a hot-plate until a surface of molten material is built up. As soon as the materials are sufficiently softened, they are removed from the plate, quickly joined together and held firmly in their proper position until the melted material has cooled to form a strong joint. The surface of the hot plate may be polished and nickel-plated in order to avoid corrosion of the metal when adhering resin decomposes on the hot-plate. A plate of solid nickel gives very good results. The hot-plate should be maintained at 250 to 300°C (preferably 275°C) to provide a rapid weld without undue decomposition of the material. Between welds, the plastic left on the plate should be removed with a putty knife. The temperature should be controlled through the use of a transformer or rheostat in the circuit, or by a thermostat.

Pressures of from 3 to 12 psi employed during the melting on the hot plate will give satisfactory melting without excessive flash. The time required for melting will vary widely, but about 10 sec of contact will give best results. The pressure between the two pieces during the actual welding union should be sufficient to press out air bubbles and to bring the surfaces into intimate contact. The greatest single factor in the production of consistently good welds is the time elapsing between removing the melted pieces from the hot plate and joining them together to form the weld. This interval should be kept at one second or less if possible.

This method is widely used in welding sections of pipe and large tubing, and it may be employed in the assembly of molded parts in which dimensions do not need to be closely held. A variation of the hot-plate method which allows for the welding of long lengths of pipe in their installed position is one in which a heated hand iron is substituted for the hot plate (Fig. 17-3). The sections of pipe to be joined are held in contact with opposite sides of the hand iron until melted. Then the iron is removed and the sections brought together.

A variation of the technique of hot-plate welding consists of replacing the hot plate with a heated shoe attached to an ordinary electric soldering iron. This method and tool are employed widely in the lap-welding of sheets to produce continuous linings for tanks. The electrically heated shoe is passed slowly between the two surfaces to be joined and is followed by a hand roller which presses the molten surfaces together (Fig. 17-4). The shoe should be kept moving and in contact with both of the sheet surfaces. No trouble with carbonizing of the plastic on the shoe is encountered so long as this precaution is observed. On the completion of a seam, the plastic left on the shoe is allowed to remain there for a moment; it will carbonize and may be easily brushed off with a fine bronze- or brass-wire brush. The shoes may be of a wide variety of design to accommodate the contour and thickness of the sheets employed. They should be made of copper, for maximum heat-transfer, and should be either heavily nickel-plated or covered with thin sheets of tantalum. Solid nickel is satisfactory, except that its heat conductivity is about only one-seventh that of copper.

The use of lubricants (waxes, stearates) to prevent sticking of the plastic

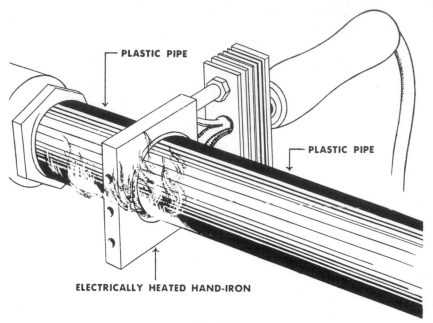

Fig. 17-3

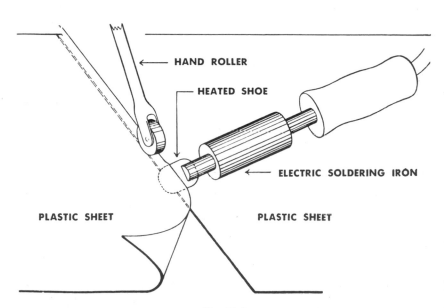

Fig. 17-4

to the hot metal is not recommended, since the weld is weakened by their presence.

Welding with Hot Gas. This method is a most versatile one and is useful with molded articles. It has been widely used with polyvinyl chloride, polyvinylidine chloride, and polyethylene plastics. The pieces to be joined are placed in their proper relative positions and held firmly, with a gap of about $1/16$ in. between them. A welding rod of similar or special composition is directed into the joint from the left with a slight steady pressure, and at an angle of 45° with the work. A blast of hot air is directed from the right at 45° and in a continuous half-diameter circular motion about the point where the rod is closest to the work.

The blast is produced by means of a hand torch designed for the purpose. Air at room temperature and at a pressure of 3 to 4 psi is fed into the torch at rates up to 3 cfm. It is heated to about 300 to 325°C (for polyvinylidine chloride) in passing through the torch, and has a temperature of about 200 to 225°C at the joint surfaces.

In welding polyethylene, it is important that an inert gas such as nitrogen be used. Oxygen and compressed air must be avoided, because these gases cause polyethylene to oxidize rapidly.

The equipment used in welding consists of a hot-gas or "flameless" torch, pressure regulator and filler rod. The torches used may be heated by either gas or electricity. The gas welding torch permits the regulation of the temperature of the stream of hot gas or air by varying the flame which heats the coil. The electric torch is regulated by a thermo-switch. The temperature of the hot gas may be further regulated through the gas pressure and also by varying the distance between the tip of the torch and the weld piece. The orifice temperature should be between 400 and 600°F.

Friction Welding. In friction welding, the plastic is melted by the heat developed between two parts which are rubbed against each other at suitable velocity and are forced together with sufficient pressure. The method is adaptable to cylindrical parts, or discs, which can be rotated against one another in a lathe or other suitable device. In this way, long cylinders may be built up by friction-welding a number of discs together.

One disc is held stationary in a tailstock adapter, while the other disc is rotated in an adapter fastened to the lathe spindle. The stationary disc is brought into contact with the rotating disc and pressure applied by means of the tailstock screw until melted resin appears at the edges of the discs. Then the lathe spindle is stopped and the pressure maintained for about 15 sec until the weld is cool enough to hold. Another disc may then be placed in the tailstock adapter and welded to the assembly in the rotating adapter. In this way a long cylinder may be built up.

In the case of a disc 3 in. in diameter, in a lathe running at 375 rpm, the rubbing velocity at the edge of the disc would be about 300 fpm. Using the same lathe speed, a 6-in. disc would have a rubbing speed of about 600 fpm, and under these conditions both sizes may be satisfactorily welded.

With experience, an operator can readily learn what pressure is sufficient to make good welds. This should be great enough to force out any bubbles which may form in the joint.

Too great a velocity, combined with too little pressure, will result in charring the resin, and the weld will be poor.

Discs of large diameter often require crowning so that the centers come into contact first and the outer portions later, as the central portions melt. This is done to minimize the effect of velocity differences and to assure melting in regions of low velocity.

This method has been used for the joining of polyvinylidine chloride pipe in butt or scarf welds and for butt-welding the pipe to flange members. Hollow cylindrical sections, such as pipe, are well adapted to friction welding because the velocities at the inner and outer edges are nearly the same.

Welding of Seams by Rotating Welding Rod. This method produces bead welds similar in appearance to electric-arc welds and employs a rotating welding rod of the same composition and softening point as the pieces which are to be joined. The rod should be about $1/4$ in. in diameter, rotated at about 5000 rpm by a high-speed drill press, hand drill, or hand grinder. Light pressure should be applied, sufficient to produce a good flow of molten plastic, and light enough to prevent whipping as the rod rotates. As the plastic melts, the rod is moved along the seam. When the proper technique has been achieved, a bead of molten plastic will follow the rod. It is possible to lay down several beads on the same seam.

An example of the use of this method is in joining sections of pipe to make a $1\frac{1}{2} \times 1\frac{1}{2} \times 1$ in. reducing pipe tee. The end of the 1-in. pipe section is cut away in a saddle shape to fit over the outside of the $1\frac{1}{2}$-in. section. Then the outside of the 1-in. pipe is beveled to form a groove in which to lay the weld bead. After welding the joint, a drill is run through the 1 in. pipe, into the side of the $1\frac{1}{2}$-in. pipe.

Mechanical Assembly of Plastics

The widespread use of plastics as components in an extensive variety of assemblies, where joining of plastic to plastic or of plastic to metal is an essential operation, has presented many novel problems in fastening. Certain characteristic properties of plastics, considered as a class of structural materials, have a direct bearing upon the choice of suitable mechanical methods of joining. The order and range of tensile strength and elongation associated with various types of plastics, as well as their response to localized stress, either instantaneous or prolonged, make it apparent that plastics must be treated with more care than metals, for instance, in designing serviceable fastening devices. A number of such devices have been accumulated through experience, and today the designer has at his disposal a choice of ingenious methods of joining.

Methods now in common use for fastening plastic components into durable assemblies are summarized below:

1. *Tapping threads in a suitable recess and using machine screws.* The holes which are threaded by tapping are either molded directly in the piece or prepared by drilling. There are certain obvious disadvantages in tapping, in that an extra operation is required and absolute tightness of fit must be sacrificed. With fibrous materials, frequently the threads are imperfect. Tapping is sometimes useful when limitations of wall thickness make other methods impracticable.

2. *Hardened self-tapping and metallic drive-screws* (*Fig. 17-5*). As in method 1, the holes in which the screws engage are either molded or drilled. In either case, the entering edge of the hole is suitably chamfered in order to prevent spalling. This is particularly important if the plastic tends to be brittle or friable.

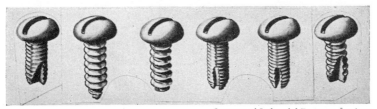

Courtesy of Industrial Fasteners Institute

Fig. 17-5. Thread-cutting and thread-forming tapping screws of various popular designs.

Self-tapping screws comprise two basic types which form their mating threads respectively by displacement and by cutting. The displacement type is more suitably used with thermoplastic materials; thread-cutting screws are better adapted to thermosetting plastics.

Particular variants of the thread-cutting type designed to distribute stresses evenly are available for use with the more friable thermosetting plastics such as urea-formaldehyde, or under conditions where strains must be minimized, as in the tapping of an island boss. Wherever a thread-cutting screw is used, a reservoir must be provided for the chips which are formed, and good design recommends that the depth of the hole be increased by $\frac{1}{32}$ in. beyond that required for engagement. Thread-cutting screws are slotted in order to provide a channel for disposing of chips, so that the fluted cutting edge is not fouled.

While self-tapping screws can be removed and replaced with no particular sacrifice in security of the joint, metallic drive-screws are used to provide a permanent assembly, since they cannot be replaced once they are removed. Special tools are available for pressing drive-screws into place.

The types of screws described above are available in a variety of metals and of plated finishes, including brass, zinc, nickel, and cadmium.

3. *Spring-type nuts used to lock on studs molded as an integral part of the plastic component (Fig. 17-6).* Units of the spring type are available in a variety of forms, among them simple washers, multi-per-

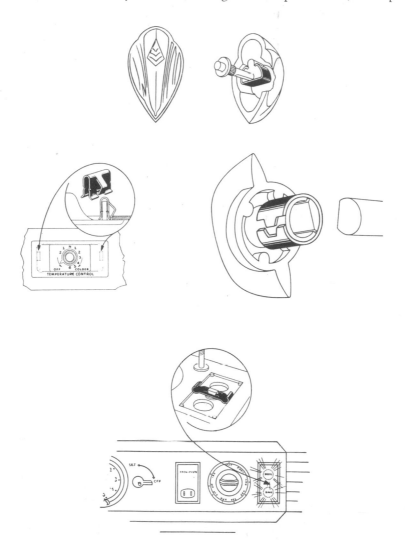

Fig. 17-6. Typical "Speed Nut" and "Speed Clip" assemblies.

forated rings, tubular devices and irregular shapes. All of them depend upon the development of spring tension when assembled in place on a stud, so that resistance to displacement is set up. Fasteners of this type offer particular advantage in rapid assembly of components on a panel without requiring access to the rear of the panel.

4. *Specially designed plastic rivets* (*Fig. 17-7*). This ingenious fastener consists essentially of a hollow body and a solid pin, the shank of the tubular body being split into four flaring prongs. The pin and body are produced as a unit by injection molding, and the fastener is available in a number of common thermoplastic compositions. This rivet

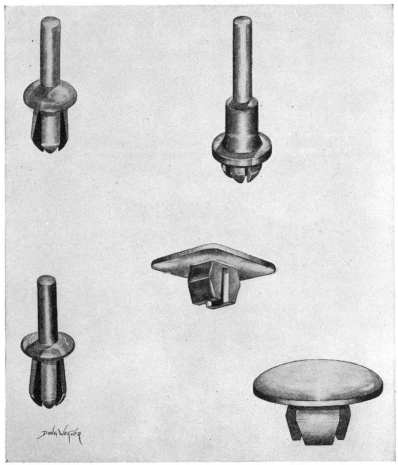

Courtesy of Shakeproof, Inc., Div. of Illinois Tool Works

Fig. 17-7

is centered over the point of joining, and then set with a sharp blow which releases the pin from the plastic collar, drives it into place in the hollow shank and in so doing sets up a positive locking action. The fastener assures good anchorage against vibration, and provides an attractive, corrosion-resistant unit.

5. *Metal rivets.* Metal rivets play a relatively small part in present-day assembly practice with plastics, but can be used with the high-impact type.

6. *Miscellaneous closure devices.* A number of means of providing movable assemblies, such as required in hinges, latches, snap locks and bead-chain attachments, are largely derived from standard devices used with common materials of construction other than plastics.

18. Assembly Gluing

Types of Resin Adhesives for Assembly Gluing

Assembly gluing may be defined as the gluing together of parts, frequently dissimilar in shape, to make a complete assembly. It is often termed secondary, subassembly, or final-assembly gluing, as contrasted to the gluing of plywood or laminates by the conventional hot-press or cold-press method.

Various types of synthetic resin adhesives are manufactured for assembly gluing. Each type has its own individual properties and fields of use. Many synthetic resins require temperatures of 200°F or higher to polymerize, or cure, them so that maximum water-resistance and strength are developed. However, the need for adhesives for assembly gluing, more durable than those made from natural substances, and capable of setting at sufficiently low temperatures to make them practical, has resulted in the development of many which will set in a reasonable time at temperatures between 68 and 211°F. These are supplied as liquids or powders. Separate hardeners or accelerators may or may not be required to be mixed in just prior to using them. Often these adhesives have been called "cold-setting." Actually, a minimum temperature of 68°F is required for even the most reactive types to accomplish setting in a reasonable time.

In this discussion, the term "room-temperature adhesives" will refer to those which set satisfactorily at 68 to 86°F, and "intermediate-temperature adhesives" will mean those which set at 87 to 211°F (it is understood that room-temperature adhesives can be set at intermediate temperatures much more rapidly than at room temperature).

In the past five years, the list of types has grown from four to ten. They are based on the following synthetic resins: phenolic, urea, melamine, resorcinol, furane, polyester, emulsion polymer, synthetic protein, mixtures of elastomer and resin, and mixtures of thermoplastic polymer and resin (cross-linking resin mixtures). The properties of these adhesives may vary considerably from one manufacturer to another. Frequent improvements and changes are being made. Hence, the following information on the different types is of necessity quite general and approximate.

As might be expected, the radical expansion of the types of assembly adhesives available has been brought about by the desire to bond materials of construction other than wood, plywood and phenol-fiber laminates, and also the new adhesives have vastly broadened the art of assembly gluing.

Phenolic Resins. These resin adhesives are used principally for making assemblies in wood, plywood, laminated wood, phenolic-fiber laminates and phenolic-paper laminates. They have a curing range from 24 hr at 90°F to 2 hr at 160°F. The allowable assembly time* is comparatively long, ½ to 2 hr. Water-resistance is high, and bond strength is comparatively unaffected by boiling water as well as cold water. These resins are not affected by temperatures that do not destroy wood; in fact, they retard the burning of wood. Their chemical resistance is greater than that of wood, and they are resistant to attack by microorganisms, such as molds and fungi. Some types using acid accelerators to speed the cure have been proven to have a deteriorating and weakening effect on wood, particularly at temperatures above 150°F. Other types having a pH close to neutral have no detrimental effect on wood and are just as durable as the familiar hot-pressed phenolic plywood adhesives.

Recently alcohol-soluble phenolics, set with acid catalyst, have become available, that cure at 75°F, require no minimum assembly time, and are not particularly weakening to wood (or plastic). Difficulty in cleaning up equipment for mixing and spreading, and unexpected shortness of working life at summer temperatures, are the main disadvantages.

Urea Resins. Urea-resin adhesives are used largely for making assemblies of wood and of plywood, although their use in gluing paper and fabrics to each other and to wood is growing. They have a setting range from 4 to 8 hr at 70 to 75°F, 1 to 2 hr at 120°F, and 10 to 20 min at 160°F. The maximum allowable time for assembly is 15 to 20 min. They have fairly good water-resistance; they withstand moderately long exposure to cold water, but are not resistant to hot water. They will not meet the more rigid specifications for water-resistance. Their heat-resistance is good up to 150°F, and their resistance to some chemicals is better than that of wood. They are resistant to molds and fungi unless excessively extended. Acid-accelerated urea resins of mild acidity are more durable than strongly acid types. Most specifications call for a lower pH limit of 2.5. Some urea-resin adhesives are supplied as liquids or powders with the hardener separate, others as powder containing the hardener already mixed in. The hardener does not take effect until the powdered adhesive is mixed with water.

Melamine Resins. As the development and understanding of melamine-urea-resin adhesives have advanced, the use of straight melamine assembly adhesives, always restricted by high cost, has very substantially decreased. Although straight melamine-resin adhesives have outstanding outdoor durability, the practical interests of economy and efficiency are best served by the mixed resins. They are used principally for assembly gluing of wood, plywood and laminated wood.

Melamine resins have been developed for use under ordinary conditions

---

* Assembly times are all open assembly times unless otherwise noted (see page 700).

of assembly gluing, to be set at temperatures not below 110°F. In general handling properties the melamine resins approach the ureas, except that melamine resins are difficult to clean up. They provide, however, a superior resistance to exposure and to such testing procedures as immersion in boiling water. Their rate of setting is dependent upon temperature. At glue-line temperature of 110°F, curing is accomplished in 6 to 8 hr; at 140°F, in about 1 hr. At 70°F, the time permissible for assembly ranges from 30 to 45 min. The pressure recommended is 100 to 250 psi. Working life is approximately 3 hr at 70°F. Melamine-urea resins are available also for setting at intermediate temperature, with a lower limit of about 140°F for curing. Adjustment of the catalyst governs the working life and the time required for cure. The melamine-urea combinations are considered intermediate in durability between the straight melamines and straight ureas. When substantial amounts of melamine resin are used, the durability is more than proportionately greater than that of the urea resin alone.

Resorcinol Resins. The resorcinol-resin adhesives are a relatively new development, but test data accumulated over the last four years indicate that when they are properly cured at room temperature they are fully as durable as the phenolic resins are when hot-pressed. They may be cured in 8 to 10 hr at 70°F, and in as little as 4 to 7 min at 180°F (temperatures are those reached at the actual glue line). The permissible assembly time for the resorcinol adhesives may be as long as 60 to 90 min at 75°F in closed assemblies (see page 700), while open assemblies at the same temperature may safely run to 20 to 40 min, provided a sufficient spread of adhesive is employed. The resorcinol adhesives are furnished as liquids with powder hardeners and as liquids with liquid hardeners. The pot life of these adhesives will range from 3 to 4 hr at 75°F to about 1 hr at 100°F. In this case the temperature referred to is, of course, the temperature of the actual mix. One of the most outstanding characteristics of the resorcinol resins is their completely neutral character, which avoids all damage to cellulosic fibers. Another valuable property of the resorcinol adhesives is their long storage life; they are not reactive until the hardener is added.

Phenol-Resorcinols. Resorcinol is inherently a relatively costly raw material, and hence efforts have recently been made to replace part of the resorcinol by phenol. Fortunately, this work has been eminently successful, in that all of the major properties of the resorcinol adhesives have been maintained. In addition, somewhat more tolerance in curing has been attained, without inducing crazing. Only in certain very special cases has there been any loss of adhesive properties.

Furane Resins. A development spurred by the valuable properties of the resorcinol-resin adhesives and involving resins based upon furane compounds has resulted in assembly adhesives having interesting properties. Like the resorcinol-resin adhesives, furane resins are practically neutral, and the uncatalyzed resins have good keeping properties. Similarly they are dark in color, and have good pot life and good durability. Unlike the resorcinol resins, they produce high bond strength without extreme rigidity or glass-hard brittleness, and thus are better suited to applications where thick glue lines are unavoidable. Perhaps most unusual is the very long time which they allow for assembly, the minimum being 30 min at 75°F, and the maximum being 4 hr. This requirement of long assembly time must not be overlooked. If working space is limited, it may be a serious inconvenience. On the other hand, it is advantageous in permitting the spreading of large areas to be completed before the adhesive loses its ability to bond; here then, is an interesting answer to this problem. Their cost is slightly lower than that of the phenol-resorcinols.

Emulsions of Thermoplastic Resins. The demands of the synthetic-rubber and certain related industries have developed to a high degree the techniques of producing emulsions and dispersions of a number of resins in liquids which contain little or no solvent. Many of these resins have long been known to be excellent adhesives, but have had little use because of their sparing solubility in expensive and generally flammable organic solvents. The application of these resins in dispersions or emulsions eliminates the need for these solvents, and permits the spreading of mixtures of adequate solids content comparable with that of older, better known resin adhesives soluble in water. Simple dispersions of some resins can be used as assembly adhesives, but usually better results are obtained by proper compounding with modifying agents, and most adhesives of this type on the market are so furnished. They have the advantages of neutrality or slight alkalinity, almost complete freedom from odor, good keeping qualities if not frozen, craze-resistance if properly compounded, flexibility, and lack of color. Their limitations are thermoplasticity and limited water-resistance in most cases, and lack of durability under extreme conditions of exposure. Work is now under way in the laboratories of a number of suppliers and users to improve the durability and to produce thermosetting forms.

These adhesives in present forms generally set by evaporation of the water, so that clamping time is similar to that for well-known water-soluble adhesives. However, unlike the older adhesives, the films do not readily redisperse. Despite this fact, their water-resistance is still limited. Assembly time is that which may be expected of a water-borne material; it is necessary only that the parts be brought together before the spread adhesive skins over appreciably, or dries out.

Synthetic Protein Resins. Since natural proteins have long been employed as adhesives, it is only natural to assume that man's success in producing protein-type substances of large molecular weight, also known as super-polyamides, would be followed by investigation of their adhesive qualities. As might also be expected, there has already been some success in this, particularly with hydrophilic materials such as wood, paper, fabrics and certain plastics, but they have not been widely adopted, because either of their high cost or their lack of advantage over better known and inexpensive phenol- or urea-formaldehyde resins.

Some of these resin-like proteins based on corn protein and nylon-type compounds are soluble only in mixed solvents, and thus develop good water-resistance by simple evaporation. Others, like most natural proteins, are insolubilized with the aid of heat. Still others are made water-resistant by cross-linking or coagulating agents.

Mixtures of Elastomer and other Resin; Mixtures of Thermoplastic Polymer and other Resin. An unusual and very promising field for synthetic resin adhesives has been developed from the discovery, born of war needs, that certain mixtures of widely divergent types of synthetic resins are highly compatible and possess a combination of outstanding adhesiveness and outstanding strength with great durability, which is not obtainable by other means. Their outstanding property is their ability to adhere to and to maintain a bond between widely dissimilar materials, such as wood and metal, rubber and metal, plastics and metal, plastics and rubber, and any of these with even glass and ceramics; of course, these adhesives will bond any of these materials to itself. Thus they are well described as polyfunctional adhesives. They are successful because of their wide affinity to materials which benefit from assembly by gluing, and also because they have within themselves a combination of resiliency with high strength which enables them to withstand the relative expansion and contraction of dissimilar materials in a joint.

As indicated by the title of this section, there are two families of adhesives in this group. These are not interchangeable, but their properties, methods of handling and types of performance are sufficiently similar to enable them to be discussed together. The principal difference is that the elastomer type provides maximum resiliency, while the thermoplastic type provides greater rigidity. There are many important minor differences, but these should be ascertained from the manufacturer.

These adhesives are almost always furnished in solution in a mixture of organic solvents, and are generally thinned, spread and cleaned up by well-known lacquer techniques. They may be brushed, sprayed, dipped, roller-coated, knife-coated or flowed onto the surfaces to be bonded.

One noteworthy exception, however, is a two-part adhesive comprising a liquid and a dry powder. The liquid is spread upon the surfaces to be joined and the dry powder is applied to the wet surfaces. This powder is not a catalyst, and the process is not to be confused with techniques wherein one surface is coated with resin and the other with catalyst. It is very important to follow in every detail the instructions of the manufacturer to ensure the performance of which this adhesive is capable. Storage life and pot life are generally indefinitely long, regardless of temperature, below the boiling point of the solvents. Very low temperatures frequently cause segregation of ingredients into layers, but these can be recombined by warming and thorough stirring. Some types contain small amounts of inert or insoluble material which may settle out and must always be redispersed before use. Some types are thixotropic and for best results should be strongly agitated before thinning or spreading, to reveal their normal consistency.

Either type can be used cold, with excellent results, simply by assembling wet and allowing sufficient time for all solvents to escape. When they are so used, the time permissible for assembly is rather short, being frequently less than 10 min because of the high volatility of the solvents, but this in turn reduces the clamping time, particularly of heavy assemblies from which solvents do not have an easy path of escape. In light assemblies, the setting is rapid enough so that they can frequently be handled after 4 hr. Heavier assemblies require setting over night. Strength continues to increase as the last traces of solvent leave the joint, but changes are of a minor order after 72 hr. Bonds made cold generally have excellent strength and good outdoor durability, but frequently do not lose their thermoplasticity or gain real solvent-resistance.

For maximum performance both types should be set by heat, following very carefully the manufacturer's instructions. Certain types are made deliberately, and permanently, partially or wholly thermoplastic, but even these give better results when set by heat. The resins used in these adhesives retain traces of their solvents with great tenacity and these traces act as plasticizers, increasing the thermoplasticity or lowering the creep-resistance, according to the type. Furthermore, even in the thermoplastic types, heat causes some cross-linking of the ingredients, with a resulting desirable increase in the softening temperature.

Bonding pressures can be as low as 15 psi or as high as 500 psi, depending upon the accuracy of fit of the parts at the joint and upon their rigidity. Thicker glue lines favor lower bonding pressures. A very common bonding temperature is 300°F, at which temperature periods under cure ranging from 10 to 20 min are common. The longer periods generally give the greatest strength and creep-resistance and durability. Shorter periods, of course, are made possible by the use of higher temperatures, which may be limited by the ability of the part to withstand the temperature, or by the accuracy of timing necessary. These adhesives are generally difficult to overcure. Shear strengths of bonds, measured in compression, range from 1000 to 9000 psi. Thus the strength of the material being bonded is frequently the limiting factor. These adhesives do not craze.

Polyester Resins. The polyester resins, which have been used in low-pressure molding, are mobile liquids or easily handled pastes containing no solvent, and by curing are transformed completely into solid, infusible, insoluble substances of considerable strength and almost devoid of any tendency to craze. Furthermore, they can be cured or set under a wide range of pressures down to and including no pressure at all. Obviously such a convenient substance would seem to make an ideal adhesive.

Thus far, however, their use as assembly adhesives has been concentrated in certain special fields. Polyester resins are relatively costly, but not more so than resorcinols and polyfunctional and polyamide types. They do not readily adhere to hydrophilic surfaces such as wood, paper or cotton fabrics without use of special techniques, and only recently have they been successfully set at room temperature. Their most important use as adhesives has been the bonding of cured polyester-resin laminates to each other and to metal, but as the variety of available types expands they seem likely to become important additions to the growing list of important assembly adhesives.

Manufacturers' recommendations must be carefully followed. Both cold-setting and hot-setting types are generally catalyzed just before use, with such agents as benzoyl peroxide or lauroyl peroxide. Cold-setting catalysts are frequently proprietary combinations tailormade to suit the resins, and must be used as directed.

Uncatalyzed resins keep well if stored in the dark at low temperature, but at room temperature they will slowly gel unless inhibited. Each producer specifies the keeping qualities of his particular resin. After the addition of catalyst, pot life may vary from about 4 to 48 hr. The adhesive may be spread by brush, spray, roller, or dipping. The coatings do not dry, and parts may be assembled immediately or from 16 to 24 hr later, according to the resin and catalyst. If a cold-setting type is used, the parts should be assembled as soon as possible after spreading. If parts coated with a hot-setting type are kept over night, they must be protected from air by overlaying with cellophane, which is easily removed before assembling.

Bonding pressures can be zero (contact) or up to 100 psi, but beyond about 15 to 20 psi care must be exercised to avoid squeezing too much adhesive out of the joint. Temperatures for curing range from about 75 to 300°F, depending on the type. Certain high temperature types are gelled at 180 to 210°F, and then, to develop utmost durability, crosslinked at 270 to 300°F.

Epoxy Resins. Epoxy or ethoxyline resins are the most recent development in thermosetting resins. While essentially thermoplastic in the uncured state, they can be converted by amines, anhydrides and other hardeners into essentially crosslinked polymers. Their outstanding characteristic is good adhesion to a wide variety of materials, notably glass and ceramics. This adhesion is accompanied by low shrinkage and high mechanical strength.

Curing can be done with contact or high pressures and is very dependent on the specific resin and hardener selected; thus a wide variety of working properties can be achieved. Temperatures for curing vary from room temperature to approximately 400°F. Resins are supplied as powders, fusible solid masses, or liquids. In working with metals, glass and ceramics, proper cleaning of surfaces is essential. Test data indicate that such adhesive systems possess good tensile, shear and impact strength, and good resistance to water and common chemicals. For certain purposes they may be extended or filled, but it is particularly important to follow closely the manufacturer's instructions as to formulation, mixing and use until these useful new adhesives are better understood.

Two disadvantages are high cost and difficulties with parting from the tooling used, due to their unique ability to adhere to most surfaces they touch. In addition, this general class of resins, unfortunately, has relatively low creep-resistance at elevated temperatures. It is expected that further development work will improve this weakness as well as lower the cost.

Extenders and Fillers. A discussion of assembly glues would not be complete without comment about the misunderstood agents generally known as extenders or fillers. Actually extenders and fillers serve different purposes, although some fillers may act as extenders.

The most common use of extenders and fillers has been as diluents for the more expensive resins to lower costs, and it is the abuse of this procedure which has brought them into disfavor, and with them even certain synthetic resin adhesives. Nevertheless, both extenders and fillers have real merit when properly used, and in some cases they are indispensable.

Common fillers are wood flour, nut-shell flour, infusorial (fuller's) earth, chopped glass fiber, powdered lignin, redwood bark, pulverized synthetic resins, and slate dust.

Fillers are valuable in certain cases for giving bulk to glue lines or desirable spreading properties to glues. Adhesives to be applied by silk-screen stencil generally will not stencil at all without fillers. Fillers frequently serve as reinforcing agents, and may be essential for maximum strength or craze-resistance. Current developments indicate that suitable use of appropriate fillers may greatly reduce the problem of bonding materials of highly dissimilar coefficients of expansion.

Common extenders are wheat and rye flours, soluble lignin, natural protein flours, pulverized partly-cured synthetic resins, and chopped, partly-cured, synthetic resin laminates.

Extenders actually have some adhesive action of their own, although it may be latent, i.e., may not develop except in the presence of a real adhesive. Here again, the principal use is to reduce cost, and the abuse of this practice carries with it the same penalties. But extenders are valuable also for modifying the physical properties of the glue line, and they frequently have reinforcing and anticrazing action as well.

The use of extenders and fillers in a manner which will not impair quality and durability is a complex subject, and is best left to the specific recommendations of the manufacturers of the resin adhesives. Many glues are formulated with the required amounts of such agents, not for purposes of cheapening, but as components essential to their proper functioning.

Function of the Glue

The function of the glue is to hold the parts together under the most extreme conditions of service to which the assembly may be subjected. Therefore, the glue line should be strong, preferably stronger than the weakest part, and should possess a high, reliable and determinable bond strength, both originally and after prolonged exposure to moisture, dryness, rot, heat, cold, mechanical stresses, sudden shock, vibrations, and any combination of these influences.

High original strength is a requirement of a good glue line, but, before an adhesive and a process are chosen for a job of assembly gluing, reasonable evidence should be developed to assure that the strength of the bond will be maintained in service.

It should be particularly noted, however, that improper assemblies, involving poor design, materials of widely different thermal or other physical properties, or unsound mating of parts, cannot be compensated for by even the best of adhesives.

Technique of Gluing

The proper technique of gluing with each resin adhesive is carefully developed by its manufacturer. Certain general rules are given here for using synthetic resin adhesives for assembly gluing, but it cannot be too strongly emphasized that each manufacturer's instructions should be very carefully followed, as different brands of even the same type of resin adhesive may require quite different mixing procedure, assembly time and curing conditions. The general information given below on storage of resin, preparation of surfaces, mixing, working life, spreading, assembly time, pressure, temperature, and aging applies to most resin adhesives for assembly gluing.

Storage. As a general rule, all resin adhesives should be stored in a cool, dry place. Some resins will react gradually at room temperature, and finally become too viscous to be usable, or become partially or wholly insoluble. The resorcinol-resin adhesives, phenol-resorcinols, furanes, emulsion-polymer adhesives, and mixtures of elastomer and thermoplastic resin are very tolerant of storage conditions, but some types have to be stored at low temperature, as recommended by the manufacturer. Quite often, the containers of such a resin bear a special label stating the safe upper limit of temperature in storage. Containers should be kept tightly closed, and labels kept clean for proper identification.

A record should be kept of the manufacturer's lot number so that it can be mentioned in any correspondence regarding the resin. It is a good idea to mark the date of receipt on each container, so that the oldest material will always be used first. Polyester resin adhesives must also be protected from light.

Preparation of Wood. In order that the adhesive may produce its expected bond, the surface of the wood must be clean and smooth and the moisture content must be within the proper range. A clean, freshly planed surface is excellent for bonding. Sometimes plywood which is highly compressed on the surface should be lightly sanded with the grain prior to gluing. After surfaces have been prepared for gluing, the wood should be handled as little as possible, and preferably glued within 8 hr. A good mechanical fit is very important, for joints having thick glue lines are inferior. There must be no grease, wax, dirt or other foreign material on the surface, for this would naturally prevent the adhesive from bonding properly. If a poor bond results which cannot be laid to obvious causes, the surface of the wood should be checked to see if it is water-repellent. If so, there may be wax, grease, or oil present as result of processing or of the use of primers, sealers or rot-inhibitors. The surface of the wood may be "nonpolar" from having been heated over 300°F, as is occasionally the case in thin plywood of some manufacture. Sanding will usually remedy either difficulty.

Most resin adhesives bond satisfactorily over a fairly wide range of moisture content. It is very important, however, that moisture content be held within the limits recommended by the manufacturer of the resin. This is particularly true in a gluing operation in which only one of the two surfaces is spread with adhesive. In this case it may be necessary to condition the unspread surface specially, in order to obtain a bond of the expected quality. Furthermore, the moisture content at the time of gluing should be approximately the same as it will be in service, to minimize the development of stresses by shrinkage or expansion. Most specifications call for a moisture content of 8 to 12 per cent, except for marine applications, where it may be a little higher. The moisture contents of different pieces of wood being glued to each other must be held very nearly the same. Trouble may be expected if they differ by more than two or three per cent.

Moisture content, i.e., the weight of water contained, expressed as percentage of the oven-dry weight, is best determined by the "oven dry" method which is widely used for airplane woods.

Oven Dry Method

Samples approximately 1 in. long are cut in the direction of the grain from representative boards. Samples are weighed immediately, before any drying takes place. They are then heated in an oven at 212°F to constant weight. The difference between the original weight (W_o) and the oven-dry weight (W_d), divided by the oven-dry weight, and multiplied by 100 is the percentage of moisture.

$$\frac{W_o - W_d}{W_d} \times 100 = \text{moisture content, per cent.}$$

Preparation of Metals. Metal surfaces to be bonded must be chemically clean and free of scale or loose deposits of oxide. Fortunately the water-film test is a reliable guide. Cold water is poured over the suspected surface and allowed to drain off. It should drain for at least 15 sec without showing any break in the film of water or any tendency of the film to crawl or pucker.

Sandblasting or other roughening may or may not be desirable, according to the adhesive used.

The manufacturer of the adhesive furnishes full instructions for cleaning the more common metals in preparation for bonding with his adhesive, but generally the procedure involves washing with solvent or degreasing with vapor if there is visible grease present. If this is not necessary, or even if it has been done, the metal is immersed in a hot alkaline cleaning bath, and scrubbed if necessary. This is followed by rinsing with fresh water, draining, and drying, preferably in a current of warm, clean air. Wiping should not be attempted. If speed is necessary, an "air knife" or "air squeegee" is used to remove rinse water quickly. For certain very critical bonds, a special acid dip followed by another rinse is interposed between the rinsing and the drying.

Certain manufacturers recommend omission of the alkaline bath, but this should be done only with approval of the manufacturer of the adhesive.

Cleaned metal should not be touched with bare hands and should be spread with adhesive within 8 hr after cleaning. Any doubt as to cleanness must be resolved by the water-film test.

Preparation of Plastics. Many plastics, particularly laminates, carry a thin film of parting agent on their surfaces. This and the normal gloss must be removed by sanding or sandblasting. This and a subsequent blast of clean, dry air to remove the dust are generally all that is required before spreading plastics with glue, but occasionally benefit is derived by priming the surface with a very dilute solution of the adhesive to be used.

Since some laminated plastics and some thermoplastics will not withstand the temperatures required by some of the new high-temperature crosslinking adhesives, it is well, before planning the use of such bonds, to make a test or to inquire of the manufacturer of the plastic involved.

Preparation of Rubber. In general, rubber to be bonded to rigid surfaces should first be cyclized on the surface, according to instructions of the manufacturer of the adhesive. Whether this is necessary is best ascertained by a test bond. One successful procedure for cyclizing rubber is as follows: after roughening the surface with sandpaper or some similar medium, the rubber is immersed for 10 min in concentrated sulfuric acid at 80°C, and then thoroughly washed with water to remove all trace of acid. It is then dried before applying adhesive.

Preparation of Sponges and End-Grain Woods. Rigid sponges, cellular hardboards and end-grain woods are given fresh cuts to eliminate dirt and contamination. A jet of clean air is then used to remove dust and particles of cut material.

It is almost mandatory to prime-coat the sponges and end-grain woods with a suitable priming adhesive, which may be a coat of the bonding adhesive itself. Some absorption of this coat is desired, and it may be necessary to cure it partially. The final glue line will then have a good foundation, with no

danger of starvation, and the surface layers of the sponge or wood will be reinforced. Cellular hardboards benefit by this treatment, but not as much. Furthermore, they are frequently composed of materials which poison the resin
glue, and they may have to be primed or washed with a solution of the catalyst
used with the resin.

Mixing. In mixing, the most important rule to follow is cleanliness.
Secondly, it is important to follow the maker's instructions. Keep scoops,
weighing pans, mixing paddles, pumps and pipe lines clean. Synthetic resin
glues which appear to be similar may be ruined if one is contaminated with the
other. The hardener used in one type may render another type unusable.
Water will spoil some mixtures, while the organic solvents used in other glues
may spoil the water-soluble ones. Exceptional care must be taken to remove
from mixing equipment all traces of animal, vegetable or casein glues when
such equipment is to be used for mixing resin glues. Copper or brass bowls
and paddles should not be used.

Keep the weighing equipment and measuring equipment clean and undamaged. Best results are obtained only by following the manufacturer's mixing formula. The weights, balances, and measuring vessels must be accurate.
Containers used for weighing glue, hardeners and water should have their
tare weights marked plainly on the outside. Containers for weighing glue
must not be interchanged with those for weighing water or other ingredients.
It is advisable to pick a workman with an aptitude for this work and to make
him responsible for the care of the equipment and the mixing. This will
minimize errors and encourage uniformity.

Particularly for weighing the small quantities of separate hardener
required by some glues, it will be found advisable to have a balance or scales
accurate at least to 15 grains or one-thirtieth of an ounce. Of course, the
water and the glue powder are better weighed on a larger balance, which can
be chosen after deciding what size of batches will be used. A general rule for
mixing, in a properly designed mixer, is to add the solvent or water to the
powder slowly. This keeps the mixture thick and, even though it takes more
mixer power, works out the lumps more quickly. If the glue is a thick syrup
which is to be thinned, stir the thinner or water gradually into the syrup. With
other equipment, better results may be obtained by adding the powdered glue
slowly to about two-thirds of the water while stirring moderately, continuing
the stirring until the mass is smooth and then adding the remainder of the
water and stirring to uniform consistency.

Some glues heat up during mixing. This may shorten their working life.
It is avoided by using a water-jacketed mixer or by mixing in a pail set in
cold water which is replaced as it becomes warmed.

The glue should be furnished to the workmen in clean containers, small
enough so that they will have none left beyond the time when the glue becomes
unusable. Waterproof paper drinking cups work satisfactorily. Containers
may be marked to show the hour at which they were distributed. Containers

and any unused glue should be collected at the end of the period recommended by the manufacturer.

Thinners and solvents other than water may be flammable or toxic or both. They should be stored in approved buildings, handled in approved containers and used under good ventilation with no possibility of flame or spark.

Evaporation before the glue is spread means loss of time and money. Simple encasing of equipment for mixing and spreading reduces the losses, and also decreases the hazards.

Working Life. Working life (pot life) is the period of time during which the adhesive is usable after it has been mixed. Naturally, adhesives that set at room temperature have a shorter working life than those requiring heat to set them. The temperature of the room affects working life; for example, an adhesive that has a working life of 6 hr at 70°F may have only 2 or 3 hr at 90°F. In general, at 70 to 75°F the room-temperature adhesives have a working life of from 2 to 4 hr and the intermediate-temperature adhesives of from 3 to 6 hr. Working life may be appreciably extended by having a cold water bath around the container. In almost all cases, the mixed adhesive is usable as long as it is sufficiently fluid to pour and spread properly. This provides a good safety factor. Manufacturers provide accurate information on safe working life of each adhesive at different temperatures.

Adhesives which contain organic solvents may thicken by simple evaporation. The remedy is suitable thinning. Those which set to a semigel by thixotropy may be restored by a few minutes of strong agitation.

Spreading. Synthetic resin glues of proper types will furnish the most durable bonds that can be made, if they are used properly. Using synthetic resin glues is no more difficult than using other glues. It is just a different procedure. A worker skilled enough to assemble wood parts correctly is sufficiently skilled to learn the minor differences in technique required by these glues.

Either one or both of the surfaces may be spread, but the techniques are different. The glue must be spread, and the parts brought together, quickly, so that the glue does not have a chance to thicken, either by evaporation, by loss of moisture to a porous part such as wood, or by partial setting, to such a point that the pressure will not be able to bring the parts into intimate contact, separated only by a very thin film of glue.

Although double spreading is preferred, i.e., coating of both of the surfaces to be joined, single spreading (coating only one surface) is generally adequate for hard, dense woods, metals, plastics, glass or other nonporous surfaces that do not soak up glue. In single spreading, the glue must be so fluid that it will readily wet the untreated surface when the two surfaces are brought together.

Double spreading is the safer method for open or porous woods or other porous materials that tend to soak up the glue. Double spreading is essential if the assembly period has to be prolonged, if the surfaces are rough, or if the surfaces present sharply sloping grain or end-grain or open cellular or sponge-like areas.

Application by machine (roller) and by brush are both satisfactory; the prime requisite is cleanliness. Spreaders with rubber rollers are preferred to steel rollers, as they give a uniform application. Application by spray is not recommended, as it requires far more skill than is justified by its advantages. The rubber on the rolls must be such that it will not be affected by the glue.

Sizing may sometimes be employed to advantage. On hard, dense woods and some plastics it facilitates the penetration of the resin into the surface. On soft, dry or porous woods or sponges and cellular boards it tends to prevent starvation of glue lines. Sizing is recommended for scarf joints, particularly where the slope is steep, or for gluing end grain.

Sizing, which is usually the regular glue in a considerably thinner mixture, should ordinarily be applied half an hour to an hour before the application of the glue itself, but the sizing coat should not be allowed to harden completely meanwhile, except in certain special cases.

The manufacturer's instructions regarding the quantity of resin adhesive to be spread on the surface should be followed. Actual tests prove that there is an optimum quantity for each adhesive on each species of wood. If insufficient adhesive is applied, the glue line is starved and the bond will be weak. If too much adhesive is applied, the glue line will be too thick and the bond may be weak. Best results are obtained when there is just sufficient glue to squeeze out into small beads along the edge when a suitable pressure is used.

In general, for a single spread, 40 to 50 lb per 1000 sq ft of joint area is satisfactory. Double spreading requires 25 to 35 lb on each surface, or a total of 50 to 70 lb.

Spreads of some of the newer polyfunctional adhesives are best specified and judged by the thickness of the dry film applied. This is because the solvents are too volatile to permit accurate weighing of the wet spread, and because frequently the glue line must be built up of a number of coats. In these types the thickness of the film of glue may be as low as 0.002 in. (total of both sides), but frequently is 0.006 to 0.010 in.

Assembly Time. If parts are put together immediately after the spreading, and pressure applied later, the procedure is called a closed assembly. In open assembly, the parts are not put together after being spread, but pressure follows immediately after the assembly. For some hard dense woods, metals and other nonporous materials, an open assembly is advisable in order to allow part of the solvent to evaporate.

Permissible assembly time is that which can be allowed between the application of the glue and the application of pressure, without risk of impairment of the quality of the bond. It is specified by the manufacturer, and varies inversely with the temperature of the room. The adhesive starts to dry and harden immediately after it has been spread. Running over the specified time is sure to prevent a good bond, by allowing premature setting of the adhesive or by permitting too much evaporation of water or solvent, which will thicken the glue prematurely, or cause a dry skin to form on the surface; dry, porous (thirsty) wood will also cause a premature thickening, by absorption of solvent. Either will cause poor bonds. Making the glue slightly more fluid (by using more water or solvent in the formula) and applying it slightly more thickly will help compensate for excessive evaporation, which occurs mainly in the winter, when rooms are steam-heated.

The room-temperature adhesives, since they set faster, naturally have shorter allowable assembly time than the intermediate-temperature adhesives. Drying is faster in open assembly than in closed, and hence the allowable time is shorter. In general, when the temperature of the room is 70 to 80°F, room-temperature adhesives have an allowable open-assembly time of from 10 to 15 min, and closed-assembly time of from 20 to 30 min. The intermediate-temperature adhesives under the same room conditions are limited to 30 to 45 min in open assembly and 60 to 90 min in closed.

Obviously, it is far safer to use too short an assembly time than too long a one. But there is one exception to this. Spreads of certain adhesives, such as the furane types, must be allowed to stand for a specified minimum time before assembly in order to produce a bond.

Two-Step Bonding. A new technique, known as two-step bond, is coming into use as the result of the development of mixtures of thermoplastics and other resins, or polyfunctional adhesives. Often the assembly must be glued cold, or for one reason or another it is not desired to use the high temperatures required by the polyfunctional adhesive. This is frequently the case if one part to be joined is metal and the other is wood or a plastic harmed by high temperatures.

In two-step bonding the cleaned metal is coated or primed with a film of the polyfunctional adhesive, which is then cured by baking in an oven, or between the platens of a partly open hot press or by means of a bank of radiant-heat (infrared) lamps. Subsequently, a cold-setting adhesive is spread on the primed metal and the other part, and the two are assembled in the usual way. Resorcinol resin glues are generally specified for the cold bonding.

Pressure

The objective of pressure is to bring into intimate contact the surfaces to be glued. It is obvious that a good mechanical fit is necessary and that surfaces must be smooth and regular to ensure close contact. Filling gaps with glue is never a satisfactory substitute for close contact achieved by proper preparation of the surfaces. The pressure must be sufficient to ensure perfect contact between surfaces which have been finished to a degree which is commercially practicable. This may mean, in some instances, pressures in excess of 150 psi on large flat surfaces of dense materials where some compression is necessary to ensure over-all contact.

Mechanical Pressure. What is called mechanical pressure is that produced by a concentrated source of pressure and uniformly distributed over a surface by means of rigid plates, but without automatic follow-up. For example, screw clamps (Fig. 18-1) may be used with a rigid caul on each side of the pressed assembly to ensure distribution of the pressure. As shown in the figure, blocks should be used in conjunction with clamps to distribute the pressure evenly. A layer of waxed paper between the pressure block and glued assembly will prevent gluing of the block to the parts being clamped. The distance between successive clamps should not be greater than twice the distance between surface and glue line on the thinner side of the lamination. For example, in gluing 1/4-in. plywood to 1-in. spruce, clamps should be spaced

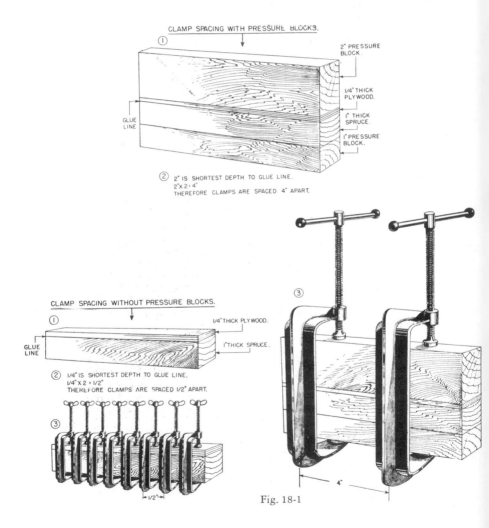

Fig. 18-1

not more than twice ¼ in., or ½ in. But putting a 2-in. pressure block on the plywood side and a 1-in. block on the spruce side enables the spacing to be increased to twice 2 in., or 4 in. Clamps and other pressure devices (except spring clamps and weights) should be kept closely adjusted for a short time after application of pressure to ensure that the full desired pressure is maintained.

Yoke clamps (Fig. 18-1A) are preferred in many cases when the two arms are capable of applying pressure. In laminating two assemblies with the same clamp, the toggle-head allows equal pressure on two assemblies that may differ slightly in thickness.

A rubber pad placed between the caul and the work gives some follow-up pressure, which is highly desirable.

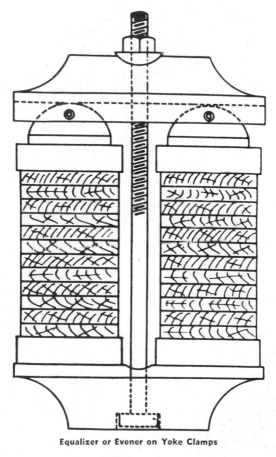

Equalizer or Evener on Yoke Clamps

Fig. 18-1A

Nail Pressure. Nail pressure, or nailing-strip pressure (Fig. 18-2), represents a practical approach where application of fluid or mechanical pressure is impracticable. Nailing-strip pressure is applied by driving nails through a narrow strip of wood so that the nails can be removed, after the adhesive has set, by pulling off the wood strip. Because of the variable techniques followed, it is not as positive as mechanical or fluid pressure. Pressure is highly concentrated at the nail and decreases sharply at a small distance.

Nailing-Strip Pressure

Fig. 18-2

However, since in many cases this method represents the only practicable means of applying pressure, it is widely used. Nail pressure has proven reasonably satisfactory for the attachment of light members to heavier construction, such as plywood skins to aircraft wing sections. It has been recommended that for such constructions the nails be spaced one inch apart in a row, that there be one row for each one-half inch width of base member, and that the nails in adjacent rows be staggered. Nails should reach at least 3/8 in. into the heavier member. Since the pressure initially applied to the glue joints tends to decrease as the glue squeezes out from between the layers or distributes itself in the joint, all nails in nailing strips should be reset before the gluing operation is completed. Heavy glue lines are an indication of irregular or inadequate pressure, or of uneven surface, or a combination of these.

While the merits of this method of applying pressure to an assembly are disputed, and in some cases it might be found better to use an alternative means of joining members, rather than resin adhesives, the practice is widely used and does represent a means found practicable in many cases.

An analogous procedure may be used in joining metal to metal or metal to plastics, when the assembly is too complex to permit easy application of pressure. Rivets or screws are used in place of nails. This procedure is used also where extreme reliability of bond is required, as in aircraft. The rivets prevent initial slip, and the glue bond takes the high distributed loads without local distortion or tearing at the rivet holes.

Dead-Weight Pressure. Pressure may be applied in many instances simply by the application of dead weight (Fig. 18-3), such as sand bags or weights attached to straps which hold the assembly firmly in place. These means are

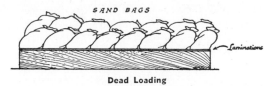

Dead Loading

Fig. 18-3

recommended only where it is impossible to apply hydraulic or fluid pressure, which are more positive and generally provide greater unit pressure.

Spring-Loaded Jigs. Spring-loaded jigs are a very desirable means of furnishing gluing pressure because of their natural following action. They are, however, rather complex for large parts and their cost is not justified unless many of the same part are to be glued.

Hydraulic Presses. Hydraulic presses give a controllable pressure over the whole area, provided proper precautions are taken to ensure even distribution of pressure.

Continued application of pressure, controlled by gauge readings, is to be preferred, but sometimes this is impracticable and the practice is to apply initial pressure hydraulically and then to clamp the assembly. Since slow plastic compression takes place, it is necessary in some cases to reapply pressure hydraulically, or to tighten the clamps, before the adhesive gels. Hydraulic jacks (Fig. 18-4), or presses, are widely used in assembly gluing. They are most satisfactory for a permanent jig or pressure mechanism, but are not readily portable.

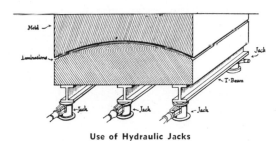

Use of Hydraulic Jacks

Fig. 18-4

Inflated-Hose (Semifluid) Pressure. Simple or complex assemblies may be pressed in a jig actuated by means of pressure of an inflated hose (Fig. 18-5). This method is most effective where compressibility of the material being glued is slight and the hose can be inflated in such a way that its cross-section remains flat rather than circular. General practice is to use mechanical means of bringing the assembly into contact with the hose in its deflated state.

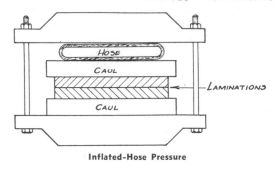

Inflated-Hose Pressure

Fig. 18-5

Then the hose is inflated and applies pressure. It is important that the cauls and blocks used in distributing the pressure be rigid enough to prevent deflection.

Fluid Pressure. Fluid pressure (Fig. 18-6) is pressure applied uniformly over, and normal to, an entire surface of irregular contour. A fluid medium is the most satisfactory means of applying pressure in the manufacture of curved plywood, the molding of plastic skins, the forming of cores, the gluing of

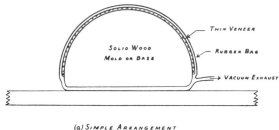

(a) SIMPLE ARRANGEMENT
FOR FORMING AND GLUING THIN VENEER WITH VACUUM BAG

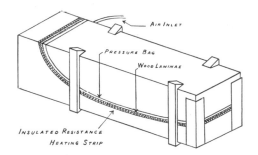

(b) TYPICAL FLUID PRESSURE JIG FOR GLUING LAMINATED PARTS

Fluid Pressure

Fig. 18-6

curved laminated sections and scarf joints, the gluing of molded plastic skins or preformed cores to another assembly, and the gluing of molded plywood or molded plastic to preshaped metal. For example, resin-coated thin veneers are fittted over a male form, the entire assembly is placed in a rubber bag, and the air is evacuated by a vacuum pump to subject the assembly to a differential pressure of about 14 psi which shapes the veneers to the exact contour of the mold.

Where thicker sections are involved, that require pressures higher than atmospheric to ensure intimate contact of the bonding surfaces, the bag may be restrained on one side by a rigid member and expanded against the assembly by the use of air, hot water, or steam. Resistance heating may be used in conjunction with air to speed up the setting of the adhesive and reduce the curing cycle to a matter of minutes instead of hours.

Heating

In some cases, it is desirable to hasten the setting of assembly glues by heating. Since the setting of synthetic resin glues is a chemical reaction, its rate is greatly influenced by even a small change in temperature. For example, a glue which sets in 4 hr at 70°F may set in 30 min at 110°F, and requires only 4 or 5 min at 160°F.

Many methods have been devised for concentrating heat on the glue line, but a complete description is not possible here. The following are the common methods employed.

Hot Platens. The simplest method of applying heat to work which is flat or of simple curvature is by the use of metal platens heated by steam or electricity and brought into contact with the work (Fig. 18-7). They serve also as a means of applying pressure. Their possibilities are limited by the size and shape of the assembly, by the difficulty of obtaining uniform contact in large curved areas, and by the cost of changes in complex shapes. They have the

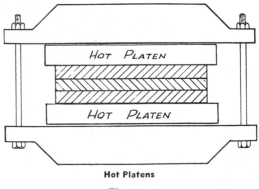

Hot Platens

Fig. 18-7

advantages of giving rapid and efficient transfer of heat to thin assemblies, and of ease of loading and unloading.

Oven Heating. Oven heating (Fig. 18-8) of assemblies is sometimes the only practicable method, particularly for complex shapes. If wood is involved, this method generally requires control of humidity, to prevent the wood from drying out. Metal clamps are apt to expand in the oven, and thus cause loss of pressure, but spring clamps may not fail in this way. If mechanical clamps are used, they should be retightened before the adhesive starts to gel.

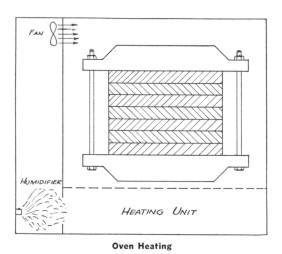

Oven Heating

Fig. 18-8

Since the rate of transfer of heat is low, oven heating necessitates long periods for curing, which may seriously reduce production unless the structure is so complex that the time for assembling far exceeds the time for curing. Where volume of production is important, some other method of heating is used if possible.

For curing bonds of metal to metal, or of other materials not disturbed by loss of moisture, oven heating is much simpler and more reliable. However, all too often, not enough attention is paid to ensuring uniformity of temperature throughout the oven, or to the speed and effectiveness of the circulation of air. A thermocouple traverse of a loaded oven should be run to make sure that the temperature is as required.

Increasing the rate of circulation of air will improve efficiency of heating and shorten the time of cure. Air, which is normally very poor heating medium, approaches steam in efficiency only at very high velocities.

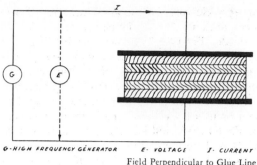

G - HIGH FREQUENCY GENERATOR   E - VOLTAGE   I - CURRENT

Field Perpendicular to Glue Line

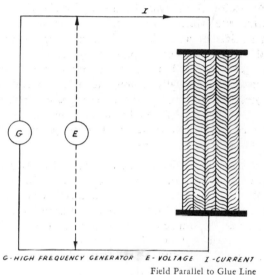

G - HIGH FREQUENCY GENERATOR   E - VOLTAGE   I - CURRENT

Field Parallel to Glue Line

G - HIGH FREQUENCY GENERATOR   E - VOLTAGE   I - CURRENT
B - PARTS BEING GLUED IN STRAY-FIELD

Stray Field

High Frequency

Courtesy Steinway and Sons

Fig. 18-9

High-Frequency Heating. Since wood and many plastics are not good conductors of heat, thick sections can be heated only slowly by application of heat from the outside. But high-frequency current (Fig. 18-9) properly applied can accomplish a rapid, uniform heating of wood, and many plastics, in thick sections, and thereby reduce curing times from hours to minutes.

It is significant that heat is developed uniformly and rapidly. This method of dielectric heating is used successfully in commercial applications at present, and a broad field of uses is indicated. Each application requires a study of proper shape of the electrode and other significant factors, together with the cost in comparison with costs by other processes.

Insulation of one of the electrodes from the work is generally desirable, to avoid a combination of resistance heating and dielectric heating.

The considerable controversy over the practical merits of this new technique is being resolved by accumulation of practical experience, which indicates that abuse and misapplication of the process have been to blame for its faults. For example, high-frequency heating used improperly may heat the glue line beyond the temperature normally recommended for the cure of the adhesive, and cause "frying" or "boiling" of the adhesive, which results in a powdery glue film and a poor bond. On the other hand, if normal cycles are used, it is increasingly evident that high-frequency heating produces excellent bonds, under proper conditions.

Resistance-Heating. Resistance-heating (Fig. 18-10) may be considered as a modification of the heating with a hot platen. By means of electrical resistance, heat is generated in thin strips of metal which may be placed in direct contact with glued assemblies. Since the resistance-heaters are generally thin strips, they may be shaped to the contours of a reasonably complex assembly. Resistance strips are subject to the limitation of the charring temperature of the wood, but constitute a very flexible means of applying heat to complex shapes.

Infrared Heating. Infrared or radiant-energy heating (Fig. 18-11) differs from convection heating principally in that it is not necessary to heat the air first, and then have the air heat the work. Infrared heat travels directly

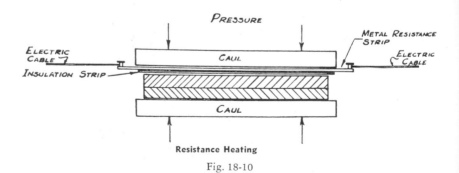

Resistance Heating

Fig. 18-10

from the source to the work. The work absorbs the infrared radiant energy and becomes heated. Infrared radiation is reflected by bright metals and so may be focused for spot heating, to provide a high concentration of heat at a desired point on the assembly. The use of radiant heat hastens materially the heating of the structure.

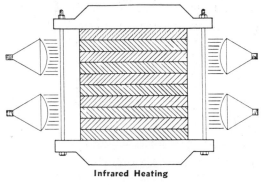

Infrared Heating

Fig. 18-11

Boiling-Water or Steam Bath. Solids, such as wood, have a film of air on their surface which acts as an insulator in convection heating, as in an oven. Bringing a heated material, such as steam or water, into direct contact with the surface eliminates this film, and rapid heating results. To accomplish this, it is possible to use a boiling-water bath (Fig. 18-12) or a steam tent. In the former, the clamped assembly is immersed in a tank of boiling water during the curing period. The steam tent (Fig. 18-13) is simply a canvas hood into which the clamped assembly is moved, and into which steam is introduced.

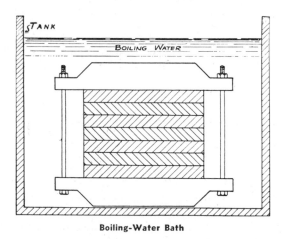

Boiling-Water Bath

Fig. 18-12

The steam produces only very slight changes in the moisture content of the assembly. Speeding up the air in an oven has the same effect of removing the insulating film of air at the surface.

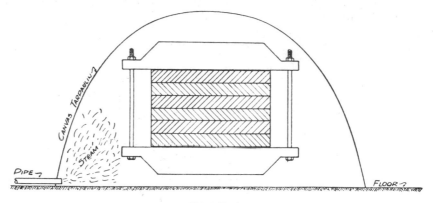

Steam Tent
Fig. 18-13

Conductive Rubber. Conductive rubber blankets (Fig. 18-14) are useful in certain cases. Current applied at the edge of the blanket heats the rubber. These blankets provide a heat-source of extreme flexibility, since they can be applied to complex shapes. Usefully high temperatures may be obtained.

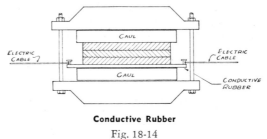

Conductive Rubber
Fig. 18-14

Aging

The manufacturers of adhesives state the minimum pressure periods for different temperatures; i.e., the minimum times as given by individual manufacturers will result in a bond sufficiently strong to withstand handling at the time pressure is released. However, the maximum bond strength does not develop in this time. The resin adhesive continues to polymerize for several days, during which time the strength of the bond increases. For this reason most specifications call for an aging period of a few days before making shear tests. Likewise, it is generally advisable to handle the assembly carefully if pressure is removed after the minimum cure period.

Suppliers

The following list of suppliers produce synthetic resin adhesives for assembly gluing. Some of them also produce resin adhesives for bonding plywood. This is not a complete list of suppliers of adhesives for plywood.

Supplier	Trade Name	Type of Adhesive
American Cyanamid Co. 30 Rockefeller Plaza New York 20, New York	Beetle Urac Melmac Melurac Laminac	urea urea melamine melamine-urea polyester
Armstrong Products Company Argonne Road Warsaw, Indiana		epoxy

Bakelite Co.
30 E. 42nd Street
New York 17, New York
	Vinylite
	
	Bakelite
	Bakelite
	Bakelite
	
	Bakelite
		vinyl acetate
		    emulsion polymer
		phenolic
		urea
		resorcinol and
		    phenol-resorcinol
		crosslinking resin mixtures

Barrett Division Allied Chemical & Dye Corp. Plaskon Laboratories Box 27, Station I Toledo 14, Ohio	Plaskon Plaskon Plaskon	urea polyester phenolic
B. B. Chemical Company 784 Memorial Drive Cambridge, Massachusetts	Bostik	elastomer and resin
The Borden Company Chemical Division 350 Madison Avenue New York 17, New York	Cascophen Cascamite Cascorez Casco Epiphen	phenolic, resorcinol urea resin emulsions elastomers epoxy
Catalin Corporation of America 1 Park Avenue New York 16, New York	Catabond Catabond Catabond	phenolic urea resorcinol
Chrysler Corporation Cycleweld Division Detroit, Michigan	Cycleweld Cycleweld Cycleweld	elastomer and resin epoxy crosslinking resin mixtures
Ciba Company, Inc. 627 Greenwich Street New York 14, New York	Araldite	epoxy

Durez Plastics & Chemicals, Inc.	Durez	phenolic
North Tonawanda, New York	Durez	resorcinol
	Durez	phenol-resorcinol
	Durez	furane
Goodyear Tire and Rubber Company	Pliobond	elastomer and resin
Chemical Products Division		
Akron, Ohio		
Irvington Varnish & Insulator Co.	Fura-tone	furane
17 Argyle Terrace		
Irvington 11, New Jersey		
Koppers Company, Inc.	Penacolite	resorcinol
Chemical Division	Penacolite	phenol-resorcinol
Koppers Building		
Pittsburgh 19, Pennsylvania		
Le Page's, Inc.	Le Page's	
40 Swanson Street	Resin Adhesive	urea
Gloucester, Massachusetts		
The Marblette Corp.	Marblette	phenolic
37-21 30th Street		
Long Island City 1, New York		
Minnesota Mining and Mfg. Co.	3-M	elastomer and resin
900 Fauquier Avenue		
St. Paul 6, Minnesota		
Monsanto Chemical Company	Lauxite	phenolic
Plastics Division	Lauxite	urea
Springfield 2, Massachusetts	Lauxite	melamine
	Lauxite	resorcinol
WESTERN DIVISION:		
911 Western Avenue		
Seattle 4, Washington		
National Casein Company		phenolic
601 West 80th Street		resorcinol
Chicago 20, Illinois		urea
		vinyl
Perkins Glue Company	Perkins	urea
44 Lake Street	Perkins	melamine-urea
Lansdale, Pennsylvania	Perkins	phenol-resorcinol
Pittsburgh Plate Glass Company	Selectron	polyester
2207 Grant Building		
Pittsburgh 19, Pennsylvania		
Reichhold Chemicals, Inc.	Plyophen	phenolic
601-607 Woodward Heights Blvd.	Plyophen	resorcinol
Detroit 20, Michigan	Plyophen	crosslinking resin mixtures
	Beckamine	urea

Resinous Products Division	Paraplex	polyester
Rohm & Haas Company	Tego	phenolic
Washington Square	Amberlite	phenolic
Philadelphia 5, Pennsylvania	Uformite	urea
	Amberlite	resorcinol
	Redux	crosslinking resin mixtures

Shell Chemical Corporation	Epon	epoxy
50 West 50th Street		
New York 20, New York		

Snyder Chemical Corporation	Synco	phenolic
Henry Street		
Bethel, Connecticut		

Swift & Company	Glubond	emulsion polymer
Glue Division		
3200 Union Stock Yards		
Chicago 9, Illinois		

Synvar Corporation	Synvaren	phenolic
415 E. Front Street	Synvarite	urea
Wilmington, Delaware	Synvarol	urea

United States Plywood Corporation	Weldwood	urea
55 West 44th Street	USP Phenol	
New York 18, New York	Resorcinol	phenol-resorcinol
	Plycozite	crosslinking resin mixtures
	Weldwood	thermoplastic emulsion
	Prestoset	resin
	Weldwood	elastomer resin
	Contact	
	Cement	

The United States Stoneware Company	Reanite	crosslinking resin mixtures
Plastics and Synthetics Division	Tygobond	vinyl-elastomer
Box 350	Tygonite	rubber-resin mixture
Akron 9, Ohio	Duralon	furane resin

Glossary of Trade Terms Used in the Industry

The brief definitions in this glossary are either general terms that have acquired a special meaning, or relatively new phrases that have been recognized recently in the industry. The terminology of the flexible-bag molding technique has been included.

A

adhesive . . . . A broader term than *glue,* which ordinarily does not include the recently developed resin adhesives. Adhesion is defined as the sticking together of substances in contact. Cf. *resin* and *glue.*

aging of plywood . . . .   A term used to designate the period, usually a
   (conditioning period)   matter of days, after the initial adhesive grip
   has become effective, and until the joint has
developed approximately its maximum strength,
and is suitable for testing. Another use of this
term is to express months or years of service or
extended exposure tests.

albumin, blood . . . . .   See *glue.*

all-veneer construction . .   Plywood without lumber cores, more frequently
multiple for strength requirements, often 7-ply
or 9-ply, to equal the thickness of conventional
lumber-core plywood. The maximum thickness
of any single sheet of veneer seldom exceeds
$\frac{1}{4}$ in.

animal glue . . . . . .   See *glue.*

assembly . . . .   The collection of and placing together in proper
order of the layers of veneer, lumber and/or
other materials, with the adhesive, ready to be
pressed and bonded into a single unit.

assembly glue . . . . . .   Denotes glues and adhesives used for assembling
parts together, as in airplanes and boats. Often
called *secondary* gluing (q.v.).

assembly time . . . . .   Usually refers to the elapsed time after the
adhesive is spread and until the pressure be-
comes effective.

autoclave . . . .   A cylindrical welded or riveted tank of suitable
size and strength to withstand the necessary
molding pressures for the flexible-bag process.
Also called *cooker* (q.v.).

B

back . . . .   Usually the rear or unexposed surface of a plywood sheet that requires normal strength, but
does not demand any selection for appearance.
Should be reasonably equivalent to the *face*
(q.v.) in thickness and strength.

bag . . . .   Flexible container in the molding process which
encloses the *layup* during the *cooking* (q.v.).

balanced construction . .   Plywood which has an odd number of plies, and
is symmetrical on both sides of its center line.

bale, or bundle . . . . . . A bundle or package of freshly glued (cold-pressed) plywood, held together by *clamp irons* (q.v.) after removal from the cold press. The bale is kept under pressure until initial adhesion is accomplished.

bastard-sawn . . . . . . Lumber or veneer, usually hardwood, in which the annual growth rings make angles of 30 to 60 degrees with the surface of the piece.

blanket . . . . Veneers which have all been laid up on a flat table. The complete assembly is placed on or in the mold all at one time; useful only on simple curved surfaces to be molded by the flexible-bag process. Also used to denote a form of "bag" made of rubber in which the edges are sealed against the mold by clamps.

bleeding . . . . Permitting the escape of a portion of the steam-air mixture during *cooking* (q.v.) to permit mixing of the steam and air and to maintain uniform temperature at all levels in the autoclave, when molding with flexible pressure.

blister (gluing error) . . A spot or area where the veneer does not adhere and bulges like a blister. It may be caused by lack of glue or adhesive or inadequate pressure. In hot pressing it may be caused by a pocket of steam, which often ruptures the veneer. In flexible-bag operations, an unglued area in one layer due to failure to vent the bag, or to excess moisture.

blood glue . . . . See *glue, albumin.*

bond . . . . The grip of the adhesive on the wood, at the line of its application.

butt joint . . . . See *joint.*

C

casein . . . . See *glue.*

catalyst . . . . Hardener for resin adhesives. A reagent that accelerates a chemical reaction, with or without heat. In the case of resinous adhesives, it accelerates setting or hardening.

caul, aluminum . . . . . Used in hot pressing, approximately $\frac{1}{16}$ in. thick and the size of the hot-press platens. Plywood assemblies are inserted between pairs of cauls, to facilitate loading the press, and to protect plywood faces from contact with the steel plates of the hot press. Earlier, plywood cauls were used in hot pressing, $\frac{1}{16}$ to $\frac{1}{4}$ in. thick. They were replaced by aluminum for quicker work and better durability.

caul, canvas-covered plywood . . . . A special type of plywood caul used in *progressive gluing* (q.v.), to control heat and moisture. Also used for two-plying fragile veneer faces in hot presses.

cauls, plywood . . . . . Used in cold-pressing with conventional glues, to assure undamaged faces and to prevent transmission of defects to adjacent assemblies. Usually $\frac{1}{4}$ to $\frac{3}{8}$ in. thick, with waxed surfaces to prevent adhesion. See also above.

cement . . . . A term sometimes used for *glue, liquid* (q.v.). In flexible-bag molding, the adhesive used to make the seams or patch the bag.

checks . . . . Small hair-line splits running parallel to the grain of the wood, caused chiefly by stresses produced in seasoning.

clamp irons . . . . . . The pressure-maintenance equipment, which includes the "I" beams or double channel irons, together with clamp screws or turnbuckle rods, to hold bales under pressure after cold gluing.

cold-pressing . . . . . . A term used to describe a glue or adhesive that does not require heat to set or harden. There should be no emphasis on cold; it merely expresses the absence of heat. Most so-called cold-setting glues and adhesives require minimum temperatures of 70°F to set in a reasonable time.

compound curve . . . . A surface curved in more than one direction, as a sphere or eggshell shape.

compregnated wood . . . **("Compreg")** **("Pregwood")** **("Jicwood")** A consolidation of the terms, compressed-impregnated wood, referring usually to an assembly of layers of veneer impregnated with a liquid resin and bonded under very high pressures. More commonly, but not always, the veneer layers have parallel grain, i.e., laminated wood construction. *"Jicwood"* is the term used in England.

conditioning period . . . See *aging*.

cooker . . . . See *autoclave;* also describes a workman who operates an *autoclave* in flexible-bag molding.

cooking . . . . Heating the assembled veneers or layup in flexible-bag molding to set or cure the adhesive.

cores, or centers . . . . . A term usually applied to the central layer of plywood, which in *lumber-core construction* (q.v.) is the principal strength factor. It is also applied to veneer cores. The term is sometimes used in the Pacific Northwest to designate the layer that is spread with glue, which agrees with the above in 3-ply, but is inconsistent when applied to 5-ply. Under this usage, *Center* is reserved to indicate the middle ply. *Core* may also refer to the remaining part of the log, too small to be cut into rotary veneer on a lathe.

crossbanding . . . . . . The transverse veneer layers that distinguish plywood from *laminated wood* (q.v.). Their presence counteracts the tendency of wood to split, as well as to shrink and swell. In standard 5-ply construction, it is the layer between the face and the core, and between the back and the core, sometimes called *"face crossing"* and *"back crossing,"* respectively.

cure of resin . . . . . . See *polymerization*. Also refers to hardening of cement in making flexible bags.

cycle tests . . . . A method of exposing plywood to alternating wet and dry conditions as a basis of determining waterproofness and durability.

D

doctor roll or bar . . . . A device for regulating the amount of liquid glue on the rollers of the spreader.

doping . . . . Coating the mold or mandrel with a substance which will prevent the molded plywood part from sticking to it, and will facilitate easy removal.

double spread . . . . . See *spread*.

E

edge joint . . . . See *joint*.

electrostatic heat . . . . See *high-frequency field*.

epoxy resin . . . . This is also known as an ethoxyline resin and is a thermosetting synthetic resin. See *resin*.

equilibrium moisture content . . . . The moisture content at which wood neither gains nor loses moisture when surrounded by air at a given relative humidity and temperature.

extenders . . . . Substances having some adhesive properties of their own and used as auxiliary ingredients in adhesives, either to reduce cost or to modify the action and behavior of the adhesives.

exterior-DFPA . . . . . A grade designation of the Douglas Fir Plywood Association for plywood made with waterproof glue, and intended for permanent exterior exposure.

F

face . . . . The veneer on the exposed surface of the plywood. Where attractive appearance is required, the figure of the veneer is carefully selected and matched. In plywood designed for strength, the emphasis on appearance is subordinated to that of strength. In some locations, like buffet doors, both sides must be of pleasing character, with more careful selection on the exterior side.

fillers . . . . Substances having no adhesive properties of their own, and used as auxiliary ingredients in adhesives, to reduce cost, to add bulk, or to modify the action and behavior of the adhesive.

film . . . . A thin, dry sheet of paper impregnated with a phenol-formaldehyde resin adhesive. *Film* sometimes is used to refer to a liquid coating of adhesive.

fixed pressure . . . . . . See *pressure*.

flat grain . . . . Grain produced in approximately a tangential direction, or plain-cut veneers.

flexible pressure . . . . . See *pressure*.

fluid pressure . . . . . . See *pressure*.

follow-up pressure . . . . See *pressure*.

formed plywood . . . . The term is more correctly applied to non-flat or curved plywood, that is formed between pairs of metal dies, in contrast to *molded plywood* (q.v.), which is made with flexible pressure on molds or mandrels. In this case, the flexible bag constitutes one half of the mold.

G

glue . . . . A term customarily applied to the older conventional cold-setting plywood adhesives, viz.:

> ALBUMIN as now used for adhesive purposes is more correctly called *soluble dried blood*. It is mixed cold and usually coagulated (set) under heat, but sometimes by chemical reagents. It is highly water-resistant, but little used. Blood is used also as an extender with other adhesives.

> ANIMAL GLUE is a derivative of bone and hide waste, usually prepared by cooking. Its application is best accomplished in a warm room with temperature of glue solution at approximately 140°F. It softens under moisture, and eventually becomes resoluble.

> CASEIN is a dried milk product, mixed cold with lime, a sodium salt and other ingredients. Its action on edge tools is abrasive, and it is weakened by soaking in water.

> JOINT GLUE is any type of glue or adhesive that may be used to bond edges, ends or surfaces together.

> LIQUID GLUE is a prepared liquid adhesive or cement, usually sold at retail. Many types have fish by-products as their base. Not important in the plywood industry.

> RESIN ADHESIVES, see *resin*.

> SILICATE OF SODA is a derivative of sand and soda ash, used with other ingredients for low-cost plywood.

> SOYA-BEAN meal is the residue of soya bean after the oil has been removed. It is

mixed cold with caustic, lime and other substances. It can be applied on wet veneers, but is likely to stain delicately-colored face veneers. It is a vegetable protein and, like casein, it is partly resoluble in water.

VEGETABLE GLUE is a starch product, usually with a cassava-root flour base. It is prepared by cooking with caustic and cooled before use. It is widely used in the furniture and plywood industries, as it gives an excellent bond dry, but it delaminates quickly under moisture.

glue joint . . . . That part of an aggregated product which comprises the adhesive (or glue) and the parts in contact therewith.

gluing, primary and secondary . . . . . . See *secondary gluing*.

gluing, progressive . . . See *progressive gluing*.

grain . . . . A rather general term applied to vertical elements of wood as it occurs in the living tree. Grain is, perhaps, most easily distinguished in certain woods by the presence of annual layers of more densely aggregated cells or by groups of prominent vessels which form the well-known growth rings. When these are severed, they may become quite conspicuous, and the effect produced is referred to as grain.

H

hairline . . . . A thin perceptible glue line, usually showing at a surface joint.

hardener for resin adhesives . . . . . . See *catalyst*.

hardwoods . . . . A general term used to designate lumber or veneer produced from broad-leafed or deciduous trees in contrast with the so-called softwoods, produced from evergreen or coniferous trees.

head block, or retainer board . . . A thick (3 to 5 in.) large piece of laminated lumber, usually with veneer crossings, used for bottom and top of a bale of plywood, during pressing and clamping.

heart, or heartwood . . . The darker-colored wood substance occurring in the center of the tree.

high-density plywood . . Plywood of special construction, made at high specific pressure, usually 500 lb and up. With the increase in pressure comes a corresponding increase in density, or specific gravity.

high-frequency field . . . A method of generating heat in an electrostatic field between electrodes connected to a high-frequency circuit. It is useful in thick assemblies where the entire assembly can be heated in a much shorter time than is possible by applying external heat from hot plates.

humidity (relative) . . . This term is used correctly to express the relative amount of moisture in air, compared to that which the air could hold if saturated at the same temperature. It should not be confused with *moisture content* (q.v.) of wood. It is determined by wet-and-dry bulb thermometer readings, but there must be active air circulation around the wet bulb.

J

jelly strength . . . . . . A method of evaluating animal glue grades.

joint or glue joint . . . . The meeting line between the edges, ends or surfaces of two adjacent pieces of wood.

BUTT JOINT describes a square joint at right angles to the grain in face veneers, or in other wood layers, as contrasted to a *scarfed joint.*

EDGE JOINT is parallel to the grain of the wood and usually square, but sometimes scarfed at an angle.

LAP JOINT is one in which the ends or edges may overlap without scarfing.

OPEN JOINT is one in which there is a visible opening at the point of joining.

PLYWOOD JOINT is the surface at which layers of veneer and lumber are bonded together with an adhesive or glue.

SCARFED JOINT is an angling or beveled joint, in veneer, lumber or plywood where pieces are spliced together. The length of the scarf is usually 12 to 20 times the thickness.

When properly made, scarf joints may be nearly as strong as the adjacent unspliced material.

STARVED JOINT is an expression used to indicate an inadequate amount of glue or adhesive, either because of insufficient spread, too rapid absorption into the wood surface, or, with dense woods, too much pressure.

SUNKEN JOINT is a term describing small, straight depressions in the plywood surface, directly above the joints in the lumber core, or in the crossbanding. This is caused by inadequate drying of the glue solvent before planing lumber cores, or by uneven thickness of the crossband veneer.

K

kiln . . . . Heating apparatus intended for drying. Sometimes applied to a drier or redrier, used to remove moisture from veneer, lumber or plywood.

L

laminated wood . . . . . An assembly of wood layers in which the wood grain or the fibres of the adjacent layers are parallel; contrasted with *plywood* (q.v.), which is characterized by cross layers or crossings, usually alternated with the parallel face, core and back layers.

lap joint . . . . See *joint, lap.*

layup . . . . In hot-press operation, the operation of assembling the various layers of veneer or lumber cores, after the glue or adhesive has been applied or inserted, and before pressing. In *molded plywood,* the veneers coated with adhesive, after the wrapping around the mold has been completed but before *cooking* (q.v.).

lumber-core construction . As contrasted with *all-veneer construction* (q.v.). The central layer is of lumber, usually edge-glued together from narrow (2- to 3-in.) strips. Lumber cores are seldom less than ⅜ in. thick, and give a lengthwise stiffness to the plywood, as well as a freedom from warp, that is not achieved by all-veneer construction.

M

mandrel . . . . Another less common term, in flexible-bag work, for *mold* (q.v.).

mixer, for adhesives
and glue . . . . An open drumlike vessel with a tapering bottom, provided with revolving blades to stir the mixture. There are two types: single or double blades on a vertical shaft; and semicircular bars on a horizontal shaft, turning inside of each other.

moisture content . . . . The amount (by weight) of water in wood (veneer or plywood), computed as a percentage on the oven-dry weight of the wood. The use of the term in connection with atmospheric *humidity* (q.v.) leads to serious confusion.

mold . . . . In flexible-bag work, the matrix upon which the plywood molding is done; generally built up of sections of soft wood glued together and shaped accurately; may be either male or female and is sometimes made of metal, concrete or plaster.

molded plywood . . . . The term is more correctly applied to curved and *monocoque* (q.v.) plywood constructions where pressure is exerted by a flexible bag. Contrasted to *formed plywood* (q.v.).

molding pressure . . . . See *pressure*.

monocoque . . . . . . A stressed-shell construction in aircraft. Usually made of *molded plywood* (q.v.), without frame members. If a minimum framework is used, it is sometimes called *semimonocoque*.

O

open joint . . . . See *joint*.

P

phenolic resin . . . . . See *resin*.

platens . . . . The heat-bearing plates of the *hot press* (q.v.). Usually of rolled steel, with drilled holes in intersecting gridiron patterns, for steam distribution.

ply . . . . A sheet or layer of veneer.

plywood . . . . An assembled product, made of layers of veneer and/or lumber and adhesive, the chief characteristic of which is the alternate cross layers, distributing the longitudinal strength of the wood. This product cannot be split, and shrinking and swelling, under the influence of moisture, is a minimum. Cf. *laminated wood,* which has no cross layers.

Plywood processes may be employed to assemble the layers of laminated wood, and both are usually made in a plywood factory.

There are also groups of intermediate construction, predominantly laminated, but with a limited number of crossings conferring plywood characteristics.

polymerization . . . . . The change that takes place when heat-hardenable (thermosetting) resins are subjected to heat, rendering them hard, strong and insoluble in water. Frequently called the curing of a resin. Cf. *setting* in conventional gluing procedure, which, however, is ordinarily accomplished by a loss of moisture.

pre-sizing . . . . See *sizing.*

press, cold . . . . A hydraulic or screw press, in which the glued members are forced together. The pressure is maintained, after removal from the press, by clamping the bale or bundle of glued members between head-blocks, with *clamp irons* (q.v.) and turnbuckle rods.

press, hot . . . . A multiplaten hydraulic press with plates or platens heated by steam, for thermosetting resin adhesives. When using thermoplastic resins, cold-water connections are provided, for circulating cooled water in the steam areas.

press, hydraulic . . . . . Platen press operated by hydraulic pressure. Accurate regulation of pressure is practicable.

press, screw . . . . . . A simple press in which the manual or mechanical turning of a screw exerts the pressure required to bond layers of veneer or lumber into plywood or laminated wood. Used only for cold-pressing. Regulation of pressure is difficult.

pressure . . . . This term varies in its application, viz.:

> FIXED — Pressure that is exerted by rigid clamps that have no follow-up to compensate for the yielding of the wood.
>
> FLEXIBLE or FLUID—Such pressure is exerted by inflating or deflating a flexible bag, e.g., of rubber. It is of the order of fluid pressure, i.e., applied perpendicular to a tangent on any concave or convex surface. It is exerted by steam, compressed air, hot water, or combinations of these or other fluids. It is sometimes called *omnidirectional* pressure, as used in making molded plywood.
>
> FOLLOW-UP—A method of applying pressure in which its intensity can be maintained uniformly, such as by a hydraulic pump. This is in contrast to fixed or rigid pressure by clamps or screws that does not compensate for any yielding of the glued assembly.
>
> OMNIDIRECTIONAL—See *flexible*.
>
> PISTON or PUMP—The pressure of the liquid medium in the hydraulic pump and press pistons, and shown on the pump pressure gauge.
>
> SPECIFIC—This is the surface pressure on the plywood and is related to the pump or piston pressure. See formula below.*

primary gluing . . . . . See *secondary gluing*.

progressive gluing . . . . A method of curing a resin adhesive in successive steps or stages of application of heat and pressure, between the platens of a hot press. Used only for plywood of larger area than the press platens.

Q

quartered wood . . . . . Wood cut to expose a radial face.

* specific pressure = pump pressure $\times \dfrac{\text{total piston area}}{\text{plywood area}}$
Pressures and areas are in pounds and square inches.

R

radio-frequency field . . . See *high-frequency field*.

resin . . . . A raw material, made synthetically, which is the basis for some of the products called plastics. Certain resins can be used to bond pieces of wood or other material, and these are called resin adhesives, less correctly resin glues. These adhesives are of relatively recent development and are much more durable than the older types of conventional glues.

> PHENOLIC resin adhesives are made from chemicals of the phenol group and formaldehyde, in general harden in the presence of heat, and are the most durable. They are available in liquid and powder form. Special types, mixed with suitable accelerators, harden at intermediate temperatures.
>
> RESORCINOL is a type of phenol.
>
> UREA resin adhesives are made from ureas and formaldehyde, harden when heated in the presence of certain chemicals (catalysts or hardeners) ; this hardening can be rapid and at moderate temperatures.
>
> MELAMINE resins are similar to the ureas, chemically.

rotary cut . . . . A manner of cutting veneer, by which the entire log or block is mounted in a lathe, and turned against a broad cutting knife, which is inclined into the log at a slight angle. The veneer is cut in a continuous sheet, from the circumference of the block, somewhat as paper is unwound from a roll.

S

sap or sapwood . . . . . The lighter-colored wood substance, usually occurring in the outer portion of the tree, nearest the bark. Cf. *heart*.

sawn . . . . Some veneers, as quarter-sawn oak, are made by sawing. It is claimed to produce more solid veneer, although much more costly than cutting because of sawkerf waste.

secondary gluing . . . . The process of gluing together wood and plywood parts in assembling wood products, such as aircraft. Contrasted with *primary gluing*, when veneers are glued into plywood. See *assembly*.

setting . . . . The hardening of an adhesive.

shim . . . . A long narrow patch glued into the panel, or into the lumber core.

single spread . . . . . . See *spread*.

sizing or presizing . . . . The application of dilute glue or adhesive on a surface on which regular glue or adhesive is to be spread. Sizing penetrates relatively deeply, and reduces subsequent absorption of the regular glue. Particularly important when woods of unlike density are joined. Sizing should not be wholly hard before glue is applied. Sizing is particularly desirable when end grain or surfaces approaching end grain are to be glued.

skin . . . . In flexible-bag operations, a molded piece of plywood; also, thin hardwood covering placed over mold to give greater durability.

slicing . . . . A manner of cutting veneer. Logs or sawn flitches are held securely against a table in a slicing machine. The table is moved down, and at an angle, across a sturdy knife, which shears off the veneer in sheets.

slip joint . . . . The method of laying up veneers in flexible-bag molding, wherein the edges are beveled and allowed to overlap over part or all of the scarfed area.

softwood . . . . A general term used to designate lumber or veneer produced from coniferous, or needle-leafed, trees, as contrasted with hardwoods from broad-leafed trees.

solid-piled . . . . . . Sometimes called *dead-piled* or *bulked-down*. Plywood fresh from clamps or hot press is piled on a solid, flat base, without stickers, and weighted down while reaching normal temperature and moisture content.

solids concentration . . . The percentage of solids present in a liquid (or content) adhesive.

solvent . . . . The liquid in which a dry powdered glue or adhesive is dissolved or dispersed.

soya bean meal . . . . . See *glue.*

spread . . . . The amount of glue or adhesive, in pounds of liquid mixture, that is applied per thousand square feet of single adhesive line. In conventional cold glues, usually 70 to 90 lb, in resin adhesives from 25 to 35 lb; on the Pacific Coast the term "spread" often applies to weight of dry glue, per thousand square feet of double line, i.e., 3-ply. This term requires adequate explanations to avoid misunderstandings. *Single spread* indicates that one of the two adjacent surfaces is spread with adhesive, while *double spread* means that adhesive is applied to both surfaces.

spreadable life . . . . . See *working life.*
   (of a glue mixture)

spreader . . . . A machine to apply coatings of adhesive on one or both sides of the veneer, preparatory to the layup.

sunken joint . . . . . . See *joint, sunken.*

super-pressed plywood . . More correctly called *high-density plywood* (q.v.).

T

tape . . . . A strip of gummed paper or cloth used to hold the edges of the veneer together, at the joint, previous to gluing.

tapeless splicer . . . . . A machine for gluing sheets of veneer together, edge to edge, without the use of gummed tape.

thermoplastic . . . . . . A material which tends to soften when heated. A thermoplastic resin, used as an adhesive, normally requires hot pressing, but the pressure cannot be released until the temperature has been reduced to a point at which the resin hardens.

thermosetting . . . . . A resin adhesive which hardens when heated, and does not again soften when reheated. No cooling is required before the release of pressure when plywood is made.

two-ply . . . . A reinforced veneer face construction in which fragile veneer, such as stump or burl, is reinforced by $\frac{1}{40}$- to $\frac{1}{60}$-in. cross-laid backing veneer of birch or maple. It is usually bonded with a resin film, and is primarily intended to prevent damage to fragile and costly veneer in handling.

U

urea resin . . . . See *resin*.

V

vegetable glue . . . . . See *glue*.

veneer . . . . A thin sheet or layer of wood, sliced, rotary-cut, half-round or sawn from a log, block or flitch. There is no sawkerf waste in a knife-cut veneer. Veneer is the raw material from which plywood and laminated wood are assembled. Thicknesses may range from $\frac{1}{100}$ to $\frac{1}{4}$ in. and are seldom greater.

W

wall board . . . . . . Plywood used in the construction trades for wall covering for interior exposure.

warp . . . . A variation from the true or plane surface, due to a number of causes, among which are uneven moisture content, unbalanced constructions, angling veneer grain, unequal exposure, etc.

working life of glues
  and adhesives . . . . . The period during which a mixture remains alive (suitable for spreading) before hardening in the receptacle, or commencing to gel appreciably.

wrinkle . . . . An unglued area caused by failure of the veneers to slip into place. Differs from *blister* (q.v.) in that surplus veneer cannot be pushed into proper place.

Section IV—Testing

19. Testing Plastics Articles

Foreword

Evaluation of physical and other characteristics of objects made from plastics is a function which the plastics engineer is frequently required to perform. The purpose may be control of quality in production, acceptance testing against specification, establishment of data for engineering and design, or other ends of substantial economic importance.

Whatever the purpose, the question of the reliability of the evaluation cannot be evaded, and when the economic importance of the evaluation is large, the reliability of the evaluation must be in proportion. Neither the authority of the engineer nor the computations performed on his data can produce reliable predictions from unreliable data; there is no substitute for a valid method of test, which must be selected before evaluation begins.

Evaluation of articles made from plastics, perhaps more than most other classes of articles, requires specialized testing methods, because of the characteristics of the resins and compounds, and of the production processes used to manufacture the articles economically. When the engineer tests a plastic object, he tests not only its material, but also the way the object was made. There are inherent variations in the articles, from lot to lot, and within each lot, and also from place to place within each individual one. This place-to-place variation establishes the rule that the characteristics of each article made from a plastic are governed not only by the material of which it is made, but also by its shape and dimensions, i.e., its design. These variations are rooted in the nature of the production process itself. The very word "plastic," meaning "readily formable," carries the concept of the economic basis of the molding processes (and it is with molded plastics articles that this chapter is chiefly concerned). Molding of plastics must be a repetitive process of high rapidity, involving rapid changes in temperature and pressure, and hence necessarily abrupt transitions from liquid, or semiliquid, to solid phase. The quality of the finished product is notably sensitive to any fluctuation in the temperature, pressure, and time characteristics of the molding cycle. Variations in characteristics of finished product, from lot to lot and even within a lot, may be both abrupt and large.

There is a considerable and useful literature on methods of test for measuring the physical and other characteristics of the various plastics as materials. Almost without exception, these methods utilize specimens of standard dimensions and shapes, prepared specifically for the purpose. The resulting data are valuable in establishing comparative characteristics of the materials themselves.

It is difficult, however, from such standard test data to predict the performance of an article made from the plastic, when it is subjected to stresses and conditions. Few plastics articles that are commercially useful will resemble, even remotely, in shape or dimensions, the standard test specimens. Even when it is feasible to cut specimens of the standard dimensions from the larger object to be evaluated, the tests of such specimens cannot be counted upon to reveal the probable performance of the integral object itself.

The plastics engineer, then, recognizing the difficulty of evaluating with reliability the probable performance of the plastic article, on the basis of either the standard test data on the material, or tests of standard-sized specimens cut from the article itself, must arrive at a method of test which is adaptable to the specific case at hand, and he may have to design one.

The literature on methods of testing plastics objects of nonstandard shapes and dimensions is not—nor, by definition, can it ever be—anything like the orderly and compact, yet comprehensive, set of guides which covers the testing of plastics simply as materials. Not only are there as many or more properties to be measured, but there is an infinity of possible different shapes and, for each possible shape, a wide range of possible dimensions. Since, by the nature of these materials and the processes by which they are molded, each specific article is likely to have its own unique set of characteristics, there can be no complete codification of methods and apparatus for testing all objects made from plastics.

Confronted with this dilemma of the plastics engineer—the inapplicability of general test methods and the impossibility of complete documentation of specific test methods—this chapter represents an attempt (in fact, the expansion of an earlier effort) at some useful classification of types of methods and equipment which may be utilized for testing articles of particular types or shapes, for measurement of certain important characteristics that are common to most types of articles made from plastics. Although the methods outlined may not meet the requirements of any given case, it is suggested that the general principles set forth herein be used in devising variations or new methods which will be suited to the particular article to be tested.

General Considerations

For testing a given article, the engineer should select the method in the light of the economic importance of the purpose which the evaluation must serve. In terms of this economic importance, the engineer will first appraise the degree of reliability required to make the test significant. He will consider whether the method will measure what it is intended to measure, and within what limits, or with what precision; what number of specimens will constitute his sample; and the means of selection of a representative sample.

If the answers to these questions leave him some freedom, he may then be able to make a choice between modifying an existing piece of test equipment or constructing an original device, and of relinquishing some unnecessary degree of precision in order to reduce the time required to perform the tests or to lessen the cost of products destroyed by the test.

Some general principles can be discussed:

Purpose. With a purpose clearly defined, it is possible to lay out the testing program and to obtain the necessary data with the least expense in time, materials and effort. "First, on paper" seems like rudimentary advice, but it is a step that is frequently overlooked, with the results that a wrong test is selected, and that the data may give unnecessary information, or too little information. No amount of computation afterward can make up for that original lapse.

Most testing of plastic articles is done for one (or several) of three purposes:

1. *To establish, and then to maintain, an economic standard of quality.* While a minimum standard is almost always applied, the practice of controlling quality within limits is being widely accepted. In either case numerical values are needed to establish the standard, although the procedure may then be simplified to a "pass-fail" test for maintaining the standard, in continuous production-lot tests.

2. *Specification testing.* This purpose of testing is usually related to acceptance by the buyer and user of the article, just as the quality-control purpose listed as (1), above, is usually associated with production inspection by the maker of the object. For this purpose, also, numerical data are needed as basis for specification standards, even though the routine acceptance test is then simplified to a "pass-fail" test.

3. *To obtain data for purposes of engineering and design.* For this purpose, not only is the emphasis upon numerical results, but the results should be in a form adaptable to statistical analysis.

Methods. The bulk of this chapter, below, will be devoted to the classification and description of methods of test. There will be no attempt to assign the particular tests or classes of tests to any of the above major purposes. Those purposes are accomplished as much by the schedule of sampling, or by the scale against which the data are interpreted, as by the method of test alone.

There are, however, two principles which must be stressed:

1. Whatever the purpose for which the test is to be made, it will invariably be much preferable to select a method which will furnish numerical data, i.e., quantitative measurements of the characteristic to be determined. A procedure which yields merely a "pass-fail" judgment has very little likelihood of being adaptable to any other testing need, nor can it readily furnish

data which can be treated statistically to point to the causes for variation in quality of product. On the other hand, a procedure which is designed to yield quantitative data can always be used for routine tests on a "pass-fail" basis.

2. It is often necessary to devise accelerated tests to simulate in a short time the effects of long-time exposure to service conditions. Caution should be exercised in avoiding overacceleration to a degree which will yield misleading results.

3. When the procedure has been agreed upon, it should be described in writing, in complete detail. It is obvious that a method of test on which will hinge commercial transactions between buyer and seller must be capable of definition. And the same is true even within a single organization, when responsibility for quality of product is divided between departments charged with research, engineering, design, production, technical service and sales. A good method of test deserves a detailed description in writing; an inadequate method stands its best chance of improvement through the same treatment.

Apparatus. In classification and description of methods of test, below, the equipment required will receive adequate description. Selection of apparatus and of procedure for tests are inseparably related, each governing the other, and the two rules suggested for guidance in choice of method apply equally to selection of apparatus; namely, the requirements of providing numerical data and of adequate written description.

The ingenious engineer will find ways to utilize the measuring and recording mechanisms of general testing equipment available to him, substituting for the standard fixtures or jaws such specific fixtures as may be needed to hold the particular article so that the test load will be applied identically to each successive specimen. The standard general testing machines have the proportions which provide rigidity, ensuring that the engineer measures the deflection "of the specimen, and not of the test equipment." There is real economy, as well as real reliability, to be gained by such adaptations of general testing equipment. There is one other advantage to such adaptation of standard general equipment—it makes it easier for engineers in other laboratories to follow the same test procedure, and is thus a step toward uniformity.

Conditions. Many plastics are moisture-sensitive, and all are affected by temperature. For reliability of results, test specimens should be exposed to specified conditions of temperature and humidity for a time previous to making the tests, and the tests themselves should be conducted in the specified atmosphere.

ASTM D618* describes the standard atmosphere for testing plastics at

* American Society for Testing Materials, 1916 Race St., Philadelphia 3, Pa.
"ASTM Standards on Plastics."

relative humidity of 50 per cent and temperature of 23°C (73.4°F). Conditioning prior to test will vary with material and with test to be performed. This ASTM method specifies common procedures and simple means for conditioning.

Many exceptions to standard conditions may properly be included in special test procedures; in fact, a prolonged exposure to an extreme atmospheric condition may in itself constitute a significant test. Whether standard or special, the condition and the period of exposure to the condition should constitute part of the method of test, and should be recorded as part of the test data.

If conditioning equipment is unavailable, readings of ambient temperature and humidity should be made at reasonably frequent intervals, and reported with the other data.

Samples. As stated above, the economic importance of an evaluation should determine the degree of reliability which a testing program must provide. Every link in the sequence of events leading to the conclusions of the test should have the same degree of reliability; stated another way, the least reliable step will determine the reliability of the whole program.

The process of sampling represents the attempt to predict the performance of all similar objects in terms of the tested performance of a relatively few. By careful random selection of his sample, the engineer plans to obtain data very nearly the same as what he would have obtained if he had tested the total number of objects. As the number of specimens tested is increased, the data tend to approach the values that would represent the whole group; on the other hand, the larger the number of specimens, the higher the cost in product destroyed and in time consumed in making the tests. The problem of sampling, then, is one of finding the happy medium, of testing enough samples to give the required reliability to the results, yet of not running the costs higher than the value of the increased reliability gained by the larger sampling.

The theory of sampling has expanded remarkably in the last few years. There is, perhaps, no area of his work in which the testing engineer will be so well rewarded by an increase in his efficiency, for a reasonable investment of his time, as in study of the modern techniques of sampling. And the importance of well-planned sampling in order to obtain meaningful test results is important because of the variations, lot to lot, within a lot, and place-to-place within an article, that arise from the nature of the plastics and the processes of molding. It is not enough to sample specimens from a batch; the sampling must take into account the possible anisotropy, or variation of properties with direction, within each specimen. In other words, the same tests must be applied in each important direction of the article.

This chapter cannot provide universal sampling tables. The reader is referred to the literature on sampling procedure, and these suggestions may be noted:

1. unless the samples are representative, the results of the test will not be reliable;

2. unless the samples are adequate in number, the results will not be reliable enough;

3. if the samples are representative and adequate in number, testing of any larger number of samples will be a waste of money.

Treatment of Data. As separate links in the sequence of events leading to the conclusion or prediction that is the result of a test, the way in which the test data are treated or the conclusions presented cannot make up for an inaccurate sampling, an inadequate method of test, or a lack of controlled atmospheric conditions. No amount of mathematical computations can produce reliable predictions from defective or inadequate data.

On the other hand, if the test procedure has been well selected, the sampling properly accomplished, and the testing carefully performed, then the data deserve professional treatment in order to extract the greatest amount of significance from them, and the results and conclusions should then be reported in terms of the purpose for which the evaluation was made. Knowledge of such purpose should include awareness of the expected readership of the report, and the facts and predictions should be presented in a form that will be understandable, with a minimum of effort, to those readers.

Reliability, to the degree required by the economic importance of the purpose of the project, is the question which cannot be evaded, and predictions of the service performance of the plastics articles that have been tested should be made with neither more nor less assurance than warranted by the facts. Techniques for statistical treatment of test data have been developed on a practical basis in recent years, and, as with sampling procedures, the engineer will find that a working familiarity with these techniques is readily acquirable and immensely useful.*

Methods of Test for Mechanical Properties

Impact. There are three general methods of testing molded articles for impact-resistance: (1) falling-weight tests, (2) pendulum tests and (3) tumbling impact tests.

(1) Falling-Weight Tests

Falling-Weight Test for Curved Surfaces. This test is made by dropping an object of given weight and dimensions from a predetermined height on a fixed specimen and examining the effect of the impact. The weight should strike the specimen in such a manner as to simulate the way in which it is most likely to be damaged in service. A single blow or repeated blows may be used. If repeated blows are used, the test becomes a fatigue test (see p. 746).

* "ASTM Manual on Quality Control of Materials."

Apparatus (see Fig. 19-1). The apparatus consists of a solid iron plate, to which a specimen is rigidly fastened, and a free-falling weight. The weight can be a steel ball, a steel rod, or a bag of shot. The steel ball can be dropped by cutting a string (Fig. 19-1a) or by demagnetizing an electromagnet (Fig. 19-1b) used to hold it. The electromagnet may be adjustable in height so as to provide a wide range of impacts. A steel rod can be guided by allowing it to fall through a pipe (Fig. 19-1c).

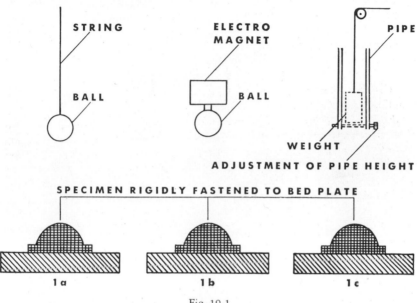

Fig. 19-1

Procedure. The steel ball or other weight is allowed to fall and strike the specimen, at a predetermined point, either once or repeatedly. The weight used and the distance of fall must be specified, for each blow. If more than one blow is employed, it should be specified whether the blow is applied to the same or different specimens.

A satisfactory means of holding and releasing a steel weight is an electromagnet. The apparatus consists of a vertical track, an electromagnet capable of supporting the required weight, and an arrangement by which the electromagnet may be fastened at any point on the track. The electromagnet is activated, the steel ball is placed in contact with it, and the magnet is raised to the desired height. The current is then turned off so that the weight falls on the specimen. The impact may be calculated in foot-pounds if so desired.

Figure 19-2 shows a 1-oz ball drop used for testing plastic dinnerware. The drop is adjustable up to 30 in. Figure 19-3 shows a magnetic

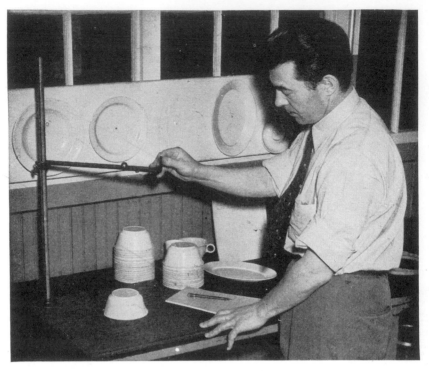

Fig. 19-2

drop mechanism which is standard for a drop test on helmet-liners. This has an adjustable drop, with a ball weighing 8 lb.

Guided Drop Test. A specimen is allowed to slide down an inclined trough so that it strikes an anvil at a specified position. This impact-fatigue test has been used rather successfully in checking production of telephone handsets.

Apparatus (see Fig. 19-4). A trough, a trough support and an anvil fastened to a solid steel plate are required for the test.

Procedure. The specimen is placed in the trough and allowed to slide freely down the trough and strike the anvil. The test usually involves a succession of drops, from gradually increased heights, until failure occurs. In some cases the pieces are dropped in several positions at each height to evaluate various parts of the molding.

Falling-Weight Method for Flat Surfaces. This method provides some measure of the resistance of shattering of laminated sheets, structural members, steering wheels, glazing, etc.

Fig. 19-3

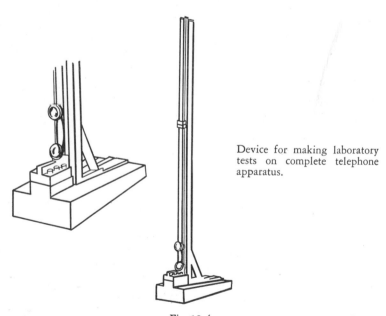

Device for making laboratory tests on complete telephone apparatus.

Fig. 19-4

Apparatus (see Fig. 19-5). The apparatus consists of a supporting frame securely mounted to a solid iron bedplate, and a steel ball or bag of shot or sand of the required weight.

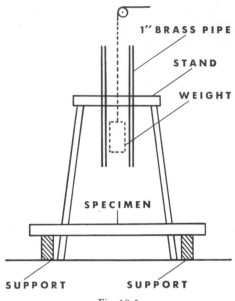

Fig. 19-5

Procedure. The test specimen is mounted in the supporting frame and a steel ball or weight is allowed to drop so as to deliver a blow at the center of the test specimen. Either single or multiple blows can be delivered, as specified.

Impact-Fatigue Test. Another example of an impact-fatigue test is shown in Fig. 19-6. The molded article is repeatedly struck by a small weight

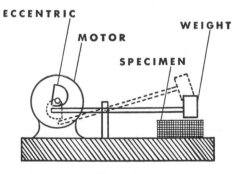

Fig. 19-6

until it fails. The time interval between the impact blows may be significant. It should be noted that the impact used in this test is much lower than that used in the single-impact test.

(2) Pendulum Tests

ASTM Test. The excess-swing type of pendulum test is more commonly used in testing specially prepared specimens. The generally accepted methods are ASTM D256, Method A, commonly known as the Izod type, and Method B, commonly known as the Charpy type. These methods are sometimes used directly for testing the article itself, by causing the pendulum to strike against a portion or portions of the article. Federal Specification L-P-406, Method No. 1071, describes a similar method.

Transmitted-Shock Test. An example is the shock test of Specification MIL-S-901 which contains several helpful sketches which can be used as a guide to design apparatus for individual requirements.

Apparatus (see Fig. 19-7). The apparatus consists of a pendulum or striker arm, adjustable to give blows of various magnitudes, a supporting frame and an anvil on which to mount the specimen.

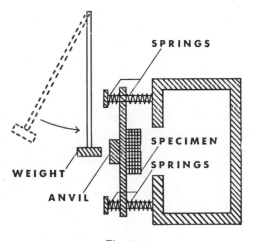

Fig. 19-7

Procedure. The specimen is mounted on the anvil so that the blow is delivered perpendicular to the specimen. Single or multiple blows can be delivered.

(3) Tumbling Impact Test

Quite frequently it may be desirable to check relative strengths of a product produced from a plastic of unknown performance against one made from a plastic whose performance is known. A number of articles are molded from the standard material and a similar number molded from the material under investigation. Both sets are then placed together in a tumbling barrel and tumbled for the specified length of time. The units are then removed and examined. The weaker of the two sets will show the greater percentage of breakage, and in that way the relative strengths can be determined.

Crushing. The purpose of these tests in general is to determine whether the article will stand up under the compressional stresses that it may encounter in service. For crushing tests, the basic procedures of ASTM D695 (Federal Specification L-P-406, Method 1021) may be modified to suit individual requirements.

Wear. It is, of course, important to know how long an article made from a plastic will stand up under the usage to which it is subjected. The plastic used for fabricating the part should be sufficiently stable and enduring to satisfy the requirements of the job. Consequently, the selection of such materials involves a knowledge of their wear and abrasion properties.

How can one measure resistance to wear and abrasion? This resistance cannot be defined in absolute terms, and there is no standard test by which it can be measured. But there are specific tests by which one can determine which plastic will provide the greatest durability when subjected to abrasion or other conditions that result in wear.

Many types of tests have been developed which give complete measurements of abrasion-resistance. A common type is the falling-abrasive test. This test generally utilizes a stream of abrasive particles, such as carborundum, which impinge upon a surface at a 45-degree angle and at a definite velocity for a fixed time. Other tests are conducted by wear machines, equipped with rotating disks, wheels or brushes to simulate conditions of actual wear. Another type is an indentation machine which presses a standard point into the plastic to produce an indentation, of which the size or depth gives a measure of "hardness."

Because there is no single method of testing that will provide complete details, it is necessary to supplement laboratory tests of abrasion with actual field tests. The primary purposes of laboratory tests are merely to save valuable time and to serve as controls in the manufacture of basic materials.

Detailed methods for measuring abrasion-resistance and hardness are given in the ASTM Standards on Plastics.

Fatigue. A plastic article, like those of other materials, may fail after repeated loading to a stress less than its short-time ultimate strength. This phenomenon is known as fatigue. Standard tests have been developed for determining the fatigue endurance limit.* This is the stress below which the material may be stressed for an infinite number of cycles (usually taken

---

* "ASTM Standards on Plastics."

as ten million) without failure. For articles which must be repeatedly stressed in service, materials should be selected with this in mind. However, since design and fabrication variables may reduce the fatigue endurance limit, it may be desirable to test articles in a manner simulating service use.

Since fatigue life is known to be dependent on frequency, amplitude, temperature and mode of stressing, as well as stress, these variables should be controlled and specified in any test.

Methods of Test for Permanence Properties

Dimensional Stability. The original shape and dimensions of a molded article are of course established primarily by the mold. Subsequent changes will be a function of the inherent properties of the material, of the molding technique, or of a combination of both. Since retention of original dimensions through long periods of service is a prime requisite of sound engineering design, our understanding of the basic causes of dimensional change, and of methods of producing such changes in the laboratory, is vital to the proper application of plastics. Too much emphasis cannot be placed on dimensional stability as an engineering property, for it is common knowledge that a high percentage of failures of plastics is due to dimensional instability.

Changes in dimensions may be caused by:

a. deformation under load (cold flow)

b. swelling or shrinking due to absorption of moisture or drying

c. aging due to cycles of absorption of moisture and drying

d. internal stresses

e. changes in temperature.

Deformation under load represents failure of the material or the article to resist change of form due to externally applied forces such as fastening devices, inserts, or stacking during shipment. It is an extremely important property where precise dimensioning is essential, such as in instrumentation of all kinds. As a group, the thermosets give little trouble with cold flow, and furthermore do not change much at elevated service temperatures. The thermoplastics are subject, to various degrees, to deformation with rising temperature.

For determinations of cold flow the constant-load system is reliable and simple to make. The article should be loaded to about its maximum service stress between two anvils. After a stipulated time, preferably not less than 6 hr, at a stipulated temperature, preferably not less than 120°F, the cold flow is measured by a dial gauge between the anvils. Cold flow is expressed as percentage of the original height. The basic features of ASTM D621, Method A (Federal Specification L-P-406, Method 1101) should be employed for tests of cold flow.

Swelling due to absorption of moisture, and shrinkage due to drying, are observed particularly in articles molded of cellulosic compounds such as cellulose acetate, cellulose acetate butyrate, and ethyl cellulose. The cellulose-filled thermosets, both molded and laminated, exhibit the tendency, but to a minor degree. Polymethyl methacrylate, polystyrene, polyvinyls, and other nonabsorbent materials do not change significantly.

For determining swelling and shrinking due to moisture and drying, Procedure 1 of ASTM D756 (Procedure I of L-P-406, Method No. 6011) should be used. It covers normalizing, humidifying, and drying, and can be used for any single set or combinations of conditions.

In materials which tend to swell when wet and shrink when dry, as exemplified by the thermoplastic cellulosics, there is a corollary tendency to undergo a progressive linear shrinkage over extended periods of time. This is generally called age shrinkage. It may be determined by subjecting the article to at least three cycles of the procedure noted in the paragraphs above. Measurements may be made at the completion of each normalizing cycle, but age shrinkage is expressed as the difference between the dimension at the completion of the initial normalizing and at the completion of the final normalizing, in mils per in.

Internal stresses in a molded article result primarily from injecting the molten plastic into too cold a die. When the plastic is suddenly chilled, some portion of the unspent force exerted by the injection ram is locked within it. This constitutes an ever-present threat to the dimensional stability of the piece, and is prevented from twisting the part out of shape only by the rigidity of the material at the temperature of service. Stresses may also be introduced in the process of extracting the article from the mold. It follows therefore that the molded articles, at some stage between original design and final acceptance, should be sampled and tested for release of stress at the highest temperature likely to be encountered in service. Many failures in applications of plastics have resulted from neglect of this important phenomenon.

A simple method for determining change of dimensions due to internal strains is as follows:

1. allow the molded article to become normalized at ordinary room conditions for at least one day;

2. measure the significant dimensions;

3. place the article in an air-circulating thermostatically controlled oven at a specified temperature and for a specified time depending on type of material and on service expected;

4. cool to room temperature;

5. remeasure;

6. if it is desired, the test may be repeated at higher or lower temperatures.

Coefficient of thermal expansion is a fundamental property of a raw material and the test is not normally applied to molded articles. Changes in dimensions due to changes of temperature are generally small in comparison to changes due to cold flow, moisture, or release of stress. However, they can become significant where plastics and metals are used jointly in precision devices, since the coefficients of expansion of plastics are several times those of metals. Thermal expansion should be determined in accordance with ASTM D696, or F.S.S.C., L-P-406.

Weathering. The problem of engineering evaluation of resistance of materials to outdoor exposure has occupied the attention of technologists the world over for many years. Like other materials, plastics are subject to change and degradation by exposure outdoors, and as a result we witness loss of engineering properties, loss of original beauty, and, in extreme cases, complete deterioration.

There is no simple way in which the weathering resistance of plastics may be determined. Installation and maintenance of exposure racks throughout the country entails expense bearable only by government agencies, organized technical societies, or large corporations. This situation is being improved by (a) the increasing number of private testing concerns which can provide test-fence facilities to small businesses at nominal cost, and (b) the establishment of such facilities through group efforts in such organizations as the American Society for Testing Materials. But in any event the procedure is rather costly in engineering effort and money.

Accelerated weathering tests conducted in the laboratory, in addition to being a continual source of controversy as to significance, require fairly elaborate equipment and a high degree of interpretive know-how, both rather expensive commodities, and are worthless except to the extent that they can be correlated with actual performance in service or under the less artificially severe conditions on the test fence. In spite of these difficulties, accelerated weathering, in the laboratory, is used extensively throughout many industries and can be safely catalogued as a laboratory technique of the highest importance.

Test fences are usually constructed of wood or metal and are located preferably at strategic points throughout the country (see Fig. 19-8). Florida and the Panama Canal zone have been used as typical of semi-tropical or tropical locations, New York and other city areas for industrial-urban exposure, and the plains of the West for dry rural exposure. Fences are generally placed facing south and at 45° from horizontal. Visual observations of specimens are made from time to time, to predict service behaviour and to serve as a calibration of accelerated tests. Such fences have been used for many years by the metals and protective-coatings industries, and the experience thus acquired is being utilized in the exposure of plastics. In some cases the materials are placed under glass-covered shelters to produce accelerated indoor exposure. Long-range programs involving test-fence exposure of plastics

Courtesy of ASTM Exposure Test Site Program

Fig. 19-8

are now being conducted by industrial organizations, by ASTM, and by the Armed Forces.

Accelerated weathering is produced by exposing the materials or articles to the influences of light, moisture, heat, thermal shock, ozone and other factors, either separately or jointly.

Weathering devices are usually rotating machines. Panels or articles are rotated around a centrally located glass-enclosed arc lamp or open-flame arc, or other source of ultraviolet energy. At predetermined intervals a spray of water or fog may be directed against the specimens, producing moist conditions as well as thermal shock. A typical machine, with controlled procedure for operating it, is described in ASTM D822. Other techniques are described in Federal Specification L-P-406, Methods 6021 and 6022 and in ASTM D795.

Various other procedures have been designed to produce unique effects, e.g., artificial sources of light to test the effects of light alone, such as changes in physical properties, fading and chemical decomposition; humidity chambers for determining loss of electrical properties by absorption of moisture, or degradation due to hydrolysis; and special devices for determining the effects of industrial gases, ozone and debris. All of these influences are part and parcel of the all-inclusive term "weathering."

Appropriate in any discussion of weathering is a review of those procedures which are generally referred to as simulated service tests. A series of such methods involving the use of extremes of temperature and humidity, such as cycling from 0 to 100 per cent relative humidity and from 75 to 175°F, are included in ASTM D756 and Federal L-P-406 Method No. 6011. The detailed methods, too long for inclusion here, are required reading for all technologists interested in this subject. Other simulated service tests include the soaking, freezing, drying, ultraviolet cycle test described in L-P-406 Method No. 6023 and the salt-spray test described in ASTM B117 and Method No. 6017.

In as much as weather varies from day to day and from place to place, it is desirable to adopt such of the controlled procedures as will reproduce the weathering influences that are of interest for the specific application in mind.

Moisture-Resistance. The physical properties directly influenced by the moisture content of the plastic are electrical insulation resistance, dielectric losses, mechanical strength, appearance and dimensions. Reference is made to procedures originally developed for tests of standard test specimens, which are usually conditioned prior to testing. Recommendations are made concerning the application of these procedures to the testing of finished shapes or of specimens cut from them.

(*Note:* Extreme caution must be exercised in attempting to estimate the serviceability of an article made of plastic on the basis of data from tests run on standard test specimens. If such tests have shown that the moisture content of the plastic has a significant effect on a particular physical property, such findings should be confirmed, when possible, by tests of the finished article.)

Whenever possible, it is recommended that the effect of water on an article made from plastic be determined by immersion of the article as a whole, rather than of specimens cut from it. This is particularly true in determining dimensional stability and surface effects. The use of cut specimens may, however, be necessitated by the difficulty of determining the percentage gain in weight of the plastic in a molded piece containing metal inserts. Since cut specimens will differ from each other and from the original piece in ratio of surface to volume, it may be desirable to note water-absorption values calculated on the basis of surface, as well as those calculated on the basis of weight.

It should be recognized, in making all observations of moisture-resistance, that where articles are to be machined for use, the samples tested should likewise be machined, since machining removes the surface skin and exposes the filler, with the result that a machined piece frequently absorbs more water than does the unmachined molded piece. This is true particularly if the filler is hygroscopic.

In immersion tests, the general principles of ASTM D570 should be followed.

The appearance should be observed carefully before and after testing. For example, immersion under severe conditions can result in blisters, cracking, wrinkles, and a mottled appearance. The nomenclature listed in ASTM D675 is recommended for describing the appearance of the molded article.

Effect of Molded-In Stresses. The possibility of dimensional change as a result of molded-in stresses has been discussed in a previous section. Such changes frequently develop when the article is subjected to heat, which softens the plastic and permits release of stress. But molded-in stresses may cause also crazing or cracking of the article, a phenomenon particularly bothersome with thermoplastics which have low elongation. Crazing or cracking is potentially possible under ordinary conditions of use, but is sharply accelerated by contact with solvents and reagents. Since the mechanics of stress-cracking are not thoroughly understood, the identity of solvents and reagents which may be troublesome with a given plastic can be established only by trials.

Molded-in stresses can be minimized by annealing. A typical procedure, devised for articles of polystyrene, consists of placing the articles for a stipulated time in an oven maintained at 20°F below the ASTM heat-distortion temperature of the material, and then slowly cooling them. The annealing time depends to some extent on the size of the moldings; it is generally felt, however, that the smallest should be heated for more than 30 minutes and that the largest should not require more than 4 hr. Although the general procedure of annealing is similar for all plastics which are subject to crazing and cracking resulting from molded-in stresses, the details as to temperature and time must be determined for each application, so that the maximum relief of stress will be accomplished with minimum change of dimensions by the relatively high annealing temperatures.

Efficacy of the annealing technique is commonly measured qualitatively by immersing the annealed articles in a reagent to which the particular plastic is sensitive. Among the better-known liquids used for this purpose are kerosene and n-heptane (for polystyrene) and ethyl alcohol (for polymethyl methacrylate). After an immersion of a few minutes the articles are removed, and observed for crazing or cracking.

Methods of Test for Thermal Properties

Effect of Temperature. Practically all organic materials, including plastics, are affected by extremes of heat or cold. The effects are mainly mechanical, although electrical properties may change to an appreciable degree. Generally speaking, within temperature range of —70 to 160°F, the thermosetting materials are less subject to change than the thermoplastics. However, all of the thermoplastics do not behave similarly. The methacrylates and polystyrenes, as examples, are only slightly affected between room temperature and low temperatures, whereas the vinyls and cellulosics undergo substantial changes. Consequently, thermoplastics are not generally used where extreme heat-resistance is an important factor in service, since they have low softening points, seldom above 200°F.

The completely assembled molded articles should be tested at a temperature which approximates that of the service conditions to be encountered. The effect of various set-screws, assembly nuts, inserts, springs, etc., on the pieces may then be observed.

The usual result of low temperature is loss of ductility or increase of brittleness, as manifested by reduction of impact strength. This is generally accompanied by increase of flexural and tensile strengths and modulus of elasticity, and decrease of elongation. Of these phenomena, the loss of impact strength is perhaps the most significant from the standpoint of serviceability.

High temperatures result in increase of ductility, as reflected in higher impact strength, greater deformation under load, lower flexural and tensile strengths, and greater elongation. Of these, the greater deformation under load is of extreme importance, since it reduces the ability of the article to maintain its dimensions at high service temperatures.

In addition to the general effects cited above, we are confronted with the fact that materials differ widely in what is sometimes called their "safe operating temperature," i.e., the temperature beyond which they are apt to be distorted badly by internal or external stresses. To this property the process of molding is a substantial contributor; therefore, such failures cannot be safely predicted from tests for deformation under load or heat-distortion, which are essentially measurements of flow. Since the result of release of stress by high service temperatures is loss of form or change in dimension, the phenomenon is discussed more fully under Dimensional Stability (p. 747).

Speaking generally, articles which are weak at room temperature will be weak at high and low temperatures. This is not rigorously true for all materials and all circumstances, but can be used as a guide. It is obvious, for instance, that an article made from cellulose acetate can be subjected to a temperature so low that it becomes no stronger in impact than a methacrylate under the same conditions. Conversely, the latter can be heated to a point where it compares favorably with the acetate. It remains true, however, that at room temperature the acetate is much the stronger, and hence is to be preferred in most applications in which impact strength is a controlling consideration.

Since testing at both low and high temperatures is expensive and arduous, it is urged that articles be evaluated at room temperature unless the conditions of service necessitate special testing. If the materials are extremely sensitive to temperature, it is recommended that the ASTM standard 23°C (73.4°F) be used.

Except for a few cases, the methods of testing at extremes of temperature are no different than at room temperature. Consequently the methods covered elsewhere in this chapter will apply. It should be pointed out, however, that greater precision is required for testing at extremes of temperature. For example, two materials or articles which are substantially different in impact strength at room temperature may be just as far apart at $-40°F$, but because of the extreme brittleness of both of them the difference may be detectable only by a precise test. The same applies to softness or flow at high temperatures.

In testing at extreme temperatures one particularly important source of error is the possibility that the specimens and testing equipment may not be held long enough at the testing temperature. It is difficult to generalize, but both should be exposed for at least 5 hr before the testing is started, and preferably for 24 hr.

The commercial aspect of testing at extreme temperatures can be stated as follows: When a drum of molding powder enters the molding room, it carries with it a certain amount of engineering knowledge of the properties which are inherent in the compound. The powder has been purchased presumably in accordance with a specification stipulated between supplier and consumer, and has been checked against the specification by one or both of the contracting parties. Therefore, before a single molding is made, the temperature-sensitivity of the material is common knowledge. If the molded article is going to be subjected to shock at low temperatures, then obviously a choice has been made of a material which is inherently strong at low temperatures, or at least strong enough.

In a somewhat separate category, but nevertheless appropriate to this discussion, is the permanent effect of heat on articles made of plastic. Here again the inherent ability of the material to withstand continuous or intermittent high temperatures should be well known before any article is molded. Testing, then, should not be necessary, unless the process of molding is believed to have an adverse effect. If testing is necessary, however, it is recommended to use the procedures outlined in ASTM D794 (Tentative Recommended Practice for Determining Permanent Effect of Heat on Plastics). The ASTM method establishes a standard procedure for conducting the tests, but leaves the permissible degree of deterioration to be stipulated between contracting parties.

Flammability. In the plastics industry, flammability is customarily determined by standard methods, which employ standard specimens of the material in question. The flammability characteristics of an article may be affected by its size and shape, and may be different from those of the test specimen.

If the flammability of the article is important, the article as such should be suitably tested.

Nondestructive Testing

The need for nondestructive testing presents a continuing challenge to every member of the plastics industry concerned with the production of high-quality merchandise at lowest possible cost. The present practice of testing to destruction a few pieces out of perhaps many thousands not only creates a false sense of security but may represent an unsound compromise between the testing of a large number of pieces in the interests of maintaining good quality and, on the other hand, the natural reluctance to destroy salable merchandise.

The problem is receiving attention in many quarters and is being diligently studied by professional groups particularly expert in this field, two examples being the American Society for Testing Materials Committee E-7 on Nondestructive Testing, organized in 1938, and the more recently established Society for Nondestructive Testing.

Most nondestructive methods of test involve far more than external visual inspection of the surfaces. Nearly every basic principle of physics has been used to obtain, nondestructively, the necessary information concerning the properties of finished articles. The great majority of methods rely upon mechanical measurements or upon a flow or transfer of energy. The energy must usually be supplied from an external source such as an X-ray tube, magnetizing coil, ultrasonic generator or mechanical force, and must be chosen so that distribution of energy within the test piece is modified by the presence of defects. Among the recognized agencies used for nondestructive testing are conduction of electric current; electromagnetic induction; magnetic field; electric (potential) field; conduction of heat; penetrating radiation (x-rays, gamma rays, etc.) ; mechanical vibration; luminous energy; chemical (spot tests) ; and static electricity.

Many of these methods originated in the technology of metals and some of them are obviously not applicable to plastics. However, there is little doubt that future testing of plastic articles will depend to an increasing extent on modifications of existing techniques or on new concepts arising from the unique needs of organic materials.

Section V— SPI Standards

20. Voluntary Commercial Standards of the Trade

Introduction

Up to the time of the release of the second edition of this handbook, The Society of the Plastics Industry has promulgated three voluntary Commercial Standards and one Simplified Practice Procedure through the United States Department of Commerce. The division of the United States Department of Commerce in charge of voluntary industry standards is known as The Commodity Standards Division, Office of Industry and Commerce.

Essentially, commercial standards are developed by manufacturers, distributors, and users in cooperation with the Commodity Standards Division. The purpose of voluntary commercial standards is to establish methods of tests, rating, certification, and labeling of commodities and to provide uniform bases for fair competition. Simplified practice recommendations, on the other hand, are promulgated in order to eliminate avoidable waste through the establishment of standards of practice for stock sizes and varieties of specific commodities that currently are in general production and demand.

One of the distinct advantages of compiling a voluntary commercial standard by these means is that industry itself writes its own specification. When 65 per cent of the volume of business approves the standard, it becomes an official document. Once a voluntary standard is promulgated, a standing committee of industry is placed in charge of the standard in order to review the standard from time to time and revise it whenever necessary.

A further advantage of voluntary commercial standards is that they are not mandatory. A manufacturer producing products which conform to a given standard may label his products, if he so desires, with the hallmark of compliance. If, on the other hand, a manufacturer does not wish to adhere to the standard, he may market his product, but may not, of course, use the hallmark of compliance.

An outline of the procedure for establishing commercial standards follows:

OUTLINE OF PROCEDURE

1. Written request from trade association or responsible producer, distributor, or user.

2. Tentative proposal obtained by one, or a combination of some, of the following processes:

   (a) Tentative draft submitted with request.

   (b) Draft prepared by a representative group of producers, distributors, laboratories, or users.

   (c) Draft prepared by the Commodity Standards Division, using data supplied by proponent and obtained from other sources, including data available in National Bureau of Standards laboratories.

3. Adjustment of tentative proposal through one, or a combination of some, of the following processes:

   (a) Tentative draft widely circulated to interested producers, distributors, users, and laboratories for written comment.

   (b) Comment summarized and referred to proponent for adjustment of draft, followed by resubmittal of draft as adjusted for further comment.

   (c) Conferences of interested groups.

   (d) General conference of producers, distributors, users and general interest.

4. Recommendations to the trade by

   (a) General conference of producers, distributors, users, and general interest; or

   (b) Concurrence of diversified interests, represented by trade associations, leading producers, and user interests.

5. Circulation of recommendation for written acceptance by producers, distributors, testing laboratories, and users.

6. Promulgation, when written acceptances represent at least 65 per cent of volume of business, in the absence of valid opposition. It consists of the following steps:

   (a) Review of the accepted standard by a technical reader and the Commercial Standards Editorial Committee of the National Bureau of Standards;

   (b) Announcement to the trade, accompanied by mimeographed copies of the standard;

   (c) Printing and distribution of the standard.

Polystyrene Plastic Wall Tiles, and Adhesives for Their Application (Commercial Standard 168-50)

(Effective July 15, 1950)

1. PURPOSE AND SCOPE

1.1 *Purpose.*—The purpose of this commercial standard is to establish a minimum standard of quality for polystyrene plastic wall tiles and for the adhesives used in their application, as a guide to producers, distributors, contractors, architects, installers, and users.

1.2 *Scope.*—This standard covers methods of test, materials, requirements for workmanship, tolerances, thickness, opacity, color-fastness, and other details of manufacture of polystyrene plastic tiles which should insure a satisfactory product for wall and/or ceiling installation in private and multiple-unit dwellings, and in commercial, industrial, and other types of buildings where a nonabsorbent, sanitary surface is desired. Requirements for the adhesive to be used for installing the tile are also included. A standard procedure and important considerations and materials in connection with the installation and maintenance are covered in the appendix.

2. MATERIALS

2.1 *Plastic compounds.*—The wall tiles shall be manufactured from a plastic conforming to the requirements of types 1, 2, or 3 in American Society for Testing Materials Tentative Specification D 703, for Polystyrene Molding Compounds. At the option of the manufacturer, fillers, pigments, and dyes may be added to produce colored wall tile.

2.2 *Composition of adhesives.*—The adhesives used in installing the tile shall be of any composition which will meet the requirements set forth herein. The adhesives shall contain not more than $1/2$ of 1 per cent of benzene or volatile chlorinated hydrocarbon solvents.

3. WALL TILE

3.1 REQUIREMENTS FOR TILES.

3.1.1 *Workmanship.*—The manufacture of the tile shall be in accordance with good commercial practice so as to produce tile meeting the requirements of this standard. The finished tile shall be free of flow marks, shrinks, warpage, blemishes, and other defects that may adversely affect its appearance and performance. The gates shall be neatly trimmed, in accordance with the best commercial practice, to produce a minimum blemish.

3.1.2 *Dimensional tolerances.*—The face size of the tiles in any shipment shall not vary one from the other, in any comparable dimension, more than by a negative tolerance of $\frac{1}{10}$ of 1 per cent or 0.005 in., whichever is greater, and by a positive tolerance of $\frac{2}{10}$ of 1 per cent or 0.010 in., whichever is greater.

3.1.3 *Thickness.*—The thickness of the plastic in tile shall be greater than 0.062 in. The lip on the tile shall extend at least 0.033 in. beyond the back of the tile.

3.1.4 *Opacity.*—Tiles in all colors, including mottled and white, shall show a contrast ratio of not less than 0.96 when tested in accordance with the procedure described in paragraph 3.2.2.

3.1.5 *Colorfastness.* No appreciable change in color shall be observed after the tile has been exposed for 50 hours to the accelerated fading test described in paragraph 3.2.3.

3.1.6 *Heat deformation.*—The tile shall not deform when tested at a temperature of 71°C (160°F) in accordance with the procedure described in paragraph 3.2.4.

3.1.7 *Cyclic service test.*—See paragraph 4.1.10.

3.2 METHODS OF TEST FOR TILE.

3.2.1 *Conditioning of test specimens.*—The test specimens shall be conditioned for 48 hours or more at 23° ±2°C (73.5° ±4°F) and 50±2 per cent relative humidity, and tested at these conditions unless otherwise specified.

3.2.2 *Opacity.*—Two specimens of each color shall be selected at random and tested as follows: Photoelectric measurements of 45°, 0° luminous directional reflectance, with the equivalent of daylight illumination, shall be made on a reflectometer for tiles backed with white vitrolite (reflectance about 90 per cent), and for the same tiles backed with black velvet (reflectance about 1 per cent). The contrast ratio of each tile shall be computed as the ratio of the reflectance obtained with the velvet backing to that obtained with the vitrolite backing. The reflectances used shall be the mean of two measurements on the central area of each tile.

3.2.3 *Colorfastness.*—The colorfastness of the tile and grouting material shall be determined in accordance with American Society for Testing Materials Tentative Method of Test·D 620. This method uses an S-1 sunlamp with the specimens exposed on a rotating table 7 inches below the bottom of the bulb.

3.2.4 *Heat deformation test.*—The specimen, loosely suspended in a wire basket, shall be immersed in a bath containing at least 1 gallon of water maintained at a temperature of 71° to 72°C (160° to 162°F) for a period of 2 minutes. The basket containing the specimen shall then be removed and allowed to hang in air for at least 5 minutes. The specimen shall then be removed from the basket and examined. The edges shall not deviate in any direction from a straight line by more than $\frac{1}{32}$ in., nor shall the face of the tile be changed from its original appearance. At least six specimens from each run or lot shall be tested. All six specimens shall meet the requirements. It is recommended that if possible the specimens be selected from different mold cavities.

3.2.5 *Cyclic service test.*—See paragraph 4.2.10.

4. ADHESIVES

4.1 REQUIREMENTS FOR ADHESIVES.

4.1.1 *Tensile-shear strength.*—The average tensile-shear strength shall be not less than the following: (a) sufficient strength to keep tiles from slipping on the vertical specimen and from separating from the under side of the horizontal specimen within 7 days after preparation of the specimens, when tested according to the procedure described in paragraph 4.2.1.1; (b) 1 psi 24 hours after preparation of the specimens when tested according to the procedure described in paragraph 4.2.1.2; (c) 10 psi 28 days after preparation of the specimens when tested according to the procedure described in paragraph 4.2.1.2.

4.1.2 *Effect of heat aging.*—The average tensile-shear strength shall be not less than 10 psi for specimens which have been heated at 65°C (149°F) in a circulating-air oven and tested in accordance with the procedure described in paragraph 4.2.2. The tensile-shear strength test shall be made in accordance with the procedure described in paragraph 4.2.1.2.

4.1.3 *Effect of moisture aging.*—The average tensile-shear strength shall be not less than 10 psi for specimens which have been immersed in water for 24 hours and tested in accordance with the procedure described in paragraph 4.2.3. The tensile-shear strength test shall be made in accordance with the procedure described in paragraph 4.2.1.2.

4.1.4 *Resistance to panel immersion.*—There shall be no visual slippage or separation when the specimen is tested in accordance with the procedure described in paragraph 4.2.4.

4.1.5 *Static loading.*—Tensile specimens shall withstand without failure a load of 0.25 psi for 28 days when tested in accordance with the procedure described in paragraph 4.2.5.

4.1.6 *Simulated aging.*—When tested in accordance with the procedure described in paragraph 4.2.6, the adhesive shall exhibit a minimum shear strength of 10 psi.

4.1.7 *Wetting.*—The adhesive shall be considered to "wet" satisfactorily, or spread easily on the surface of the tile, if it meets the requirements of the test procedure described in paragraph 4.2.7.

4.1.8 *Heat resistance.*—There shall be no visible slip or movement of tile at or below 60°C (140°F) when bonded panels are tested as described in paragraph 4.2.8.

4.1.9 *Shrinkage.*—The maximum shrinkage in the center of the mounted tiles shall be not greater than 0.015 in. when they are tested in accordance with the procedure described in paragraph 4.2.9.

4.1.10 *Cyclic service test.*—There shall be no visible slip or movement of the tiles, warping or cracking of the tiles, or loosening of the bond when a test panel is prepared and tested in accordance with the procedure described in paragraph 4.2.10.

4.1.11 *Chemical attack.*—Visible chemical attack (noticeable, for example, as small erupted pin points or craters, bulging surface "out of flat," or soft, bubbly, or crazed surface) shall not occur on the exposed surface of the tiles when tested in accordance with the procedure described in paragraph 4.2.11.

4.1.12 *Mildew resistance.*—A disk of the adhesive shall not support growth of mildew when tested in accordance with the procedure described in paragraph 4.2.12.

4.1.13 *Grouting in joints.*—Any composition used between the tiles as a grouting material shall show no appreciable change in color after exposure for 50 hours to the accelerated fading test described in paragraph 3.2.3. Neither shall appreciable change in color take place after immersion in water for 7 days at 23°C (73.5°F).

4.2 Methods of Test for Adhesives.

4.2.1 *Tensile-shear strength.*

4.2.1.1 The panels for the slippage test shall consist of ¾-in., 5-ply exterior grade Douglas fir plywood, approximately 14 in. by 14 in., on which shall be mounted three field tiles which have been applied according to the adhesive manufacturer's recommendation, except that the tiles shall be unpointed or ungrouted. The three field tiles shall be mounted, unsupported, in a straight horizontal row in the center of the board while the board is in a vertical position. A suitable marking shall be made on the tile and the plywood by which any slippage can be noted after 7 days.

A simulated ceiling surface composed of ¾-in., 5-ply exterior grade Douglas fir plywood, on which nine field tiles are applied in accordance with the adhesive manufacturer's recommendations, shall be prepared. These tiles shall be visually examined for separation from the panel after 7 days.

4.2.1.2 The tensile-shear strength test shall be made with a single lap-jointed specimen. The specimen is prepared by bonding, with the adhesive, a strip of polystyrene wall tile, 1 in. wide by 4 in. long, to a plywood strip (¾-in., 5-ply exterior grade Douglas fir plywood) of the same size. The polystyrene strip shall overlap the plywood for an area of 2 sq. in. The specimen shall be broken in a suitable tensile testing machine (such as a Scott Model J-2) at a rate of jaw separation of 2 in. per minute. The specimens shall be held in the grips so that the outer 1.5 in. of each end are in contact with the jaws and so that the long axis of the test specimen shall coincide with the direction of applied force through the center line of the grip assembly. Separate blocks, the thickness of the adherents, shall be used in the grips to insure that the adhesive bond is loaded in shear and not in cleavage. Ten such specimens shall be used to obtain each average tensile-shear strength value. The method of test is similar to the American Society for Testing Materials Tentative Method of Test D 1002, for Strength Properties of Adhesives in Shear by Tension Loading (Metal to Metal).

4.2.2 *Effect of heat aging.*—Ten tensile-shear-strength specimens shall be prepared from $3/4$-in. 5-ply exterior grade Douglas fir plywood, and shall be aged at $23° ±2°C$ ($73.5° ±4°F$) and $50 ±2$ per cent relative humidity, for 21 days. The specimens shall then be aged in a circulating-air oven at $65° ±2°C$ ($149° ±4°F$) and a relative humidity of less than 10 per cent, for 7 days. The specimens shall be conditioned to temperature equilibrium, by allowing them to stand at $23° ±2°C$ ($73.5° ±4°F$) for 1 hour, and then tested immediately.

4.2.3 *Effect of moisture aging.*—Ten tensile-shear-strength specimens shall be prepared from $3/4$-in., 5-ply exterior grade Douglas fir plywood, and shall be aged at $23° ±2°C$ ($73.5° ±4°F$) and 50 per cent $±2$ per cent relative humidity, for 21 days. The specimens shall be immersed in water at $23° ±2°C$ ($73.5° ±4°F$) for 24 hours. After conditioning according to paragraph 3.2.1, the assemblies shall be tested according to paragraph 4.2.1.2.

4.2.4 *Panel immersion test.*—A simulated wall section 10 in. by 10 in., composed of $3/4$-in., 5-ply exterior grade Douglas fir plywood, on which four field tile mounted to form a square approximately $8½$ in. on a side are applied in accordance with the adhesive manufacturer's recommendations, shall be prepared, except that the tile shall be unpointed and ungrouted. This assembly shall then be conditioned for 21 days at room temperature. The assembly shall then be immersed and held in a vertical position in water at $23° ±2°C$ ($73.5° ±4°F$) for 7 days, and visual examination of slippage or separation shall be noted.

4.2.5 *Static load test.*—An inverted field tile shall be fastened to a surface by means of five screws. The exposed surface of the tile shall be bonded with the adhesive to a plywood disk $½$ in. thick, and with a diameter equal to the diagonal of the tile. This disk shall be fastened with an adhesive according to the adhesive manufacturer's recommendations. A screw hook shall then be located exactly in the center of the plywood disk; the specimen shall then be conditioned for 3 days at room temperature, after which the assembly shall be inverted to simulate a ceiling installation, and weights shall be added to the hook to bring the total load to 0.25 psi, including the plywood disk and hook.

The adhesive shall be considered as failing if any separation from the back of the tile is noted within 28 days.

4.2.6 *Simulated-aging test.*—The specimen shall be prepared by bonding with the adhesive a strip of polystyrene wall tile, 1 in. wide by 4¼ in. long, to paper-covered plasterboard ⅜ in. by 4 in. by 4 in., as illustrated in Fig. 20-1, below. The adhesive shall be applied according to the manufacturer's recommendations. The assemblies shall be allowed to dry 1 week at room temperature and then shall be placed in a circulating-air oven at 50° ±2°C (122° ±4°F) for a period of 90 days. After conditioning according to paragraph 3.2.1 the assemblies shall be tested according to paragraph 4.2.1.2.

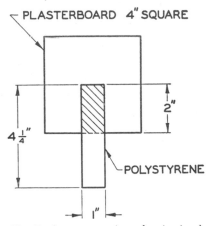

Fig. 20-1. Tensile-shear test specimen for simulated-aging test.

4.2.7 *Wetting test.*—A small gob of adhesive shall be pressed gently against a test surface and then, by reversing the pressure on the spatula, the gob shall be lifted from the surface. The stain and adhering adhesive shall be examined to observe whether failure occurs in cohesion or adhesion. The adhesive is considered "wetting" the surface if failure is in cohesion. Surfaces to be tested shall be polystyrene, plasterboard, plywood, Masonite, bare plaster, painted plaster, and concrete.

4.2.8 *Heat resistance test.*—A sheet of ¾-in., 5-ply exterior grade Douglas fir plywood 15 in. by 20 in. shall be coated with adhesive by trowel, and three rows of four tiles per row shall be installed in accordance with the procedure recommended by the manufacturer. After 3 days of aging at room temperature, heat shall be applied to the assembly by placing it in a vertical position in a circulating-air oven at 60° ±2°C (140° ±4°F) and maintaining the temperature for 6 hours. While the assembly is heating, the tile shall be examined at intervals to determine if the tile slips or warps under its own weight. If slippage or warpage is observed, the temperatures of adhesive and tile face shall be recorded. If the tile slips or warps at a temperature below 60° ±2°C (140° ±4°F), the adhesive or the tile shall be considered to be unsatisfactory. The test is to simulate the installation of tile over walls containing hot-air ducts.

4.2.9 *Shrinkage test.*—The test panel shall be a piece of flat 5-ply exterior grade Douglas fir plywood measuring approximately $\frac{3}{4}$ in. by 14 in. by 14 in. The adhesive under test shall be applied to this panel according to the recommendations of the manufacturer. Nine flat unribbed tiles, measuring $4\frac{1}{4}$ in. by $4\frac{1}{4}$ in., and having a thickness of 0.065 in. (±0.003 in.) and a cavity depth of 0.035 in. (±0.002 in.), shall be mounted on this panel according to recommended procedure, and the assembly shall be allowed to dry for 90 days in a circulating-air oven held at 50° $\pm2°C$ (122° $\pm4°F$). After removing from the oven the assembly shall be brought to standard conditions and the maximum "cupping" of the tiles (or deflection from "flat") shall be determined in both diagonal directions on each tile by use of the test instrument shown in Fig. 20-2 below.

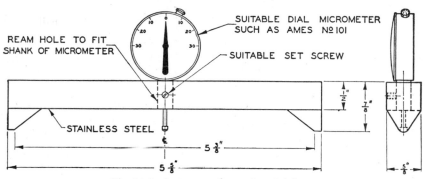

Fig. 20-2. Instrument for testing shrinkage.

Note. A zero reading on the micrometer must be obtained on a flat surface before attempting to measure deflection of tiles.

4.2.10 *Cyclic service test.*—The test panel shall be made by bonding 16 polystyrene plastic tiles, in a 4 by 4 pattern, to a piece of 5-ply exterior grade Douglas fir plywood, 18 in. by 18 in. by $\frac{3}{4}$ in. thick; the adhesive to be applied in accordance with the directions given by the manufacturer. The test panel shall be aged for 14 days at room conditions and then subjected to five cycles of the following set of conditions:

Period	Temperature		Relative humidity
	(°C)	(°F)	(%)
2	60	(140)	88
2	0	(32)	(ca) 100
2	60	(140)	10
2	60	(140)	88
16	60	(140)	10

The tile shall not warp or crack, and the bond between the plywood and the tile shall not fail.

4.2.11 *Chemical attack.*—The test panel shall consist of tile bonded to a piece of plate glass measuring approximately 5 in. by 14 in. The adhesive under test shall be applied to the panel according to the recommendations of the manufacturer. Three unribbed tiles measuring 4¼ in. by 4¼ in., and having a thickness of 0.065 in. (±0.003 in.) and a cavity depth of 0.035 in. (±0.002 in.), shall be mounted on this panel and a "grout" shall be applied around the outside of the three butted tiles (in order to simulate practical use where air circulation under each tile is reduced to a minimum by the sealing action of adjacent tiles). The assembly shall be allowed to dry for 90 days in a circulating-air oven held at 50° ±2°C (122° ±4°F). After removal from the oven, careful visual examination of the exposed surface of each tile shall be made.

4.2.12 *Mildew resistance*—The test specimen is prepared by drying a disk of the adhesive on a glass plate at 50°C (122°F) until it is of such consistency that it can be lifted from the plate and handled.

4.2.12.1 *Test apparatus.*—The apparatus for the mildew test shall be as follows:

(a) *Autoclave.*—The autoclave shall be capable of being operated at a steam pressure of 15 psi and an exhaust temperature of 121°C (249.8°F) for sterilization of media and test specimens.

(b) *Leaching.*—The leaching apparatus shall consist of as many quart jars as are necessary. Tap water shall be delivered to the bottoms of the jars at a rate of flow to give five changes per hour. The water shall be maintained at 27° to 30° C (80.6° to 86° F), and pH shall be as close to neutral as practicable, in the range of 6.0 to 8.0. The leaching period shall be 24 hours.

(c) *Petri dishes.*—10-cm-diameter petri dishes shall be used.

(d) *Room.*—A dust-free sterile room shall be maintained for inoculating the specimens. In addition, sterilamps or antiseptic sprays may be used to maintain sterile conditions.

(e) *Incubator.*—A room or cabinet shall be maintained at a a temperature of 28° to 30° C (82.4° to 86° F) and a relative humidity of 85 to 95 percent for incubating the the specimens after inoculation.

4.2.12.2 *Test medium.*—The culture medium shall have the following composition:

Ammonium nitrate	3. 0 g.
Potassium dihydrogen orthophosphate	2. 5 g.
Potassium monohydrogen orthophosphate	2. 0 g.
Magnesium sulphate—7 molecules water of crystallization	2. 0 g.

Agar... 20. 0 g.
Distilled water to make... 1,000. 0 ml.
Sucrose.. 30. 0 g.

Adjust pH to between 6.4 and 6.8 with HCl or NaOH, if necessary.

4.2.12.3 *Organism.*—The organism used shall be *Aspergillus niger,* USDA 215-4247 (ATCC 6275).

4.2.12.4 *Preparation of culture plates.*—The culture medium in flasks shall be sterilized in the autoclave for 20 minutes at a steam pressure of 15 psi and an exhaust temperature of 121°C (249.8°F). About 20 ml of the hot, sterile agar medium shall be poured into sterile petri dishes under aseptic conditions. The plates shall be covered and left undisturbed until the agar medium has hardened.

4.2.12.5 *Inoculum.*—Scrapings from a ripe fruiting culture of *Aspergillus niger* (10 to 14 days old), which completely cover a 10-cm petri dish or equivalent surface, shall be added to an Erlenmeyer flask containing 100 ml of sterile water. The transfer shall be made with a sterile loop made from nicrome, platinum, or tungsten wire. The black spore clusters shall be shaken in the flask with sterile glass beads until the tiny spores can be seen to go into suspension. Other equally satisfactory procedures for forming a suspension may be used.

The test medium for growing the *Aspergillus niger* shall be as described in paragraph 4.2.12.2.

4.2.12.6 *Inoculation of mycelial mats.*—The hardened agar medium shall be inoculated by first loading a sterile camel's hair brush with spores from the inoculum and then brushing the surfaces of the sterile agar medium uniformly.

4.2.12.7 *Incubation of mycelial mats.*—The inoculated medium in petri dishes shall be incubated for a period of 42 to 48 hours, or until the white mycelium is evident over the entire surface of the agar medium at 28° to 30° C (82° to 86° F), and at a relative humidity of 85 to 95 percent.

4.2.12.8 *Incubation of specimens.*—Specimens shall be wetted thoroughly with water and laid on the mycelial mats, then further incubated at 28° to 30° C (82° to 86° F) and at a relative humidity of 85 to 95 percent, for 14 days. *Do not use a wetting agent.*

4.2.12.9 *Results.*—Satisfactory specimens shall show no growth of *Aspergillus niger.*

5. IDENTIFICATION

5.1 *Labels and literature.*—In order that purchasers may be assured that the plastic tiles and adhesive purchased actually comply with all requirements of this commercial standard, it is recommended that manufacturers include the following statement in conjunction with their name and address on labels, invoices, sales literature, etc.:

These (this) .... comply (complies) with Commercial
    (trade name of tiles or adhesive)

Standard CS168-50, as developed by the trade, under the procedure of the Commodity Standards Division, and issued by the U. S. Department of Commerce.

5.1.1 The following abbreviated statement is suggested when available space on labels is insufficient for the full statement:

Complies with CS168-50, as developed by the trade, and issued by the U. S. Department of Commerce.

5.2 *Hallmark.*—Polystyrene plastic wall tile and adhesive containers may carry the following hallmark (see Fig. 20-3) to indicate compliance with this commercial standard:

Fig. 20-3. Hallmark.

6. EFFECTIVE DATE

6.1 Having been passed through the regular procedure of the Commodity Standards Division, and approved by the acceptors hereinafter listed, this commercial standard was issued by the United States Department of Commerce, effective from July 15, 1950.

7. HISTORY OF PROJECT

7.1 In October 1947 manufacturers of polystyrene plastic wall tiles, through the Plastic Wall Tile Manufacturers Institute and the Society of the Plastics Industry, requested the assistance of the Commodity Standards Division of the National Bureau of Standards in establishing a commercial standard for their product. The phenomenal boom in building construction had created an active market for plastic wall tiles, and the very rapid growth of this comparatively new industry emphasized the need for a standard as a guide to those contemplating the use of such tile. Producers, too, felt the need for a standard by which to control the quality of their expanding production.

7.2 With a view to developing a commercial standard for polystyrene plastic wall tiles and the adhesives used in their application, representatives of the molders and of the raw material producers met several times during 1948 and 1949 with representatives of the National Bureau of Standards to discuss the various requirements to be included in the standard.

7.3 The preliminary draft that was evolved from these discussions and from laboratory tests of the materials was circulated to leading manufacturers, Government agencies, and others concerned for their advance review and comment. Some helpful suggestions were received as a result. These were included in the adjusted draft of the recommended standard sent on November 29, 1949, to manufacturers, distributors, contractors, architects, installers, and users, for their consideration and approval.

7.4 Written acceptances representing adequate support by manufacturers, distributors, and users resulted from this circularization, together with a few additional suggestions for modification of the standard. After careful consideration of these suggestions by the proponents, certain adjustments were made in the standard with the general concurrence of the acceptors. On June 15, 1950, an announcement was issued that the standard, designated CS168-50, had been approved for promulgation and publication, effective from July 15, 1950.

APPENDIX

Installation and maintenance.—The following instructions on installation and maintenance should be followed in order to insure best results with plastic tiles and adhesives conforming to this commercial standard:

(1) *Installation.*

(a) *Temperature.*—Polystyrene wall tiles and adhesives should not be installed at temperatures less than 21° C (70° F). The room temperature should also be not less than 21° C (70° F).

(b) *Condition of adhesives.*—All adhesives should be clean and thoroughly mixed to a uniform composition.

(c) *Condition of wall.*—All adhesives should be installed over plaster, wood, plywood, concrete, cement, wallboard, or any wall surface that is structurally solid. The walls should be straight, even, clean, dry, and free from high or low spots. All corners should be square and plumb. Wallpaper, linoleum, and oilcloth should be removed and the old adhesive washed off the wall before the tiles are installed. Improperly bonded paint, lacquer, and enamel should be removed before the tiles are installed. Water-soluble paint surfaces should first be removed. Tiles should not be installed over any surface of wall through which moisture may penetrate unless the wall is treated with an adequate moisture barrier.

(d) *Job layout.*—Where possible, all installations should be planned so that the joint lines will be level at wainscot height. When tiles are applied to ceilings, start at the center of the ceiling and work out in all directions.

(e) *Water.*—The tiles should be installed in a manner to prevent water from getting into the supporting surface in back of the tile. This requires adequate sealing particularly around sinks, wash bowls, bathtubs, shower bases, etc.

(f) *Heat.*—Hot-air ducts, chimneys, registers, radiators, heaters, stoves, etc., should be shielded or insulated in such a manner that the wall tile temperature shall not exceed 60° C (140° F). Tiles should not be installed when hot water or air will cause the temperature of the installed tiles to exceed 60° C (140° F).

(g) *Cutting.*—The tiles should be cut by guillotine-type cutters, coarse-tooth hacksaws, coping saws, or power-driven cutting tools. The tiles should not be cut with scissors, metal shears, or knives, or by scribing and cracking.

(h) *Application of adhesive.*—The adhesive should be combed onto the walls with a wavy motion by using a specially notched trowel. The coating of adhesive should be of such thickness that when the tile is pressed firmly against the wall the ridges of adhesive formed by the notched trowel will flatten and contact at least 60 percent of the back of the tile. All tiles should be pressed firmly into position to insure good adhesion.

(i) *Joints.*—The tiles should be laid in such a manner that they are not set tightly edge to edge. There should be a slight space of at least 0.005 in. between each tile, or 0.001 in. per inch of tile face, whichever is greater.

(j) *Wall fixtures.*—Towel bars, soap holders, paper holders, pull bars, tooth-brush holders, etc., should be of the types that are inset in the wall or fastened directly to the subconstruction. Accessories should not be fastened to the plastic wall tile.

(k) *Finishing.*—Excessive adhesive should be removed from the face of the tile with a suitable cleaner before it dries. It is recommended that the surface of the plastic tile be coated with a suitable destaticizer and/or wax.

(2) *Maintenance.*

(a) *Cleaners.*—Suitable cleaners should not etch, mar, or otherwise attack the plastic or the dried adhesive. They should not leave any residual film that detracts from the appearance of the tile. Warm, soapy water is the best cleaning agent for polystyrene wall tile after installation. Abrasive cleaners, gasoline, paint thinners, turpentine, carbon tetrachloride, or similar cleaning agents should be avoided.

(b) *Waxes.*—If waxes are used they should not etch, mar, or otherwise attack the plastic or the dried adhesive. They should withstand a minimum of 10 cold-water rinses and 5 warm, soapy-water washes. Most paste waxes and all oil-base waxes will attack the tile and should be avoided.

(c) *Plastics.*—Where vinyl-type plastic curtains are used, they should not be in prolonged contact with polystyrene wall tiles.

(d) *Insecticides.*—Direct contact of the tiles with insecticides should be avoided.

(3) *Flammability.*

(a) Polystyrene-tiled walls do not contribute any more to the fire hazard of structures in which they are located than the woodwork, wall covering, or the paint on which they are often mounted, or in fact than the furniture, floor coverings, or window hangings in common use. It is true that exposed edges of tile can be made to burn if held in an open flame. When ignited, polystyrene is rated as a "slow burning" plastic according to American Society for Testing Materials Method of Test D 635-44. However, it is known that polystyrene tile, molded and mounted as decorative wall coverings according to these specifications, do not constitute a greater fire hazard than other well-known organic building materials, such as wood and paint.

Heavy-Duty Alpha-Cellulose-Filled Melamine Tableware (Commercial Standard 173-50)
(Effective from December 15, 1950)

1. PURPOSE

1.1 The purpose of this commercial standard is to foster maintenance of the quality of heavy-duty alpha-cellulose-filled melamine tableware, and to provide a nationally recognized specification for the information of producers, distributors, and users.

2. SCOPE

2.1 This commercial standard covers chemical and physical properties and methods of test for heavy-duty tableware molded from alpha-cellulose-filled melamine materials. The materials used are composed of melamine-for-maldehyde resin combined with alpha-cellulose as the filler. An identifying hallmark and recommended statement of compliance are included.

3. REQUIREMENTS

3.1 *Thickness.*—Tableware conforming to this commercial standard shall have a thickness of not less than 0.100 inch over not less than 90 percent of the surface area, and the remainder shall not be less than 0.090 inch in thickness.

3.2 *Finish.*—The surface of all tableware shall have a high luster produced by molding, and not by the application of finish or protective coating or lacquer, or by the use of other adulterants. Flash or parting lines only shall be buffed to a high polish.

3.3 *Resistance to boiling sulfuric-acid solution.*—When tested in accordance with paragraph 4.2, tableware shall show no chalking and/or loss of gloss that is readily perceptible without close examination.

3.4 *Resistance to boiling water.*—When tested in accordance with paragraph 4.3, the tableware shall not develop cracks, or show surface chalking or any other defects that might impair the serviceability or appearance of the tableware.

3.5 *Resistance to dry heat.*—When tested in accordance with paragraph 4.4, the tableware shall show no cracks.

4. METHODS OF TEST

4.1 The methods of test are especially designed so that they can be conducted by purchasers, distributors, or molders without the use of costly equipment, and by personnel that need not be specially trained. Meeting these tests is evidence of proper molding.

4.1.1 Five specimens chosen at random shall be tested to determine conformance of tableware with each of the requirements of section 3. If one of the five specimens fails to meet the requirements of a given test, five additional specimens shall be subjected to that test, all of which shall be required to pass the test in order to indicate conformance of the tableware with this commercial standard. If more than one of the original five specimens for a given test fails, the tableware shall be reported as failing to conform with this commercial standard.

4.2 *Sulfuric acid test.*

4.2.1 *Materials:*

    (a) Aqueous solution of sulfuric acid 0.8 percent by weight. This solution can be obtained from a local druggist or chemical supply house.

    (b) Porcelain-enameled or stainless-steel pail, with cover, about 2- to 3-quart capacity (2000 to 3000 ml). Enameled ware must not be used if the inside surface is chipped, exposing bare metal.

(c) Heater, preferably a gas burner of about 4 to 5 inches in diameter. In any event, it should have sufficient capacity to keep the acid solution boiling fairly vigorously.

4.2.2 *Procedure.*—Five untested specimens shall be used for this test. From the molding to be tested, cut a cross-section strip about 3 inches wide, if a plate, dish, or saucer is being tested. If testing a cup, cut a section of about one-half of the molded part, taking for the test that part which includes the handle. The entire piece of tableware may be used if it is desired not to destroy it by cutting.

Heat to boiling a fresh portion of acid solution, keeping the container covered. Immerse the test piece(s) and re-cover the vessel. Keep boiling. Remove test piece(s) after 10 minutes, ±0.5 minute, rinse in cold water, and dry. Inspect for conformance with paragraph 3.3.

4.2.3. *Precautions.*

4.2.3.1 The acid solution is corrosive, and care should be taken that it is not splashed on one's person or clothing, or about the premises.

4.2.3.2 Use fresh acid solution for each test run.

4.2.3.3 The solution must be kept boiling during the 10 minutes of the test. If too many test pieces are put in at once, the solution will be cooled to such an extent that it will stop boiling, thus endangering the accuracy of the test. By trial and error, one can determine the maximum number of parts which can be properly tested at one time.

4.2.3.4 Test pieces can be attached to fairly heavy cord or string, and be removed by this means when the test is completed.

4.2.3.5 Test pieces should be kept separated during boiling so that the acid bath has free access to all surfaces.

4.2.3.6 Dispose of waste acid solution by allowing it to cool, then flushing it down the toilet, using plenty of water.

4.3 *Resistance to boiling water.*—Five untested specimens shall be used for this test. Each sample of tableware shall be placed in boiling water for 30 minutes, removed, and allowed to stand for 1 hour at room temperature. This cycle shall be immediately repeated three times to give a total of four such cycles. The tableware shall be allowed to stand for 48 hours in air at room temperature. In cases of dispute, a temperature of 23° ±1.1°C (73.5° ±2°F), and a relative humidity of 50 percent ±4 percent shall be maintained. Inspect the tableware for conformance with paragraph 3.4.

4.4 *Resistance to dry heat.*—Five untested specimens shall be used for this test. Place the tableware in a circulating-air oven for 8 hours at 170° F. Cool to room temperature, and inspect for conformance with paragraph 3.5.

5. MARKING AND IDENTIFICATION

5.1 *Hallmark.*—Pieces of heavy-duty alpha-cellulose-filled melamine tableware may carry the hallmark shown in Fig. 20-4, which shall constitute the manufacturer's declaration of compliance with this commercial standard.

Fig. 20-4. Enlarged reproduction of hallmark.

5.2 *Marking.*—In order that purchasers may be assured that pieces of heavy-duty alpha-cellulose-filled melamine tableware purchased actually comply with all requirements of this commercial standard, it is recommended that manufacturers include the following statement in conjunction with their name and address on labels, invoices, sales literature, etc.:

> This (these) article(s) of heavy-duty alpha-cellulose-filled melamine tableware complies (comply) with Commercial Standard CS173-50, as developed by the trade under the procedure of the Commodity Standards Division, and issued by the U. S. Department of Commerce.

5.3 When available space on labels is insufficient for the full statement in legible type, an abbreviated statement, as follows, is recommended:

> Complies with CS173-50, as developed by the trade, and issued by the U. S. Department of Commerce.

6. EFFECTIVE DATE

6.1 Having been passed through the regular procedure of the Commodity Standards Division, and approved by the acceptors hereinafter listed, this commercial standard was issued by the United States Department of Commerce, effective from December 15, 1950.

7. HISTORY OF PROJECT

On April 26, 1949, the Society of the Plastics Industry, Inc., requested the cooperation of the National Bureau of Standards in the establishment of a commercial standard for heavy-duty alpha-cellulose-filled melamine tableware.

Following receipt of this request by the Bureau, copies of a proposed commercial standard for heavy-duty alpha-cellulose-filled melamine tableware, endorsed by the proponent organization, were circulated to selected representatives of manufacturers, distributors, purchasers, testing laboratories, and Government agencies for advance comment. The specification was adjusted in accordance with majority viewpoint as indicated by the comment.

With the unqualified endorsement of a number of interested organizations, the recommended commercial standard was submitted to the trade for written acceptance on September 18, 1950. Having received acceptances in writing estimated to represent a satisfactory majority, announcement was issued on November 15, 1950, that the standard would become effective for new production on December 15, 1950.

General Purpose Vinyl Plastic Film
(Commercial Standard CS192-53)

(Effective May 22, 1953)

1. PURPOSE, SCOPE AND GENERAL DESCRIPTION OF PRODUCTS COVERED

1.1 *Purpose.*—The purpose of this commercial standard is to promulgate minimum standards in order to maintain the quality of the materials in question for the mutual protection of manufacturers and consumers.

1.2 *Scope.*—This standard covers methods of test and requirements of general purpose vinyl plastic film to insure satisfactory products for consumer use. The requirements and methods of test specify thickness tolerances, yield per roll, width tolerances, shrinkage at elevated temperatures, contamination, appearance, crocking, tensile properties, tear resistance, volatility of plasticizer, water extraction, low temperature impact and flammability. Suggested forms for declaring compliance with the standard and an identifying hallmark are included.

1.3 *General description of products covered.*—The material covered is nonrigid, unsupported, vinyl plastic film 10 mils and less in thickness, including transparent, translucent and opaque material, and whether plain, embossed, molded or otherwise surface treated.

2. DIMENSIONAL TOLERANCES

2.1 *Thickness.*—The average thickness of the film shall be within ±10% of that specified. The average thickness shall be determined from 5 uniformly-spaced readings taken across the width of the sheet. The referee test method for average thickness shall be the method described in paragraph 4.1.

2.1.1 *Average thickness based on yield per roll.*—The yield of material in any one roll shall be based on average thickness of the film, which shall be ±5% of the thickness specified, calculated as follows:

$$\text{Average thickness (mils)} = \frac{770 \times \text{Net Weight (lbs.)}}{\text{sp. g.} \times \text{length (yds.)} \times \text{width (in.)}}$$

2.2 *Width.*—The film shall be held to a tolerance of +½ −0 in. of the width specified by the purchaser and agreed to by the manufacturer. This tolerance shall apply when the material is in roll form on the core.

2.3 *Length.*—The length of material, excluding that which has been subjected to embossing, printing, etc., shall be continuous in any one roll and the total length in a roll shall be as agreed to by the manufacturer and the purchaser.

3. REQUIREMENTS

3.1 *Shrinkage at elevated temperatures.*—The average dimensional change shall be not greater than 7% in any direction when tested at a temperature of 100° C for 30 minutes in accordance with the method referred to in paragraph 4.2.

3.2 *Contamination.*—The material shall be as free as is commercially practical from pinholes, particles of foreign matter, and undispersed raw materials. The material shall have no visible holes.

3.3 *Appearance.*—The material shall be as free as is commercially practical from visual defects, e.g., "cold-checks," "crow's feet," "pine trees," "streaks," and "blisters." It shall also have smooth edges, free from cuts and nicks.

3.4 *Crocking.*—The amount of color transferred from the specimen under examination to the white test square shall not be perceptible when tested in accordance with the method described in paragraph 4.3.

3.5 *Tensile properties.*—The minimum average tensile strength of the material when tested in accordance with the method referred to in paragraph 4.4 shall be 2100 psi when tested with the pendulum-type machine and 2300 psi when a static controlled separation-type machine is used. Either of the above methods may be used. If the film meets the requirement by any one method, the film shall be considered as passed. The minimum ultimate elongation of the materials shall be 150%.

3.6 *Tensile tear resistance.*—The minimum average tensile tear strength (either plain or after embossing, if embossed) in any direction shall be 200 lb/in. when tested in accordance with the method referred to in paragraph 4.5.

3.7 *Elmendorf tear resistance.*—The minimum average Elmendorf tear strength (either plain or after embossing, if embossed) in any direction shall be 180 grams *per sheet* for film 3 mils or less in thickness and 60 g. *per mil* for film greater than 3 mils in thickness when tested in accordance with the method referred to in paragraph 4.6. The average shall be determined from measuring five samples taken across the width of the sheet, two of which samples shall be taken directly adjacent to the longitudinal edges of the sheet, the remaining three being equally spaced between these two.

3.8 *Plasticizer volatility.*—The average weight loss based on initial film weight shall be not more than 10% for film 3 mils or less in thickness; 9% for 4 mils; 7½% for 6 mils; 5% for film 8 mils in thickness, when tested at a temperature of 70° ±2°C (158° ±3.6°F) for 24 hours in accordance with the method referred to in paragraph 4.7.

3.9 *Water extraction.*—The material shall show not more than 1% average loss by weight when tested in accordance with the method referred to in paragraph 4.8.

3.10 *Low temperature impact.*—Not more than two specimens out of ten shall fail when tested at a temperature of −17.8° ±2°C (0° ±3.6°F) in accordance with the method described in paragraph 4.9.

3.11 *Flammability.*—The rate of burning shall not exceed 1.2 in./sec. as judged by the average of five determinations lengthwise and five determinations transverse to the direction of processing, when tested with the SPI Flammability Tester in accordance with the method described in paragraph 4.10.

NOTE: *Light stability.*—At the industry meeting on November 18, 1952, the desirability of including a requirement for light stability was discussed at some length.

The Society of the Plastics Industry Committee which prepared the recommended Commercial Standard for general purpose vinyl plastic film recognized the value and need of such a requirement. However, after years of work by the Society of the Plastics Industry group which was assigned the problem of selecting or developing a suitable method of test for light stability, as well as the enormous amount of work done by the American Society for Testing Materials and various governmental agencies such as the National Bureau of Standards, no suitable method has been found or developed. Two major difficulties have been encountered as follows:

(1) The poor degree of reproducibility between different pieces of apparatus of the same type;

(2) The poor degree of correlation between laboratory light stability tests and service behavior.

The SPI group working on light stability hopes to have a reasonably satisfactory method in a year or two. It was the opinion of the committee recommending this specification for promulgation as a Commercial Standard that it would be more of a detriment to the plastic film industry than a benefit to wait for at least another two years to issue this standard because of the lack of this one test. When a suitable test method is developed, the Commercial Standard can be revised. Any help which anyone can offer to the SPI group will be appreciated.

4. METHODS OF TEST

4.1 *Average thickness (weight method)*.

4.1.1 *Apparatus.*

- (a) Analytical balance, equipped with pan straddle or other stationary support, sensitive to 0.0005 g.

- (b) Class S. Weights.

- (c) Beaker, 250 ml.

- (d) Fine non-absorbent thread or wire.

- (e) Thermometer, 0-100° C, graduated in 1° divisions.

- (f) Die or template, for cutting test specimens, 10 cm. $\times$ 10 cm., with dimensional tolerance of ± 0.01 cm. per side.

- (g) Sharp knife or razor.

4.1.2 *Test specimens.*—Five 10 cm. $\times$ 10 cm. specimens taken uniformly across the width of the sheet shall be tested.

4.1.3 *Test conditions.*—The specimens shall be conditioned and tested in accordance with Procedure A of ASTM D618, Tentative Methods of Conditioning Plastics and Electrical Insulating Materials for Testing.

4.1.4 *Procedure.*

4.1.4.1 By means of the die or template and the sharp knife or razor, cut 5 specimens from the sample of material.

4.1.4.2 Weigh each specimen to the nearest 0.5 mg on the analytical balance. Record the weight as W.

4.1.4.3 Following the procedure of ASTM D792, Methods of Test for Specific Gravity of Plastics, Method A, determine the specific gravity of each specimen and record as D. Use of a wetting agent is recommended.

4.1.5 *Calculations.*—Calculate the average thickness of each test specimen, using the following formula, and average the two values:

$$T = \frac{394W}{100D} = 3.94 \, \frac{W}{D}$$

Where T = average thickness of test specimen in mils
W = weight of test specimen in grams
D = density of test specimen in grams per cc
   (specific gravity = density in metric units)
394 = conversion factor, cm to mils
100 = area of specimen in sq cm.

4.2 *Shrinkage at elevated temperatures.*—The dimensional change shall be determined in accordance with ASTM D1204, entitled Method of Test for Measurement of Changes in Linear Dimensions of Nonrigid Thermoplastics Sheeting and Film.

4.3 *Crocking.*

4.3.1 *Definition.*—Color fastness to rubbing (crocking) is understood to be resistance to physical transfer of color from the material under test to a piece of white cotton under the conditions of the test.

4.3.2 *Apparatus.*—AATCC crockmeter. (Crockmeter and cloth, 2 × 2 in. test squares, may be obtained from the secretary of the American Association of Textile Chemists and Colorists, Lowell Textile Institute, Lowell, Mass.)

4.3.3 *Materials.*—White bleached cotton cloth, starch-free, cut into 2 in. test squares. Lawns, percales or print cloths are suitable. (See par. 4.3.2.)

4.3.4 *Test specimens.*—Two 2 × 5 in. specimens of film shall be used, one for the dry test and one for the wet test.

4.3.5 *Procedure.*—The test specimen shall be preconditioned in accordance with ASTM D618, Procedure A, Tentative Methods of Conditioning Plastics and Electrical Insulating Materials for Testing. The test specimen shall then be placed on the base of the crockmeter so as to rest flat on the abrasive cloth with its long dimension in the direction of the rubbing. The square of white testing cloth is mounted over the end of the finger which projects downward from the slide, with the weave oblique to the direction of rubbing, and is held in place by the spiral clip. The covered finger of the slide is then placed on the test specimen and is slid back and forth for 20 rubbings, i.e., for 10 steady turns of the crank at the rate of one turn per second.

For wet rubbing (crocking) tests, the white testing square is thoroughly wet out in distilled water, squeezed and then passed through a wringer between two sheets of filter paper just before use. Otherwise the procedure for wet rubbing is the same as for dry rubbing.

Accidental damage to the rubbing finger, spiral clip, or abrasive cloth may be repaired when noticeable as follows: The abrasive cloth is neatly renewed; the clip is bent further open or shut over an inserted rod of the correct diameter as required; the finger is resurfaced by movement on an extra piece of fine emery cloth in a manner simulating regular use.

4.4 *Tensile properties.*—The tensile strength and elongation shall be determined in accordance with Method B of ASTM D882, entitled Methods of Test for Tensile Properties of Thin Plastic Sheets and Films, using specimens 1 in. wide. The thickness of the specimens tested shall be determined as described in par. 4.1.

4.5 *Tensile tear resistance.*—The tensile tear strength shall be determined in accordance with ASTM D1004, entitled Method of Test for Tear Resistance of Plastic Film and Sheeting. The Thickness of the specimens tested shall be determined as described in par. 4.1.

4.6 *Elmendorf tear resistance.*—The Elmendorf tear strength shall be determined in accordance with ASTM D689, entitled Method of Test for Internal Tearing Resistance of Paper, except that readings obtained where the tear deviates more than 10 mm ($\frac{3}{8}$ in.) from the line of the initial slit shall not be rejected when obtained with embossed films. The thickness of the specimens tested shall be determined as described in par. 4.1.

4.7 *Plasticizer volatility.*—The plasticizer volatility shall be determined in accordance with ASTM D1203, entitled Method of Test for Volatile Loss from Plastic Materials.

4.8 *Water extraction.*—The percentage loss in weight from extraction by distilled water shall be determined in accordance with ASTM D1239, entitled Method of Test for Resistance of Plastic Films to Extraction by Chemicals, except that the specimens shall be preconditioned for three hours at 50° ±3°C (122° ±5.4°F), removed from the oven, placed in the desiccator and allowed to cool to room temperature before weighing. Also, the immersion test shall be made for 24 hours at 50° ±3°C (122° ±5.4°F) in distilled water only.

4.9 *Low temperature impact.*

4.9.1 *Apparatus.*—Cold chambers at least 18×18×18 in. that open from the top are preferable. Dry ice cabinets cooled by circulated air and solid carbon dioxide that are equipped with heater units perform well for this test.

The impact machine shown in Figs. 20-5 and 20-6 is constructed of cold rolled steel except for the bolts, screws and rubber stopper. All structural parts (i.e., base, anvil, arm, arm supports and shaft) may be chromium plated.

The arm including rubber stopper and bolt shall weigh 6 lb. and 13 oz. ±1 oz.

Lubricants are not usually necessary. However, if lubrication is necessary, suitable low-temperature lubricants shall be used.

A 2×5¾ in. die, a good desk type of stapler with metal base and stop mounted on base exactly ½ in. back of the center of the groove that turns the staple, 2×5 in. cards of regular 5×8 in. index file card stock.

4.9.2 *Procedure.*—The impact machine shall be in the cold chamber at −17.8° ±2°C (0° ±3.6°F) at all times. The temperature shall be measured in close proximity to the test specimen.

Ten specimens shall be cut with a die with the long dimension parallel with the transverse direction of the film or sheet. Each 2×5¾ in. specimen

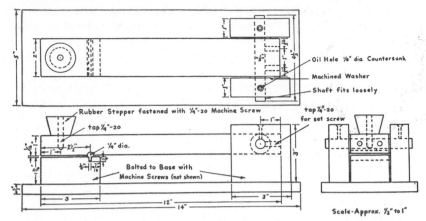

Oil Hole ⅛" dia. Countersunk

Machined Washer

Shaft fits loosely

Rubber Stopper fastened with ¼"-20 Machine Screw

tap ¼"-20 for set screw

tap ¼"-20

¼" dia.

Bolted to Base with Machine Screws (not shown)

Scale-Approx. ½" to I"

Fig. 20-5

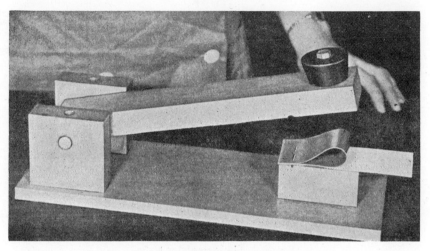

Fig. 20-6

shall be cut and folded lengthwise with normal loop at room temperature. The two ends of the folded specimen and one end of the 2×5 in. card shall be matched exactly with the loop lying on the card. Two staples shall be crimped, ½ in. from and parallel to the 2-in. end of the stack.

The mounted specimens with loops up shall be placed in the cold chamber at the desired testing temperature for a conditioning period of an hour.

The card with specimen (after conditioning) shall be placed on the anvil with the crimped ends of the staples on the back of the card fitted into the groove in the anvil (see Fig. 20-6). The card shall be handled—not the sample. The arm shall be allowed to fall free from a position within 5° off perpendicular to the base. In order to facilitate this, a mechanical release device may be employed. The arm shall then be raised, the sample on the card shall be removed from the anvil, and the next specimen shall be positioned and struck, etc.

The removed specimen shall be examined for failure which shall consist of breaking into two or more pieces.

4.10 *Flammability.*

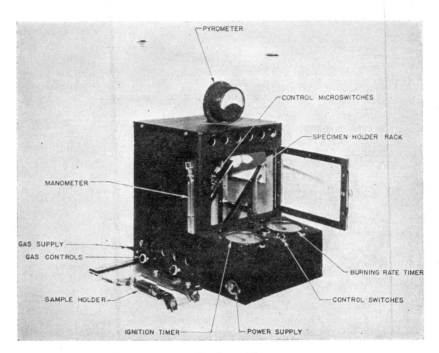

Fig. 20-7. SPI flammability tester.

4.10.1 *Apparatus and Materials.*—The apparatus shall be constructed essentially as shown in Fig. 20-7 and shall consist of the following:

4.10.1.1 *Specimen holder.*—A removable, flat, specimen holding rack, the upper and lower sections of which are separate, shall have the shape and dimensions shown in Fig. 20-8. (Sketch of sample holding rack.) The specimen is supported by tight closure of the upper and lower sections around the sides of the specimen. The center section of the rack contains an open U-shaped area in which burning of the specimen takes place. At the open end of the rack the forked sides are at an angle of 45° for the last inch. Thus, when the rack is slid into the cabinet on runners mounted at a 45° angle, the

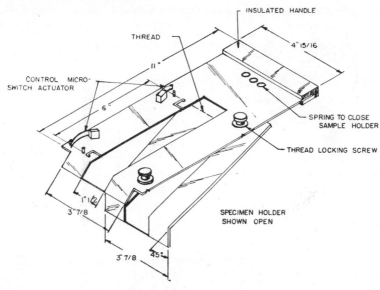

INSULATED HANDLE

THREAD

4" 15/16

CONTROL MICRO-
SWITCH ACTUATOR

11"

6"

SPRING TO CLOSE
SAMPLE HOLDER

THREAD LOCKING SCREW

1" 1/2

3" 7/8

SPECIMEN HOLDER
SHOWN OPEN

3' 7/8   45°

Fig. 20-8

bent portion of the specimen adjacent to the igniter flame is vertical and the remainder is at 45°.

The switch activators consist of suitable springs mounted on the side of the rack, one just beyond the curved portion at the open end, and the other at the closed end of the U-shaped holder. The springs are depressed and held in position prior to ignition by means of cotton thread suitably wound across the specimen and securely attached to the rack. As flame reaches these threads, the springs are released, thus activating the microswitches of the stop clocks.

4.10.1.2 *Igniter flame.*—The igniter flame shall be produced at the tip of a No. 22 hypodermic needle jet. The igniter shall be so located in the cabinet that the tip of the needle is $9/16$ in. from the surface of the specimen when the specimen rack is in place.

4.10.1.3 *Cabinet.*—The cabinet shall protect the igniter flame and specimen from air currents during test yet contain a suitable door or window for visual operation, provision for inserting the specimen holder, and adjustable vents to supply sufficient air for combustion of the specimen. It should also be capable of rapid ventilation following a test so that all combustion products can be removed between tests. A hood may be used if its exhaust fan is turned off during the test.

4.10.1.4 *Timing mechanism.*—The burning rate shall be determined by a stop clock through microswitches mounted on the specimen holder rack. The clock is started when the specimen flame burns the first thread, and is stopped when the thread at the upper end of the holder 6 in. from the first thread burns apart. The timing mechanism shall be capable of indicating time interval to 0.1 second.

4.10.1.5 *Butane.*—Butane gas, unless otherwise specified, shall be used for the igniter flame.

4.10.1.6 *Thread.*—J. & P. Coats heavy duty white cotton thread.

4.10.1.7 *Microburner.*

4.10.2 *Test specimens.*

4.10.2.1 Test specimens shall be 3 in. in width and 9 in. in length. They shall be free from folds or wrinkles. Five specimens from each direction (machine and transverse) of a given material shall be tested.

4.10.2.2 *Conditioning.*—The conditioning procedure shall conform to the requirements of Procedure B, Methods of Conditioning Plastics and Electrical Insulating Materials for Testing, ASTM Designation D618.

4.10.3 *Procedure.*

4.10.3.1 After preparing the specimens, the holder shall be threaded so as to depress the switch activators (springs) at least $\frac{1}{4}$ in. from the edge of the holder. Each activator shall be separately threaded, the thread passing down through the J-slots and under the upper jaws so that the thread is adjacent to the specimen when the holder is closed.

4.10.3.2 The specimen shall be inserted into the holder so it extends down into the lock springs and is held firmly between the two wires at the open end of the burning channel. These wires insure that the end of the specimen is always the correct distance from the igniter flame. The sample shall be free from wrinkles or distortion when the holder is closed. The specimen should not extend beyond the outer edge of the lower plate, otherwise the rack may not slide freely on the slide channel on introducing it into the cabinet.

4.10.3.3 Prior to introducing the specimen and holder into the cabinet, both electrical switches shall be set for automatic timing. The needle valve regulating the butane flow shall be adjusted to provide a $\frac{1}{2}$-in. flame. (When the specimen is in place its surface is $\frac{9}{16}$ in. from the tip of the needle and the flame is just barely flattened against the specimen. This can be checked by using a specimen made of asbestos in place of a plastic specimen.)

4.10.3.4 With the hood fan off, clocks zeroed, and flame adjusted as mentioned, the door is closed and the specimen holder is then inserted at a constant rate. The holder should be allowed to slide down the rails by gravity, taking about $\frac{1}{2}$ second to travel the length of the slide. Any hesitation in bringing the specimen holder fully into burning position may cause erroneous ignition results.

4.10.3.5 The burning time shall be read from the stop clock and the rate of burning calculated. Results that deviate from the mean value of all tests should be rejected if the deviation of the doubtful value is more than 5 times the average deviation from the mean obtained by excluding the doubtful value. Such doubtful values shall be discarded and retests made.

5. IDENTIFICATION

5.1 *Labels and literature.*—In order that purchasers may be assured that the general purpose vinyl film actually complies with all requirements of this commercial standard, it is recommended that manufacturers include the following statement in conjunction with their name and address on labels, invoices, sales literature, etc.:

These (this) .... comply (complies) with Commercial Standard CS192-53, as developed by the trade, under the procedure of the Commodity Standards Division, and issued by the U. S. Department of Commerce.

5.1.1 The following abbreviated statement is suggested when available space on labels is insufficient for the full statement:

Complies with CS192-53, as developed by the trade and issued by the U. S. Department of Commerce.

Fig. 20-9

5.2 *Hallmark.*—General purpose vinyl film may carry the hallmark shown in Fig. 20-9 to indicate compliance with this Commercial Standard.

6. EFFECTIVE DATE

6.1 Having been passed through the regular procedure of the Commodity Standards Division, and approved by the acceptors hereinafter listed,

this Commercial Standard was issued by the United States Department of
Commerce, effective from May 22, 1953.

7. HISTORY OF PROJECT

In a letter dated August 6, 1952, the Society of the Plastics Industry requested the cooperation of the Commodity Standards Division, Office of
Industry and Commerce, in the establishment of a Commercial Standard for
general purpose vinyl film, and submitted as a basis for the standard a specification developed by a committee of the SPI.

The Commodity Standards Division distributed copies of the proposed
Commercial Standard to representative producers, distributors, testing laboratories, users, and Government agencies, for constructive comment. All comments that were received were discussed at a general conference of the
industry held at the National Bureau of Standards on November 18, 1952.
Substantially all of the suggestions for modification contained in the comments were approved by the conference, and the Commodity Standards Division was instructed to submit the revised draft to the industry generally for
written acceptance.

Accordingly, the recommended Commercial Standard was circulated to
the trade on January 28, 1953. On April 22, the Commodity Standards Division issued an announcement that acceptances had been received representing
a satisfactory majority of the general purpose vinyl plastic film business, and
that the standard, designated Commercial Standard 192–53, would become
effective May 22, 1953.

Plastic Tableware
(Simplified Practice Recommendation 249-52)

(Effective April 1, 1952)

Purpose and scope.—The purpose of this recommendation is to establish,
as a useful standard of practice, a simplified schedule of standard shapes and
sizes of articles of plastic tableware for the guidance of hospitals, sanatoriums,
and other users; and to enable these consumers to realize the particular benefits
inherent in the adoption and use of standard sizes of tableware, as set forth
below.

Table 20-1 lists the capacities and diameters, with tolerances, for the
recommended standard stock items.

TABLE 20-1. CAPACITIES AND DIMENSIONS OF PLASTIC TABLEWARE.

No.	Item	Nominal capacity	Over-all diameter	Tolerances [1] Capacity	Over-all diameter
		Ounces	Inches	Ounce	Inch
1	Compartment or grill plate	....	$9\frac{9}{16}$	....	$\pm\frac{1}{8}$
2	......do	....	9	....	$\pm\frac{1}{8}$
3	Plate	....	10	....	$\pm\frac{1}{8}$
4	......do	....	9	....	$\pm\frac{1}{8}$
5	......do	....	8	....	$\pm\frac{1}{16}$
6	......do	....	$7\frac{1}{8}$	....	$\pm\frac{3}{16}$
7	......do	....	$6\frac{1}{2}$	....	$\pm\frac{1}{8}$
8	......do	....	6	....	$\pm\frac{1}{4}$
9	......do	....	$5\frac{1}{2}$	....	$\pm\frac{1}{8}$
10	Cup with handle [2]	7	....	$\pm\frac{1}{2}$	....
11	......do.[2]	8	....	$\pm\frac{1}{2}$	....
12	Mug	10	....	$\pm\frac{1}{2}$	....
13	Bouillon cup	$7\frac{1}{2}$	....	$\pm\frac{1}{2}$	....
14	Saucer [2]		$5\frac{1}{2}$	....	$\pm\frac{1}{8}$
15	......do.[2]	....	6	....	$\pm\frac{1}{8}$
16	......do.[2]	....	$6\frac{1}{2}$	....	$\pm\frac{1}{8}$
17	Vegetable dish	$4\frac{3}{4}$	....	$\pm\frac{1}{4}$	....
18	......do	$3\frac{3}{4}$	....	$\pm\frac{1}{4}$	....
19	Soup or miscellaneous bowl (with rim or lug)	10	....	$\pm\frac{1}{2}$	....
20	......do	12	....	$\pm\frac{1}{2}$	....
21	......do	14	....	$\pm\frac{1}{2}$	....
22	Bowl (rimless)	$10\frac{1}{2}$	....	$\pm\frac{1}{2}$	....
23	......do	14	....	$\pm\frac{1}{2}$	....
24	......do	$15\frac{1}{2}$	....	$\pm\frac{1}{2}$	....
25	Creamer	1	....	$\pm\frac{1}{8}$	....
26	......do	4	....	$\pm\frac{1}{4}$	....

[1] The products of all manufacturers making the recommended standard stock sizes should fall within these tolerances. The products of any one manufacturer will have much finer tolerances.

[2] Cups and saucers should match.

EFFECTIVE DATE

Having been passed through the regular procedure of the Commodity Standards Division, and approved by the acceptors hereinafter listed, this simplified practice recommendation was issued by the United States Department of Commerce, effective April 1, 1952.

HISTORY OF THE RECOMMENDATION

In January 1948, the American Hospital Association, which had been interested for some time in simplification and standardization of sizes and shapes of plastic tableware for hospital use, requested the Commodity Standards Division to cooperate in the development of a simplified practice recommendation for this product.

The importance of standard sizes of plastic tableware for hospitals was stressed in a report submitted by representatives of the Association, and among the reasons given for the need for standardization were the following: (1) Food trays are limited in size and it is important that service for a complete meal be set on the tray. (2) From the dietetic standpoint it is important that the tableware be of standard sizes for control of portions served. The same is true also with respect to cost control in hospitals. (3) Plates should be of such size as to accommodate standard plate covers, many of which are of stainless steel and will be in service for many years. (4) Correlation of size of the bread and butter plate with the soup bowl is important because many hospitals make a practice of placing the bread and butter plate on top of the soup bowl to keep the soup warm during transit between the serving point and the patient. (5) Articles of standard size are important also for storage in serving counters equipped with dish wells and a spring arrangement to maintain the top dish at the serving level.

PROCEDURE FOLLOWED IN DEVELOPMENT OF RECOMMENDATION

First, the simplification and standardization committee of the American Hospital Association conducted a comprehensive survey to obtain information on the use of plastic tableware in hospitals. At the same time the manufacturers, at the hospital committee's request, prepared a list of shapes and sizes of plastic tableware being manufactured, which, together with the information derived from the hospital survey, was considered at a joint meeting of representatives of the AHA and of the Society of the Plastics Industry, on May 23, 1950. The list approved at this meeting provided the basis for the proposed simplified practice recommendation for plastic tableware that was mailed on February 23, 1951, to hospitals, sanatoriums, and other users, as well as to manufacturers and distributors, for acceptance or comment.

As a result of the comments and suggestions that were received, the proposed recommendation was modified in some respects, and again submitted for approval to those concerned on August 22, 1951.

A considerable number of individual firms and hospitals made known their approval by authorizing one of their officers to fill in an acceptance form worded as follows: "We believe that the proposed simplified practice recommendation for plastic tableware constitutes a useful standard of practice, and we individually plan to utilize it as far as practicable in the (a) production, (b) distribution, or (c) use of plastic tableware. We reserve the right to depart from it as we deem advisable."

In addition to these signed acceptances, a number of suggestions for listing other sizes or for further reducing the number of sizes were also offered.

However, in view of the substantial and representative list of acceptors, it was felt that the needs of the majority would be adequately served by the proposed list of sizes. The recommendation, therefore, was approved for promulgation and publication.

This recommendation represents the initial effort of the industry to simplify and standardize sizes of plastic tableware. If, subsequently, as a result of changes in demand or new industry developments the need for adjustments in the list of sizes is demonstrated, the recommendation can then be revised in accordance with the established procedure.

The sponsors of this recommendation believe that the adoption of standard sizes is desirable for all concerned at this point in the development of the industry. The recommendation will serve as a guide to all manufacturers in buying or making new dies as changes in design occur, or when old dies or molds are replaced for any reason. Adoption of the standard sizes with the tolerances indicated should eliminate the necessity for scrapping costly equipment or for investment in new equipment to meet specific size requirements on various large institutional orders.

Index

A

I

N

O